APPLIED MATHEMATICS: AN INTRODUCTION
Mathematical Analysis for Management

IRWIN SERIES IN QUANTITATIVE ANALYSIS FOR BUSINESS

Consulting Editor

ROBERT B. FETTER *Yale University*

Applied Mathematics: an Introduction

Mathematical Analysis for Management

By

CHRIS A. THEODORE, Ph.D.

Professor of Business Administration
Graduate Division
College of Business Administration
Boston University

1965

RICHARD D. IRWIN, INC.

HOMEWOOD, ILLINOIS

TO ATHENA

PREFACE

This volume, *Applied Mathematics: An Introduction,* has been exclusively designed to serve the special and growing needs of business education. It is not an ordinary textbook in mathematics with respect to underlying assumptions, content, or orientation.

Within the span of a few years, mathematics has become an integral part of the curriculum in an increasing number of collegiate schools of business. The changing conditions which have brought about this recent development may certainly be the subject of lively speculation. Suffice it to say here that two of these conditions must be held largely responsible: the advent of computers, which have made the application of sophisticated mathematical tools in business operations economically feasible, and the greater emphasis on analytical thinking in business education.

But while considerable unanimity exists on the need for mathematics, there is considerable diversity of opinion over the content and orientation of subject matter. Those who have studied the place of mathematics in business education have suggested topics from traditional mathematics such as analytic geometry and calculus, as well as topics from modern mathematical analysis such as Boolean algebra, matrix algebra, and probability.[1] The situation is further complicated since the background, as well as the aptitude, of business students is likely to be more heterogeneous in mathematics than in almost any other subject. Thus, mathematics courses are likely to be as diverse with respect to rigor of presentation and depth of subject matter as they are with respect to content.

Considerations such as the above have been important in setting up a number of design directives:

1. An introductory textbook in mathematics for business students must require a satisfactory high-school background in ordinary algebra and plane geometry.

---

[1] See, for example, R. K. Gaumnitz and O. H. Brownlee, "Mathematics for Decision Makers," *Harvard Business Review,* Vol. XXXIV, No. 3 (May-June, 1956), p. 48; G. A. W. Boehm, "Mathematics II: The New Uses of the Abstract," *Fortune,* Vol. LVIII, No. 1 (July, 1958), p. 124; R. A. Gordon and J. F. Howell, *Higher Education for Business* (New York: Columbia University Press, 1959), pp. 159–63; F. C. Pierson *et al., The Education of American Businessmen* (New York: McGraw-Hill Book Co., Inc., 1959), pp. 186–90; S. Goldberg, "Mathematics for Business Students," in *Views on Business Education* (Chapel Hill: School of Business Administration, University of North Carolina, 1960).

2. Aside from the above requirement, each part of such a textbook must be as self-contained as possible.

3. Instead of treating one or two mathematical fields at length, such a book must contain a shorter treatment of as many important topics relevant to a curriculum in business administration as possible.

4. The book must allow for a wide choice of alternatives without seriously impairing logical continuity so that it may be easily used for curricula under a semester, quarter, or other system.

5. The core material of the textbook must be designed to meet the requirements of a two-semester equivalent terminal course for undergraduates; however, it must include a wide assortment of problems and optional sections which, in addition to introducing flexibility, may be used for an accelerated course for upper classmen or, together with outside reading assignments, for graduate students.

6. An introductory textbook in mathematics for business students must strike a balance between the objectives of mathematics as such, and the pedagogical objectives of a curriculum in business management: mathematical systems and their theorems must be introduced to the extent that they serve to develop the student's analytical faculties, to expose him to the process of decision making, and to demonstrate applications of mathematics to "real-world" problems drawn from economics and the various functional areas of business administration.

7. Finally, such an introductory textbook must express the managerial viewpoint by emphasizing the analytical process of decision making for optimizing under structured conditions, and by pointing out the potentialities as well as the limitations of the developed quantitative techniques.

In writing the present volume I have made a special effort to follow the above-mentioned design requirements. The book is divided into five parts which, with the exception of the mathematical background requirement mentioned earlier, are self-contained or nearly so. From my teaching experience I have found that our task may be considerably simplified if students are introduced into logic after they have been exposed to sets and set operations. Thus, Chapter 1 deals with sets and set operations as analytical devices, introduces the students to Boolean algebra as a mathematical system, and lays down the conceptual foundations for a unified approach to the majority of the topics in this volume. Logic, as another application of Boolean algebra, occupies Chapters 2 and 3. This ordering of topics leaves it to the instructor to decide whether to confine his course to sets and set operations or to cover logic as an additional rigorous exercise in analytical thinking. Chapter 4, the last of Part I, is devoted to voting coalitions, two-digit number systems, and the design and operation of digital computers as special applications of Boolean algebra. In sum, the student is introduced into the mathematical system of Boolean algebra and is shown how the tools of this system may be applied to empirical situations which are relevant to business activity.

The same approach is followed in the treatment of other mathematical fields. Thus, Part II, Chapters 5, 6, and 7, introduces the systems of ordinary algebra and analytical geometry and emphasizes the application of certain tools of these systems to business operations; Part III, Chapters 8, 9, and 10, deals with the mathematical systems of the algebra of vectors and matrices and shows their relevance to linear programming; Part IV, Chapters 11, 12, and 13, deals with the system of calculus and includes some applications of this system to marginal analysis and optimization; finally, Part V, Chapters 14, 15, and 16, introduces probability and Bayesian applications of this system to business decision making.

Sets and logic of Part I may be considered valuable tools for the first step in the process of decision making, namely, analysis of a situation into its mutually exclusive and collectively exhaustive components and exposure to deductive reasoning. The mathematical systems introduced in Parts II, III, and IV supply quantitative tools for making decisions under the condition of certainty, while probability, in Part V, deals with quantitative techniques for making decisions under the condition of uncertainty. Throughout the book motivating examples illustrate the application of the developed mathematical tools so that each topic is given an empirically meaningful ending.

Flexibility for planning a course is achieved by arranging the text material in 26 core and 19 optional sections, as shown in the accompanying schematic diagram. Each section is denoted by chapter and serial number. The core sections of each part are contained in a circle with arrows pointing at the optional sections in boxes. A two-semester course may be designed covering the core sections of all five parts. Since most optional sections are more sophisticated and demanding than core ones, the instructor can step up the pace as well as increase the difficulty of his course at will, by covering optional sections as suggested by the solid-line arrows to the boxes. A one-semester course may be very easily planned with the core sections of Part I, III, and V without loss of continuity, or with the core sections of Parts II, III, and IV with a very short introduction to set concept and notation. In either case, however, omitting sections 8.1 and 8.2 of Part III does not impair subject matter continuity.

Additional flexibility for planning a course is introduced with the material arrangement in Parts I and III. The core sections 2.1, 2.2, and 3.1 of Part I represent a unit on logic with special problems at the end of section 3.1, summarizing the major points of the optional sections 3.2, 3.3, and 3.4 on the same subject. If desirable, however, the instructor may skip even the core sections on logic without loss of continuity. Furthermore, with a short introduction to matrix notation, the instructor may skip the optional sections 9.1 and 9.2 of Part III and move from the core sections 8.1 and 8.2 to the optional 10.1 and

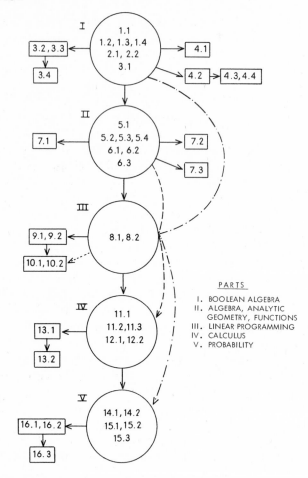

PARTS

I. BOOLEAN ALGEBRA
II. ALGEBRA, ANALYTIC
    GEOMETRY, FUNCTIONS
III. LINEAR PROGRAMMING
IV. CALCULUS
V. PROBABILITY

10.2, thus emphasizing the computational rather than the mathematical aspects of linear programming. The above suggestions for planning a course are by no means exhaustive.

In addition, several optional sections in this volume may be advantageously used as outside assignments in courses from the functional areas of business administration and economics. These sections, their topics, and the area(s) or course in which they may be used are shown below:

Section(s)	Topic	Suggested area or course
4.1	Voting coalitions	Personnel management or human relations
4.2–4.4	Binary arithmetic-cumputers	Computer systems
7.1	Demand and supply functions	Economics

Section(s)	Topic	Suggested area or course
7.2	Growth and decline functions	Marketing-production
7.3	Mathematics of investment and finance	Accounting-finance
9.1–10.2	Linear programming	Economics-marketing
13.1, 13.2	Calculus in business operations I, II	Marketing-production-finance
16.1, 16.2	Expected value	Statistics-economics
16.3	Binomial distribution	Statistics-production

Of course, it is assumed that students in a regular mathematics course have had the core sections in this volume or equivalent material from another textbook before they are assigned the corresponding optional sections.

Each section is divided into topics which are denoted by section and serial number. The same system is followed for denoting examples, tables, and diagrams. Such items are referred to by section and serial number only unless they belong to a different chapter than the one in which they are cited. Optional sections are marked with an asterisk. Also, problems or parts of problems whose answers appear at the end of the book are starred for easy recognition. A limited bibliography appears at the end of each chapter. The number in parentheses at the end of each source refers to the section or sections of this volume to which the source material is relevant.

Encouragement and assistance for the preparation of this volume came from many persons and it is with great pleasure that I thank some of them publicly.

My greatest debt by far is to Samuel Goldberg of Oberlin College for reviewing an early draft of a sample of chapters, and subsequently a later version of the manuscript. As a severe yet encouraging critic, his many valuable specific suggestions have been very helpful. Although neither in substance nor in style have I attained the high standards he has set, I am grateful to him for making me work harder and to better effect.

My thanks go to Howard Raiffa of Harvard University Graduate School of Business for his favorable and encouraging comments, especially in Part V on probability. But my greatest debt to him is indirect, for, as my teacher at the Harvard Institute of Basic Mathematics for Application to Business (1959–60), sponsored by the Ford Foundation, he, with Samuel Goldberg, Allen Spivey of the University of Michigan, and Ronald Howard of the Massachusetts Institute of Technology, did much to imbue me with a sense of admiration and humility towards mathematics, as well as to provide me with the necessary background and inspiration without which this volume might not have been written.

Also, this volume owes much to the consulting editor for the Irwin Series in Quantitative Analysis for Business, Robert B. Fetter of Yale University, for his suggestions as well as his unshakable confidence in the pedagogical merits of the approach followed in this book; to my colleague and friend Samuel Hanna of Boston University for his highly valuable editorial assistance on format and presentation of text material; to Norman Goldman of the Computational Laboratory at Boston University for his suggestions on Sections 4.3 and 4.4 on computers; to K. T. Wallenius of Yale University for reading the galleys; and to many others. By naming a few, I mean to thank all.

Furthermore, I would like to thank wholeheartedly the administration of Boston University for their encouragement and generous help which came in many forms; the administration of the University of Hawaii for their assistance which was graciously offered during my stay there on a visiting appointment; and my publisher, Richard D. Irwin, Inc., for generous editorial assistance.

No less grateful am I to my students, both undergraduates and graduates, who have been exposed to most of the material in this volume. Their difficulties and comments have contributed much to this book, while their motivation and enthusiasm have given me the greatest reward for my toils. In this connection, I am especially thankful to my former students, Leland Doane, Suk Hyun Lim, Richard Rosen, and Alexander Safer.

Needless to say, I assume full responsibility for the shortcomings in this volume, and I shall be grateful to any reader who calls my attention to serious errors of omission or commission.

CHRIS A. THEODORE

Honolulu, Hawaii
January, 1965

TABLE OF CONTENTS

* Sections with an asterisk are optional.

PART I

Boolean Algebra with Applications

Boolean algebra (named after the English logician, George Boole, 1815–64, who developed it) is a mathematical system. Like other systems in mathematics, such as ordinary algebra and geometry, Boolean algebra consists of abstract laws and theorems derived from these laws.

We shall deal with the abstract laws and, to a limited extent, with mathematical proofs of this system in Chapter 1. At the same time, we shall have the opportunity to introduce the system's first application, namely, sets. Logic or deductive reasoning, the second application we shall be concerned with, occupies Chapters 2 and 3. Inclusion of these two topics may raise a crucial question. If our ultimate objective is to study mathematical tools for solving real-world managerial problems, in what way does Boolean algebra help us toward achieving this goal? In general, Boolean algebra will help us organize our thinking and develop our analytical faculties; it will enable us to survey the whole of a situation, to grasp what is fundamental or relevant and what is secondary or irrelevant, and to see the interrelationships which may exist between the parts and the whole. In particular, with set operations we shall be able to analyze or combine elements of a business situation representing alternative possibilities; and with logic we shall be able to examine such possibilities as mutually exclusive and collectively exhaustive events. In this sense, both set operations and deductive reasoning are intimately associated with managerial problems and the decision-making process of solving them. After all, no problem exists unless there is more than one course of action; and no decision may be wisely made unless all logically possible courses of action are analyzed and an optimal one is chosen.

Furthermore, the use of sets and logic is demonstrated in situations which are related to business management and economics. Although this is done throughout Chapters 1, 2, and 3, two important applications are given special emphasis: one is decision-making bodies; and the other is the design and operation of digital computers. They occupy Chapter 4.

Finally, the study of the mathematical system of Boolean algebra not only establishes a unifying theoretical frame of reference for its numerous applications but also prepares the reader, conceptually, for the introduction of functions, linear programming, calculus, and probability which follow.

Chapter 1

SETS AND SET OPERATIONS

THE FIRST application with which we shall be concerned is the Boolean algebra of sets. After introducing the concept of a set and basic notation, we shall explain set equality and set inclusion. These two topics will, in turn, enable us to demonstrate basic operations on sets. Last, we shall enunciate the abstract laws of set operations, which in fact are also the laws of Boolean algebra itself.

1. THE NOTION OF A SET; BASIC NOTATION

1.1. Definition of a Set. *A collection or an aggregate of objects of any kind such as books, people, numbers, etc., is defined as a set.* Thus, we can speak of the set of the board of directors of a corporation, the set of trustees of an institution, the set of employees of a firm, the set of suppliers of a manufacturer, the set of consumers of a product, the set of sales records, the set of a company's inventory, the set of accounts of a firm, and so forth and so on. But the objects contained in a set need not be as concrete as the ones already mentioned. They can be abstract concepts such as the set of positive integers, the set of real numbers which satisfy the equation $x^2 + 2x - 3 = 0$, or any other equation. We can see that the notion of a set is very general and can be easily understood. Yet, a collection of objects must meet the following conditions in order to form a set:

A. The collection or aggregate of objects must be *well defined*. This means that for a given set we must be able to determine unequivocally whether or not any object belongs to that set. Consider the set of the board of director of Johnson, Inc. It must be possible to give a yes or no answer to the question, "Is Mr. Williams a member of the board of directors of Johnson, Inc.?", so that of the "yes" and "no" answers, one and only one will be correct.

B. The objects of a set must be *distinct*; in other words, no object in a set appears twice. Consequently, in listing the objects in a set no object is repeated after it is once recorded. The set of price quotations of a

3

common stock during one day, $10, 10^{\frac{1}{4}}$, $10, $12, 10^{\frac{1}{4}}$, is a set which does not contain the five numbers, but the three distinct numbers $10, 10^{\frac{1}{4}}$, $12. For the same reason the set of letters in the word "Mississippi" is a set containing the four distinct letters M, i, s, and p.

C. If the objects of a set can be enumerated, the *order* in which they may be listed is *immaterial*. Thus, the set of letters a, b, c is the same as the set of letters b, c, a or c, b, a. This condition is closely related to the equality of sets which we shall discuss in the next section.

1.2. Set Membership.

An object which *belongs to* or is a *member of* or is *contained in* a set is said to be an element of this set. Let o be an object and P a set. If o belongs to P, then this relation may be denoted by $o \in P$, read "object o is an element of set P." If o does not belong to P, then this relation may be denoted by $o \notin P$, read "object o is not an element of set P." We shall follow the general practice of denoting sets with capital letters. Lowercase letters will be used to denote elements of a set.

Example 1.1. Let w be Mr. Williams and J the set of directors on the board of Johnson, Inc. Then $w \in J$ means that Mr. Williams is a member of the board of directors of Johnson, Inc., and $w \notin J$ that he is not.

1.3. Number of Elements in a Set.

The number of elements in a set may be finite or infinite. Sets such as the set of employees of a firm, the set of suppliers of a manufacturer, and other examples from the business world are *finite* because we can enumerate the elements of each set in some order by counting its elements one by one until a last element is reached. On the other hand, the set of positive integers, $1, 2, 3, \ldots$, is *infinite* because the process of counting can never end. Practical business problems may involve infinite sets. In quality control, for example, statisticians may study a machine as a process which turns out an infinite set of parts. It may be noted, however, that a set, such as the molecules of sea water, can contain a vast number of elements, yet be a finite set.

In addition to finite and infinite sets, it is pertinent at this point to introduce the notion of a set with no elements in it. Such a set is called an *empty* or *null* set and is denoted by the symbol $\varnothing$. Since there can be one and only one set with no elements in it, we shall refer in our discussion to *the* empty or *the* null set.

1.4. Specifying Sets.

Basically a set is specified in two different ways: the roster method and the descriptive or defining method. The *roster method* consists of enclosing in braces { } a list of the elements in the set.

Example 1.2. Let Smith, Brown, and Lord be the set P representing the partners of Lehigh Metal Company. By the roster method this set may be denoted by

$$P = \{Brown, Lord, Smith\}.$$

The *descriptive or defining property method* consists of stating in braces the rule or condition on the basis of which it can be determined whether or not a given object is an element of the set.

Example 1.3. Consider the previously specified set P of Smith, Brown, and Lord, partners of Lehigh Metal Company. By the descriptive method set P may be specified as follows:

$$P = \{x|x \text{ is a partner of Lehigh Metal Company}\}.$$

It is read "P is the set of those elements x such that x is a partner of Lehigh Metal Company." The vertical bar | means "such that" or "for which." The symbol x denotes any one element of set P. Of course, any other symbol such as y, z, or an asterisk *, or any other would be equally suitable to denote an element of a set.

Frequently, the descriptive method is denoted in a different way. In any analysis of a particular situation a fixed collection of elements is defined which is called the *universal set*, denoted by $\mathcal{U}$. Then a particular set is specified by referring to the universal set.

Example 1.4. Let the universal set $\mathcal{U}$ be the set of all people. Then the set P of Brown, Smith, and Lord may be denoted by

$$P = \{x \in \mathcal{U}|x \text{ is a partner of Lehigh Metal Company}\},$$

read "P is the set of those elements x of $\mathcal{U}$ for which x is a partner of Lehigh Metal Company." This notation can be further abbreviated into a more general form. Let $p(x)$ be the condition on x; i.e., "x is a partner of Lehigh Metal Company." Then the set of those elements x of $\mathcal{U}$ which satisfy the condition $p(x)$ may be written as

$$P = \{x \in \mathcal{U}|p(x)\}.$$

Some mathematicians call these methods of specifying sets *set builders* because they convert a collection of objects or a condition to a set.

1.5. A Few Additional Examples. The following examples further illustrate the notation of set building.

Example 1.5. At the end of the first month in business the accounts of the Quick Service Garage owned by Thomas Deane and Stephen Hill showed the following transactions:

Initial investment of $11,000 by each partner ...	$22,000
Mortgage payable	15,000
Automobile Supply Company, payable	10,000
Value of land and building	35,000
Gas, spare parts, other supplies in stock	10,000
Office furniture	2,000

Let P be the set of partners, and the letters A, L, and W the sets of transactions representing assets, liabilities, and net worth, respectively. Then these sets can be specified by using the roster method:

$$P = \{\text{Thomas Deane, Stephen Hill}\},$$
$$A = \{\$35{,}000, \$10{,}000, \$2000\},$$
$$L = \{\$15{,}000, \$10{,}000\},^{\cdots}$$
$$W = \{\$22{,}000\}.$$

The likelihood of having more than one transaction with the same amount would render this method unsatisfactory since the elements of each set must be distinct. One way of overcoming this difficulty would be to write down the amount and the nature of each transaction. But then the roster method becomes cumbersome, especially when each set contains a large number of elements. A more efficient way out would be to use the descriptive method as follows:

$P = \{x|x \text{ is a partner of Quick Service Garage}\}$,

$A = \{y|y \text{ is a transaction of Quick Service Garage representing assets}\}$,

$L = \{w|w \text{ is a transaction of Quick Service Garage representing liabilities}\}$,

$W = \{z|z \text{ is a transaction of Quick Service Garage representing net worth}\}$.

Example 1.6. Let R be the universal set representing all real numbers. Let Q be the set of numbers which satisfy the equation $x^2 + 2x - 3 = 0$. Then by the descriptive method

$$Q = \{x \in R | x^2 + 2x - 3 = 0\},$$

and by the roster method
$$Q = \{1, -3\}.$$

Example 1.7. Let R be the set of all real numbers; and let P be the set of real numbers which satisfy the equation $x^2 = -25$. Then the set

$$P = \{x \in R | x^2 = -25\}$$

has no elements, since the square of any real number is nonnegative. Thus, set P is the empty or null set $\varnothing$.

Example 1.8. Consider the infinite set P of all positive integers. Listing all the elements in the set is impossible. An abbreviation may be used for specifying the set as follows:

$$P = \{1, 2, 3, 4, \ldots\},$$

where the three dots indicate the omitted elements of the set. However, this notation must be used with care. A sufficient number of elements must be listed in order to indicate the correct pattern. Otherwise, the roster method may be misleading.

Let Q be the set of those numbers of the form $n^2 + (n-1) \cdot (n-2) \cdot$

$(n-3)$, where n is any positive integer. Then we may be tempted to specify the set Q as follows:

$$Q = \{1, 4, 9, \ldots\},$$

where 1, 4, and 9 represent the first three elements of Q when $n = 1, 2, 3$. Observing that the listed elements of Q are consecutive squares, i.e., $1 = 1^2, 4 = 2^2, 9 = 3^2$, we may readily conclude that the next element is 16. Actually, for $n = 4$ the next element is 22, not 16.

Thus, in specifying an infinite set it may be better to use the descriptive or defining property method. By this method the set P of all positive integers is

$$P = \{x \mid x \text{ is a positive integer}\}$$

and for Q is

$$Q = \{x \mid x = n^2 + (n-1) \cdot (n-2) \cdot (n-3)\}$$

for some positive integer n.

PROBLEMS

1.1. In each case below indicate which sets are the same and which sets are different. Explain why.

a) $P = \{1, 2, 3\}$, $Q = \{3, 4, 1\}$, $R = \{3, 2, 1\}$.

b) $P = \{a, e, i, o, u\}$,
   $Q = \{x \mid x \text{ is a vowel in the English alphabet}\}$,
   $R = \{e, o, i, a, j, u\}$,
   $S = \{x \in \mathcal{U} \mid x \text{ is a vowel}\}$,
   where $\mathcal{U}$ is the set of letters in the English alphabet.

c) $P = \{x \mid x \text{ is an amount representing an asset of XYZ Company}\}$,
   $Q = \{\$1000, \$3555, \$3000, \$50,000\}$,
   $R = \{\$3555, \$1000, \$50,000, \$3000\}$,
   where sets Q and R contain all transactions of XYZ Company representing assets.

d) $P = \{x \mid x^2 - 2x = 0\}$,
   $Q = \{x \mid x - 2 = 0\}$,
   $R = \{x \mid x^2 - x - 2 = 0\}$.

1.2. For each set as defined in the example discussed in the text, indicate whether each statement below is true or false.

a) Example 1.2:
   i) "Smith $\in P$."
   ii) "Burke $\notin P$."

b) Example 1.5:
   i) "$\$22,000 \notin W$."
   ii) "$\$10,000 \notin P$."
   iii) "$\$35,000 \in A$."

c) Example 1.6:
   i) "$-1 \notin Q$."
   ii) "$-3 \in Q$."

    d) Example 1.7:
      i) "2 ∈ *R*."
      ii) "−5 ∈ *P*."
      iii) "0 ∈ *P*."
    e) Example 1.8:
      i) "5 ∉ *P*."
      ii) "16 ∈ *Q*."
      iii) "600 ∉ *Q*."

1.3. For each set listed below, state whether it is finite or infinite, and express it in set notation by both the roster method, whenever feasible, and by the descriptive method:

    a) The set of Rainbow, Inc., Quality Paints Company, and Packard Paint Manufacturers, suppliers of Homes and Buildings Care Company.
    b) The set of $20 million common stock, $2 million preferred stock, $10 million bonds representing the book value capital investment of Loomis Products Corporation.
    c) The set of $700 thousand cash, $12 million U.S. Government Bonds, and $100 million common stock representing the current market value of the investment portfolio of Sayles Investment Fund.
    d) The set of transactions $100, $500, $10,000, $22,000, $500, $1,000, representing the current assets of Bliss Industrial Cleaning Company.
    e) The set of letters in the word "profitability."
    f) The set of even positive integers.
    *g) The set of real numbers satisfying the equation $x^2 + 2x = 8$.
    h) The set of real numbers satisfying the equation $x^2 - 3x - 6 = 0$.

*1.4. Let the set $\mathcal{U}$ be a sample of one hundred cigarette smokers who were interviewed about their smoking habits. The table below shows the distribution of the sample by sex and kind of cigarettes consumed.

Kind of Cigarettes Consumed	(1) Men	(2) Women	Total
Filter	30	40	70
Nonfilter...................	20	10	30
Total	50	50	100

Express each of the *eight* classes of smokers in set notation using the descriptive method.

1.5. From each of the following subjects select a set and express it in the set notation using either the roster or the descriptive method.
    a) Accounting.
    b) Behavioral science.
    c) Economics.
    d) Finance.
    e) Marketing.
    f) Production.
    g) Statistics.

1.6. Let P be the set of owners or partners of a firm, and the letters A, L, and W the sets of transactions representing assets, liabilities, and net worth, respectively. Express the sets which are included in (a) and (b) below by both the roster and descriptive methods.

*a) John Baker buys a store building at a price of $50,000. He pays $35,000 of his own money and borrows the balance from Essex Savings Bank by placing a mortgage on the property in the amount of $15,000.

b) The Mason-Allen Service, Inc., a package delivery firm, had the following transactions at the time it was established:

Initial investment (G. Mason and K. Allen $10,000 each)	$20,000
Purchase of 5 trucks	27,500
Prepaid monthly rental	500
Office supplies, paid	100
Loan for the purchase of trucks	10,000
Office equipment, paid.............................	900
Cash	1,000

What difficulties may one encounter in using the roster method? Show how you may overcome these difficulties.

1.7. The set of elements satisfying equation $x^2 + 2x - 3 = 0$ in Example 1.6 can be specified as follows: $Q = \{x \in R \mid x^2 + 2x - 3 = 0\} = \{1, -3\}$. Solve the equations below using this form. If form $\{1, -3\}$ is not appropriate, use the descriptive method. In each case indicate whether the set is finite or infinite.

a) $2x + 6 = 0$.
b) $x^2 - 9 = 0$.
c) $3x - 6 = 0$.
*d) $x^2 - 5x + 6 = 0$.
e) $x + 2 > 0$.
f) $x - 1 \leqslant 0$.
g) $2x^2 - 5x + 3 \geqslant 0$.
h) $2x^2 - x < 0$.

1.8. Indicate whether the following statements are true or false. Justify your answer.

a) $3 = \{3\}$.
*b) $3 \in \{3\}$.
c) $0 = \varnothing$.
d) $0 \in \varnothing$.

1.9. For a full semester assignment read the stories about the great mathematicians of the world from James Newman (ed.), *The World of Mathematics* (New York: Simon & Schuster, Inc., 1956), paperback edition, Vol. I, the following topics:

a) "Great Mathematicians," pp. 75–168.
b) "Archimedes," pp. 179–87.
c) "Johann Kepler," pp. 220–34.
d) "Isaac Newton, the Man," pp. 277–85.
e) "Gauss, the Prince of Mathematicians," pp. 294–339.
    Write a short essay on the major contributions which these mathematicians have made to the development of scientific knowledge.

2. SET EQUALITY AND SUBSETS

In this section our task will be to discuss set equality, to distinguish between set equality and subsets, and to determine the number of subsets which can be formed from a given set.

2.1. Set Equality. *Two given sets P and Q are said to be equal, i.e., $P = Q$, if and only if every element of P is also an element of Q and every element of Q is an element of P.*

Example 2.1. Let the sets

$$P = \{\text{Lord, Brown, Smith}\}$$

and

$$Q = \{\text{Brown, Lord, Smith}\}$$

be given. Sets P and Q are equal because they contain identical elements.

Note that the notion of set equality illustrated above implies the condition that the order in which the elements of a set may be listed is immaterial. Furthermore, the notion of set equality indicates that two or more sets specified by the descriptive method can be equal in spite of the fact that their defining properties may be entirely different.

Example 2.2. Consider the sets P and Q specified in Example 2.1. Let the sets

$$P = \{x|x \text{ is a partner of Lehigh Metal Company}\}$$

and

$$Q = \{y|y \text{ is the son-in-law of J. B. Lehigh}\}$$

be given.
Although the defining property of set P is different from that of set Q, $P = Q$ since the two sets have identical elements; namely, the three individuals named Smith, Brown, and Lord.

By contrast, two given sets P and R are unequal, i.e., $P \neq R$, if one set contains an element which is not contained in the other.

Example 2.3. Let the sets

$$P = \{\text{Brown, Lord, Smith}\}$$
$$R = \{\text{Brown, Lord}\}$$

be given. Then $P \neq R$ since set P contains the element Smith which is not an element of set R.

2.2. Subsets. *A set P is a subset of another set Q, denoted by $P \subseteq Q$, if each and every element of P is also an element of Q.*

Example 2.4. Let Q be the set representing all partners in the United States; and let

$$P = \{x|x \text{ is a partner of Lehigh Metal Company}\}$$

Then $P \subseteq Q$.

Example 2.5. Let the universal set $\mathfrak{U}$ be all the transactions of a firm during a fiscal year; and let the sets A, L, and W consist of such transactions representing assets, liabilities, and net worth, respectively. Then $A \subseteq \mathfrak{U}$, $L \subseteq \mathfrak{U}$, and $W \subseteq \mathfrak{U}$.

Note that in any analysis of a situation once the universal set $\mathfrak{U}$ is defined all other sets in the same analysis are subsets of $\mathfrak{U}$.

At this point a question readily comes to our mind: Is a set a subset of itself? Since each and every element of a set P is naturally an element of the same set, P is a subset of itself, i.e., $P \subseteq P$ is always true. Also, the convention is adopted to call the null set $\varnothing$ a subset of every set.

Example 2.6. Let $P = \{1, -3\}$. Then $P \subseteq P$. Let Q be the null set $\varnothing$ and $R = \{x \mid x$ is a real number$\}$. Then $Q \subseteq P$ and $Q \subseteq R$.

2.3. Set Equality and Subsets.

Earlier, it was said that two sets are equal if and only if every element of one set is also an element of the other set. The fact that a set is a subset of itself leads to the proposition that any two equal sets are subsets of each other. Thus, set equality may be restated concisely as follows: *Two sets P and Q are said to be equal if and only if $P \subseteq Q$ and $Q \subseteq P$.*

However, set inclusion, i.e., the process of a set being a subset of another set, is a much broader concept than set equality. For two sets P and Q may be unequal, yet set P *may be* a subset of Q.

Example 2.7. Let

$$P = \{a, b, c\}$$

and

$$Q = \{a, b, c, f\}$$

be given. Then $P \neq Q$ inasmuch as letter f is an element of Q but not of P; but $P \subseteq Q$ since each and every element of P is also an element of Q.

But if two sets are unequal, neither *need be* a subset of the other. This is the case where each of the two unequal sets contains elements which are not elements of the other.

Example 2.8. Consider the following sets:

$$R = \{a, b, c, d\},$$
$$Q = \{a, b, c, f\}.$$

Then $R \neq Q$ since d is an element of R only and f an element of Q only. In such a case of set inequality neither $R \subseteq Q$ nor $Q \subseteq R$ is true.

2.4. Subset Forming.

As explained before, once the universal set $\mathfrak{U}$ in a particular situation is defined, all sets which can be formed from the elements of $\mathfrak{U}$ are subsets of $\mathfrak{U}$. It is obvious that the total number of all possible subsets depends on the number of elements in $\mathfrak{U}$.

Let us now develop a general rule which will give us the total number of subsets for any number, say n, of elements in $\mathcal{U}$.

If $\mathcal{U}$ has no elements so that $n = 0$, then $\mathcal{U} = \emptyset$ and the only subset of $\emptyset$ is $\emptyset$ itself. Hence, the number of subsets of $\mathcal{U}$ is 1 which can be written as 2^0. Let $\mathcal{U} = \{a\}$ so $n = 1$. Then there is one decision to be made; and since we can make this decision in 2 ways, namely, to include or exclude a, the subsets are $\emptyset$ and $\{a\}$, 2^1 subsets in all. Let $\mathcal{U} = \{a, b\}$ so $n = 2$. Then there are two decisions; and since we can make these decisions in $2 \cdot 2 = 4$ ways, the subsets are $\emptyset$, $\{a\}$, $\{b\}$, $\{a, b\}$, 2^2 subsets in all. Hence, if $n \geqslant 1$, the process of forming subsets of $\mathcal{U}$ requires a decision to be made for each element in $\mathcal{U}$ with two alternatives, either to include or exclude an element in a subset.

We may observe that the number of subsets which can be formed are 2^0, 2^1, 2^2 when there are 0, 1, 2 elements in $\mathcal{U}$. Can we guess what the number of subsets is when $n = 3$, $n = 4$, or any other number? If $n = 3$, then the number of subsets is 2^3. If $n = 4$, then there are 2^4 subsets. And if there are n elements in $\mathcal{U}$, there are n decisions to be made and we can make these decisions in $2 \cdot 2 \cdot 2 \ldots \cdot 2$, or 2^n ways. Therefore, the general rule is that for a given $\mathcal{U}$ having n elements where n is any positive integer, the number of subsets of $\mathcal{U}$ is 2^n. This general rule is an application of the *fundamental principle of counting* which is explained in Chapter 15, Section 3.

It is not difficult to imagine the large number of new sets that subset forming can generate. Even for a universal set with a moderately small number of elements, say 30, we can generate 2^{30} or more than one billion different subsets! But let us illustrate subset forming with a universal set containing three elements only.

Example 2.9. Let the universal set

$$\mathcal{U} = \{a, b, c\}$$

be given. Since $n = 3$, the subsets of $\mathcal{U}$ are $2^3 = 8$ as shown below:

$$\emptyset, \{a\}, \{b\}, \{c\}, \{a, b\}, \{a, c\}, \{b, c\}, \{a, b, c\}.$$

In addition to the number of subsets, there is another important point in set forming. Let $\mathcal{U}$ be any set. Then the set whose elements are all the subsets in $\mathcal{U}$ is called the *power set* of $\mathcal{U}$ and is denoted by $2^{\mathcal{U}}$. Now, if there are n elements in $\mathcal{U}$, then the number of elements in the power set $2^{\mathcal{U}}$ is 2^n.

Example 2.10. Consider the universal set $\mathcal{U}$ specified in the previous example. Then the eight subsets of $\mathcal{U}$ are the elements of the power set $2^{\mathcal{U}}$ as follows:

$$2^{\mathcal{U}} = \{\emptyset, \{a\}, \{b\}, \{c\}, \{a, b\}, \{a, c\}, \{b, c\}, \{a, b, c\}\}.$$

Observe the difference in notation. The subsets of $\mathcal{U}$ become elements of $2^{\mathcal{U}}$ by enclosing the subsets of $\mathcal{U}$ in braces. Thus, while $\{a\}$ is a subset of $\mathcal{U}$ it is only an element of $2^{\mathcal{U}}$, i.e., $\{a\} \subseteq \mathcal{U}$ and $\{a\} \in 2^{\mathcal{U}}$. The correct notation for denoting $\{a\}$ as a subset of $2^{\mathcal{U}}$ is $\{\{a\}\} \subseteq 2^{\mathcal{U}}$.

2.5. Recapitulation. While specifying sets is a way of classi-fying a collection of objects, set inclusion is a method of subclassifying such a collection. As we shall see presently, this classification process becomes an important analytical tool because we can perform certain operations on sets which are in many respects analogous to the opera-tions in algebra.

PROBLEMS

2.1. Let the universal set $\mathcal{U} = \{1, 2, a, 3, b, 4, c\}$. Explain why each of the following statements is true or false:

a) $P = Q$, where $P = \{2, a, 3, b\}$ and $Q = \{a, b, 2, 3\}$.

*b) $P = Q$ and $P \subseteq Q$, where $P = \{1, c, 3\}$ and $Q = \{3, 1, c\}$.

c) $P \neq Q$ and $P \subseteq Q$, where $P = \{4, b, c\}$ and $Q = \{c, 1, 4, b\}$.

d) $P \neq Q$ and $P \subseteq Q$, where $P = \{3, b, d, 4\}$ and $Q = \{3, b, d, 2\}$.

e) $P \neq Q$, but $P \subseteq \mathcal{U}$ and $Q \subseteq \mathcal{U}$, where $P = \{1, a, b, c\}$ and $Q = \{2, 3, 4\}$.

2.2. Let the set $\mathcal{U} = \{1, 2, 5, a, c\}$. Write down four sets which are equal to set $\mathcal{U}$.

2.3. Explain with examples of your own in what sense subset forming is a broader concept than set equality and a narrower concept than set inequality.

2.4. From each of the following subjects cite an example of your own illustra-ting the concept of subset:

a) Accounting.

b) Behavioral science.

c) Economics.

d) Finance.

e) Marketing.

f) Production.

g) Statistics.

2.5. Find which of the following statements involves a subset relation and express it in set notation by using for set symbols the letters in paren-theses. Explain why the other statements do not involve a subset relation.

*a) Some wholesalers (W) are retailers (R).

*b) All partnerships (P) are business (B) organizations.

c) Stockholders (S) are owners (O) of capital.

d) No consumer (C) is a price-conscious person (P).

e) Bondholders (B) are creditors (C).

2.6. Using the definition of set equality show that—

a) There is one and only one empty set.

b) A set is a subset of itself.

2.7. Let $P = \{a, b, c\}$. Specify all sets Q if $\{a\} \subseteq Q$, $Q \subseteq P$, and $Q \neq P$.

2.8. Specify the set Q if there is only one set P such that $P \subseteq Q$.

2.9. Let the universal set $\mathfrak{U} = \{1, 2, 3, 4\}$. Write down in proper set notation:
  a) The subsets of $\mathfrak{U}$.
  b) The elements of $2^{\mathfrak{U}}$.
  c) Find whether each of the following statements is true or false. If false, indicate correct notation.
  *i) $\{1, 2\} \in \mathfrak{U}$.
  *ii) $\{1, 2\} \subseteq 2^{\mathfrak{U}}$.
  iii) $\{\{2, 3, 4\}\} \in 2^{\mathfrak{U}}$.
  iv) $\{2, 3, 4\} \subseteq \mathfrak{U}$.

2.10. Let the set $P = \{$Lord, Smith, Brown$\}$. List the elements of the power set 2^P and explain why the following statements are true:
  a) $\varnothing \notin P$, but $\varnothing \in 2^P$.
  b) Lord $\in P$, but Lord $\notin 2^P$.
  c) $\{$Smith$\} \notin P$, but $\{$Smith$\} \in 2^P$.
  d) P is an element, but is not a subset of 2^P.
  e) $\{P\}$ is not an element, but a subset of 2^P.

2.11. Let $\mathfrak{U} = \{a, b, c, d\}$, representing the members of a decision-making body, say a committee.
  a) List the elements of the power set $2^{\mathfrak{U}}$. Each element can represent a voting *coalition* casting votes for a specific measure. If each committee member has one vote and if three votes are needed to carry a motion, a set of any three committee members represents a *winning* coalition, while a set of any one member is a *losing* and any two members a *blocking* coalition.
  b) Specify the winning, the losing, and the blocking coalitions of the set $2^{\mathfrak{U}}$.
  c) Let the four members of the decision-making body represent the shareholders of a corporation with 100 shares of stock outstanding, and let a own 50 shares, b, 20 shares, and c and d, 15 shares each. If each share has one vote and a simple majority, i.e., 51 votes, can carry a motion, list the winning, losing, and blocking coalitions of the set $2^{\mathfrak{U}}$.
  d) Do the same as in (*c*) but assume that stockholder b has sold one share to a.

3. BASIC OPERATIONS ON SETS

While subset forming is the process which generates new sets from the elements of a given universal set, operations on sets consist of different devices by which sets can be combined to form other sets. To put it in a different way, set operations is the machinery by which the process of set formation can be performed systematically and efficiently. Furthermore, demonstrating the basic operations on sets, namely, the complement, the intersection, and the union of sets, is a necessary step toward the abstract laws of set operations.

3.1. Complement. *Let P be any subset of a universal set* $\mathcal{U}$. *Then the complement of P, denoted by P′, is the set of elements of* $\mathcal{U}$ *which are not members of P.* In symbols, the definition of the complement is

$$P' = \{x \in \mathcal{U} | x \notin P\},$$

read "not P is the set of those elements x of $\mathcal{U}$ for which x is *not* an element of *P.*"

Example 3.1. Let the universal set be

$\mathcal{U} = \{x | x$ is a board director of any corporation in the United States}.

Also, let the set

$P = \{$Rothmund, Hemeon, Green, Gross, White$\}$

represent the board of directors of Rothmund Steel Corporation. Then the set P' contains the directors of all corporations in the United States who are *not* board directors of Rothmund Steel Corporation.

The complement of a set can be visualized with a diagram shown in Figure 3.1. Diagrams such as this are called *Venn diagrams* (after the English logician John Venn, 1834–83). In Figure 3.1 the rectangle represents the universal set $\mathcal{U}$, the circle drawn inside the rectangle the set P, and the shaded part of the rectangle outside the circle the set P'; i.e., the complement of P.

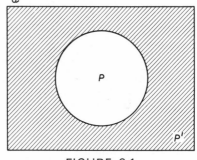

FIGURE 3.1.

It is of interest to note that the complement of the universal set $\mathcal{U}$ is the null set $\varnothing$ and conversely, the complement of the empty set is the universal set, i.e., $\mathcal{U}' = \varnothing$ and $\varnothing' = \mathcal{U}$.

3.2. Intersection. *Let P and Q be any subsets of a universal set* $\mathcal{U}$. *Then the intersection of P and Q, denoted by* $P \cap Q$, *is the set of elements of* $\mathcal{U}$ *which are members of both P and Q.* In symbols the definition of the intersection is

$$P \cap Q = \{x \in \mathcal{U} | x \in P \text{ and } x \in Q\},$$

read "*P* intersection *Q* is the set of those elements x of $\mathcal{U}$ such that x is both an element of *P* and an element of *Q.*"

Example 3.2. Let

$P = \{$Rothmund, Hemeon, Green, Gross, White$\}$

represent the board of directors of Rothmund Steel Corporation and

$$Q = \{\text{Clement, Rothmund, Hemeon, Lyon, Jenkins}\}$$

represent the board of directors of Mesabi Coal Company. Then their intersection is

$$P \cap Q = \{\text{Rothmund, Hemeon}\}.$$

It contains the individuals who are board directors of both Rothmund Steel Corporation *and* Mesabi Coal Company.

The intersection of sets P and Q involves two possibilities that are of utmost significance in subsequent discussions. The two sets may be joint or disjoint. The sets P and Q are said to be *joint* if they have one or more elements in common.

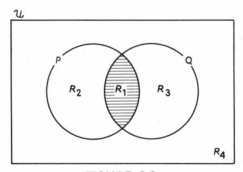

FIGURE 3.2.

Example 3.3. Let P and Q be the sets specified in the previous example. Then these sets are joint since

$$P \cap Q = \{\text{Rothmund, Hemeon}\}$$

is not the empty set. It can be seen from Figure 3.2 that $P \cap Q \neq \emptyset$. It is represented by the shaded area designated R_1.

On the other hand, two sets P and Q are said to be *disjoint* or *mutually exclusive* if they have no common elements; i.e., if the intersection of the two sets is the null set $\emptyset$.

Example 3.4. Consider the sets

$$P = \{1, 2, 3\}$$

and

$$Q = \{a, b, c\}.$$

They are disjoint or mutually exclusive since $P \cap Q = \emptyset$. We can very easily visualize this relation if we imagine that the circles in Figure 3.2 representing the sets P and Q are not overlapping.

3.3. Union. *Let P and Q be any subsets of a universal set $\mathcal{U}$. Then the union of P and Q, denoted by $P \cup Q$, is the set of elements of $\mathcal{U}$ which are members of either P or Q or both.* In symbols, the definition of the union is

$$P \cup Q = \{x \in \mathcal{U} \mid x \in P \text{ or } x \in Q\},$$

read "*P* union *Q* is the set of those elements *x* of $\mathcal{U}$ for which *x* is an element of either *P* or *Q* or both."

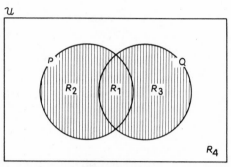

FIGURE 3.3.

Example 3.5. Consider the sets

$$P = \{\text{Rothmund, Hemeon, Green, Gross, White}\}$$

and

$$Q = \{\text{Clement, Rothmund, Hemeon, Lyon, Jenkins}\}$$

specified earlier. The union of these sets is

$$P \cup Q = \{\text{Rothmund, Hemeon, Green, Gross, White, Clement,}$$
$$\text{Lyon, Jenkins}\}.$$

It represents individuals who are board members of Rothmund Steel Corporation *or* of Mesabi Coal Company.

The union of two sets *P* and *Q* is illustrated in a Venn diagram shown in Figure 3.3. The set $P \cup Q$ is represented by the shaded area designated R_1, R_2, and R_3.

It is important to point out that in the union of sets the word "or" is used in its *inclusive* sense. For *P* union *Q* means the elements of *P* or the elements of *Q* or the elements that belong to both *P* and *Q*. The connective "or" in mathematics is *not* used in its *exclusive* sense whereby *P* or *Q* means the elements of *P* or the elements of *Q* but not the elements that belong to both *P* and *Q*.

3.4. Set Forming with Basic Operations. The discussion so far may be well summarized by emphasizing the fact that the words *not, and,* and *or* are the key words for remembering the complement, intersection, and union of sets. The complement of a set P is an operation similar to subtraction since $P' = \mathcal{U}$ minus P. Also, $P \cup Q$ is sometimes called the logical sum while $P \cap Q$ the logical product of P and Q because these operations obey several of the laws of the ordinary algebra of numbers.

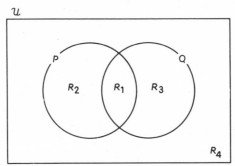

FIGURE 3.4.

We have seen that an effective way of illustrating the complement, intersection, and the union of sets P and Q is the use of regions of a Venn diagram. In fact, the four nonoverlapping regions of the Venn diagram in Figure 3.4 correspond to the four possibilities for any element of the universal set $\mathcal{U}$ as follows:

$$R_1 : \{x \in \mathcal{U} | x \in P \text{ and } x \in Q\} = P \cap Q,$$

$$R_2 : \{x \in \mathcal{U} | x \in P \text{ and } x \notin Q\} = P \cap Q',$$

$$R_3 : \{x \in \mathcal{U} | x \notin P \text{ and } x \in Q\} = P' \cap Q,$$

$$R_4 : \{x \in \mathcal{U} | x \notin P \text{ and } x \notin Q\} = P' \cap Q';$$

and any set which is formed by applying basic operations on sets P and

TABLE 3.1.

$\cap$ = Common

$\cup$ = one of each

Set	Area in Figure 3.4
$\mathcal{U}$	R_1 & R_2 & R_3 & R_4
P	R_1 & R_2
Q	R_1 & R_3
P'	R_3 & R_4
Q'	R_2 & R_4
$P \cap Q$	R_1
$P \cup Q$	R_1 & R_2 & R_3
$P \cap Q'$	R_2
$P' \cap Q$	R_3
$(P \cup Q)'$	R_4
$(P \cap Q)'$	R_2 & R_3 & R_4

Q can be expressed in terms of combinations of the above four regions. For example, the set $(P \cup Q)'$ contains the elements of $\mathfrak{U}$ which are not in the set $P \cup Q$, i.e., not in the area formed by the combinations of regions R_1, R_2, and R_3; therefore, $(P \cup Q)'$ represents region R_4. In contrast, the set $(P \cap Q)'$ contains the elements which are not in $P \cap Q$, i.e., not in region R_1; consequently, the set $(P \cap Q)'$ represents the area formed by the combination of regions R_2, R_3, and R_4.

These sets, plus others expressed in terms of regions as shown in Figure 3.4, are conveniently summarized in Table 3.1. The reader may verify that each listed set is represented by the corresponding region or regions.

Example 3.6. Consider the sets

$$P = \{\text{Rothmund, Hemeon, Green, Gross, White}\},$$
$$Q = \{\text{Clement, Rothmund, Hemeon, Lyon, Jenkins}\},$$

given previously, and

$$S = \{\text{Evans, Green, Rothmund, Clement, McCoy}\},$$

which represents the board of directors of Erie Shipping Company.
Applying the basic operations on these sets, we obtain

$$(P \cup Q) \cap S = \{\text{Rothmund, Green, Clement}\},$$
$$P' \cap (P \cap Q) = \varnothing,$$
$$(P \cap Q') \cap S' = \{\text{Gross, White}\},$$
$$(P \cap Q) \cap S' = \{\text{Hemeon}\}.$$

These, as well as other subsets of $\mathfrak{U}$, can be illustrated with a Venn diagram shown in Figure 3.5. One can imagine that the joint subsets

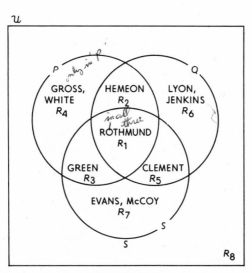

FIGURE 3.5.

P, Q, and S of $\mathcal{U}$ represent a case of interlocking directorates of an industrial complex in a miniature form or the case of an industrial empire with the set $P \cap (Q \cap S) = \{\text{Rothmund}\}$ representing Rothmund Enterprises, a holding company having controlling interests in Rothmund Steel Corporation, Mesabi Coal Company, and Erie Shipping Company. Interlocking directorates and holding companies are a few of the many developments which in the past have led to the concentration of economic power in business, a subject which is studied in economics courses.

A number of sets which can be formed by applying basic operations on three given subsets of $\mathcal{U}$ are shown in Table 3.2 where each set is

TABLE 3.2.

Set	Area in Figure 3.5
$\mathcal{U}$	R_1 & R_2 & R_3 & R_4 & R_5 & R_6 & R_7 & R_8
P	R_1 & R_2 & R_3 & R_4
Q	R_1 & R_2 & R_5 & R_6
S	R_1 & R_3 & R_5 & R_7
$P \cap Q$	R_1 & R_2
$Q \cap S$	R_1 & R_5
$P \cap S$	R_1 & R_3
$P \cup Q$	R_1 & R_2 & R_3 & R_4 & R_5 & R_6
$(P \cup Q) \cap S$	R_1 & R_3 & R_5
S'	R_2 & R_4 & R_6 & R_8
$S' \cap (P \cap Q')$	R_4

expressed in terms of a region or combination of regions as shown in Figure 3.5. It is left for the reader to verify that each listed set is represented by the corresponding region(s).

Example 3.7. The panel is one of the techniques used in marketing research. Under this method a scientifically selected sample of people are interviewed more than once at different time intervals with regard to a particular product or service. Suppose a sample of 1000 housewives are asked whether they are using "Gee-Whiz" soap or other brands for washing dishes. Six months later the same housewives are interviewed again to find out whether they are still using "Gee-Whiz" soap. A third interviewing of the same respondents for the same purpose takes place six months later. If we let P, Q, and R denote the sets of respondents who reported using "Gee-Whiz" soap during the first, second, and third interviews, respectively, then all the respondents who represent the universal set $\mathcal{U}$ can be classified into the eight categories or disjoint subsets shown in the Venn diagram of Figure 3.6.

In Table 3.3 a few of the subsets of $\mathcal{U}$ are identified. Suppose only the data in Table 3.3 are available to us. Can we find the respondents who belong to each of the eight disjoint subsets shown in Figure 3.6? This can be done by working from the bottom of the above list to the top. Since

TABLE 3.3.

Set	Respondents Using "Gee-Whiz" Soap	Interview
P	250	First
Q	325	Second
R	400	Third
$P \cap Q$	175	First and second
$P \cap R$	200	First and third
$Q \cap R$	250	Second and third
$P \cap (Q \cap R)$	150	First, second, and third

the disjoint region, $P \cap (Q \cap R)$, contains 150 elements and since subset $Q \cap R$ contains 250 elements, the set $(Q \cap R) \cap [P \cap (Q \cap R)]'$ contains 250–150 or 100 elements. Hence, there are 100 respondents who reported using "Gee-Whiz" soap during the second and third interviews but not during the first. Similarly, the set $(P \cap R) \cap [P \cap (Q \cap R)]'$ contains 200–150 or 50 respondents who reported using "Gee-Whiz" soap during the first and third interviews but not during the second. By repeating this process of subtraction we can obtain the number of respondents in each of the eight categories or disjoint subsets of $\mathcal{U}$.

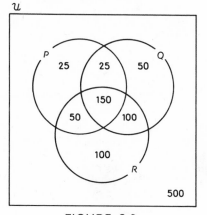

FIGURE 3.6.

Assume that after the first interview a one-year advertising campaign is launched for "Gee-Whiz" soap. From the Venn diagram in Figure 3.6 we can read that use of this soap increased from 25 percent (250/1000) before advertising had begun to 40 percent (400/1000) a year later. But of the 250 respondents who reported using "Gee-Whiz" soap during the first interview, only 150 or 15 percent kept using it throughout the year while the remaining 100 or 10 percent were less consistent.

PROBLEMS

*3.1. Let the universal set $\mathcal{U} = \{a, b, c, d\}$ and the sets $P = \{a, d\}$ and $Q = \{b, c\}$.

    a) List the elements of the following sets: P', Q', $P \cup Q$, $P \cap Q$, $P \cup Q'$, $P' \cup Q$, $(P \cup Q)'$, $(P \cap Q)'$.

    b) Refer to the Venn diagram in Figure 3.4 and determine the region or regions which each of the sets in (a) represents.

3.2. Let the universal set $\mathfrak{U} = \{a, b\}$ and the sets $P = \{a\}$ and $Q = \{b\}$.

   a) List the elements of the following sets: P', Q', $P \cup Q$, $P \cap Q$, $P \cup Q'$, $P' \cup Q$, $(P \cup Q)'$, $(P \cap Q)'$.

   b) Construct a Venn diagram showing the sets $\mathfrak{U}, P$, and Q as specified above and determine the region or regions which each of the sets in (a) represents.

3.3. Draw a Venn diagram with $\mathfrak{U} = \{1, 2, 3\}$, $P = \{1\}$, and $Q = \{1, 2\}$.

   a) List the elements of the following sets: P', Q', $P \cup Q$, $P \cap Q$, $P \cup Q'$, $P' \cup Q$, $(P \cup Q)'$, $(P \cap Q)'$.

   b) Let the elements of $\mathfrak{U}$ correspond to regions R_1, R_2, R_3, respectively. Determine the region or regions which each of the sets in (a) represents.

   c) By definition of the problem every element of P is also an element of Q. Using a Venn diagram verify that the following assertions are equivalent; i.e., each gives the information that every element of P is also an element of Q: $P \subseteq Q, P \cap Q' = \varnothing, P = P \cap Q, Q = P \cup Q$.

   d) If $P = Q$, will the above assertions be equivalent?

3.4. Let $\mathfrak{U} = \{1, 2, 3, 4, 5, 6, 7, 8\}$, $P = \{1, 2, 3, 4\}$, $Q = \{1, 2, 5, 6\}$, and $S = \{1, 3, 5, 7\}$.

   *a) List the elements of the following sets: $P \cap Q$, $P \cap S$, $Q \cap S$, $(P \cap Q)', (P \cap S)', (Q \cap S)', P \cup Q, P \cup S, Q \cup S, (P \cup Q)', (P \cup S)', (Q \cup S)', (P \cap Q) \cap S, (P \cup Q) \cap S, S', S' \cap (P \cup Q), [(P \cup Q) \cup S] \cap [(P \cap Q) \cap S]'$.

   b) Refer to the Venn diagram in Figure 3.5 and indicate the region or regions which each set in (a) represents.

3.5. The Central Supply Company, an all-metal screws distributor, has purchased a large lot of screws at an auction. A sample of 500 screws disclosed that they could be used for three different operations as indicated below:

   > 255 for operation A,
   > 240 for operation B,
   > 215 for operation C,
   > 125 for operation A and B,
   > 75 for operation A and C,
   > 60 for operation B and C,
   > 50 for all three operations.

   a) Draw a Venn diagram and determine the number of screws which can be used *exclusively* for operations A, B, and C, i.e., the elements of $A \cap (B \cup C)'$, $B \cap (A \cup C)'$, and $C \cap (A \cup B)'$.

   *b) Determine the number of screws in set $[(A \cup B) \cup C]'$. For which of the three operations can the screws of this set be used?

3.6. In a consumer survey housewives were asked the following question: Which brands of cold cereal did you serve your family during the last four weeks? brand A, brand B, or brand C? The response of the 100 interviewed housewives is shown below. (Note: In place of numbers of respondents percentages may be used also without difficulty.)

Brand A	Brand B	Brand C	Respondents
Yes	Yes	Yes	6
Yes	Yes	No	7
Yes	No	Yes	8
Yes	No	No	10
No	Yes	Yes	0
No	Yes	No	14
No	No	Yes	25
No	No	No	30

Total Number of Respondents .. 100

*a) Draw a Venn diagram and place the number of respondents shown above in the appropriate disjoint subset.

b) Find the number of elements and explain the meaning of each of the following sets: A, B, C, $A \cap B$, $A \cap C$, $B \cap C$, $[(A \cup B) \cup C]'$.

c) Is it appropriate to conclude that the brand with the largest number of respondents is the most popular brand? Explain why it is or it is not appropriate.

3.7. Verify that the following statements are true by referring to the regions of the Venn diagram in Figure 3.4.

a) If $P \subseteq Q$, then $Q' \subseteq P'$.

b) $\mathfrak{U}' = \varnothing$.

c) $\varnothing' = \mathfrak{U}$.

d) $(\mathfrak{U}')' = \mathfrak{U}$.

e) $(\varnothing')' = \varnothing$.

f) If $P \cup Q = \varnothing$, then P and Q are empty sets.

g) If $P \cap Q = \varnothing$, then it does not follow that $P = \varnothing$ or $Q = \varnothing$.

3.8. Verify that each of the following pairs of sets is represented by the same region or regions in the Venn diagram of Figure 3.5.

*a) $(P \cup Q)'$ and $P' \cap Q'$.

b) $(P \cap Q)'$ and $P' \cup Q'$.

c) $(P \cup Q) \cup S$ and $P \cup (Q \cup S)$.

d) $(P \cap Q) \cap S$ and $P \cap (Q \cap S)$.

e) $P \cap (Q \cup S)$ and $(P \cap Q) \cup (P \cap S)$.

3.9. Let P be a subset of the universal set $\mathfrak{U}$. By shading the appropriate regions of a Venn diagram verify the following statements:

*a) $P \cup P' = \mathfrak{U}$.

b) $P \cap P' = \varnothing$.

c) $(P')' = P$.

d) $\mathfrak{U}' = \varnothing$ and $\varnothing' = \mathfrak{U}$.

e) From (a) and (b) above formulate a definition of complement.

3.10. Let P and Q be subsets of the universal set $\mathfrak{U}$. By shading the appropriate regions of a Venn diagram verify that
$P \cap Q' = \varnothing$, if $P \subseteq Q$, and
$P \subseteq Q$, if $P \cap Q' = \varnothing$.

3.11. Let P be the power set $2^{\mathfrak{U}}$ as defined in Problem 2.11. Consider part 2.11(b) and show that—

a) A losing coalition is the complement of a winning coalition.

b) A blocking coalition is the complement of a blocking coalition.

c) Also show that $P = W \cup W'$ where W is the set of winning coalitions and W' is the set of nonwinning coalitions with respect to the power set $2^{\mathfrak{U}}$.

*3.12. Let P, Q, and R be subsets of a universal set $\mathfrak{U}$. Arrange the sets shown below in such an order that each set is a subset of the following sets:

$P \cap Q$, $P \cup Q$, $\mathfrak{U}$, Q, $P \cup (Q \cup R)$, $\varnothing$, $(P \cup Q) \cup R$, $(P \cap Q) \cap R$, $Q \cap P$, $\varnothing'$, $P \cap (Q \cap R)$.

3.13. Consider the data in Problem 1.4 where the major subsets of $\mathfrak{U}$ can be defined as follows:

$M = \{x \in \mathfrak{U} \,|\, x$ is a male respondent$\}$,
$W = \{x \in \mathfrak{U} \,|\, x$ is a female respondent$\}$,
$F = \{x \in \mathfrak{U} \,|\, x$ is a respondent smoking filter cigarettes$\}$,
$N = \{x \in \mathfrak{U} \,|\, x$ is a respondent smoking nonfilter cigarettes$\}$,

* a) Construct a diagram of set $\mathfrak{U}$ and its subsets.

b) Find the number of respondents in each of the following sets: $M \cap W$, $M \cap F$, $W \cap N$, $F \cap N$, $(F \cap M) \cup (N \cap M)$, $(M \cup N) \cap (W \cup N)$, $\mathfrak{U} \cap (N \cup M)'$, $(N \cup M)' \cap (N \cup W)$.

c) Explain why the following sets are disjoint: M & W, F & N.

d) Explain why the following sets are joint: M & F, W & N, M & N, W & F.

e) The set of respondents who are neither males nor smokers of nonfilter cigarettes is the set $(M \cup N)'$. Express the following statements in similar set notation using the basic operations of $'$, $\cap$, and $\cup$:

i) The set of respondents who are neither women nor smoke nonfilter cigarettes.

ii) The set of respondents who are women and do not smoke nonfilter cigarettes.

3.14. A sample of 586 families is distributed below by annual income and number of television sets owned:

TV Sets Owned	(1) Less than $3000	(2) $3000 to $5499	(3) $5500 to $8000	(4) More than $8000	Total
Two or more	5	87	42	47	181
One	76	154	57	23	310
None............	35	25	10	25	95
Total......	116	266	109	95	586

Let the universal set $\mathfrak{U}$ be the set of all families in the sample and the following subsets of $\mathfrak{U}$ be defined:

$T = \{x \in \mathfrak{U} \,|\, x$ is a family owning two or more TV sets$\}$,
$O = \{x \in \mathfrak{U} \,|\, x$ is a family with one TV set$\}$,

$P = \{x \in \mathcal{U} \,|\, x \text{ is a family with less than \$3000 income}\}$,
$Q = \{x \in \mathcal{U} \,|\, x \text{ is a family with \$3000 to \$5499 income}\}$,
$R = \{x \in \mathcal{U} \,|\, x \text{ is a family with \$5500 to \$8000 income}\}$.

a) Find the number of responding families in each of the following sets: $P \cap O$, $T \cup R$, $(T \cup O)' \cap R$, $(P \cup Q \cup R)' \cap (T \cup O)'$.

b) A number of sets are specified below. Express each of them in set notation using the basic operations of $'$, $\cap$, and $\cup$.

   i) $\{x \in \mathcal{U} \,|\, x \text{ is a family with one TV set and an income of less than \$5500}\}$.

   ii) $\{x \in \mathcal{U} \,|\, x \text{ is a family with no TV set and more than \$8000 income}\}$.

   iii) $\{x \in \mathcal{U} \,|\, x \text{ is a family with two or more TV sets or an income of \$5500 to \$8000}\}$.

   iv) $\{x \in \mathcal{U} \,|\, x \text{ is a family with no TV set}\}$.

3.15. The statements in Problem 2.5 can be expressed in set notation using only the symbols $\varnothing$, $'$, $\cap$, $\cup$, $=$, and $\neq$. For example, the statement, "Some wholesalers (W) are retailers (R)," means that there is at least one wholesaler who is a retailer. Thus, this statement can be expressed with $W \cap R \neq \varnothing$. Similarly, the statement, "All partnerships (P) are business (B) organizations," means that the set of partnerships is a subset of the set of business organizations, i.e., $P \subseteq B$. But since we are not allowed to use the set inclusion symbol, the subset notation is equivalent to $P \cap B = P$, $P \cup B = B$, or $P \cap B' = \varnothing$. Express the following statements in set notation using as set symbols the letters in parentheses:

a) No stockholder (S) is a creditor (C).

b) Some wholesalers (W) are not retailers (R').

c) If a person is a bondholder (B), then he is a creditor (C).

d) Some stockholders (S) are neither creditors (C) nor business managers (M).

e) Some bondholders (B) are creditors (C) and financiers (F).

f) A person is a bondholder (B) if and only if he is a creditor (C).

3.16. Let P and Q be subsets of the universal set $\mathcal{U}$. By means of Venn diagrams show that $P = Q$ if and only if $P \subseteq Q$ and $Q \subseteq P$.

3.17. Let $n(\mathcal{U})$, $n(P)$, and $n(Q)$ denote the number of elements in the universal set $\mathcal{U}$ and its subsets P and Q.

   a) Construct a Venn diagram and show in terms of regions that

   i) $n(P \cup Q) = n(P) + n(Q)$ if $(P \cap Q) = \varnothing$.

   ii) $n(P \cup Q) = n(P) + n(Q) - n(P \cap Q)$ if $(P \cap Q) \neq \varnothing$.

   Prove proposition (*a*)(ii) algebraically.

   b) From formula in (*a*)(ii) above show how one can derive the formula $n(\mathcal{U}) = n(P) + n(P')$.

4. THE ABSTRACT LAWS OF SET OPERATIONS

The discussion on subsets demonstrated the process of set formation while that on basic operations supplied the tools of combining sets.

Thus, we have found that there are many relationships among the newly formed sets. These relationships obey a number of abstract laws which form the subject matter of this section.

Our task will be to list the most important of these laws, stress the similarities which exist between laws of set operations and the laws of ordinary algebra, and show how the former can be proved by means of Venn diagrams, membership tables, or algebraically.

4.1. Laws of Set Operations. Let A, B, and C be any subsets of a universal set $\mathcal{U}$. Then the most important laws governing operations on sets are listed in Table 4.1. Laws 1 through 10 follow from the previously defined universal set $\mathcal{U}$, the empty set $\varnothing$, set equality, and operations denoted by $'$, $\cap$, and $\cup$. Two additional operations, denoted by $-$ and Δ, are introduced and explained in topic 4.5 of this section.

TABLE 4.1.

A. *Laws governing union and intersection*:
*1a. $A \cup \varnothing = A$.	1b. $A \cap \mathcal{U} = A$.
*2a. $A \cup B = B \cup A$.	2b. $A \cap B = B \cap A$.
*3a. $A \cup (B \cup C) = (A \cup B) \cup C$.	3b. $A \cap (B \cap C) = (A \cap B) \cap C$.
*4a. $A \cup (B \cap C) = (A \cup B) \cap (A \cup C)$.	4b. $A \cap (B \cup C) = (A \cap B) \cup (A \cap C)$.
*5a. $A \cup \mathcal{U} = \mathcal{U}$.	5b. $A \cap \varnothing = \varnothing$.
6a. $A \cup A = A$.	6b. $A \cap A = A$.

B. *Laws governing complements*:
*7a. $A \cup A' = \mathcal{U}$.	7b. $A \cap A' = \varnothing$.
*8a. $(A')' = A$.	
9a. $(A \cup B)' = A' \cap B'$.	9b. $(A \cap B)' = A' \cup B'$.
10a. $\mathcal{U}' = \varnothing$.	10b. $\varnothing' = \mathcal{U}$.

C. *Laws governing set-differences*:
11a. $A - B = A \cap B'$.
12a. $A \Delta B = (A \cap B') \cup (A' \cap B)$.

4.2. Boolean and Ordinary Algebra. The similarities between these laws and the laws of elementary algebra of numbers are numerous. From the latter we have learned that zero is an identity number with respect to addition, since $a + 0 = a$ and one is an identity number with respect to multiplication since $a \times 1 = a$ for any number a. The laws 1a and 1b in Table 4.1 are sometimes called *identity laws* because the empty set $\varnothing$ is an identity set with respect to union since $A \cup \varnothing = A$, and the universal set $\mathcal{U}$ is an identity set with respect to intersection since $A \cap \mathcal{U} = A$.

Also, from ordinary algebra we know that the order of the terms in the sum or product of two numbers can be interchanged or commuted without changing the result of these operations. In other words, addition and multiplication are commutative since

$$a + b = b + a \quad \text{and} \quad a \times b = b \times a$$

for any numbers a and b. Similarly, the laws 2a and 2b in Table 4.1 are considered to be *commutative laws* on set operations since

$$A \cup B = B \cup A \quad \text{and} \quad A \cap B = B \cap A;$$

i.e., the order in which two sets are written does not affect their union or intersection.

Furthermore, the laws 3a and 3b in Table 4.1 are analogous to the *associative laws* of ordinary algebra; i.e.,

$$a + (b + c) = (a + b) + c \quad \text{and} \quad a \times (b \times c) = (a \times b) \times c$$

for any number a, b, and c. For this reason it is not necessary to use parentheses in order to show the union or intersection of three or more sets. Thus, by analogy to the associative laws of ordinary algebra

$$A \cup (B \cup C) = (A \cup B) \cup C = A \cup B \cup C$$

and

$$A \cap (B \cap C) = (A \cap B) \cap C = A \cap B \cap C.$$

By contrast, for any number a, b, and c there is only one *algebraic distributive* law, namely,

$$a \times (b + c) = (a \times b) + (a \times c)$$

which is analogous to 4b, only one of the two distributive laws for sets.

A word of caution should be introduced, however, lest the analogy between the two groups of laws be considered perfect. We have said that because of numerous similarities between algebraic laws and abstract laws of set operations, $A \cup B$ is sometimes called the logical sum and $A \cap B$ the logical product of the sets A and B. But $a + a = 2a$ and $a \times a = a^2$, if a is a number; while laws 6a and 6b in Table 4.1, called *idempotent laws*, show that $A \cup A = A$ and $A \cap A = A$, if A is a set.

4.3. Venn Diagrams.

Any of the laws in Table 4.1 can be verified with a Venn diagram. We shall use two examples in order to illustrate.

Example 4.1. Let A and B be subsets of the universal set $\mathfrak{U}$. Then the Venn diagram in Figure 4.1 can be used to verify law 9a,

$$(A \cup B)' = A' \cap B',$$

called De Morgan's law. Since $A \cup B$ is represented by the regions R_1 & R_2 & R_3 in Figure 4.1, its complement $(A \cup B)'$, the left-hand side of law 9a, is represented by R_4.

Also, since A' is represented by R_3 & R_4 and B' by R_2 & R_4, their intersections $A' \cap B'$, the right-hand side of law 9a is represented by R_4.

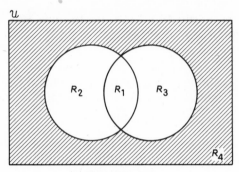

FIGURE 4.1.

Thus, it has been shown that the two sides of De Morgan's law are represented by the same shaded region designated R_4 in Figure 4.1.

Example 4.2. Let A, B, and C be subsets of the universal set $\mathcal{U}$. Then the distributive law 4a,

$$A \cup (B \cap C) = (A \cup B) \cap (A \cup C),$$

can be verified by using the Venn diagram in Figure 4.2.

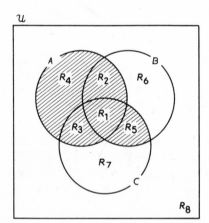

FIGURE 4.2.

Find the Area of $A \cup (B \cap C)$:

Since $B \cap C$ is represented by the regions R_1 & R_5, its union with A, i.e., $A \cup (B \cap C)$, is represented by R_1 & R_2 & R_3 & R_4 & R_5, the left-hand side of law 4a.

Find the Area of $(A \cup B) \cap (A \cup C)$:

Also, from Figure 4.2 we can see that $A \cup B$ is represented by R_1 & R_2 & R_3 & R_4 & R_5 & R_6 and $A \cup C$ by R_1 & R_2 & R_3 & R_4 & R_5 & R_7. Then the intersection of these two sets, i.e., $(A \cup B) \cap (A \cup C)$, is represented by R_1 & R_2 & R_3 & R_4 & R_5, the right-hand side of law 4a.

Thus, the two sides of law 4a are represented by the shaded area in Figure 4.2.

4.4. Membership Tables. Earlier, we introduced the notation for set membership. Let A and B be any sets of the universal set $\mathcal{U}$ and let x be any element of $\mathcal{U}$. Then with respect to sets A and B there are four possibilities for an element x which are given in Table 4.2, columns 2 and 3. Observe that these possibilities correspond to the regions R_1, R_2, R_3, and R_4 of a Venn diagram such as the one shown in Figure 4.1 and to the possibilities found by the application of the fundamental

TABLE 4.2.

Regions (1)	Possibilities A B (2) (3)	Complement A' (4)	Intersection $A \cap B$ (5)	Union $A \cup B$ (6)
R_1	$\in$ - $\in$	$\notin$	$\in$	$\in$
R_2	$\in$ - $\notin$	$\notin$	$\notin$	$\in$
R_3	$\notin$ - $\in$	$\in$	$\notin$	$\in$
R_4	$\notin$ - $\notin$	$\in$	$\notin$	$\notin$

principle of counting discussed earlier. These regions are shown in column 1 of Table 4.2.

With respect to the complement of set A there are two possibilities for an element x of $\mathfrak{U}$. Either x belongs to A or not; but if x belongs to A, then x does not belong to A'; and if x does not belong to A, then x belongs to A'. Thus, the membership table for A', shown in column 4 of Table 4.2, has an $\notin$ where the membership table for A has an $\in$ and an $\in$ where the membership table for A has an $\notin$.

With respect to the intersection of two sets A and B, any element x of $\mathfrak{U}$ belongs to $A \cap B$ if and only if x is an element of both A and B. Hence, the membership table for $A \cap B$, shown in column 5 of Table 4.2, has an $\in$ in possibility $\in$ - $\in$ and an $\notin$ in the other three remaining possibilities.

Finally, with regard to the union of A and B, an element of $\mathfrak{U}$ belongs to $A \cup B$ if x is an element of either A or B or both. Thus, the membership table for $A \cup B$, shown in column 6 of Table 4.2, has an $\notin$ in the fourth possibility $\notin$ - $\notin$ since this is the only possibility where an element x of $\mathfrak{U}$ does not belong to $A \cup B$.

The above membership tables of basic operations may be used to verify any of the laws in Table 4.1.

Example 4.3. In order to verify De Morgan's law 9a,

$$(A \cup B)' = A' \cap B',$$

we first prepare columns 1 and 2 of Table 4.3 which contain the four possibilities for an element x of $\mathfrak{U}$.

TABLE 4.3.

(1) A	(2) B	(3) $A \cup B$	(4) $(A \cup B)'$	(5) A'	(6) B'	(7) $A' \cap B'$
$\in$	$\in$	$\in$	$\notin$	$\notin$	$\notin$	$\notin$
$\in$	$\notin$	$\in$	$\notin$	$\notin$	$\in$	$\notin$
$\notin$	$\in$	$\in$	$\notin$	$\in$	$\notin$	$\notin$
$\notin$	$\notin$	$\notin$	$\in$	$\in$	$\in$	$\in$

Find the Membership Table of $(A \cup B)'$:

The set $A \cup B$ in column 3 is obtained by using the basic membership table for the union of two sets. In column 4 the membership table of the left-hand side of De Morgan's law is obtained by applying the basic membership table for complements to set $(A \cup B)$.

Find the Membership Table of $A' \cap B'$:

Columns 5 and 6 in Table 4.3 are obtained from columns 1 and 2, respectively, by using the basic membership table for complements. Then the intersection $A' \cap B'$ in column 7 is obtained by following the rule of the basic membership table for the intersection of two sets.

We now observe that columns 4 and 7 are identical; i.e., whenever an element of $\mathfrak{U}$ belongs to $(A \cup B)'$, it also belongs to $A' \cap B'$. In other words,

$$(A \cup B)' \subseteq A' \cap B'.$$

In addition, whenever an element of $\mathfrak{U}$ does not belong to $(A \cup B)'$, it does not belong to $A' \cap B'$ either. By definition of the complement of a set, it follows that every element that belongs to $A' \cap B'$ must also belong to $(A \cup B)'$; i.e.,

$$A' \cap B' \subseteq (A \cup B)'.$$

Recalling that two sets A and B are equal if and only if $A \subseteq B$ and $B \subseteq A$, we conclude that

$$(A \cup B)' = A' \cap B'.$$

Example 4.4. Verification of the distributive law 4a,

$$A \cup (B \cap C) = (A \cup B) \cap (A \cup C),$$

TABLE 4.4.

(1) A	(2) B	(3) C	(4) $B \cap C$	(5) $A \cup (B \cap C)$	(6) $A \cup B$	(7) $A \cup C$	(8) $(A \cup B) \cap (A \cup C)$
$\in$	$\in$	$\in$	$\in$	$\in$	$\in$	$\in$	$\in$
$\in$	$\in$	$\notin$	$\notin$	$\in$	$\in$	$\in$	$\in$
$\in$	$\notin$	$\in$	$\notin$	$\in$	$\in$	$\in$	$\in$
$\in$	$\notin$	$\notin$	$\notin$	$\in$	$\in$	$\in$	$\in$
$\notin$	$\in$	$\in$	$\in$	$\in$	$\in$	$\in$	$\in$
$\notin$	$\in$	$\notin$	$\notin$	$\notin$	$\in$	$\notin$	$\notin$
$\notin$	$\notin$	$\in$	$\notin$	$\notin$	$\notin$	$\in$	$\notin$
$\notin$	$\notin$	$\notin$	$\notin$	$\notin$	$\notin$	$\notin$	$\notin$

by membership tables is shown in Table 4.4. It can be seen that columns 5 and 8 of the table, representing the two sides of law 4a, are identical. By following the same reasoning as in the previous case, we reach the conclusion that the two sides of this law must be equal. The procedure of obtaining columns 5 and 8 is different from the case in Example 4.3 in two respects. Since there are three subsets, there are eight possibilities. Also, in cases such as this where parentheses are involved, it is important in using the basic membership tables to work out from inside the parentheses.

4.5. Verifying Laws of Set-Differences. Law 11a defines the *relative complement* or *difference* of sets A and B, read "A minus B." Also, law 12a defines the *symmetric difference* of sets A and B, read "A delta B." It may be of interest to note that $A \triangle B = (A \cap B') \cup (A' \cap B) = (A \cap B') \cup (B \cap A')$ by law 2a. But the latter expression is equivalent to $(A - B) \cup (B - A)$ by law 11a. Because these laws are important in later discussions, they are verified with both Venn diagrams and membership tables.

Example 4.5. The difference $A - B$ and the symmetric difference $A \triangle B$ are represented by the shaded areas shown in Figures 4.3 and 4.4, respectively.

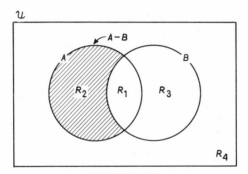

FIGURE 4.3.

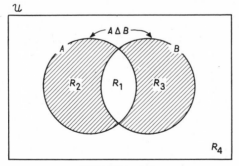

FIGURE 4.4.

Find the Area of $A - B$:
The set $A \cap B'$ is represented by region R_2 in Figure 4.3. Since $A - B = A \cap B'$, the difference $A - B$ is also represented by R_2.

Find the area of $A \triangle B$:

It has been shown that $A \cap B'$ is represented by R_2; similarly, $A' \cap B$ is represented by R_3 as shown in Figure 4.4. Since $A \triangle B = (A \cap B') \cup (A' \cap B)$, the symmetric difference $A \triangle B$ is represented by R_2 & R_3.

The membership tables of $A - B$ and $A \triangle B$ are shown in Table 4.5, columns 5 and 7, respectively.

TABLE 4.5.

(1) A	(2) B	(3) A'	(4) B'	(5) $A \cap B'$	(6) $A' \cap B$	(7) $(A \cap B') \cup (A' \cap B)$
$\in$	$\in$	$\notin$	$\notin$	$\notin$	$\notin$	$\notin$
$\in$	$\notin$	$\notin$	$\in$	$\in$	$\notin$	$\in$
$\notin$	$\in$	$\in$	$\notin$	$\notin$	$\in$	$\in$
$\notin$	$\notin$	$\in$	$\in$	$\notin$	$\notin$	$\notin$

4.6. The Duality Principle and Proofs.

Now that we have illustrated how the laws in Table 4.1 can be verified by Venn diagrams and membership tables, we are ready to discuss the *duality principle* and illustrate how set laws can be proved algebraically.

If, in any law, the sets $\varnothing$ and $\mathfrak{U}$ are interchanged and the set operations $\cup$ and $\cap$ are interchanged, then the result is again a law called the *dual* of the original law. For example, from 1a we can obtain its dual 1b by substituting $\cap$ for $\cup$ and $\mathfrak{U}$ for $\varnothing$. The dual of 2a can be derived by changing $\cup$ with $\cap$. Thus, for each of the laws shown on the left-hand side of Table 4.1, we are able to obtain its dual which is shown on the right-hand side of that table. Laws 8a, 11a, and 12a are said to be self-duals since the dual of each law is the law itself.

Furthermore, from the proof of *any* law we can obtain the proof of its dual by invoking the duality principle.

Example 4.6. To prove the idempotent law 6a, let A be any subset of the universal set $\mathfrak{U}$. Then

$$(4.1) \qquad A \cup A = A.$$

Proof:

$$
\begin{aligned}
A \cup A &= (A \cup A) \cap \mathfrak{U} && \text{[by 1b]} \\
&= (A \cup A) \cap (A \cup A') && \text{[by 7a]} \\
&= A \cup (A \cap A') && \text{[by 4a]} \\
&= A \cup \varnothing && \text{[by 7b]} \\
&= A && \text{[by 1a]}
\end{aligned}
$$

Invoking the dual of the law which justifies each of the steps in proving (4.1) we can obtain the proof of its dual law 6b,

$$(4.2) \qquad A \cap A = A.$$

Proof:

$$A \cap A = (A \cap A) \cup \varnothing \qquad \text{[by 1a]}$$
$$= (A \cap A) \cup (A \cap A') \qquad \text{[by 7b]}$$
$$= A \cap (A \cup A') \qquad \text{[by 4b]}$$
$$= A \cap \mathfrak{U} \qquad \text{[by 7a]}$$
$$= A \qquad \text{[by 1b]}$$

4.7. The Laws of Set Operations and Boolean Algebra.

The laws in Table 4.1 marked with an asterisk can be considered "fundamental" in the sense that all other laws can be deduced from them without drawing Venn diagrams or using membership tables, or even defining the meaning of the symbols ', $\cap$, and $\cup$. *Moreover, we can think of "set" as an abstract undefined term subject to several interpretations.* Thus the mathematical system of Boolean algebra which the "fundamental" laws in Table 4.1 specify has several applications. One such application is the algebra of sets which we have already considered. Defining the term "set" as statement and using the basic operations ', $\cap$, and $\cup$, we are led to another important application of Boolean algebra, namely, the logical analysis of statements or deductive logic. This topic will be taken up next.

PROBLEMS

4.1. State in words what each of the laws in Table 4.1 asserts.

4.2. Four rows were required in verifying law 9a by means of membership tables, while eight rows were necessary for law 4a. How many rows are required in a membership table for a law which contains four subsets? five subsets? n subsets where n is any positive integer? About what rule on subsets does your answer remind you? Compare the application of the rule in the two cases.

4.3. Of the laws shown in Table 4.1 only 4a, 9a, 11a, and 12a have been verified with Venn diagrams and membership tables.
  a) Verify the remaining laws in Table 4.1 by constructing membership tables.
  b) Verify the same laws by drawing Venn diagrams. Number each region of the diagram to correspond to the row of the membership table you have constructed in (*a*) for each law.

*4.4. Simplify the following sets by using De Morgan's law 9a and its dual 9b.
  a) $[A' \cup (B \cap C)]'$.
  b) $[(A' \cap B') \cup C']'$.
  c) $[(A' \cap B') \cup (B' \cap C') \cup (A' \cap C')]'$. *argument*

4.5. The following are special arguments called syllogisms. Each consists of two hypotheses and a conclusion.
  *i) (1) All farm (F) prices are unstable (N).
      (2) All farm incomes (I) depend on farm (F) prices.
      _____
      Therefore, all farm incomes (I) are unstable (N).

    ii) (1) All bondholders (B) are creditors (C).

       (2) No creditors (C) are shareholders (S).

      Therefore, no shareholders (S) are bondholders (B).

  a) Translate the statements of the two syllogisms into set equalities or inequalities using for set symbols the letters in parentheses (see Problem 3.15).

  b) An argument is valid if the conclusion is true whenever both hypotheses are true. Prove that each argument quoted above is valid. Justify each step of your proof by invoking one of the hypotheses or one of the laws in Table 4.1.

  c) Hypothesis (2) and the conclusion in syllogism (ii) above may be actually false. But the argument is valid and the conclusion is implied. How do you explain this "inconsistency"?

4.6. Let p be "food prices are rising" and q be "the cost of living index is rising." Also, let the expressions "not" or "it is not true that" correspond to the basic operation $'$, "and" to $\cap$, and "or" to $\cup$.

  a) Write down a verbal translation for each of the following statements:

    i) p'.   vi) $p' \cap q'$.

    ii) q'.   vii) $p' \cup q'$.

    iii) $p \cap q$.   viii) $(p \cap q)'$.

    iv) $p \cap q'$.   ix) $(p \cup q)'$.

    v) $p \cup q'$.   x) $(p' \cup q')'$.

  b) Simplify statement (x) in (*a*) by invoking De Morgan's law 9a and translate the simplified statement.

  c) Substitute "True" for $\in$ and "False" for $\notin$ and find the "truth" table of the following statements:

  *i) $(p \cup q) \cup (p \cup q)'$.

  ii) $(p \cup q) \cap (p \cup q)'$.

  d) Translate statements (i) and (ii) in (*c*) and explain why you would be inclined to call them logically true and logically false, respectively.

  e) What may this new application of Boolean algebra be called?

4.7. Let A be a subset of a universal set $\mathfrak{U}$ and consider the following laws of relative complements:

  *i) $\mathfrak{U} - A = A'$.   iii) $A - \varnothing = A$.   v) $A - A = \varnothing$.

  ii) $A - \mathfrak{U} = \varnothing$.   iv) $\varnothing - A = \varnothing$.

  a) Express, if possible, the set equality between the two sides of each of the above laws in terms of Venn diagrams.

  b) Verify each law by means of a membership table.

  c) Prove that these laws follow from the laws in Table 4.1.

4.8. Let A, B, and C be any subsets of a universal set $\mathfrak{U}$. Do (*a*), (*b*), and (*c*), as specified in Problem 4.7, for the following laws of relative complements:

  *i) $A - (B - C) = (A - B) \cup (A \cap C)$.

  ii) $(A - B) - C = A - (B \cup C)$.

  iii) $A \cap (B - C) = (A \cap B) - (A \cap C)$.

  iv) $A \cup (B - C) = (A \cup B) - (C - A)$.

4.9. Let the set A be a subset of $\mathcal{U}$. Do (a), (b), and (c) as specified in Problem 4.7 for the following laws of symmetric difference:

*i) $\mathcal{U} \Delta A = A \Delta \mathcal{U} = A'$.   iii) $A \Delta A = \varnothing$.
ii) $A \Delta \varnothing = \varnothing \Delta A = A$.   iv) $A \Delta A' = \mathcal{U}$.

4.10. Let the sets A, B, and C be any subsets of $\mathcal{U}$. Do (a) and (b), as specified in Problem 4.7, for the following laws of symmetric difference:

*i) $A \Delta B = B \Delta A$.
ii) $A \Delta (B \Delta C) = (A \Delta B) \Delta C$.
iii) $A \cap (B \Delta C) = (A \cap B) \Delta (A \cap C)$.

4.11. Let A, B, and C be any subsets of a universal set $\mathcal{U}$. Draw appropriate Venn diagrams and construct membership tables to verify the following laws:

*a) $(A \cup B) \cap (A \cup B') = A$.
b) $(A \cap B) \cup (A \cap B') = A$.
c) $A \cup B = (A \cap B) \cup (A \cap B') \cup (A' \cap B)$.
d) $[A' \cup (B \cup C)]' = A \cap B' \cap C'$.
e) $[A' \cup (A \cap B)']' = A \cap B$.
f) $A \cap (A \cup B) = A$.
g) $B \cup (A \cup B) = A \cup B$.
h) $A \cap B = (A' \cup B')'$.
i) $A \cup B = (A' \cap B')'$.
j) $(A' \cup B')' \cup (A' \cup B)' = A$.

4.12. Consider the laws *(a), (b), (c), (d), (e), (f), (g), (h), (i), (j) given in Problem 4.11. Prove each one algebraically. Justify each step of your proof by citing the law or laws you invoke from Table 4.1.

4.13. On the basis of the laws in Table 4.1 prove that

$$(A \cap B) \cup (A' \cap B) \cup (A \cap B') \cup (A' \cap B') = \mathcal{U}.$$

4.14. Prove law 10a in Table 4.1. Show how its dual 10b is proved by invoking the duality principle.

4.15. Prove De Morgan's law 9a and its dual 9b shown in Table 4.1.
(*Hint:* Given that $(A \cup B)$ and $(A' \cap B')$ are sets, show that their union is the universal set $\mathcal{U}$ while their intersection the empty set $\varnothing$, and prove the law by using the laws governing complements.)

4.16. Prove that there is one and only one null set $\varnothing$.

SUGGESTED REFERENCES

1. ALLENDOERFER, C. B., AND OAKLEY, C. O. *Principles of Mathematics*, pp. 103–12. New York: McGraw-Hill Book Co., Inc., 1955. **(1–4)**

2. GOLDBERG, SAMUEL. *Probability: An Introduction*, pp. 1–38. Englewood Cliffs, N.J.: Prentice-Hall, Inc., 1960. **(1–4)**

3. KEMENY, JOHN G., *et al.* *Introduction to Finite Mathematics*, pp. 54–70. Englewood Cliffs, N.J.: Prentice Hall, Inc., 1957. **(1–4)**

4. MATHEMATICAL ASSOCIATION OF AMERICA. COMMITTEE ON THE UNDER-
   GRADUATE PROGRAM. *Elementary Mathematics of Sets with Applications*,
   pp. 1–6. 1959. **(1–4)**
5. RICHARDSON, M. *Fundamentals of Mathematics*, pp. 176–84. Rev. ed. New
   York: The Macmillan Co., 1958. **(3, 4)**
6. ROSE, I. H. *A Modern Introduction to College Mathematics*, pp. 3–17.
   New York: John Wiley & Sons, Inc., 1960. **(1, 2)**
7. WESTERN, D. W., AND HAAG, V. H. *An Introduction to Mathematics*,
   pp. 153–67. New York: Henry Holt & Co., Inc., 1959. **(3, 4)**

Chapter 2

SETS AND LOGICAL STATEMENTS

CHAPTER 1 dealt exclusively with sets, whereas this and the following chapter deal with statements. Statements are the basic units of deductive logic, and deductive logic is another application of Boolean algebra. We shall, therefore, proceed in this chapter by defining statements, examining the different ways statements can be compounded, and showing how the truth value of a compound statement can be determined from the known truth value of its component parts. In developing these topics, we shall build upon our previous knowledge by discussing the similarities and differences between sets and statements from the conceptual standpoint as well as with respect to basic operations, truth tables, and Venn diagrams. In closing this chapter, we shall deal with logical propositional statements and logical possibilities.

1. FROM SETS TO STATEMENTS

1.1. Definition of a Statement. What constitutes a statement is somewhat more difficult to define than what constitutes a set. There is no universal rule for determining whether a given sentence or word is a statement because almost any generalization about statements has exceptions. Nevertheless, we shall attempt to specify a working understanding of the concept of a statement, knowing that our remarks may require further clarification in a more sophisticated treatment of the subject.

A statement is a verbal or written assertion which is either hypothetically or actually true or false but not both. This working definition of a statement involves the following three conditions:

-A. Only *declarative sentences,* i.e., sentences which assert that something is true or false, are statements. For example, the sentence, "New England is the birthplace of textile manufacturing in the United States," is a true statement asserting that New England is the birthplace of the American textile industry. The same assertion may be expressed by

37

another sentence, "The American textile industry started in New England," or by another declarative sentence in English or any other language. We can see that an assertion can be expressed by more than one sentence, since there are alternative ways of phrasing a given truth or falsehood. Therefore, an assertion is the nucleus of a statement. Consequently, interrogatory, exclamatory, hortatory, optative, and imperative sentences, and, in most instances, isolated nouns or adjectives are not statements. For nothing is asserted to be true or false by expressions such as "How is business?", "How progressive is the mangement of XYZ Company!", "Let's try to raise a bond issue.", "Let x be interest.", "Attention! Sales clearance.", "Comparative advantage," etc.

B. It is not necessary for a statement to be *actually* true or false; it can also be *hypothetically* true or false. "New England is the cradle of the industrial revolution in the United States" can be actually true or we may assume that it is true.

C. A given statement is either true or false *but not both*; there can be *no middle ground.* The previous statement, "New England is the birthplace of textile manufacturing in the United States," can be either true or false, there can be no in-between classification. This rule is a combination of two fundamental laws of logic which will be discussed in the next section.

1.2. Propositional and Set Statements.   For the sake of convenience in studying logic, statements may be classified into two categories. A statement which asserts a proposition may be called a *propositional statement*. For example, the previously quoted statements about New England are propositional statements. A statement which asserts a relation between sets may be called a *set statement*. For instance, the statement "All farm prices are unstable" is a set statement because it asserts a relation between the set of farm prices and the set of things which are unstable. Similarly, the statement "Some cars are white" is a set statement for it asserts a relation between the set of cars and the set of white objects.

We shall follow the general practice of denoting propositional and set statements with lowercase letters. Thus, the statements

$p =$ "New England is the birthplace of the American textile industry" and
$q =$ "All farm prices are unstable,"

previously quoted, are clearly distinguished from sets. Note that statements are further distinguished from sets by using quotation marks instead of braces.

Although conversion of propositional statements to set statements and vice versa is usually possible, their separate analysis is important enough to occupy two major topics in deductive logic: namely, the *logic*

of propositions and the *logic of classes or sets.* They will be the subject
matter of subsequent discussion.

1.3. Simple Set Statements and Boolean Algebra.
Simple set statements indicate a single relation between a *subject* and a
predicate. The subject represents the set about which the statement
makes an assertion or denial, while the predicate denotes the set asserted
or denied. For example, the statement "All farm prices are unstable"
asserts the predicate *unstable things* of the subject *farm prices*; and the
statement "Some cars are not white" denies the predicate *white cars* of
the subject *cars.*

Simple set statements may be expressed in terms of equations or
inequalities of sets by direct application of basic operations of Boolean
algebra.

Example 1.1. Express the simple set statement

$$p = \text{"All smokers are drinkers"}$$

in terms of set operations.

Let $\mathcal{U}$ be the set of all people and

$$P = \{x \in \mathcal{U} \,|\, x \text{ is a person who smokes}\},$$

$$Q = \{x \in \mathcal{U} \,|\, x \text{ is a person who drinks}\}.$$

Then, since according to our statement all smokers drink, the set P is a
subset of Q, i.e., $P \subseteq Q$. But the latter subset relation is equivalent to

$$P \cup Q = Q, \text{ or } P \cap Q = P, \text{ or } P \cap Q' = \varnothing.$$

Hence, the statement p can be expressed by any one of the above three set
equations.

In general, let P and Q be any two sets other than the null set $\varnothing$. Then
four basic types of simple set statements can be formed, each representing

TABLE 1.1.

Statement Notation (1)	Basic Forms of Simple Set Statements (2)	Corresponding Set Representation (3)
p	="All P is Q"	$P \cap Q = P$
q	="Some P is Q"	$P \cap Q \neq \varnothing$
r	="No P is Q"	$P \cap Q = \varnothing$
s	="Some P is not Q"	$P \cap Q' \neq \varnothing$

a different relation between sets P and Q. Their general forms are conveniently summarized in column 2 of Table 1.1 with some of their
corresponding set representations shown in column 3. Since we have

already illustrated statement p, we shall explain the other remaining three types of set statements.

Example 1.2. Let P and Q be the sets defined in Example 1.1 and consider the set statement

$$q = \text{``Some smokers are drinkers.''}$$

Since this set statement indicates that there is at least one smoker who drinks, the intersection of P and Q is not the null set $\varnothing$ and q may be expressed by

$$P \cap Q \neq \varnothing$$

as shown in Table 1.1.

Similarly, the set statement

$$r = \text{``No smokers are drinkers''}$$

may be expressed by the set equation

$$P \cap Q = \varnothing$$

since the set statement r indicates that the intersection of sets P and Q is the null set $\varnothing$.

Finally, since the set statement

$$s = \text{``Some smokers are not drinkers''}$$

indicates that the intersection of P and Q' is not the null set $\varnothing$, statements may be expressed by

$$P \cap Q' \neq \varnothing.$$

It is left for the reader to visualize these four types of set statements with a Venn diagram.

Now that we have shown the connection between simple set statements and Boolean algebra, we may turn to the study of propositional statements.

1.4. Basic Operations on Propositional Statements.

The basic of operations $'$, $\cap$, $\cup$, of Boolean algebra can be applied to *simple* or *atomic* propositional statements to form new statements, called negation, conjunction, and disjunction, respectively.

Let p and q be any two simple or atomic propositional statements. Then,

I. The *negation* of statement p is denoted by p' and read "not p" or "it is not true that p."

Example 1.3. Let p be the statement

$p = $ "New England is the birthplace of textile manufacturing in the United States."

Then the negation of p is

$p' =$ "New England is *not* the birthplace of textile manufacturing in the United States"

or

$p' =$ "*It is not true* that New England is the birthplace of textile manufacturing in the United States."

II.   The *conjunction* of p and q is denoted by $p \cap q$ and read "p and q."

Example 1.4. Let p be the statement specified in Example 1.3 and

$q =$ "New England is the cradle of the industrial revolution in the United States."

Then the conjunction of p and q is

$p \cap q =$ "New England is the birthplace of textile manufacturing *and* the cradle of the industrial revolution in the United States."

III.   The *disjunction* of p and q is denoted by $p \cup q$ and read "p or q" (or in its inclusive sense).

Example 1.5. Let p and q be the statements specified in Examples 1.3 and 1.4, respectively. Then the disjunction of p and q is

$p \cup q =$ "New England is the birthplace of textile manufacturing *or* the cradle of the industrial revolution in the United States."

1.5. Basic Truth Tables. In discussing the basic operations of Boolean algebra on sets we introduced membership tables for the complement, intersection, and union of sets. The corresponding truth tables for the negation, conjunction, and disjunction of propositional statements are shown in Table 1.2 where the four possibilities between any

TABLE 1.2.

Row	Possibilities of p & q		Negation p'	Conjunction p∩q	Disjunction p∪q
(1)	(2)	(3)	(4)	(5)	(6)
1	T - T		F	T	T
2	T - F		F	F	T
3	F - T		T	F	T
4	F - F		T	F	F

two simple propositional statements p and q are shown in columns 2 and 3.

We are now concerned with the truth or falsity of propositional statements. Note that the only difference between the truth tables in Table 1.2

and the corresponding basic membership tables (Table 4.2, Chapter 1) is the substitution of T for ∈ and of F for ∉. From columns 2 and 4 of Table 1.2 we may conclude that *the negation of a true statement is false and the negation of a false statement is true.* From column 5 we see that *the conjunction of two statements p and q is true if and only if both statements are true; otherwise it is false.* Finally, column 6 shows that the *disjunction of two statements p and q is true if and only if at least one of the statements is true; otherwise it is false.*

1.6. Compound Statements and Their Truth Value.

We have seen how the basic operations of Boolean algebra ', ∩, and ∪, originally applied to sets, can be applied to simple statements. Thus, these operations, now called negation, conjunction, and disjunction can be used to form complex compound propositional statements.

Example 1.6. Let p and q be the statement specified in Examples 1.3 and 1.4, respectively. Then, by applying the basic operations of Boolean algebra, we have

$(p \cap q)' =$ "It is not true that New England is the birthplace of textile manufacturing and the cradle of the industrial revolution in the United States."

By De Morgan's law 9b in Table 4.1 of Chapter 1, the above statement is equivalent to

$p' \cup q' =$ "Either New England is not the birthplace of textile manufacturing or New England is not the cradle of the industrial revolution in the United States."

Furthermore, truth tables may be used to verify the abstract laws of Boolean algebra (Table 4.1, Chapter 1) the same way that membership tables have been used earlier to verify these laws. We shall give only one example to illustrate this point.

Example 1.7. Verify De Morgan's law

$$(p \cap q)' = p' \cup q',$$

invoked in Example 1.6, using the basic truth tables.

Find the Truth Value of $(p \cap q)'$:

From the four possibilities of p and q shown in columns 1 and 2 of Table 1.3, we can find the truth value of $p \cap q$ shown in column 3 by using the basic truth table for conjunction. The truth value of $(p \cap q)'$, the left-hand side of De Morgan's law, shown in column 4, is obtained from the truth table of $p \cap q$ by using the basic truth table for negation.

Find the Truth Value of $p' \cup q'$:

From the truth tables p and q, shown in columns 1 and 2 of Table 1.3, we obtain the truth value of p' and q', shown in columns 5 and 6, respectively, by using the basic truth table for negation. The truth value of

TABLE 1.3.

(1) (2) $p \quad q$	(3) $p \cap q$	(4) $(p \cap q)'$	(5) p'	(6) q'	(7) $p' \cup q'$
T - T	T	F	F	F	F
T - F	F	T	F	T	T
F - T	F	T	T	F	T
F - F	F	T	T	T	T

$p' \cup q'$, the right-hand side of De Morgan's law shown in column 7, is obtained from p' and q' by using the basic truth table for disjunction.

Thus, De Morgan's law is verified. Statement $(p \cap q)'$, representing the left-hand side, is equivalent to statement $p' \cup q'$, representing the right-hand side of the law, since their truth tables are identical.

In addition, the above verification of De Morgan's law leads to a definition of equivalent statements. *In general, two propositional statements are equivalent if and only if their truth tables are identical.*

Finally, truth tables allow us to study the truth or falsity of compound statements as a function of the truth of constituent parts.

Example 1.8. Let p and q be

$$p = \text{"costs go down,"}$$
$$q = \text{"prices go up."}$$

Assuming that p is *true* and q is *false*, find whether the statement

$$(p \cup q)' \cap q$$

is true.

The sequence of operations on the given truth value of the constituent parts of the compound statement can be illustrated with the diagram shown in Figure 1.1.

	Explanation
1.	Statement
2.	Given truth value
3.	Disjunction
4.	Negation
5.	Conjunction

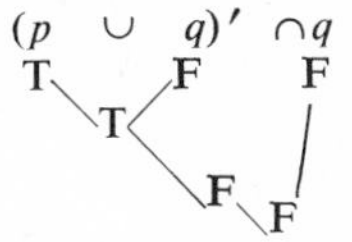

FIGURE 1.1.

Since p is given to be true and q is given to be false, their disjunction $p \cup q$ is true, the negation $(p \cup q)'$ is false, and the conjunction $(p \cup q)' \cap q$ is false. Thus, the given compound statement is false.

Note that the analysis in Figure 1.1, like the similar analysis for sets, proceeds from inside the parentheses out. Truth tables will be used later on for determining the truth value of more complex compound propositional statements.

1.7. Relationship between Sets and Propositional Statements.
The close connection between set operations and operations on propositional statements can also be illustrated with Venn diagrams such as the one in Figure 1.2. Let p and q be any statements and let $\mathcal{U}$ be the set of their true and false logical possibilities, i.e., all possible ways that two propositional statements can be related. Since each statement can be either true or false, the number of ways that two statements can be logically related is $2^2 = 4$. Thus, the number of logical

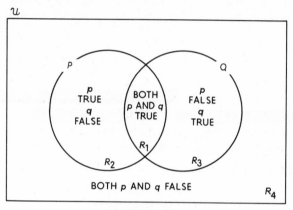

FIGURE 1.2.

possibilities of two or more statements is a direct application of the general rule for determining the number of rows in a membership table or a truth table.

Let P and Q be the subsets of $\mathcal{U}$ for which statements p and q are true, respectively. Then P and Q are called the *truth sets* of p and q. To statement p we assign a set P for which that statement is true while to p', the negation of p, we assign a set P', the complement of P, for which statement p is false. This process is repeated for statement q. Similarly, to the conjunction $p \cap q$ and the disjunction $p \cup q$ we assign the sets $P \cap Q$ and $P \cup Q$, respectively, for which these statements are true. Since each statement can be either true or false, there are 2^2 or 4 compound statements corresponding to an equal number of subsets which form the universal set $\mathcal{U}$. This process of assigning statements to sets holds true for n statements where n is any positive integer. Thus, we can convert a problem about compound propositional statements into a problem about sets.

Example 1.9. Verify De Morgan's law

$$(p \cap q)' = p' \cup q'$$

by means of a Venn diagram.

Let the set P and Q, shown in Figure 1.2, represent the truth sets of p and q, respectively. Then, in order to verify the above law, it is sufficient to show that the truth sets of $(p \cap q)'$ and $p' \cup q'$ represent the same areas of the Venn diagram in Figure 1.2.

Find the Area of $(P \cap Q)'$:
Since $P \cap Q$ is represented by region R_1, $(P \cap Q)'$ is represented by R_2 & R_3 & R_4.

Find the Area of $P' \cup Q'$:
Since P' is represented by R_3 & R_4 and Q' by R_2 & R_4, their union $P' \cup Q'$ is represented by R_2 & R_3 & R_4.

Thus, the truth sets $(P \cap Q)'$ and $P' \cup Q'$ are equal and the corresponding statements $(p \cap q)'$ and $p' \cup q'$ are equivalent.

We have seen that both set and propositional statements can be symbolically expressed in terms of sets. There is, however, a basic difference between these two forms of symbolic expression. Basic set operations are applied to two sets, the subject and the predicate, in order to construct *simple* set statements in the form of set equalities or inequalities. In contrast, the same operations are applied to two or more simple propositional statements in order to form *compound* propositional statements. Furthermore, in the former case we make direct use of sets, while in the latter the use of sets is indirect by assigning a truth set to each propositional statement.

PROBLEMS

1.1. Indicate whether each of the following sentences is a statement and, if it is, whether it is a set or a propositional statement. Justify your answer in each case.

*a) "All accounts receivable are assets."
*b) "How large is XYZ Company?"
*c) "XYZ Company is a price leader in the steel industry."
d) "Imagine what the National Income of the United States will be in the year 2000!"
e) "Do not ask questions about prices; ask questions about costs."
f) "No worker in this plant is a union member."
g) "The most important selling point of this new product is quality."
h) "Let us bargain first instead of striking for higher wages."

1.2. After expressing the following statements in the symbolic form of set equalities or inequalities, discuss each statement in terms of regions of a Venn diagram.

*a) "Some teen-agers are car drivers."
*b) "All teen-agers are car drivers."
*c) "No teen-ager is a car driver."
*d) "Some teen-agers are not car drivers."
e) "No car drivers are teen-agers."
f) "Some car drivers are teen-agers."

g) "All car drivers are teen-agers."

h) "Some car drivers are not teen-agers."

1.3. Set statement (*a*) in Problem 1.2 can be expressed in general form as follows:

"Some *T*'s are *D*'s,"

where *T* stands for teen-agers and *D* for drivers. Express in a similar form the remaining set statements of that problem.

1.4. Express the following statements in symbolic form, letting

$$p = \text{"Costs are reduced"}$$

and

$$q = \text{"Prices are reduced,"}$$

and find the truth value of each statement.

*a) "Costs are reduced and prices remain the same."

*b) "Prices are reduced and costs remain the same."

*c) "Either costs are not reduced or prices are not reduced."

d) "Both costs and prices remain the same."

e) "Both costs and prices are reduced."

f) "Either costs or prices are reduced."

g) "Either costs are reduced or prices remain the same."

h) "It is not true that both costs and prices remain the same."

1.5. Assuming that both *p* and *q* are true, find which of the compound statements in **(a)*, **(b)*, **(c)*, (*d*), (*e*), (*f*), (*g*), and (*h*) of Problem 1.4 are true.

1.6. Find the truth set of each compound statement in **(a)*, **(b)*, **(c)*, (*d*), (*e*), (*f*), (*g*), and (*h*) of Problem 1.4 by means of Venn diagrams.

1.7. Find one set and one propositional statement from each of the following subjects:

a) Accounting.

b) Behavioral science.

c) Economics.

d) Finance.

e) Marketing.

f) Production.

g) Statistics.

1.8. Letting

$$p = \text{"Stock prices are rising"}$$

and

$$q = \text{"The stock market is bullish,"}$$

express the following compound statements in words and find the truth value of statements (*a*) through (*j*):

*a) $p \cap q$.
*b) $p \cup q$.
*c) $p \cap q'$.
d) $q \cap p'$.
e) $p \cup q'$.
f) $q' \cup p$.
g) $(p \cap q)'$.
h) $(p \cup q)'$.
i) $(p' \cap q')'$.
j) $(p' \cup q')'$.

1.9. Using Boolean algebra simplify statements *(*i*) and (*j*) in Problem 1.8, and express the simplified statements in words. Do they convey the same idea of the original statements? Find their truth value and compare them with the truth value of the original statements.

1.10. Let p and q be any statements. Show that the following pairs of statements are equivalent by means of truth tables and Venn diagrams.
   a) p and $p \cup (p \cap q)$.
   b) $(p \cup q)'$ and $p' \cap q'$.
   c) $p \cap q'$ and $(p' \cup q)'$.

1.11. Let p and q be the statements defined in Problem 1.4 and

$$r = \text{"Profits have increased."}$$

Express the following statements in symbols and find their truth value:
   a) "Either costs are reduced or prices are not reduced and profits have increased." $_{and}$
   b) "Neither costs nor prices are reduced, but profits have increased."
   c) "It is not true that costs and prices are not reduced while profits have increased."

1.12. Find the truth set of each compound propositional statement in *(*a*), (*b*), and (*c*) of Problem 1.11.

1.13. Assuming statements p and q in Problem 1.11 are true and statement r is false, find the truth value of the compound propositional statements in *(*a*), (*b*), or (*c*) of Problem 1.11.

1.14. Let p, q, and r be the statements given in Problems 1.4 and 1.11. Express in words the following compound propositional statement and show that each pair is equivalent by means of truth tables and Venn diagrams.
   a) $(p \cap q) \cup r$ and $(p \cup r) \cap (q \cup r)$.
   b) $(p \cup q) \cap r$ and $(p \cap r) \cup (q \cap r)$.
   c) $(p' \cap q')' \cap r$ and $(p \cup q) \cap r$.

1.15. The working definition of a statement p which is given in the text implies the following fundamental laws of logic:
   a) For all p, p is equivalent to p.
   b) For all p, the statement $p \cap p'$ is always false.
   c) For all p, the statement $p \cup p'$ is always true. Assigning a set P to statement p, express the above laws in appropriate set notation.

2. LOGICAL STATEMENTS AND LOGICAL POSSIBILITIES

After showing the relationship between sets and statements we now turn to a systematic study of logically true or false statements and logical possibilities. Our primary objective will be to distinguish between factual and logical statements and examine their anatomy. This division is essential to our subject matter inasmuch as deductive logic may be said to deal with the analysis of logical statements. Although in this section we shall be concerned with propositional statements, we should keep in mind that the principles discussed here are applicable to set statements as well. The logical possibilities of set statements are studied in connection with probability theory in Part V of our course.

2.1. Factual Propositional Statements. *A simple statement is factual if its truth or falsity depends on some fact, situation, circumstance, or state of affairs which either exists or is assumed to exist in the real world.*

Example 2.1. Consider the previously quoted simple statement

$p = $ "New England is the birthplace of textile manufacturing in the United States."

Its truth or falsity depends on historical events. Hence, it is a factual statement.

However, a statement is factual although its truth or falsity may depend on some unavailable fact.

Example 2.2. The simple statement

$q = $ "There is gold under the White House"

is factual. For its truth or falsity depends on the assumption we may make about the outcome of mining in the designated area.

Similarly, compound propositional statements can be factual as the following example illustrates.

Example 2.3. Let the following compound propositional statements be given,

$p \cap q = $ "The United States is a monopolistic and a laboristic economy," and
$p \cup q = $ "The United States is a monopolistic or a laboristic economy."

Some economists may consider the above statements to be true because they wish to emphasize the economic controls which large corporations and big unions may be capable of exerting in our economy. Other economists may believe that such emphasis is overexaggerated and therefore that the statements are false. Whatever their opinion, however, it depends on *facts or observations* which exist in the real world. Accordingly, we may conclude that the statements are factual.

But in order to understand why the statements in the above examples are factual we must explain further in what sense the truth or falsity of factual statements depends on observations, existing or assumed, of the real world. We can do that only by studying the anatomy of compound statements with truth tables and Venn diagrams.

Example 2.4. Let us consider again the statements specified in Example 2.3. We may recall that the conjunctive statement $p \cap q$ is true if and only if p and q are both true; otherwise it is false. In other words, it is not exclusively true or exclusively false in all possible combinations of p and q. In this sense, the truth or falsity of $p \cap q$ *depends* on whether the simple statements p and q are considered true or false either as the result of real-world observations or by assumption. For the same reason, the disjunctive statement $p \cup q$ is never true or false in all four possible combinations of p and q. Its truth or falsity *depends* on whether the simple statements p and q are true or false either on the basis of fact or by assumption. Thus, $p \cup q$ is true if either p or q is true and false if both p and q are false.

Furthermore, we can easily realize that the truth sets $P \cap Q$ and $P \cup Q$ assigned to the statements $p \cap q$ and $p \cup q$, respectively, represent neither the universal set $\mathfrak{U}$ nor the empty set $\varnothing$.

The above points can be easily verified with truth tables and a Venn diagram.

In sum, *a simple or compound propositional statement is factual if its truth or falsity depends on existing or assumed real-world observations in the sense that its truth value is not in all possible ways true or false and the truth set assigned to the statement is neither the universal set $\mathfrak{U}$ nor the empty set $\varnothing$.* Thus the dependence of factual statements on the "real world" takes on a special meaning which does not depend on the content of statements. Indeed, all the propositional statements we have quoted in Section 1 are factual.

2.2. Logical Propositional Statements.

At this point the reader may be able correctly to define logical statements. It might be desirable, however, to proceed with examples.

Example 2.5. Let the following disjunctive propositional statement be given,

$p \cup p' =$ "The United States is a monopolistic economy or it is not."

By the definition of statements, there are two possibilities for p; it can be either true or false. But if p is true, then its disjunction with p' yields the statement $p \cup p'$, which is true. Also, if p is false, then its disjunction with p' yields the same result. This means that the statement $p \cup p'$ is true in all possible ways. The reader may verify the fact that the truth value of $p \cup p'$ is always T. Also, the truth set $P \cup P'$ assigned to the statement $p \cup p'$ represents the universal set. The reader can easily verify this point with a Venn diagram.

Statements such as the one considered in Example 2.5 are called *logically* or *universally true* statements. We turn now to an example illustrating *logically false* statements, also called *self-contradictions.*

Example 2.6. Consider the following conjunctive propositional statement:

$p \cap p' =$ "The United States is a monopolistic economy and it is not."

If p is true, then its conjunction with p' yields the statement $p \cap p'$ which is false. If p is false, then its conjunction with p' yields the same result. Hence, the statement $p \cap p'$ is false in all possible ways; it is logically false. Thus, the truth value of statement $p \cap p'$ is always F; and the truth set $P \cap P'$ assigned to statement $p \cap p'$ is the null set. Again, the reader can easily verify these points using truth tables and a Venn diagram.

From the above two examples it can be seen that the truth or falsity of a logical statement does not depend upon some fact or historical event which exists or is assumed to exist in the real world; it would be true or false of a world on Mars or other planets; it is true or false for all times and places. In conclusion, *a logical propositional statement is true (false) independently of any fact, situation, circumstance, or state of affairs which exist or are assumed to exist in the real world in the sense that it is true (false) in all possible ways and the truth set assigned to the statement is the universal set* $\mathcal{U}$ *(the empty set* $\varnothing$*).*

Although all quoted logical statements are compound, this is not always the case. Neither is classification of a given statement as factual or logical always a clear-cut case. But further discussion on this point belongs to a more sophisticated treatment of the subject. What the reader should bear in mind is that *in all statements each word must have the same meaning whenever it occurs.*

We have indicated that whether a statement is factual, logically true, or logically false can be determined with truth tables and Venn diagrams. We further illustrate this technique with the following example.

Example 2.7. Let the following be any unspecified propositional statements:

$(p \cup q)'$; $(p \cup q) \cup (p \cup q)'$; and $(p \cup q) \cap (p \cup q)'$.

We wish to determine whether the statements are factual, logically true, or logically false.

TABLE 2.1.

(1) (2) $p \quad q$	(3) $(p \cup q)$	(4) $(p \cup q)'$	(5) $(p \cup q) \cup (p \cup q)'$	(6) $(p \cup q) \cap (p \cup q)'$
T T	T	F	T	F
T F	T	F	T	F
F T	T	F	T	F
F F	F	T	T	F

Statement $(p \cup q)'$:

The truth value of this statement is shown in column 4 of Table 2.1. It can be seen that its truth value is sometimes F and sometimes T. Its truth table consists of neither a solid column of T's nor of F's'. Also, the truth set $(P \cup Q)'$ assigned to the statement is represented by area R_4 in Figure 2.1; it is neither the universal set nor the null set. Hence, statement $(p \cup q)'$ is factual.

Statement $(p \cup q) \cup (p \cup q)'$:

From column 5 of Table 2.1 it can be seen that the truth value of this statement is always T since its table consists of a solid column of T's.

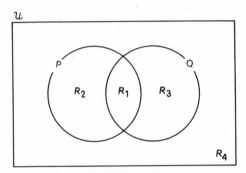

FIGURE 2.1.

Also, the truth set $(P \cup Q) \cup (P \cup Q)'$ in Figure 2.1 assigned to this statement is the universal set. Hence, the statement is universally or logically true.

Statement $(p \cup q) \cap (p \cup q)'$:

In contrast, from column 6 of Table 2.1 we can see that this statement is universally or logically false since its truth value is always F. Its table consists of a solid column of F's; and the truth set $(P \cup Q) \cap (P \cup Q)'$ in Figure 2.1 assigned to this statement is the null set.

We may stress the point here that determining whether a statement is logically true is independent of the content of that statement; it is the way simple statements are combined to form compound statements that counts. The significance of this observation will be fully appreciated when the same technique is used later to find the truth value of special types of compound statements.

2.3. Logical Possibilities and Laws of Logic. In defining statements we have mentioned the rule that a given statement is either true or false but not both; there can be no middle ground. This rule underlines two fundamental laws of logic which we shall explain briefly.

We have already seen that the statement $p \cup p'$ is universally true. This statement enunciates a law of logic called the *law of the excluded middle.* It asserts that the disjunction of a statement p and its negation p' exhausts the alternatives. Also, statement $p \cap p'$ found to be universally false or a contradiction enunciates another law of logic called the *law of contradiction.* It asserts that in the conjunction of a statement p and its negation p' the one statement excludes the other. In sum, *a statement p and its negation p' represent all logical possibilities, i.e., all collectively exhaustive and mutually exclusive alternatives.* This observation is of paramount importance because a situation gives rise to a decision problem when there is more than one alternative. Thus, analysis of logical possibilities is central to the process of making decisions.

The following example, although unrelated to business and unsophisticated, amply illustrates the decision-making process of considering the outcomes of alternative courses of action to arrive at an inevitably true conclusion.

Example 2.8. An urn contains three white balls and two black balls. This ball composition is known to James, Carpenter, and White who draw one ball each from the urn. Each person is allowed to see the color of the ball which the other two individuals have drawn but not his own. James is asked to guess the color of the ball he has drawn. He replies that he cannot tell. When Carpenter is asked the same question he in turn admits that he is unable to tell. But White, *without seeing* the color of the balls drawn by the others, guesses correctly.

Question: What was his answer and how did he arrive at it?

Answer: White guessed the color of his ball to be white. But how? White started with the following propositional statement

$$p \cup p' = \text{"I have either a white or a black ball"}$$

and employed the following reasoning:

Let us assume that $p' = $ "I have a black ball" is true. Then Carpenter would have reasoned as follows: "I see a black ball in White's hand. If I also have a black ball, James would have seen two black balls and concluded that his own ball is white. Since James could not tell, he must have seen a white ball in my hand. Hence, I have a white ball." Also, James would have reached the same conclusion following the same reasoning. But this conclusion is false since neither of them could tell. Therefore, White reasons, my assumption that

$$p' = \text{"I have a black ball"}$$

must be *false* and statement

$$p = \text{"I have a white ball"}$$

must be true.

Observe that White's conclusion is based on the laws of the excluded middle and of contradiction. White considers the two mutually exclusive and collectively exhaustive outcomes that either p or p' but not both must be true. He arrives at his inevitably true conclusion that p must be true indirectly by concluding that the other alternative p' cannot be true.

2.4. Logic and Scientific Inquiry. In conclusion, it is worth emphasizing that logical statements may sound trivial, yet it is this triviality which makes them important. The division between factual and logical statements is intimately related to any scientific inquiry. Factual statements such as "The demand for a commodity and its supply determine price," or "In periods of general optimism the stock market is bullish." or "Mass-media selling is an important activity in our economy," or "Smoking reduces longevity" are generalizations whose truth or falsity is based on empirical evidence which was obtained from the real world through observing, surveying, and experimenting. Unlike logical statements these generalizations are informative rather than trivial; probable rather than certain; dependent for their truth or falsity on facts from the real world rather than being true or false in all possible worlds. Thus, analyzing factual statements and determining their truth or falsity involves a process of thinking called *induction* or *inductive reasoning* which arrives at probable conclusions on the basis of empirical evidence.

Deductive logic, on the other hand, as already stated, is the analysis of logical statements. It is the process of abstract thinking which builds a whole system of logically or universally true statements on the basis of certain fundamental assertions (called assumptions, postulates, or axioms) which are taken for granted. Boolean algebra, for example, is such a mathematical system. It is based on the abstract laws of "set" operations, marked with an asterisk in Table 4.1, Chapter 1, together with the property of "set" equality. Therefore, while inductive reasoning is the basis of experimental science, deductive logic is the backbone of mathematics in the sense that *every mathematical proof must be the result of deductive reasoning.* This latter remark does not mean that induction is foreign to mathematical thinking. It simply means that although induction may lead to a mathematical generalization, this generalization remains a factual statement, a probable conclusion. It does not become a universally or logically true statement unless it is proved by deductive reasoning. For example, by observing that

$$6 = 3 + 3,$$
$$8 = 3 + 5,$$
$$10 = 3 + 7 \quad \text{or} \quad 5 + 5,$$
$$12 = 5 + 7,$$
$$14 = 3 + 11 \quad \text{or} \quad 7 + 7,$$

etc., we may induce that "any even number greater than 4 is the sum of two odd primes." But this statement is only factual since its truth is based on a number of observations. No amount of additional observation will make the statement logically true. Hence, we do not know if the statement is universally true because in spite of great efforts on the part of some great mathematicians, no proof of it has been found to date.

Finally, analysis of logical possibilities is a process basic to almost any scientific investigation. Such analysis of real phenomena leads through induction to the formulation of empirically justified conclusions or factual statements. In turn, these probable conclusions lead by deduction to logically true statements. The latter are checked against available facts to formulate new empirically justified conclusions, and the cycle of reasoning, sometimes called *reflective thinking*, repeats itself. Mathematical model building for the solution of business and economic problems is a case which may explicitly involve these two phases of thinking. Thus, inductive and deductive reasoning complement, reinforce, and check each other in the formulation of scientific knowledge and in the process of problem solving and decision making.

PROBLEMS

2.1. Find one simple factual propositional statement from each of the following subjects and explain in what sense each statement may be true or false.
  a) Accounting.
  b) Behavioral science.
  c) Economics.
  d) Finance.
  e) Marketing.
  f) Production.
  g) Statistics.

2.2. With truth tables verify that—
  a) Statement $p \cup p'$ in Example 2.5 is logically true.
  b) Statement $p \cap p'$ in Example 2.6 is logically false.

2.3. Determine by means of truth tables whether the following statements are factual, logically true, or logically false:
  a) $(p \cap q) \cup r$.
  b) $(p \cap q)' \cup r$.
  c) $(p \cap q \cap r) \cup (p \cap q \cap r)'$.
  d) $(p \cap q \cap r) \cap (p \cap q \cap r)'$.
  e) $(p \cup q \cup r) \cup (p \cup q \cup r)'$.
  f) $(p \cup q \cup r) \cap (p \cup q \cup r)'$.
  g) $p \cap [(q \cap p') \cup (r \cap p')]$.
  h) $\{q \cup [(p \cap q') \cup (r \cap q')]\} \cup (p \cup q \cup r)'$.

2.4. Let P, Q, and R be the truth sets assigned to statements p, q, r, respectively. Find whether the statements in *(a)*, *(b)*, *(c)*, *(d)*, *(e)*, *(f)*, *(g)* and *(h)* of Problem 2.3 are factual, logically true, or logically false by means of Venn diagrams.

2.5. Make a verbal translation of the three statements in Example 2.7, if

p = "The United States is a monopolistic economy"

and
$$q = \text{"The United States is a laboristic economy."}$$

2.6. Let the following statements be given,

$$p = \text{"Food prices go up,"}$$
$$q = \text{"The cost of living rises."}$$

Express the statements below in symbolic form and find whether they are factual, logically true, or logically false by means of truth tables and Venn diagrams.

a) "Food prices go up and the cost of living rises, but it is not true that both food prices and the cost of living rise."

b) "Food prices go up, but the cost of living does not rise."

c) "It is not true that neither food prices go up nor the cost of living rises or it is not true that food prices go up and the cost of living rises."

2.7. After expressing the statements given in *(a)*, (b), (c) of Problem 2.6 in symbolic form, find their truth value under the following conditions:

a) When both p and q are true.

b) When p is true and q is false.

c) When p is false and q is true.

d) When both p and q are false.

e) Compare your results in steps (a) through (d) and draw your conclusion.

2.8. For each of the following pairs of statements,

i) Write down the verbal expression of one logically true and one logically false statement, and

ii) Verify your examples by means of truth tables and Venn diagrams.

a) "Credits to the company's customers represent accounts receivable." "Credits from the company's suppliers represent liability accounts."

b) "Bond prices depend on interest rates." "Stock prices depend on dividends."

c) "Impulse buying is prevalent among supermarket shoppers." "Buying of industrial goods is basically rational."

d) "The demand for factors of production is a derived demand." "The demand for factors of production is a joint demand."

e) "Labor unions are strong in the United States." "The United States has become a laboristic economy."

2.9. Prove the following propositions:

a) A statement is logically true if and only if the assigned set is $\mathfrak{U}$.

b) A statement is logically false if and only if the assigned set is $\varnothing$.

2.10. Let t be universally true, s a self-contradictory, and p any other statement.

i) Prove that the following pairs of statements are equivalent, and

ii) Verify your proof by means of truth tables and Venn diagrams.

a) $(p \cap t)$ and p.

b) $(p \cup t)$ and t.

c) $(p \cap s)$ and s.

d) $(p \cup s)$ and p.

2.11. Invoking the appropriate laws of set operations, prove the following:
  a) The negation of a logically true statement is logically false.
  b) The negation of a logically false statement is logically true.

2.12. Let the sets P and Q be assigned to statements p and q, respectively. Then p implies q, i.e., q is a logical consequence of p, if and only if $P \subseteq Q$. Prove this theorem and verify it with a truth table and a Venn diagram.

2.13. Refer to G. Polya, *Mathematics and Plausible Reasoning*, Vol. I: Induction and Analogy in Mathematics (Princeton, N.J.: Princeton University Press, 1954), chap. i, pp. 7–8, and do the following:
  a) Write down the rules for inductive attitude in scientific investigations.
  b) Cite two examples from this reference which illustrate the formulation of mathematical generalizations (factual statements) arrived at through inductive reasoning.

2.14. The following steps prove that $6 = 3$.
  (1) Let $x = 3$,
  (2) Then $x^2 = 3x$,   on multiplying (1) by x,
  (3) And $x^2 - 9 = 3x - 9$,   by subtracting 9 from (2),
  (4) And $(x - 3)(x + 3) = 3(x - 3)$,   by factoring;
  (5) Then $x + 3 = 3$,   when (4) is divided by $(x - 3)$,
  (6) And $3 + 3 = 3$,   on substituting (1) into (5).
  (7) Therefore $6 = 3$.
  What is wrong with this proof?

2.15. Consult E. R. Stabler, *An Introduction to Mathematical Thought* (Reading, Mass.: Addison-Wesley Publishing Co., Inc., 1953) pp. 11–19, 23–24, 28–29; and M. Richardson, *Fundamentals of Mathematics* (rev. ed.; New York: The Macmillan Co., 1958), pp. 437–58, and answer the following:
  a) What are the postulates upon which the following mathematical systems of geometry are based?
    i) Euclidean.
    ii) Lobachevskian.
    iii) Riemannian.
  b) To what logically true statement about the sum of the angles of a triangle does each system lead? Why?
  c) In what sense are mathematical truths relative?

2.16. Give a summary of the steps involved in reflective thinking from John Dewey, *How We Think* (New York: D. C. Heath & Co., 1910), chap. vi, pp. 68–78. Which steps would you call predominantly inductive and which deductive?

2.17. From *Mathematical Models and Methods in Marketing* edited by Frank M. Bass *et al.* (Homewood, Ill.: Richard D. Irwin, Inc., 1961), read the editorial commentary to any one article and write a one-hundred-word essay describing the inductive and deductive reasoning which is employed in the article you have selected.

SUGGESTED REFERENCES

1. ALLENDOERFER, C. B., AND OAKLEY, C. O. *Principles of Mathematics*, pp. 1–25. New York: McGraw-Hill Book Co., Inc., 1955. **(1, 2)**

2. JOHNSTONE, HENRY W. *Elementary Deductive Logic*, pp. 1–22. New York: Thomas Y. Crowell Co., 1959. **(1, 2)**

3. KEMENY, JOHN G., *et al. Introduction to Finite Mathematics*, pp. 1–10, 19–30, 63–69. Englewood Cliffs, N.J.: Prentice-Hall, Inc., 1957. **(1, 2)**

4. MATHEMATICAL ASSOCIATION OF AMERICA, COMMITTEE ON THE UNDERGRADUATE PROGRAM. *Elementary Mathematics of Sets with Applications*, pp. 17–22. 1959. **(1, 2)**

5. RICHARDSON, M. *Fundamentals of Mathematics*, pp. 6–21. Rev. ed. New York: The Macmillan Co., 1958. **(1, 2)**

6. WESTERN, D. W., AND HAAG, V. H. *An Introduction to Mathematics*, pp. 1–25. New York: Henry Holt & Co., Inc., 1959. **(1, 2)**

Chapter 3

THE LOGIC OF STATEMENTS

IN CHAPTER 2 we defined statements, distinguished between sets and propositional statements, and showed how the basic operations on sets can be used to form compound statements from simple or atomic statements. In fact, we demonstrated that statements, like sets, represent another interpretation of the undefined symbols in Table 4.1 of Chapter 1 which, together with the basic operations denoted by ′, ∩, ∪, and the equivalence relation, constitute the mathematical system of Boolean algebra. Furthermore, we carefully drew the distinction between factual and logical propositional and set statements and we dealt in detail with logical possibilities. Our purpose was to accomplish two objectives—on the one hand, to make a gradual transition from sets to statements and, on the other hand, to establish the conceptual framework which is necessary for the analysis of logical statements, in other words, for deductive logic.

In the first two sections of this chapter we shall continue enriching our conceptual inventory by discussing logical relations and conditional statements. This background will enable us to deal with testing the validity of compound propositional statements in the third and compound set statements in the last section of this chapter.

1. IMPLICATION AND CONDITIONAL STATEMENTS

After explaining briefly unrelated and related statements, our attention in this section is focused on the relation of implication which is one of the most important concepts in the study of deductive logic. In turn, the notion of implication will give us the opportunity to introduce two new compound statements, namely, the conditional and the biconditional.

Conceptually, these topics constitute a single unit. For the sake of convenience, however, conditional statements and the related concepts of validity and inference will be discussed in this section and variations of the conditional and biconditional statements in the next. Although we shall deal formally with propositional statements, from the conceptual standpoint both the relation of implication and the conditional are essential for testing the validity of set statements as well.

1.1. Unrelated and Related Statements. *Any two statements p and q are said to be logically unrelated if each of the four truth table possibilities can occur.*

Example 1.1. Let the statements

$$p = \text{``Food prices rise''}$$

and

$$q = \text{``The cost-of-living-index rises''}$$

be given. All four logical possibilities can actually occur; p and q can be both true or false, p can be true and q false, and p can be false and q true. Food prices may rise and the cost-of-living-index may rise; but while food prices may rise, the cost-of-living index may not because prices of other commodities included in the index may have declined at the same time, thus offsetting the effect of food prices. Similarly, the other two possibilities can occur as shown in Table 1.1.

TABLE 1.1.

Possibilities p q	Region in Figure 1.1
T - T	R_1
T - F	R_2
F - T	R_3
F - F	R_4

Assigning the truth sets P and Q to the above quoted statements p and q, respectively, the four possibilities correspond to the four regions listed in Table 1.1 and shown in the Venn diagram of Figure 1.1. Since all four possibilities can occur, none of the four regions represents the empty set.

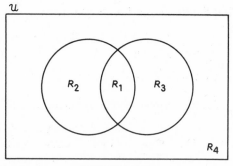

FIGURE 1.1.

The statements "Food prices rise" and "The cost of living rises" are unrelated.

If any one or two of the four possibilities between p and q cannot occur, then the two statements are said to be related. Of all possible relations, six are of interest: four with one possibility excluded, called *onefold* relations, and two with two possibilities excluded, called *twofold* relations. These relations appear as an exercise in the next section. Here, we shall deal with only the onefold relation of implication where of the four possibilities shown in Table 1.1, logical possibility T-F is excluded.

1.2. Implication. Although the relation of implication may be defined in terms of the excluded possibility T-F, the following definition may help subsequent discussions. Let p and q be any two propositional statements: *Then p implies q if q is true in all logical possibilities for which p is true.*

Example 1.2. Consider the truth value of statements $p, q, p \cap q$, and $p \cup q$ given in Table 1.2.

TABLE 1.2.

p	q	$p \cup q$	$p \cap q$
T	T	T	T
T	F	T	F
F	T	T	F
F	F	F	F

Statement p implies statement $p \cup q$ because the latter is true in all logical possibilities for which p is true. Observe that p implies $p \cup q$ since possibility T-F between the two statements is excluded.

On the other hand, statement p does not imply statement $p \cap q$ since possibility T-F occurs and consequently the latter is not true in all possibilities for which p is true.

The notion of implication may be also conveyed using the familiar concept of subsets.

Example 1.3. Let the statements

$$p = \text{"Evans is a Vermont businessman"}$$

and

$$q = \text{"Evans is a New England businessman"}$$

be given; and let P represent the set of all Vermont and Q the set of all New England businessmen. If we assert that "Evans is a Vermont businessman" is true, then the statement "Evans is a New England businessman" must also be true since all Vermont businessmen are New England businessmen, i.e., since $P \subseteq Q$. In other words, q is true in all possibilities for which p is true; if p is true, then q is necessarily true. This is the essence of implication.

Observe that in this case the possibility T-F between statements p and q is excluded. This is equivalent to saying that set P is a subset of Q where in terms of a Venn diagram, such as the one Figure 1.1, region R_2 is the null set.

The reader may explain for himself why the statement q in Table 1.2 implies $p \cup q$ and does not imply $p \cap q$. Also, using the Venn diagram in Figure 1.1, he may express the same relations in terms of sets assigned to the corresponding statements.

1.3. The Conditional and Implication. Let p and q be any two propositional statements. *Then the conditional of p and q is a statement which is false if p is true and q is false; otherwise it is true.* Such a statement is denoted by $p \rightarrow q$, which is read "if p then q." Its truth value is shown in Table 1.3. Observe that the conditional $p \rightarrow q$ is false

TABLE 1.3.

Regions in Figure 1.1	Possibilities p q	Conditional $p \rightarrow q$
R_1	T - T	T
R_2	T - F	F
R_3	F - T	T
R_4	F - F	T

only in possibility T-F which corresponds to region R_2 in Figure 1.1. Statement p is called the *antecedent* and statement q the *consequent* of the conditional $p \rightarrow q$.

The conditional is so closely associated with the relation of implication that the two terms are sometimes used as if they were interchangeable. It is important to remember that *the conditional is not a logical relation but a new compound statement.*

In order to appreciate the close affinity, as well as the difference between the conditional statement and the relation of implication, it is necessary to study the anatomy and truth table of the conditional. The truth value of the conditional shown in Table 1.3 is consistent with the definition of implication for the logical possibilities T-T and T-F where p cannot be true unless q is true. Thus, if both p and q are true, then $p \rightarrow q$ is true, while if p is true and q is false, then $p \rightarrow q$ is false. But what about the truth value of the other two logical possibilities; i.e., F-T and F-F? They cannot be left undefined since this would violate the principle that all true-false possibilities between two statements must be considered. The arbitrary rule is established that the conditional is true whenever p is false and regardless of the truth value of q. Yet, this rule does not seem completely arbitrary if we observe that the truth table of the conditional is reduced to the relation of implication if the T-F logical possibility is excluded; i.e., if R_2 represents the null set. Thus, any conditional statement is reduced to an implication if we assume that the antecedent is true if and only if the consequent is true. The conditional "If New England is the birthplace of textile manufacturing, then the six-state area is the cradle of the industrial revolution in the United States" is reduced to an implication if *we assume* that New England cannot be the birthplace of textile manufacturing without being also the cradle of the American industrial revolution. The association between implication and the conditional may be summarized by saying that p *implies q if and only if p → q is logically true.* We hasten to emphasize that the new connective → does not indicate any causal relationship between the antecedent and the consequent.

With the above distinction between the conditional and the notion of implication in mind, let us introduce new compound propositional statements called arguments and study briefly their validity.

1.4. Arguments and Their Validity. *An argument is an assertion that a certain statement called conclusion is implied by other statements called premises.*

Example 1.4. Consider the statement

$[(p \cup q) \cap q'] \to p =$ "There is either a wage or a price inflation in the United States. In fact there is no price inflation. Therefore, there is a wage inflation."

It is an argument. The statements in brackets [ ] represent the premises, and the statement p connected with the premises by the new operation → represents the conclusion of the argument. The argument asserts that the conclusion follows from the premises.

In studying arguments we like to know whether or not in a particular argument the premises imply the conclusion. If the premises of an argument imply its conclusion then such an argument is called *valid*; if the premises of an argument do not imply its conclusion then such an argument is called *invalid*. The validity of an argument may be tested with truth tables.

TABLE 1.4.

(1) p	(2) q	(3) $p \cup q$	(4) q'	(5) $(p \cup q) \cap q'$	(6) $[(p \cup q) \cap q'] \to p$
T	T	T	F	F	T
T	F	T	T	T	T
F	T	T	F	F	T
F	F	F	T	F	T

Example 1.4.—*Continued.* Find whether the above argument is valid. Using the basic truth tables for the operations ', ∩, ∪, and → shown in Table 1.4 we find that the given argument is logically true. Therefore, the premises of the argument imply its conclusion; the argument is valid.

Example 1.5. Test the validity of the following argument:

$p \rightarrow q$ = "If Evans is a Vermont businessman, then he is a New England businessman."

q = "But Evans is a New England businessman."

∴ p = "Evans is a Vermont businessman."

Observe that a new form is used with this argument. The connective → between the premises $[(p \rightarrow q) \cap q]$ and the conclusion p is replaced with a line and the symbol ∴ which means therefore. The truth value of this argument is shown in column 5 of Table 1.5. The argument is invalid since it is not a logically true statement but a factual statement.

TABLE 1.5.

(1) p	(2) q	(3) $p \rightarrow q$	(4) $(p \rightarrow q) \cap q$	(5) $[(p \rightarrow q) \cap q] \rightarrow p$
T	T	T	T	T
T	F	F	F	T
F	T	T	T	F
F	F	T	F	T

It is important to realize that the conclusion of an argument may be empirically true and the argument invalid or the conclusion empirically false and the argument valid; in other words, whether the conclusion of an argument is in fact true or false is irrelevant to the validity of the argument.

In sum, an argument is valid if and only if it is a logically true statement; otherwise it is a factual statement and therefore invalid. Nonvalid arguments are also called *fallacies,* although the latter term is much broader than the former.

Since testing the validity of arguments occupies an important position in the analysis of statements, this topic is further discussed in the optional Sections 3 and 4 on logic. In the meantime we conclude this section by introducing another important concept closely related to the notion of implication.

1.5. Implication and Inference. The user of an argument has two intentions. First, the arguer claims that there is a relation of implication between the premises and the conclusion. Second, the arguer affirms the premises and consequently the conclusion, thus crossing the bridge from premises to conclusion.

Example 1.6. Let sets A and B be assigned to statements a and b, respectively. Then

$p \rightarrow q$ = "If statement a implies statement b, then $A \subseteq B$."
p = "But statement a implies statement b," i.e., b is true whenever a is true.

$\therefore q$ = "$A \subseteq B$," i.e., every element of A is an element of B.

In order to verify that this argument is valid, the reader may find its truth value for himself.

Note that an arguer claims that the conditional "If statement a implies statement b, then $A \subseteq B$" depicts an implication, a bridge between p and q. Then the arguer affirms the premises by asserting that "a implies b" and consequently the conclusion. In this manner, he crosses the bridge from premises to conclusion.

This process of inferring the conclusion from the premises of an argument is called *inference, demonstration, deduction,* or *proof.*

The above argument illustrates a simple mathematical proof. It is important to realize that in a mathematical proof the premises are simply asserted, but not themselves proved. In order to prove these premises we shall have to invoke some other statements which imply these premises and which in turn we must assert, but not prove, and so on and so forth. This means that *not every statement can be proved.* The unproved statements constitute the axioms or postulates on the basis of which other statements—theorems—are proved through inference. The two kinds of statements together form a mathematical system such as Euclidean geometry, linear algebra, Boolean algebra, and others. Thus, statements of any mathematical system are relative since their truth depends on statements which are asserted but not themselves proved. As Einstein pointed out, "As far as the laws of mathematics refer to reality, they are not certain; and as far as they are certain, they do not refer to reality."

The validity of propositional and set statements will be studied systematically after a discussion of the variations of the conditional and biconditional statements.

PROBLEMS

1.1. From the given six statements below select a complete set of four statements so that no one statement implies any of the others. Verify your answer by expressing the selected statements in symbolic form and by showing their truth table.

a) "There is full employment and prosperity."
b) "If there is full employment, then there is prosperity."
c) "It is not true that there is full employment and there is prosperity."
d) "There is full employment but there is no prosperity."

e) "It is not the case that there is full employment or there is no prosperity."

f) "It is not true that there is full employment or prosperity."

*1.2. Draw a Venn diagram and verify the fact that none of the truth sets assigned to the statements you found in Problem 1.1 is a subset of any other.

1.3. By means of truth tables find whether the following pairs of statements are related or unrelated; and, if related, draw the appropriate Venn diagrams and shade the regions which represent the null set.

a) $p \to (q \cup r)$ and $(q \cup r)' \to p'$.

b) $[p' \cup (q' \cap r')]$ and $p \to [p \cap (q \cup r)']$.

1.4. Indicate whether or not each of the following conditional statements express a relation of implication. Explain why. If a conditional does not express an implication, explain the condition under which it is reduced to an implication.

*a) "If there is full employment, then there is prosperity."

*b) "If Black is our customer, then his credit account represents receivables."

c) "If the production process is in control, then not more than 0.1 percent of the produced parts should be defective."

d) "If Mr. Perkins is from Maine, then he is a New Englander."

1.5. Illustrate the logical relation of implication by giving examples from the following subjects:

a) Accounting.

b) Behavioral science.

c) Economics.

d) Finance.

e) Production.

f) Marketing.

g) Statistics.

1.6. Prepare truth tables for each of the following statements: $(A)p'$, $(B)q'$, $(C)p \cap q$, and $(D)p \cup q$. In each of the six pairs of statements shown below, find whether the first statement implies the second.

*a) $A, B.$ *d)* $B, C.$

b) $A, C.$ *e)* $B, D.$

c) $A, D.$ **f)* $C, D.$

1.7. For each relation of implication you find in Problem 1.6, draw a Venn diagram and shade the region which represents the null set.

1.8. Consider the following statements:

(A) "Interest rates determine bond prices."

(B) "Dividends determine stock prices."

(C) "Either interest rates do not determine bond prices or dividends do not determine stock prices."

(D) "Dividends do not determine stock prices and interest rates do not determine bond prices."

Express each statement in symbolic form, construct its truth table, and find whether in each of the following six pairs of statements the first statement implies the second.

*a) A, B.   d) B, C.
b) A, C.   e) B, D.
c) A, D.   *f) D, C.

1.9. Verify the following equivalence relations by using truth tables for statements and membership tables for sets.

a) $p \to q = p' \cup q$.
b) $P' \cup Q = (P - Q)'$.

*1.10. Construct truth tables for each of the following compound statements, arrange them in such a way that each statement implies all the statements which follow, and verify each implication by showing that the conditional of two adjacent statements is logically true.

a) $p \cup (p' \to q)$.
b) $p \cap q'$.
c) $p \to (q \to p)$.
d) $[p \to (p' \to q)]'$.
e) $[(p \to q) \cap (q \to p)]'$.

1.11. Let the sets P and Q be assigned to statements p and q, respectively. For each of the statements in Problem 1.10 draw a Venn diagram and verify the fact that each statement implies all the statements which follow by shading the region(s) which represents the truth set in each case.

1.12. Find whether each of the following arguments is logically true and, therefore, valid or otherwise invalid and, hence, a fallacy, by means of truth tables.

*a) $[(p \to q) \cap p'] \to q'$.
b) $[(p \to q) \cap (q \to r)] \to r$.
c) $[(p \to q') \cap (q' \to p')] \to (p \to p')$.
d) $[(p \to q) \cap q'] \to p'$.
e) $[(p \to q) \cap (q \to p')] \to (p \to p')$.
f) $[(p \to q) \cap q] \to p$.
g) $[(p \to q) \cap (r \to q) \cap (p \cup r)] \to q$.

1.13. Let the following be given:

p = "The wheat market is perfectly free,"
q = "A single farmer cannot affect wheat prices."

Translate in words the conditional argument $[(p \to q) \cap q'] \to p'$ and discuss the distinction between implication and inference.

*1.14. Test the validity of the conditional argument in Problem 1.13 by means of truth tables.

1.15. Let the sets P and Q be assigned to the statements p and q, respectively. Show with membership tables that the subset relation $P \subseteq Q$ assigned to the conditional is equal to the complement of the difference of P and Q, i.e., $(P - Q)'$.

1.16. Draw the distinction between mathematical inference and statistical inference.

The following problems summarize the major points on logic treated in subsequent sections. They may be assigned instead of the optional Sections 2, 3, and 4 of this chapter.

1.17. Let p and q be any two propositional statements. Then the statement $q \to p$ is called the *converse* of the conditional $p \to q$. For each pair of statements given below:
  i) Form the conditional $p \to q$ and its converse $q \to p$.
  ii) Find whether both statements involve implications.
    a) $p = $ "$x = 2$ and $y = 3$" and $q = $ "$x + y = 5$."
    b) $p = $ "$x + y = 10$" and $q = $ "$x = 10 - y$."
    c) $p = $ "White is a customer," and
       $q = $ "White's account represents assets."
    d) $p = $ "The price of wheat is raised from \$4.00 to \$4.50 per bushel," and
       $q = $ "Demand for wheat falls from 12 to 11 million bushels."

1.18. The conjunction of a conditional statement $p \to q$ and its converse $q \to p$ is equivalent to a new statement $p \leftrightarrow q$ called biconditional. It is read "p if and only if q" which is true if p and q are either both true or both false; otherwise, it is false. Using basic truth tables find that the truth value of $(p \to q) \cap (q \to p) = p \leftrightarrow q$. Also, using truth tables find whether each of the following biconditional statements are logically true and identify the abstract law (if any) of set operations from Table 4.1 of Chapter 1 to which each biconditional statement may correspond.
    a) $(p \cap q)' \leftrightarrow (p' \cup q')$.
    b) $(p \cap q) \leftrightarrow (q \cap p)$.
    c) $(p \to q) \leftrightarrow (p' \cup q)$.
    d) $(p \to q) \leftrightarrow (q' \to p')$.

1.19. In mathematics, as well as in scientific inquiries and everyday conversation, the antecedent, p, of a conditional statement, $p \to q$, is frequently omitted and only the consequent, q, is stated. When, for example, we assert that "$x + 3 = 5$," we implicitly understand that "if $x = 2$, then $x + 3 = 5$" is the complete mathematical assertion. For lack of a better term, statements such as "$x + 3 = 5$" may be called *hidden conditionals*. Consider the following statements as hidden conditionals and find a statement which may be used as the missing antecedent.
    a) $x + y = 12$.
    b) $x^2 + 2x + 1 = 0$.
    c) "The sum of the angles of a triangle is 180 degrees."
    d) "The sum of the angles of a triangle is more than 180 degrees."
    e) "The sum of the angles of a triangle is less than two right angles."
    f) "There are three million persons currently unemployed in the United States."

1.20. Let $p = $ "The contract is valid" and $q = $ "Goodwill and Company is liable" be given. Then express each of the following arguments in the form introduced in Example 1.5 and test their validity.
    a) $[(p \to q) \cap p] \to q$.
    b) $[(p \to q) \cap p'] \to q'$.

      c) $[(p \to q) \cap q'] \to p'$.
      d) $[(p \to q) \cap q] \to p$.
      e) $[(p \cap q)' \cap p] \to q'$.
      f) $[(p \cap q)' \cap p'] \to q$.
      g) $[(p \cup q) \cap p'] \to q$.
      h) $[(p \cup q) \cap q] \to p'$.

1.21. For each argument given below:
    i) Express it in the form introduced in Example 1.5.
    ii) Test its validity.
    iii) Discuss the validity of the argument in relation to the empirical truthfulness of the conclusion.
      a) $[(p \to q) \cap q] \to p$, where
         p = "The United States is a capitalistic economy,"
         q = "Most means of production in the United States are privately owned."
      b) $[(p \to q) \cap q'] \to p'$, where
         p = "There is communism in the Soviet Union,"
         q = "Most means of production in the Soviet Union are owned by the state."

1.22. Consider the argument

$$[(p \to z) \cap (z \to r) \cap (r \to q)] \to (p \to q),$$

where
p = "Productivity increases,"
q = "Consumers benefit,"
r = "Prices fall,"
z = "Costs per unit of output decrease."
    a) Express the argument in the form introduced in Example 1.5.
    b) Test the validity of the argument.

1.23. Express the following arguments in symbolic form and test their validity.
    a) "It is not true that there is an international crisis and a sharp drop in stock market prices. But there is an international crisis. Therefore, stock market prices have not declined."
    b) "Either there is an international crisis or there is a sharp decline in stock market quotations. But there is a decline in stock market prices. Therefore, there is no international crisis."
    c) "If there is an international crisis, then stock market prices drop sharply. But the stock market is bullish. Therefore, there is no international crisis."

1.24. Set statements may form special types of arguments called syllogisms such as the one below:
      (1) "All farm (F) prices are unstable (N)."
      (2) "All farm incomes (I) depend on farm (F) prices."

    ∴(3) "All farm incomes (I) are unstable (N)."

Here the set statements (1) and (2) are the premises and (3) the conclusion. Though the validity of this syllogism cannot be tested with

truth tables, it may be tested with the following Venn diagram, where
F, I, and N represent the sets of "farm prices," "farm incomes," and
"unstable things," respectively.

Since premise (1) of the syllogism indicates that $F \subseteq N$, the region of F representing the empty set is shaded with horizontal lines. Since by premise (2) $I \subseteq F$ the region of I representing the null set is shaded with vertical lines. Note that in the process of diagramming the premises we have indeed diagrammed the conclusion (3) of the syllogism since R_1, representing the set of "All farm incomes," is a subset of set N, i.e., $I \subseteq N$. Hence, the syllogism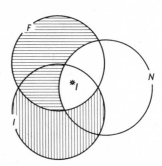
is valid. On the basis of the above illustration determine the validity
of the following syllogism with a Venn diagram:

a) "All Americans are thrifty."
   "All thrifty people are wealthy."
   _____
   "All Americans are wealthy."

b) "All bondholders are creditors."
   "No creditors are shareholders."
   _____
   "No shareholders are bondholders."

c) "All creditors are bondholders."
   "No creditors are stockholders."
   _____
   "No stockholders are bondholders."

*2. VARIATIONS OF THE CONDITIONAL; BICONDITIONAL STATEMENTS

2.1. Variations of the Conditional.
Like subsets the conditional of two statements lacks symmetry, i.e., $p \rightarrow q$ is not equivalent to its *converse* $q \rightarrow p$. Since the conditional is a more important source of faulty reasoning than the other connectives, perhaps because of this lack of symmetry, a closer study of it and its variations, shown in

TABLE 2.1.

(1) (2) p & q	(3) Conditional $p \rightarrow q$	(4) Converse of Conditional $q \rightarrow p$	(5) Contra- positive $q' \rightarrow p'$	(6) Converse of Contrapositive $p' \rightarrow q'$
T - T	T	T	T	T
T - F	F	T	F	T
F - T	T	F	T	F
F - F	T	T	T	T

Table 2.1, is necessary. Comparing their truth values we can see that the conditional is equivalent to the *contrapositive*, while the converse of the conditional is equivalent to the converse of the contrapositive. Also, if the third row logical possibility is excluded from column 4, the converse of the conditional is reduced to a relation of implication, namely, that q implies p. The reader can readily visualize this logical relation by means of a Venn diagram.

The following example illustrates the conditional and its variations.

Example 2.1. Let the statements

$$p = \text{"Evans is a Vermont businessman"}$$

and

$$q = \text{"Evans is a New England businessman"}$$

be given. We have already seen that if we assert p, the conditional $p \to q$ is logically true; in other words, it is inescapably true that Evans is a New England businessman. But its converse $q \to p$ is not logically true because asserting that Evans is a New England businessman does not necessarily imply that he is a Vermont businessman. He may be a Vermonter or a resident of another New England state. On analogous grounds, if we assert that Evans is not a New England businessman, the contrapositive $q' \to p'$ is logically true; i.e., it is inescapably true that Evans is not a Vermont businessman. By contrast, the converse of the contrapositive $p' \to q'$ is not logically true since asserting that Evans is not a Vermont businessman does not necessarily imply that Evans is not a resident of another New England state.

2.2. Forms of the Conditional. Consider the statement:

"Evans is a Vermont businessman *only if* he is a New England businessman."

It is of the form "p only if q." How is it related to the conditional of the form "if p then q"? This statement can be interpreted as follows: "If Evans is not a New England businessman, then he is not a Vermont businessman." But the latter statement is of the form "if q' then p'," the contrapositive of the conditional, and hence equivalent to the conditional "if p then q." Consequently, the statement under consideration is equivalent to the statement "If Evans is a Vermont businessman, then he is a New England businessman."

Less frequently, a conditional statement is phrased as follows:

"Evans is a New England businessman *if* he is a Vermont businessman."

"Evans is a New England businessman *provided that* he is a Vermont businessman."

These conditionals are of the form "q if p" and "q provided that p," respectively. Both of these idiomatic expressions are considered to have the same logical meaning as the standard conditional form "if p then q."

Very frequently mathematicians express a conditional statement by using the phrases "p is a sufficient condition for q" or "q is a necessary condition for p."

Example 2.2. Let the statement "If $x = 2$ and $y = 3$, then $x + y = 5$" be given. Then, asserting that the antecedent "$x = 2$ and $y = 3$" is a sufficient condition for the consequent "$x + y = 5$" means that the former statement is sufficient to satisfy the latter. Similarly, asserting that the consequent "$x + y = 5$" is a necessary condition for the antecedent "$x = 2$ and $y = 3$" means that when the former is false the latter *must* be also false.

In general, the statement "p is a sufficient condition for q" is of the form "if p then q," while the statement "p is a necessary condition for q" is equivalent to "q only if p." Observing that the latter statement is equivalent to "if q then p," we can conclude that the *assertion of a necessary condition is the converse of the assertion of a sufficient condition.*

In conclusion, any statement of the form

"p only if q"
"q if p"
"q provided that p"
"p is a sufficient condition for q"
"q is a necessary condition for p"

is equivalent to the standard form "if p then q" of the conditional $p \rightarrow q$.

2.3. The Biconditional.   Let p and q be any propositional statements. Then *the biconditional, denoted by $p \leftrightarrow q$ and read "p if and only if q" is a statement which is true if p and q are either both true or both false; otherwise it is false.*

Example 2.3. Let the statements

$$p = \text{"Food prices rise"}$$

and

$$q = \text{"The cost-of-living index rises"}$$

be given. Then

$$p \leftrightarrow q = \text{"Food prices rise \textit{if and only if} the cost-of-living index rises."}$$

The truth value of the biconditional statement is shown in Table 2.2. When possibilities T-F and F-T are excluded, then the biconditional statement reduces to an equivalence relation where $p = q$.

TABLE 2.2.

(1) (2) $p \& q$	(3) $p \leftrightarrow q$
T - T	T
T - F	F
F - T	F
F - F	T

Example 2.4. Let the statements

$$p = \text{“}x + y = 15\text{”}$$

and

$$q = \text{“}x = 15 - y\text{”}$$

be given. Then

$$p \leftrightarrow q = \text{“}x + y = 15 \text{ if and only if } x = 15 - y\text{”}$$

where $p = q$ since possibilities T-F and F-T are excluded.

The reader may verify with a Venn diagram that the truth set of the biconditional $p \leftrightarrow q$ is the set $(P' \cup Q) \cap (P \cup Q')$.

The above example points out that the standard form of the biconditional "p if and only if q" is equivalent to "if p then q and if q then p," i.e., the biconditional is the conjunction of the conditional and its converse. This is verified in Table 2.3 where the truth value of the conjunc-

TABLE 2.3.

(1) p	(2) q	(3) $p \to q$	(4) $q \to p$	(5) $(p \to q) \cap (q \to p)$	(6) $(p \leftrightarrow q)$
T	T	T	T	T	T
T	F	F	T	F	F
F	T	T	F	F	F
F	F	T	T	T	T

tion of the conditional and its converse, column 5, is equal to the truth value of the biconditional, column 6.

Frequently, conditional statements require careful analysis in order to determine whether the person making the assertion means the conditional, its converse, or for that matter the biconditional. The following example illustrates such a case.

Example 2.5. Table 2.4 shows the relationship between price and quantity of wheat demanded, a relationship which economists call a "demand schedule" for wheat.

Assuming "pure" or perfect competition, this table indicates the quantity of wheat which can be sold to consumers at a given price or the

TABLE 2.4.

(1) Price per Bushel (Dollars)	(2) Quantity (Million Bushels)
5.00	10
4.50	11
4.00	12
3.50	16
3.00	21

price at which a given quantity of wheat will be demanded. If the price
of wheat is raised, a smaller quantity will be demanded; and if the price is
lowered, a greater quantity will be sold. Consider the following statement:

$p \to q$ = "If the price of wheat is raised from \$4.00 to \$4.50
per bushel, then the demanded quantity falls from 12 to 11
million bushels."

Asserting the above statement we also assert the statement

$q \to p$ = "If the demanded quantity falls from 12 to 11 million
bushels, then the price of wheat is raised from \$4.00
to \$4.50 per bushel."

But the latter statement is the converse of the former and by asserting
the conditional $p \to q$ we in fact assert the biconditional:

$p \leftrightarrow q$ = "The price of wheat increases or decreases if and
only if the quantity of wheat demanded decreases or
increases."

2.4. Hidden Conditionals.
The importance of the conditional
and, to a lesser degree, of its variations, can hardly be exaggerated.
Many statements in mathematics are conditional, i.e., of the form "if p
then q." But more frequently than not, the antecedent, p, of a conditional
is usually omitted and only the consequent, q, is stated. When, for example, we assert that "$x + 3 = 5$," we implicitly understand that "if $x = 2$,
then $x + 3 = 5$" is the complete mathematical assertion. For lack of a
better term, statements such as "$x + 3 = 5$" may be called *hidden
conditionals*.

The antecedents of a conditional must be explicitly stated or implicitly understood; otherwise it is not a complete mathematical assertion.
For example, we cannot say whether the statements "The sum of the
angles of a triangle is 180 degrees," "The sum of the angles of a triangle
is less than 180 degrees," and "The sum of the angles of a triangle is
more than 180 degrees" are logically true or false. However, their
respective conditionals are logically true since their conclusions are

implied by the antecedent or premises of Euclidean and non-Euclidean geometries. Thus the above-quoted statements are logically true if they are intended to read, "If the axioms of Euclidean geometry are accepted, then the sum of the angles of a triangle is equal to two right angles," "If the axioms of Lobachevskian geometry are accepted, then the sum of the angles of a triangle is less than two right angles," and "If the axioms of Riemannian geometry are accepted, then the sum of the angles of a triangle is more than two right angles." Thus, the obvious inconsistency between the hidden conditionals is clearly understood to originate from different hypotheses.

Hidden conditionals may become the source of inconsistencies, contradictions, and confusion not only in scientific inquiries but also in everyday conversation. To cite just one example: Statements about the magnitude of the unemployed labor force in periods of "economic recession" are invariably in disagreement. Labor union representatives may state that "there are 5 million persons currently unemployed in the United States"; the Chamber of Commerce may declare that "current unemployment is not more than 3.2 million persons"; while the Bureau of Labor Statistics may report that "unemployment has currently reached approximately 3.8 million individuals." Unless the definitions, conditions, and hypotheses which constitute the antecedents of these hidden conditionals are well understood, no meaningful evaluation of them can be made.

PROBLEMS

2.1. For each of the following logical relations draw a Venn diagram and shade the region(s) which represent the null set.

*a) p implies q.

b) q implies p.

c) Equivalence.

2.2. Let the following statements be given:

$$p = \text{"The price of steel is raised,"}$$
$$q = \text{"There is inflation."}$$

Write down the statements indicated below and discuss the conditions under which each statement is logically true.

a) $p \rightarrow q$.

b) $q' \rightarrow p'$.

c) $p' \rightarrow q'$.

d) $q \rightarrow p$.

*2.3. Let the statements

$$p = \text{"Wages are raised,"}$$

and

$$q = \text{"Prices are raised."}$$

Express each of the following statements in symbolic form:

a) "Prices are raised provided that wages are raised."

b) "If prices are raised, then wages are raised."

c) "If wages are not raised, then prices are not raised."

d) "If prices are not raised, then wages are not raised."

*2.4. Let statements

$$p = \text{"There is full employment,"}$$

and

$$q = \text{"There is prosperity."}$$

Put each of the following statements into symbolic form and identify its type:

a) "There is full employment only if there is prosperity."

b) "Full employment is a necessary and sufficient condition for prosperity."

c) "There is prosperity provided that there is full employment."

d) "There is prosperity if there is full employment."

e) "Full employment is a sufficient condition for prosperity."

f) "Prosperity is a necessary condition for full employment."

g) "Full employment is a necessary condition for prosperity."

2.5. Let the statements

$$p = \text{"Inflation continues,"}$$

and

$$q = \text{"The federal government imposes price controls."}$$

Write down the following statements in standard conditional "if . . . then . . ." or biconditional ". . . if and only if . . ." forms.

a) p only if q.

b) q provided that p.

c) p is a sufficient condition for q.

d) q only if p.

e) p is a necessary condition for q.

f) p is a necessary and sufficient condition for q.

*2.6. Let the statements

$$p = \text{"White is a customer,"}$$

and

$$q = \text{"White's account represents assets,"}$$

Form the conditional $p \to q$ and its converse $q \to p$. Do both compound statements involve implications? Explain why they do or they do not.

2.7. Express the following biconditional statements in form $(p \to q) \cap (q \to p)$.

*a) "There is prosperity if and only if there is full employment."

b) "Production costs are reduced if and only if the plant is run more efficiently."

c) "The financial manager is successful if and only if he strikes a balance between the chance of making greater profits and the risk of being unable to meet the financial obligations of the firm because of fluctuating earnings."

2.8. Find a biconditional statement from each of the following subjects:
   a) Accounting.
   b) Behavioral science.
   c) Economics.
   d) Marketing.
   e) Finance.
   f) Production.
   g) Statistics.

2.9. Verify the following equivalence relations by using truth tables for statements and membership tables for sets.
   a) $p \leftrightarrow q = (p' \cup q) \cap (p \cup q')$.
   b) $(P' \cup Q) \cap (P \cup Q') = (P \triangle Q)'$.

2.10. Prove that the conjunction of the conditional and its converse is equivalent to the biconditional.

2.11. The following is what economists call a "supply schedule" for wheat. It shows the relationship between price and quantity of wheat supplied.

(1) Price per Bushel (*Dollars*)	(2) Quantity (*Million Bushels*)
5.00	20
4.50	18
4.00	12
3.50	10
3.00	9

Assuming "pure" or perfect competition, the above schedule shows the quantity of wheat which can be sold by the suppliers at a given price or the price at which a given quantity of wheat will be supplied. Do the same analysis which is done in Example 2.5 of the text.

2.12. From each of the following subjects find a *hidden conditional* statement and express it in a proper conditional form.
   a) Accounting.
   b) Behavioral science.
   c) Economics.
   d) Finance.
   e) Marketing.
   f) Mathematics.
   g) Production.
   h) Statistics.

2.13. Find with truth tables whether each of the following biconditional statements are logically true and identify the abstract law (if any) of set operations from Table 4.1 of Chapter 1 to which each biconditional statement may correspond.
   *a) $(p \cap q)' \leftrightarrow (p' \cup q')$.

b) $(p \cup q)' \leftrightarrow (p' \cap q')$.
c) $(p \cap q) \leftrightarrow (q \cap p)$.
d) $(p \cup q) \leftrightarrow (q \cup p)$.
e) $(p \rightarrow q) \leftrightarrow (p' \cup q)$.
f) $(p \rightarrow q)' \leftrightarrow (p \cap q')$.
g) $(p \leftrightarrow q) \leftrightarrow [(p \rightarrow q) \cap (q \rightarrow p)]$.
h) $(p \leftrightarrow q) \leftrightarrow [(p \cap q) \cup (p' \cap q')]$.
i) $p \leftrightarrow [(p')']$.
j) $(p \rightarrow q) \leftrightarrow (q' \rightarrow p')$.

2.14. The following excerpt is from the *Christian Science Monitor*, November 13, 1961, p. 10. "A labor union economist says the United States may have more unemployment than government statistics show—up to 8.3 per cent of the labor force if part-time workers who want full-time jobs are included . . ."

a) Express the conditional about unemployment in "if *p* then *q*" form.
b) Refer to the *Statistical Abstract of the United States*, 1961, and express the reported percentage of unemployed labor force for the United States for 1961 in "if *p* then *q*" conditional form.
c) Explain the difference between the two conditional propositions with respect to their conclusions or their consequents by comparing their premises.

2.15. The six important logical relations which can be obtained from the basic connectives of conjunction, disjunction, conditional, and biconditional are shown below:

Possibilities Excluded		*Logical Relation*	*Alternative Definition*
Region(s) = ∅	*Truth Table(s)*		
R_1	T-T	Contraries	$p \cap q$ logically false
R_4	F-F	Subcontraries	$p \cup q$ logically true
R_2	T-F	*p* implies *q*	$p \rightarrow q$ logically true
R_3	F-T	*q* implies *p*	$q \rightarrow p$ logically true
R_2, R_3	T-F and F-T	Equivalents	$p \leftrightarrow q$ logically true
R_1, R_4	T-T and F-F	Contradictories	$q \leftrightarrow p$ logically false

For each logical relation draw the appropriate Venn diagram and shade the region(s) which represents the null set.

2.16. Let the truth values of statements 3 through 7 shown in the table below be given:

(1) *p*	(2) *q*	(3) $p \rightarrow q$	(4) $p' \cup q$	(5) $(p \cap q)'$	(6) $(p' \cup q')'$	(7) q'
T	T	T	T	F	T	F
T	F	F	F	T	F	T
F	T	T	T	T	F	F
F	F	T	T	T	F	T

On the basis of the information given in the table in Problem 2.15 about the six important logical relations, find what relation exists between the following pairs of statements: (3,4), (3,5), (3,6), (3,7), (4,5), (4,6), (4,7), (5,6), (5,7), (6,7).

*3. VALID AND INVALID PROPOSITIONAL STATEMENTS

In demonstrating the use of the new compound statements—the conditional and the biconditional—we dealt briefly with arguments. We said that if an argument is logically true, i.e., if the conjunction of the premises implies the conclusion, then the argument is valid; otherwise it is invalid. In this section we shall study systematically, although not exhaustively, the validity of arguments which are made up of propositional statements.

Such arguments can be classified into different groups depending on the kind of compound propositional statements they contain in their premises. Thus, arguments with a conjunction in their premises are called *conjunctive*. Analogously, we have *disjunctive, conditional,* and *biconditional arguments* if their premises contain one or more disjunctive, conditional, or biconditional statements. All above forms are *simple* arguments. In contrast, if two or more of the above four basic compound statements appear in the premises of an argument, such an argument is called *complex*.

The interested reader will find at the end of this section problems involving all the above-mentioned types of arguments. However, since most of them are of minor importance, we shall concentrate our attention on the analysis of different forms of conditional and complex arguments.

3.1. Simple Conditional Arguments. Four simple conditional arguments can be obtained by considering the conjunction of the conditional $p \to q$ with the four logical possibilities between p and q. They are shown in Table 3.1. If p is true, the only possibility which

TABLE 3.1.

Row	(1)	(2)	(3)	(4)	(5)
1.	$[(p \to q) \cap p] \to q$	Asserting p	T-T	Valid	*Modus ponendo ponens*
2.	$[(p \to q) \cap q'] \to p'$	Denying q	F-F	Valid	*Modus tollendo tollens*
3.	$[(p \to q) \cap p'] \to q'$	Denying p	F-?	Invalid	Fallacy
4.	$[(p \to q) \cap q] \to p$	Asserting q	?-T	Invalid	Fallacy

yields a valid argument is when q is true. Hence, we obtain the first valid argument shown in row 1. It is called *modus ponendo ponens* since we, by asserting (*ponendo*) the antecedent p, assert (*ponens*) the consequent q. If, on the other hand, q is false, the only possibility which yields a valid argument is when p is also false, leading to the second valid argument in row 2. It is called *modus tollendo tollens*, i.e., we, by denying (*tollendo*) the consequent q, deny (*tollens*) the antecedent p. Contrastingly, when either p is false or q is true, their conjunction with the conditional does not yield valid arguments since in neither case does the conjunction of the premises imply the conclusion. The reader may test the validity of the four arguments in Table 3.1 by means of truth tables. Furthermore, he may find it useful to refer to Example 1.6 which is a *modus ponendo ponens* argument. We give two additional examples below.

Example 3.1. Let the conditional statement

$p \rightarrow q =$ "If the contract is valid, then Goodwill and Company is liable."

be given. To the above conditional we may add the premise

$p =$ "The contract is valid"

and argue validly by *modus ponens* the conclusion

$q =$ "Goodwill and Company is liable."

Alternatively, adding to the conditional the premise

$q' =$ "Goodwill and Company is not liable,"

we are led by arguing validly *modus tollens* to the conclusion

$p' =$ "The contract is not valid."

In contrast, those who add to the conditional the premise

$p' =$ "The contract is not valid"

and draw the conclusion

$q' =$ "Goodwill and Company is not liable"

are arguing invalidly: they are committing the *fallacy of denying the antecedent*. Their argument is fallacious because the premise $p \rightarrow q$ does not rule out the possibility that Goodwill and Company may be liable for other than the contract in question, say for an industrial accident in a plant of the company. On similar grounds, those who assert the premise

$q =$ "Goodwill and Company is liable"

and reach the conclusion

$p =$ "The contract is valid"

are committing the *fallacy of asserting the consequent*. They argue invalidly because the premise $p \rightarrow q$ does not exclude the possibility that Goodwill and Company's liability may stem from other sources. The reader may notice that the latter fallacy arises from the confusion of the conditional with its converse (cf. Examples 2.1 and 2.5).

Whether the conclusion of an argument is empirically true or false is independent of the validity of the argument. In other words, the conclusion may be empirically true while the argument is invalid or the conclusion empirically false and the argument valid, as the following example illustrates.

Example 3.2. Let us examine the argument

$p \rightarrow q$ = "If the United States is a capitalistic economy, then most means of production are privately owned."

q = "Most means of production in the United States are privately owned."

$\therefore p$ = "The United States is a capitalistic economy."

Naturally the conclusion is empirically true; but the argument is invalid since we have committed the fallacy of asserting the consequent of the conditional.

Similarly, compare the following case:

$p \rightarrow q$ = "If there is communism in the Soviet Union, then most means of production are owned by the State."

q' = "Most means of production in the Soviet Union are privately owned."

$\therefore p'$ = "There is no communism in the Soviet Union."

The conclusion is empirically false; but the argument is valid since the conclusion is implied by the premises. Of course the paradox disappears as soon as we realize that the second premise q' is empirically false.

3.2. Chain Arguments.

This kind of argument, otherwise called "pure hypothetical syllogism," deserves special attention. A chain argument is a conditional argument of the form

$$[(p \rightarrow r) \cap (r \rightarrow q)] \rightarrow (p \rightarrow q).$$

A peculiar feature of a chain argument is that all of its premises and its conclusion are conditional statements. The validity of a chain argument depends on two conditions: (a) the eliminated simple statement r occurs once as an antecedent and once as a consequent in the premises of successive conditionals; (b) the antecedent p of the conclusion is the antecedent of the first premise, and the consequent q of the conclusion is the consequent of the last premise. We may observe that the above symbolic form depicts a valid chain argument since it meets both conditions. Finally, a chain argument may have more than two conditional statements as premises. We demonstrate the above features of chain arguments with an example.

Example 3.3. Assuming conditions of free competition let us consider the argument "If prices fall (r), then consumers benefit (q). If costs per unit of output do not decrease (z'), then productivity does not increase (p'). If costs per unit of output decrease (z), then prices of goods fall (r). Therefore, if productivity increases (p), then consumers benefit (q)."

In order to determine whether the conclusion "If productivity increases, then consumers benefit" follows from the premises, we need to test the validity of the chain argument. Using the letters in parentheses which follow each simple statement we can express the given argument in its symbolic form, shown in Table 3.2, column 1. Obviously, this form does

TABLE 3.2.

(1)	(2)	(3)
$r \to q$	$r \to q$	$p \to z$
$z' \to p'$	$p \to z$	$z \to r$
$z \to r$	$z \to r$	$r \to q$
$\therefore p \to q$	$\therefore p \to q$	$\therefore p \to q$

not meet the conditions necessary for a valid chain argument. But it can be reduced to its valid form. For one thing, the second premise $z' \to p'$ is the contrapositive of the conditional $p \to z$. Since they are equivalent, the former is replaced by the latter in the step shown in column 2. For another thing, we can change the order of the premises as shown in column 3. Now the argument is valid since it meets the two previously mentioned conditions and the conclusion "if productivity increases, then consumers benefit" follows from the premises.

3.3. Indirect Method of Proof.

At this point we are ready to explain the direct and indirect methods of inference or proof. In the former case we show directly that a conditional premise $p \to q$ is an implication when we assert the consequent q by asserting the antecedent p. *Modus ponendo ponens* and the chain argument already analyzed are examples of direct method of proof. Frequently, however, it is more convenient and sometimes the only way to show indirectly that a conditional premise $p \to q$ is an implication when we deny the antecedent p by denying the consequent q. *Modus tollendo tollens* is an example of the indirect method of proof. Although indirect proof utilizes several types of arguments, their common characteristic is to show that the conditional $p \to q$ is an implication by actually showing that its equivalent contrapositive $q' \to p'$ is an implication. Although the indirect method of proof may be used in any scientific inquiry as well as in everyday discussion, we shall illustrate the method with three examples from mathematics by using *modus tollendo tollens* and two chain arguments other than the kind already used.

Example 3.4. We wish to prove the statement "Any two empty sets are equal." Converting this statement to its equivalent conditional and using the latter as a premise we have the following argument.

$p \rightarrow q$ = "If any given two sets are empty, then they are equal."
q' = "For two sets to be unequal means for one of the sets to contain an element not in the other."

$\therefore p'$ = "The two given sets are not empty."

We may observe that by *modus tollendo tollens* we have arrived at the conclusion "The two given sets are not empty" which is contradictory to the hypothesis "If any two given sets are empty." Thus, indirectly we prove the original statement "any two empty sets are equal," which justifies the conclusion that there is one and only one empty set—*the* null set by showing that the contrapositive $q' \rightarrow p'$ is implied.

Example 3.5. A prime number is a positive integer which is greater than 1 and divisible only by 1 and itself. We wish to prove the following conditional statement:

$p \rightarrow q$ = "If an integer greater than 2 is prime, then it is an odd number."

Substituting the word "integer" for "integer greater than 2" we use the following chain argument:

$q' \rightarrow r$ = "If an integer is not odd, then it is even."
$r \rightarrow z$ = "If it is even, then it is divisible by 2."
$z \rightarrow p'$ = "If it is divisible by 2, then it is not a prime by above definition of primes."

$\therefore q' \rightarrow p'$ = "If an integer is not odd, then it is not a prime."

The conclusion $q' \rightarrow p'$ is implied since the chain argument is valid. But the contrapositive $q' \rightarrow p'$ is equivalent to the conditional $p \rightarrow q$. Thus, by showing that the former is implied, we have proved indirectly the latter statement "If an integer greater than 2 is a prime, then it is an odd number."

Example 3.6. The chain argument

$$[(p \rightarrow q') \cap (q' \rightarrow p')] \rightarrow (p \rightarrow p')$$

called *reductio ad absurdum* (reduction to absurdity) is a well-known indirect method of proof. We illustrate its use with the famous Euclid's proof of the theorem "There are infinitely many primes."

Let us assume that there were only a *finite* number of primes. Let all of them be 2, 3, 5, 7, ..., a where prime a is the largest of them. Also, let us consider the number $b = 2 \cdot 3 \cdot 5 \cdot 7 \ldots \cdot a + 1$. The argument runs as follows:

$p \rightarrow q'$ = "If a is the largest prime, then b is not a prime since if it were that would be contradictory to our hypothesis."

$*q' \rightarrow p' = $ "If b is not a prime (q'), then this means that b is divisible by some factor other than 1 and itself (r). But b is not divisible by any of the given primes since if b is divided by either 2, 3, 5, 7, . . . , or a there is always a remainder of 1 (r'). Therefore, b is a prime, by definition of prime numbers in Example 3.5 (q); then a is not the largest prime (p')."

$\therefore p \rightarrow p' = $ "If a is the largest prime, then a is not the largest prime."

From this obviously contradictory statement $p \rightarrow p'$ we *always* conclude (why?) that—

$p' = $ "There is no largest prime, i.e., there are infinitely many primes."

It is important to realize that using the letters in parentheses which follow each simple statement of the above given argument, statement $*q'$ is equal to

$$\{[(q' \rightarrow r) \cap r'] \rightarrow q\}$$

and the complete chain argument is

$$[(p \rightarrow q') \cap (\{[(q' \rightarrow r) \cap r'] \rightarrow q\} \rightarrow p')] \rightarrow (p \rightarrow p').$$

3.4. Biconditional and Complex Arguments.

It is difficult to imagine someone committing a logical error by arguing from a biconditional. Nevertheless, mathematical inference or proof of biconditional statements are of special importance because they require testing the validity of both the sufficient condition $p \rightarrow q$ and the necessary condition $q \rightarrow p$. For this reason problems involving biconditional arguments are provided at the end of this section. We terminate our present discussion with an example of a complex argument.

Example 3.7. Consider the following complex argument: "If there is no price stability (p'), then the federal government will impose economic controls (q). If economic controls are imposed (q), then there is no economic recession (r'). There is either an economic recession (r) or overproduction (z). In fact, according to economic indicators there is no overproduction (z'). Therefore, there is price stability (p)."

Using the symbols provided, the argument is

$$\begin{array}{cccc} (1) & (2) & (3) & (4) \end{array}$$
$$[(p' \rightarrow q) \cap (q \rightarrow r') \cap (r \cup z) \cap z'] \rightarrow p,$$

where the numbers in parentheses indicate the premises of the argument.

Since the argument contains four simple statements, testing its validity would require a truth table with $2^4 = 16$ rows. This is a time-consuming task which, in addition, increases the likelihood of error.

We can accomplish the same objective as follows:

Step	Argument	Premise(s)	Implied Statement
1	$[(r \cup z) \cap z'] \to r$	(3) and (4)	r
2	$[(q \to r') \cap r] \to q'$	(2)	q'
3	$[(p' \to q) \cap q'] \to p$	(1)	p

Since all the above three simple arguments are valid (the reader may verify them by means of truth tables), the complex argument is valid and the conclusion

$$p = \text{"There is price stability"}$$

is implied by the premises of the argument.

It should be noted that two rules have been utilized: (*a*) We have introduced the four premises piecemeal when needed—premises (3) and (4) in step 1, (2) in step 2, and (1) in step 3. (*b*) We have derived new simple implied statements which in turn have been used as premises—statement r in step 1 as premise in step 2 and statement q' in step 2 as premise in step 3.

We conclude with the remark that the valid arguments of this section may be used as a basis for developing a workable strategy for testing the validity of many other more complex propositional statements.

PROBLEMS

3.1. For each group of arguments indicated below, test the validity of each argument with a truth table and visualize the relationship between premises and conclusion by drawing a Venn diagram.

a) Conditional arguments in Table 3.1.

b) Conjunctive arguments in table below:

Row	(1)	(2)	(3)
1.	$[(p \cap q)' \cap p] \to q'$	Asserting p	Valid
2.	$[(p \cap q)' \cap q] \to p'$	Asserting q	Valid
3.	$[(p \cap q)' \cap p'] \to q$	Denying p	Fallacy
4.	$[(p \cap q)' \cap q'] \to p$	Denying q	Fallacy

c) Disjunctive arguments shown below:

Row	(1)	(2)	(3)
1.	$[(p \cup q) \cap p'] \to q$	Denying p	Valid
2.	$[(p \cup q) \cap q'] \to p$	Denying q	Valid
3.	$[(p \cup q) \cap p] \to q'$	Asserting p	Fallacy
4.	$[(p \cup q) \cap q] \to p'$	Asserting q	Fallacy

3.2. Let the following statements be given:

$$p = \text{``Wages rise,''}$$
$$q = \text{``Prices rise.''}$$

Using the above two statements, form the four conjunctive arguments shown in Problem 3.1(b).

3.3. Let the following statements be given:

$$p = \text{``Our economy is in a state of recession,''}$$
$$q = \text{``Our economy is in a state of prosperity.''}$$

Using the above two statements, form the four disjunctive arguments shown in Problem 3.1(c).

*3.4. It is very important to realize that the disjunctive fallacies in Problem 3.1.(c) are the result of the fact that the premise $p \cup q$ is *inclusive*. Let $p \underline{\cup} q$ represent an *exclusive* disjunction, where $p \underline{\cup} q$ is true if and only if one of the statements is true and the other false. Using the statements given in Problem 3.3, form the two disjunctive fallacies and show by means of truth tables that they become valid arguments if the exclusive disjunction is used as a premise.

3.5. Test the validity of the following arguments with truth tables:
  *a) $[(p \rightarrow r) \cap (r \rightarrow q)] \rightarrow (p \rightarrow q)$.
  b) $[(q' \rightarrow r) \cap (r \rightarrow z) \cap (z \rightarrow p')] \rightarrow (q' \rightarrow p')$; (Example 3.5).
  c) $[(p \rightarrow q') \cap (\{[(q' \rightarrow r) \cap r'] \rightarrow q\} \rightarrow p')] \rightarrow (p \rightarrow p')$; (Example 3.6).
  d) $[(p' \rightarrow q) \cap (q \rightarrow r') \cap (r \cup z) \cap z'] \rightarrow p$; (Example 3.7).

3.6. The following is a selective group of biconditional arguments. Test the validity of each with truth tables and visualize the relationship between its premises and its conclusion with a Venn diagram.
  *a) $[(p \leftrightarrow q) \cap p] \rightarrow q$.
  b) $[(p \leftrightarrow q) \cap p'] \rightarrow q'$.
  c) $[(p \leftrightarrow q) \cap (q \leftrightarrow r)] \rightarrow (p \leftrightarrow r)$.
  d) $[(p \leftrightarrow q) \cap (q \cup r)] \rightarrow (p \cup r)$.
  e) $[(p \leftrightarrow q) \cup p] \rightarrow q$.

3.7. Express the following arguments in symbolic form and test their validity with truth tables.
  *a) "It is not true that there is an international crisis and a sharp drop in stock market prices. But there is an international crisis. Therefore, stock market prices have not declined."
  b) "Either there is an international crisis or there is a sharp decline in stock market quotations. But there is a decline in stock market prices. Therefore, there is no international crisis."
  c) "If there is an international crisis, stock market prices drop sharply. But the stock market is bullish. Therefore, there is no international crisis."
  d) "There is an international crisis if and only if there is a sharp decline in the stock market. In fact, stock prices dropped sharply. Therefore, there is an international crisis."

3.8. Let the following statements be given:

p = "A consumer is a person who has wants,"
q = "A businessman's job is to satisfy consumer wants profitably."

Write in words one valid argument and one fallacy for each of the following forms of simple arguments by using the above statements.
a) Conditional arguments.
b) Biconditional arguments (a) and (e) in Problem 3.6.
c) Conjunctive arguments [defined in Problem 3.1(b)].
d) Disjunctive arguments [defined in Problem 3.1(c)].

3.9. For each of the following arguments provide a conclusion to complete one valid and one invalid argument.
 *a) "A full-employment economy can produce more butter or more guns. It can produce more butter. Therefore, ..."
 b) "It is not true that a full-employment economy can produce more butter and more guns. It cannot produce more butter. Therefore, ..."
 c) "If a full-employment economy can produce more butter, then it produces fewer guns. In fact, it does not produce fewer guns. Therefore, ..."
 d) "A full-employment economy produces more butter if and only if it produces fewer guns. In fact, it does not produce more butter. Therefore, ..."

3.10. The premises of three arguments are given below. For each argument find a valid conclusion by doing the following steps:
 i) Prepare the truth table of the conjunction of the premises.
 ii) Since in a valid argument the conclusion must be true whenever the premises are true, find a compound statement (if there is one) which is implied by the premises and therefore makes the arguments valid.
 *a) $[(p \to q) \cap (r' \to q')] \to$?
 b) $[(p' \leftrightarrow q) \cap (q \cup r) \cap r'] \to$?
 c) $[(p \cup q) \cap (q \to r') \cap (p \cup r)] \to$?

*3.11. Express the following argument in symbolic form, test its validity, and identify type of argument:

"Demand for the new product will increase provided that advertising is effective. But if production costs for the new product are reduced, its price will be reduced also. In fact, if more units of the new products are sold, then production costs will be lower. Actually, more units of the new product can be sold if the demand for it increases. Therefore, advertising is effective only if prices for the new product will be reduced."

(Use letters d, a, c, p, s for symbols.)

*3.12. Translate the following argument into symbols, test its validity, and identify type of argument.

"Farmers have more income only if they work hard and nature cooperates. If they work hard and nature cooperates, they will have a bumper crop of wheat. But if they have a bumper crop, wheat prices will fall and if prices fall, farmers will not have more income. Therefore, if farmers have more income, then they will not have more income."

From the above argument can you imply that "farmers will not have more income"? Explain why or why not.

3.13. Let x and y be any integers. Prove by *modus tollendo tollens* the following statements:

a) "If x^2 is an even integer, then x is an even integer."

b) "If xy is an odd number, then x and y are both odd."

*3.14. Express the following complex argument in symbolic form and test its validity by the method illustrated in Example 3.7. Then verify your answer by testing the validity of the argument with a truth table.

"There will be inflation if either wages or prices rise. If there is inflation, then either the government must impose controls or the cost of living will rise. But the government will be unpopular if the cost of living rises. The government will not impose controls. So the government will not be unpopular. Therefore, wages or prices will rise."

(Use letters w, p, i, c, l, u for symbols.)

*3.15. Consider the following argument:

"If the market of steel is perfectly free, then a single producer cannot affect prices. If a single producer cannot affect prices, then there is a large number of producers. In fact, the number of steel producers is large because the steel industry is diversified. Therefore, the steel market is perfectly free."

Is the conclusion implied by the premises of the argument? Use letters f, p, l to test the argument's validity by the method illustrated in Example 3.7. Then verify your answer with a truth table. How would the meaning of the terms "steel market" and "steel industry" determine whether the conclusion of the argument is factually true or false?"

3.16. The reader is referred to Example 4.3 of Chapter 1 which proves De Morgan's law 9a. After observing that the membership tables of sets $(A \cup B)'$ and $A' \cap B'$, columns 4 and 7 of the table, are identical, prove the biconditional statement

$$p \leftrightarrow q = \{(A \cup B)' \text{ is equivalent to } A' \cap B' \text{ if and only if } (A \cup B)' = A' \cap B'\}.$$

[*Hint:* Prove

a) The sufficient condition $p \to q$;

b) The necessary condition $p' \to q'$; and

c) The biconditional $(p' \to q') \leftrightarrow (q \to p)$.

3.17. Write a book report of W. W. Fearnside and W. B. Holther, *Fallacy: The Counterfeit of Argument* (Englewood Cliffs, N.J.: Prentice-Hall, Inc., 1959).

*4. VALID AND INVALID SET STATEMENTS

While the previous section dealt with the *logic of propositions*, this section, the last of Chapter 3, deals with the *logic of classes or sets*, i.e., with the analysis of arguments whose premise(s) and conclusion consist of set statements. After a general discussion of the four types of simple set statements, space limitations will allow us to concentrate on the analysis of only one kind of compound set statement or argument, called syllogism. We shall study the anatomy of the syllogism, determine its validity with Venn diagrams, and show how the validity of certain syllogisms may be proved with set operations. Last, we shall briefly discuss the general forms of valid syllogisms.

4.1. Basic Types of Set Statements.
The structure of set statements was discussed in terms of sets in Section 1, Chapter 2. The reader may find it helpful to review the appropriate topic. At that time, set statements were defined as denoting a single relation between a subject, i.e., a set about which the statement makes an assertion or denial and a predicate, i.e., a set which is asserted or denied. Now it is necessary to study this relationship between subject and predicate more systematically.

Let S and P be sets denoting the subject and predicate of a set statement, respectively. Then all possible inclusions or exclusions between the sets S and P can form four types of statements whose general form is shown in Table 4.1. The following example illustrates these four types of set statements.

TABLE 4.1.

	Universal	Particular
Affirmative.........$A =$ "All S is P"		$I =$ "Some S is P"
Negative ....$E =$ "No S is P"		$O =$ "Some S is not P"

Example 4.1. Let the sets
$$S = \{x|x \text{ is a smoker}\}$$
and
$$P = \{x|x \text{ is a drinker}\}$$
be given. Then we can form the following four types of statements:

$A =$ "All smokers are drinkers,"
$I =$ "Some smokers are drinkers,"
$E =$ "No smokers are drinkers,"
$O =$ "Some smokers are not drinkers,"

where the set of smokers is the subject and the set of drinkers the predicate.

Statements of type *A* and *E* are called *universal* because each statement refers to the whole subject. Statements of type *I* and *O* are called particular since each of them refers to a part of the subject. The two *affirmative* types of statements are designated by letters derived from the first two vowels of the Latin verb AffIrmo (I affirm) while the letters of the two *negative* types are derived from the verb nEgO (I deny). Observe that statement *E* is not equivalent to the negation of *A*, i.e., to *A'*. Neither is statement *O* equivalent to the negation of *I*, i.e., to *I'*. Universal statements of type *A* and *E* are called *existential* if the person who makes such a statement *implies* that some elements of the subject-set, in Example 4.1 smokers, really exist. If no such implication is made, such a universal statement is called *hypothetical*. Hence, which statement is involved in a particular situation depends on whether the person who makes the statement is committed to the weak hypothetical or to the strong existential form of a universal statement.

We have followed the convention of denoting the general forms of the four types of statements with the capital *A*, *I*, *E*, and *O* whose origin has already been explained. In studying specific cases of the most important compound set statements or arguments called syllogisms, however, we shall follow our practice of denoting set statements by lowercase letters.

4.2. The Anatomy of a Syllogism.

An argument involving a syllogism consists of two set statements representing its premises and one set statement representing its conclusion. But in order to understand syllogisms we need to study their anatomy.

Example 4.2. Consider the following arguments consisting of set statements:

(4.1) $p =$ "All Americans are thrifty."
           $q =$ "All thrifty people are wealthy."
           _____
           $\therefore r =$ "All Americans are wealthy."

(4.2) $p =$ "No rank-and-file member runs the union."
           $q =$ "Some active union members run the union."
           _____
           $\therefore r =$ "Some active union members are not rank-and-file members."

The above arguments have some resemblance to chain arguments since the conclusion is reached by eliminating something from the premises. Perhaps this mild resemblance may explain why we have called chain arguments pure hypothetical syllogisms while arguments such as (4.1) and (4.2) are called *categorical syllogisms* or simply *syllogisms*.

But this resemblance is superficial. What is eliminated in both syllogisms is not a statement but a set—the set of thrifty people in (4.1) and the set of workers who control the union in (4.2). A chain argument may have any number of premises while (4.1) and (4.2) or any other syllogism cannot have more than two. Furthermore, the inner structure of a syllogism is quite different from a chain argument. Each premise of a chain argument is a conditional propositional statement, while each premise of (4.1) and (4.2) consists of a simple set statement. In addition to the basic connectives $\cap$ and $\rightarrow$ in the quoted syllogisms, new words such as "all" and "some" called *quantifiers* have been introduced. In fact, it may be argued that the logic of classes is the study of the meaning of words such as the above quoted. Last but not least, the symbolic expression of a syllogism is of the form $(p \cap q) \rightarrow r$ whose validity cannot be tested with truth tables. In a sense, therefore, the logic of classes is an extension of the logic of propositions.

The set which occurs in both premises is called the *middle term*. In (4.1) it is the set of thrifty people, and in (4.2) it is the set of workers who run the union; the predicate of the conclusion is the *major term*, and the subject the *minor term*. Correspondingly, the premise with the major term is called the *major premise*, and the premise with the minor term *minor premise*. Thus, in (4.1) statement p is the minor and q the major premise, while the reverse is true in (4.2). Usually, the major premise is placed first. This practice will be followed as a matter of convenience.

4.3. Determining the Validity of Syllogisms with Venn Diagrams.

We have already pointed out that the validity of syllogisms cannot be tested with truth tables. However, Venn diagrams offer an unsophisticated method for determining the validity of syllogisms.

Example 4.3. Let the sets

$$A = \{x | x \text{ is an American}\}$$
$$T = \{x | x \text{ is a thrifty person}\}$$
$$W = \{x | x \text{ is a wealthy person}\}$$

be given. Then the validity of syllogism (4.1), with the major premise q first, can be determined with the Venn diagram shown in Figure 4.1.

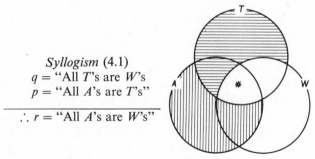

Syllogism (4.1)
$q =$ "All T's are W's"
$p =$ "All A's are T's"
──────────────
$\therefore r =$ "All A's are W's"

FIGURE 4.1.

Since the major premise "All thrifty people are wealthy" indicates that $T \subseteq W$, the region of the diagram representing the empty set is shaded with horizontal lines. Similarly, the region representing the empty set for the minor premise "All Americans are thrifty," which indicates that $A \subseteq T$, is shaded with vertical lines. But we may observe that in the process of diagramming the premises we have at the same time diagrammed the conclusion. The region marked with an asterisk and representing "All Americans" is a subset of set W, containing "All wealthy people." Hence, the syllogism is valid.

It is important to realize that the validity of a syllogism does not depend on whether the premises and the conclusion are really true or false. In argument (4.1) all three set statements are in reality false, yet the syllogism is valid.

Example 4.4. Determine the validity of syllogism (4.2) with a Venn diagram. Let the sets

$$F = \{x|x \text{ is a rank-and-file union member}\}$$
$$R = \{x|x \text{ is a union member who runs the union}\}$$
$$M = \{x|x \text{ is an active union member}\}$$

be given. Then we can determine the validity of syllogism (4.2) with the Venn diagram shown in Figure 4.2. We first shade the empty set which

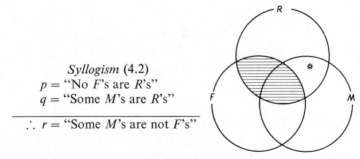

Syllogism (4.2)
$p =$ "No F's are R's"
$q =$ "Some M's are R's"

$\therefore r =$ "Some M's are not F's"

FIGURE 4.2.

represents the universal statement "No rank-and-file member runs the union." Then, we mark with an asterisk the region of the diagram which depicts the particular statement "Some active union members run the union." Could the asterisk be placed on the shaded part of the set $R \cap M$? No, because this would mean that at least one active member who runs the union is a rank-and-file member, which is inconsistent with the universal statement that no rank-and-file member runs the union. Therefore, the argument is valid since there is at least one active member, as the position of the star indicates, who is not rank and file.

In sum, determining the validity of syllogisms with Venn diagrams involves the following procedure:

a) *Shade the region(s) of the diagram for the universal premise(s) first.*
b) *Next, star the region(s) of the diagram which depict the meaning of the particular premise(s).*
c) *Finally, see if the diagramming of the premises agrees with the diagramming of the conclusion.*

4.4. Proving the Validity of Syllogisms with Set Operations.

The validity of syllogisms whose all three set statements are universal, either affirmative or negative, can be proved with set operations. The following example illustrates this case. Another case appears as a problem at the end of this section.

Example 4.5. Let the sets A, T, and W be defined as in Example 4.3. Then prove with set operations syllogism (4.1) expressed in terms of set relations as follows:

$q = $ "All thrifty people are wealthy" $T \cup W = W$ (1)
$p = $ "All Americans are thrifty" $A \cup T = T$ (2)

$\therefore r = $ "All Americans are wealthy" $\therefore A \cup W = W$

In order to prove the validity of the above statement we must show that the conclusion is true whenever the hypotheses are both true.

Proof:

$$
\begin{aligned}
A \cup W &= A \cup (T \cup W) && \text{[by hypothesis (1)]} \\
&= (A \cup T) \cup W && \text{[by law 3a of Table 1.4.1, Ch. 1]} \\
&= T \cup W && \text{[by hypothesis (2)]} \\
&= W && \text{[by hypothesis (1)]}
\end{aligned}
$$

Since we have proved that $A \cup W = W$, the argument is valid.

4.5. General Forms of Valid Syllogisms.

Since there are four basic types of set statements from which we can perform the three tasks of choosing the major and minor premises and the conclusion of a syllogism, there are $4 \times 4 \times 4 = 64$ possible arrangements, called *moods*. A mood such as AAA or AAI denotes the type of statement as defined in Table 4.1 which occupies the major premise, the minor premise, and the conclusion in a syllogism in that order. Letting the letters M, S, and P denote the middle, minor, and major terms of a syllogism, respectively, we can obtain four patterns, called *figures*. They are shown in Table 4.2, column 1. Since each of the 64 moods may occur in any of the four figures, there are $64 \times 4 = 256$ possible types of syllogisms. Proving the theorems which are necessary to determine which of the 256 types are valid lies beyond the scope of this book. Suffice it to say that only a limited number of them are valid. If universal statements are interpreted hypothetically, there are only 15 valid types, shown in column 2 of Table 4.2. Under the existential interpretation of universal statements nine *additional* types, column 3 of Table 4.2, are valid.

TABLE 4.2.

	Types of Valid Syllogisms	
Figures (1)	Hypothetical (2)	Existential (3)
1. [(*MP*) & (*SM*)], then *SP*	*AAA, AII, EAE, EIO*	*AAI, EAO*
2. [(*PM*) & (*SM*)], then *SP*	*AOO, AEE, EAE, EIO*	*AEO, EAO*
3. [(*MP*) & (*MS*)], then *SP*	*AII, EIO, OAO, IAI*	*AAI, EAO*
4. [(*PM*) & (*MS*)], then *SP*	*AEE, EIO, IAI*	*AAI, AEO, EAO*

This list of valid types greatly facilitates the *formal* analysis of syllogisms for determining their validity. Discovering, however, whether a given argument is syllogistic in form is not an easy task because of the incomplete or ambiguous character of linguistic expressions encountered in the normal course of reading and conversation.

4.6. A Few Final Remarks. In this part of the course we have seen how sets and deductive logic involve the mathematical system of Boolean algebra. Deductive logic, however, as a method of reasoning is closely affiliated with another great body of thought, namely, philosophy. In fact, deductive reasoning as a method of scientific inquiry has greatly contributed to the development of both mathematics and philosophy.

PROBLEMS

4.1. Indicate the kind of basic set statement involved in each of the following sentences. Express your answer in terms of symbols shown in Table 4.1.
a) "Some forms of nonprice competition are not desirable."
b) "Most investments are savings."
c) "Some corporations are not big."
d) "A few types of consumer credit involve excessive interest charges."
e) "Business firms are profit organizations."
f) "No partnership in the United States is big business."
g) "The majority of business firms are single proprietorships."

4.2. Convert the following syllogism into a chain argument and discuss the similarities and differences between these two types of arguments.

$$p = \text{"All } x\text{'s are } y\text{'s"}$$
$$q = \text{"All } y\text{'s are } z\text{'s"}$$

$$\therefore r = \text{"All } x\text{'s are } z\text{'s"}$$

4.3. Illustrate each of the following sets of premises with a Venn diagram. What valid syllogism(s) (if any) can you obtain from each set of premises?

a) "All *P* is *R*,"   "All *Q* is *P*."
b) "No *P* is *Q*,"   "All *R* is *P*."
c) "Some *P* is *Q*," "No *P* is *R*."
d) "All *P* is *Q*,"   "All *Q* is *R*,"
      with both the hypothetical and existential interpretation of *P*.
e) "Some *P* is *Q*," "All *P* is *R*."
f) "All *P* is *Q*,"   "All *R* is *Q*."
g) "All *P* is *Q*,"   "All *Q* is *R*."

4.4. Test the validity of the syllogism in Problem 4.2 by means of a Venn Diagram. Verify your answer by referring to Table 4.2.

4.5. For each of the following arguments:
  i) Find the major, minor, and middle terms and express the argument in syllogistic form.
  ii) Write the mood of the syllogism.
  iii) Identify the feature to which each mood belongs.

a) "All investments are savings; no consumption is savings; therefore, no consumption is investment."

b) "Some corporations are big; some corporations are monopolies; therefore, some monopolies are big."

c) "Some corporations are business giants; no corporation is a monopoly; therefore, some monopolies are not business giants."

d) "Every regimentation of the United States economy is undesirable because it curtails individual freedoms; every measure for the purpose of achieving full employment is a form of regimentation; therefore, every measure for full employment is undesirable."

e) "Some types of consumer credit involve excessive interest charges; all types of consumer credit involve instalment buying of one or another kind; some instalment buying involves excessive interest charges."

f) "Some of the best cigarettes in the market are *mellow* cigarettes because they are mild."

g) "No form of nonprice competition is desirable because no trading stamps are desirable and all trading stamps are forms of nonprice competition."

h) "No trading stamps are desirable because all trading stamps are forms of nonprice competition and no form of nonprice competition is desirable."

i) "Some bondholders are stockholders since all stockholders are equity owners and some bondholders are equity owners."

j) "Business firms are living organisms because firms are born, grow, and die; and everything which is born, grows, and dies is a living organism."

k) "General Motors has a payroll larger than any other business firm. The U.S. government has a payroll larger than General Motors.

Therefore, the U.S. government is the largest employer in our economy."

4.6. Test the validity of each argument in (*a*), (*b*), (*c*), (*d*), (*e*), (*f*), (*g*), (*h*), (*i*), (*j*), and (*k*) of Problem 4.5 by means of a Venn diagram. Verify your answer by referring to Table 4.2.

4.7. We have pointed out in the text "that the validity of a syllogism does not depend on whether the premises and the conclusion are factually true or false." Discuss along similar lines each of your answers to (*a*), (*b*), (*c*), (*d*), (*e*), (*f*), (*g*), (*h*), (*i*), (*j*), and (*k*) of Problem 4.6.

4.8. Express each of the following syllogisms in terms of set symbols and prove its validity with set operations.
a) Problem 4.5(*a*).
b) Problem 4.5(*d*).
c) Problem 4.5(*g*).
d) Problem 4.5(*h*).

4.9. Find one valid and one invalid syllogism from each of the following subjects and test their validity with a Venn diagram.
a) Accounting.
b) Behavioral science.
c) Economics.
d) Finance.
e) Marketing.
f) Production.
g) Statistics.

4.10. What type of a set statement (if any) can you supply as a conclusion to make a valid syllogism from each of the following pairs of premises (first letter being the major premise)? For what figures and interpretation (hypothetical or existential) does each of your answers give a valid syllogism?
a) *AI*.
b) *AA*.
c) *EA*.
d) *IO*.
e) *IA*.
f) *AO*.
g) *EI*.
h) *II*.

4.11. Construct a valid syllogism from each of the following groups of three sets (the first being the major and the last the middle term):
a) "Personal income," "management profits," and "wages."
b) "Employment," "exports," "investments."
c) "American cars," "foreign cars," "cars having a rear engine."
d) "Retailers," "wholesalers," "people selling directly to consumers."

4.12. In each case construct a valid syllogism having one of the following set statements as a conclusion.

*a) "Only price and wage controls can prevent inflation."
 b) "All decision makers consider several logically possible solutions of a problem."
 c) "Some persons who consider all logically possible solutions of a problem are decision makers." (Some decision makers exist.)
 d) "Some wholesalers are manufacturers."
 e) "Not all wholesalers are manufacturers."
 f) "No industrial product is a fashion good."

SUGGESTED REFERENCES

1. ALLENDOERFER, C. B., AND OAKLEY, C. O. *Principles of Mathematics,* pp. 25–38. New York: McGraw-Hill Book Co., Inc., 1955. (1–3)
2. BLACK, MAX. *Critical Thinking,* pp. 114–58. Englewood Cliffs, N.J.; Prentice-Hall, Inc., 1952. (4)
3. JOHNSTONE, HENRY W. *Elementary Deductive Logic,* pp. 23–159. New York: Thomas Y. Crowell Co., 1959. (1–4)
4. KEMENY, JOHN G., *et al. Introduction to Finite Mathematics,* pp. 10–15, 30–48. Englewood Cliffs, N.J.: Prentice-Hall, Inc., 1957. (1–3)
5. RICHARDSON, M. *Fundamentals of Mathematics,* pp. 22–40, 182–84, 185–89. Rev. ed. New York: The Macmillan Co. 1958. (1–3)
6. STABLER, E. R. *An Introduction to Mathematical Thought,* pp. 43–101. Reading, Mass.: Addison-Wesley Publishing Co., Inc., 1953. (1–4)
7. SUPPES, PATRICK. *Introduction to Logic,* pp. 3–42. New York: D. Van Nostrand Co., Inc., 1957. (1–3)
8. TARSKI, ALFRED. *Introduction to Logic and the Methodology of Deductive Sciences,* pp. 3–152. Rev. ed. New York: Oxford University Press, 1946. (1–4)
9. WESTERN, D. W., AND HAAG, V. H. *An Introduction to Mathematics,* pp. 25–32. New York: Henry Holt & Co., Inc., 1959. (1, 3)

Chapter 4

ADDITIONAL APPLICATIONS OF
BOOLEAN ALGEBRA

WE BEGAN our study of mathematics with sets and set operations. From sets we moved to statements and the testing of the validity of arguments. In this last chapter of Part I we shall consider further applications of the mathematical system of Boolean algebra. In Section 1 we shall use our knowledge about sets to study the voting coalitions which can control a decision in a set of people who form a decision-making body. We shall deal with two-digit number systems, especially the binary number system, in Section 2. Finally, in Sections 3 and 4 we shall demonstrate how Boolean algebra is utilized in the design and operation of digital computers.

*1. DECISION-MAKING BODIES AND VOTING POWER

Managerial decisions in business and other social organizations are frequently made by a group of people on the basis of simple or complicated voting rules. It behooves us, therefore, to study what coalitions within a given decision-making group of people can or cannot carry a proposal and how the voting power of each individual member in such a group can be measured by means of an index.

1.1. Basic Terminology and Notation.

Let the universal set $\mathcal{U}$ be the set $\{a, b, c, d\}$ representing a decision-making body, say a committee of four people, each with one vote. Let $P = 2^{\mathcal{U}}$ be the power set of $\mathcal{U}$. According to the discussion in Section 2 of Chapter 1 there are 2^4 or 16 subsets of $\mathcal{U}$ which are elements of the power set P, shown in Table 1.1. Each element of P, including $\varnothing$ and $\mathcal{U}$, can represent a *voting coalition* in the sense that no committee member, or any one member, any two, any three, or all four members may vote for (as well as against) a given motion.

If a simple majority vote (at least three out of four) is required to carry a vote in our committee, set W shown in Table 1.1. is called the set of *winning coalitions*. Then its complement W' is the set of *nonwinning coalitions*. Since each coalition can be either winning or not, sets W and W' are disjoint and $P = W \cup W'$.

TABLE 1.1.

$$P = \{\varnothing, \{a\}, \{b\}, \{c\}, \{d\}, \{a,b\}, \{a,c\}, \{a,d\}, \{b,c\}, \{b,d\}, \{c,d\}, \{a,b,c\}, \{a,b,d\}, \{a,c,d\}, \{b,c,d\}, \{a,b,c,d\}\}$$

$$W = \{\{a,b,c\}, \{a,b,d\}, \{a,c,d\}, \{b,c,d\}, \{a,b,c,d\}\}$$

$$W' = \begin{bmatrix} L = \{\varnothing, \{a\}, \{b\}, \{c\}, \{d\}\} \\ B = \{\{a\,b\}, \{a,c\}, \{a,d\}, \{b,c\}, \{b,d\}, \{c,d\}\} \end{bmatrix}$$

A nonwinning coalition is called a *losing coalition* if its complement is a winning coalition. Let $S = \{a\}$. Then S is an element of the set of losing coalitions L, shown in Table 1.1, since $S' = \{b, c, d\}$ is an element of W. Thus, the set L is defined by

$$L = \{S \,|\, S \,\epsilon\, W' \quad \text{and} \quad S' \,\epsilon\, W\}.$$

It is important to note that W' is the complement of W with respect to the power set P whose elements are sets of people called coalitions, while S' is the complement of S with respect to the universal set $\mathcal{U}$ whose elements are people-members of the committee.

Similarly, a nonwinning coalition is called a *blocking coalition* if its complement is a nonwinning coalition. Let $S = \{a, b\}$. Then S is an element of the set B of blocking coalitions, shown in Table 1.1, since $S' = \{c, d\}$ is an element of the set of nonwinning coalitions W'. In symbolic terms, the set of blocking coalitions is defined as follows:

$$B = \{S \,|\, S \,\epsilon\, W' \quad \text{and} \quad S' \,\epsilon\, W'\}.$$

The above terminology and notation applies to a set forming a decision-making body with n members where n is any finite number of people. In general, we should keep in mind that *given the voting rules of a particular group of people deliberating for a decision, a winning coalition is a set of people who control enough votes to carry a motion.* The complements of the winning coalitions are losing coalitions while all remaining subsets of $\mathcal{U}$ are blocking coalitions.

1.2. Selective Cases of Voting Coalitions.   Since voting rules determine voting coalitions, we shall consider a few cases of decision-making bodies with varying voting patterns.

Example 1.1. Suppose individual a who is the chairman of the four-member committee previously considered has, in addition to one vote, the right to break ties when voting *for* a motion. Then, there are no blocking coalitions since the blocking coalitions $\{a, b\}$, $\{a, c\}$, $\{a, d\}$

become winning coalitions while the remaining blocking coalitions become losing coalitions. Giving the chairman the right to break ties has the same effect on coalitions as giving him two votes. The reader may verify the fact that the redistribution of blocking coalitions is the same when the chairman is given two votes.

Example 1.2. J. B. Gordon and Sons is a father-and-two-sons partnership operating a chain of novelty shops. Let set $\mathfrak{U} = \{G, J, B\}$ be the set of the three partners. We may consider the following possibilities:

Case 1: Let us assume that each partner has one vote. We obtain the following sets of coalitions:

$$W = \{\{G, J\}, \{G, B\}, \{J, B\}, \{G, J, B\}\},$$
$$L = \{\varnothing, \{G\}, \{J\}, \{B\}\}.$$

There are no blocking coalitions.

Case 2: Let G be the father who, in a patriarchal setup, can make decisions without needing any of his sons to vote with him. Then, assuming that a deliberating body still exists, the coalitions of the "partnership" are distributed as follows:

$$W = \{\{G\}, \{G, J\}, \{G, B\}, \{G, J, B\}\},$$
$$L = \{\varnothing, \{J\}, \{B\}, \{J, B\}\}.$$

Again, there are no blocking coalitions. But now no coalition is winning without G being a member of it. In fact, $\{G\}$ is a winning coalition irrespective of whether any or both sons vote with him or against his measure. In such a case G is called a *dictator*, while J and B are called *powerless* members of the partnership.

Case 3: Suppose the agreement has been made that each partner has the right to block any measure proposed by any other partner, i.e., each partner has *veto power* over others. This is a "troika" type of voting arrangement where there is only one winning coalition $\{G, J, B\}$ and one losing $\varnothing$, all the other coalitions being blocking coalitions. Decisions can be made only with a unanimous vote.

Case 4: But according to the doctrine of "mutual agency" provided in the partnership law, each partner has rather broad powers to act as an agent, thus committing the whole partnership. Let us assume that such broad powers are equivalent to each partner's being a "dictator." Then we can interpret this partnership arrangement as follows: First, we may consider that all coalitions, except $\varnothing$, are winning coalitions; and since only one partner can carry a measure, the other partners are powerless members in two-member and three-member coalitions. Second, we may consider that only one-member coalitions are winning coalitions; yet, each partner is liable for the consequences of the decisions made by the other partners. Finally, we may conclude that under the above-mentioned partnership conditions no deliberating body exists. Thus, such an arrangement may indicate one of the major disadvantages of partnership over the other forms of business organization.

It is not always necessary to list all winning coalitions. In the case of the equal-vote partnership of the last example, if coalition $\{G, J\}$ is winning, then coalition $\{G, J, B\}$ is also winning. In general, if a coalition S is winning then any other set which has S as a subset is also winning. Thus, a coalition which does not contain any smaller winning coalitions as subsets is called *minimal winning coalition*. In the equal-vote partnership coalitions $\{G, J\}$, $\{G, B\}$, and $\{J, B\}$ are minimal winning coalitions. In other words, a winning coalition is minimal if and only if a defection of any *one* of its members will make the coalition no longer winning. The following examples illustrate the use of this new concept.

Example 1.3. Let the universal set $\mathfrak{U}$ be the set of n stockholders of the XYZ corporation, where n is a finite number. A "large" stockholder owns 50 per cent of the shares, while the remaining shares are owned by $n - 1$ "small" stockholders. Each share represents one vote. A simple majority vote, i.e., 50 percent plus one vote is needed to carry a motion. The minimal winning coalitions are the two-member coalitions consisting of the "large" stockholder and any one other shareholder. All coalitions having minimal winning coalitions as subsets are winning coalitions. There are only two blocking coalitions—that of the "large" stockholder with 50 percent ownership and that of all the $n - 1$ "small" stockholders put together. All other coalitions are losing coalitions.

Suppose the single "large" stockholder acquires one more share, then there is no more power to be gained: he is a dictator and all other $n - 1$ stockholders are powerless members of losing coalitions.

Example 1.4. Let the set $\mathfrak{U}$ be the ten-member board of directors of Rothmund Enterprises, a holding company discussed earlier and shown in Figure 3.5, Chapter 1. Let us also assume that each member of the board has one vote but, in addition, Rothmund, Hemeon, Green, and Clement each have the right to veto any motion. It takes six out of ten votes to carry a motion. Since a decision must not be vetoed in order to pass, the minimal winning coalitions consist of the "Big Four," i.e., the board members with veto power, and any two other members. Sets containing no more than four nonveto board members are losing coalitions. Sets consisting of five or six nonveto members are blocking coalitions. Finally, any nonwinning coalition with at least one of the Big Four as a member is a blocking coalition.

1.3. A Power Index. But the number of votes which a member of a decision-making body controls is not necessarily in itself an accurate measure of his voting power. Consider, for instance, a committee consisting of an odd number of members with the chairman having the right to vote in order to break ties. He has as much power as anybody else since he can be the last voting member of a minimal winning coalition as frequently as another committee member. And we have seen in Example 1.3 that the large stockholder, while only a blocking coalition for owning 50 percent of the voting shares, becomes a dictator as soon as he acquires a single additional share: no additional shares can formally enhance his power. It is, therefore, necessary to develop an index for measuring more accurately voting power than the number of votes controlled.

We may observe that in a decision-making body an individual member's power depends on the chance he has of being the last voting member of a minimal winning coalition; in other words, the chance he has to be a *pivot*. Hence, we can conceive the *power index of a given member of a decision-making body as the ratio with the denominator representing the total number of possible ways all members can align for voting on a motion and the numerator representing the number of alignments in which that member is a pivot.*

Let us take up again our original four-member committee $\{a, b, c, d\}$ with each member having one vote. We must find the number of all possible voting alignments. There are four voting positions. Since the first position can be occupied by any one of the four committee members, the second by any of the remaining three members, etc., there are $4 \cdot 3 \cdot 2 \cdot 1 = 24$ alignments. (These orderings are called *permutations*. For any positive integer n, the product of the integers from 1 to n is denoted by $n!$ and is called n *factorial*. Thus 1 factorial is $1! = 1$, 2 factorial is $2! = 2 \cdot 1 = 2$, $3! = 3 \cdot 2 \cdot 1 = 6$, $4! = 4 \cdot 3 \cdot 2 \cdot 1 = 24$, and so on for any positive integer n. By convention 0! equals 1. Both permutations and factorials are discussed and used more extensively later in Part V on probability.) The 24 voting permutations of the committee members are shown in Table 1.2 where the pivot member in

TABLE 1.2.

	Pair I		Pair II		Pair III	
	(1)	(2)	(1)	(2)	(1)	(2)
1.	cdab	dcab	bdac	dbac	bcad	cbad
2.	cdba	dcba	adbc	dabc	acbd	cabd
3.	bdca	dbca	adcb	dacb	abcd	bacd
4.	bcda	cbda	acdb	cadb	abdc	badc

each alignment is underlined. Since committee member a is a pivot in 6 out of 24 alignments, his power index is $\frac{6}{24} = \frac{1}{4}$. It can be seen that the value of the power index is $\frac{1}{4}$ for each of the other three committee members.

In fact, in this particular case the value of the power index for each committee member is not different from the number of votes controlled by each member over the total votes. This observation points out another way of measuring the voting power of each committee member. Since there are four committee members, there are four voting positions; but only the third voting position is pivotal. Since each of the four members has an equal chance of being pivotal, each member has $\frac{1}{4}$ voting power.

The above computation of the power index involves the fact that under the voting rules each committee member is treated symmetrically and the power indices of all members add up to 1. We further illustrate the use of the *symmetry* and *additivity* rules with an example.

Example 1.5. Consider a four-member board with the chairman having two votes and each of the other three members one vote. There are four voting positions corresponding to the four members. Since the chairman is the pivot in two—second and third—out of four positions, his power index is $\frac{1}{2}$. By the additivity rule the voting power for the other three members is the difference of the chairman's power index from 1 or $\frac{1}{2}$, and by the rule of symmetry each member has $\frac{1}{6}$ voting power.

This result can be easily verified by consulting Table 1.2. Let a be the chairman of the four-member committee. Then he is the pivot in the six voting alignments shown in row 1 of the table. However, since the chairman has two votes, he will also be the pivot in the three remaining alignments under column 2 in pairs II and III. Therefore, he will be the pivot in $6 + 3 + 3 = 12$ of the 24 alignments. Any other committee member, say b, will be the pivot in only four of the six alignments shown in row 2. Hence, the chairman's power index is $\frac{1}{2}$ while each of the three committee members has a power index of $\frac{1}{6}$ as found previously.

We can proceed now to the development of a power index formula. The alignments in Table 1.2 are listed in pairs. Each pair contains one minimal winning coalition having the same committee member as the pivot. The only difference between the two paired alignments is in the ordering of the first two members to which the same pivot member is added. Knowing, for example, that member a is the pivot in alignment $cd\underline{a}b$, we also know that it is the pivot in $dc\underline{a}b$, since in both cases the same set $\{c, d\}$, turns to a minimal winning coalition when member a is added. By holding member a in the pivotal voting position while re-ordering the other committee members among the other three voting positions we obtain all six alignments shown in the top row of the table. Each row of alignments is obtained in the same way.

All possible ways of building up coalitions correspond to all orderings $(i_1, i_2, \ldots, i_n)$ of the n members of a set $\mathfrak{U}$ representing a decision-making body. From such an ordered set of members we can define a chain of coalitions $S_0 = \varnothing$, $S_1 = \{i_1\}$, $S_2 = \{i_1, i_2\}, \ldots$, $S_n = \{i_1, i_2, \ldots, i_n\}$ which starts from the coalition with no voting members and builds up to the coalition with all n members by adding one i member at a time. On the basis of our previous discussion it is evident that at some point in this chain there is a minimal winning coalition S_p with all preceding coalitions $S_0, \ldots, S_{p-2}, S_{p-1}$ being nonwinning and all following coalitions $S_{p+1}, S_{p+2}, \ldots, S_n$ being winning. We can imagine this chain of coalitions as follows:

$$S_0 \subseteq S_1 \subseteq S_2 \subseteq \ldots \subseteq S_{p-1} \subseteq S_p \subseteq S_{p+1} \subseteq \ldots \subseteq S_n,$$

where

$\subseteq$ = the symbol that each coalition is a subset of the one which follows:

$S_{p-1} = \{i_1, i_2, \ldots i_{p-1}\}$;
$S_p = \{i_1, i_2, \ldots, i_{p-1}, i_p\}$; and
i_p = a pivotal member.

A nonwinning coalition S_{p-1} turns to a minimal winning coalition S_p by adding the pivot i_p. In every reordering of $i_1, i_2, \ldots, i_{p-1}, i_p, i_{p+1}, \ldots, i_n$ of $\mathfrak{A}$ we permute the first $p - 1$ members among themselves and the last $n - p$ members among themselves, while we keep the pivotal members i_p fixed; and every reordering corresponds to a new set of alignments such as the ones shown in each row in Table 1.2. Hence, the number of permutations for the pre-pivotal and the post-pivotal members are $(p - 1)!$ and $(n - p)!$ respectively; and the total number of alignments with the ith pivot member are $(p - 1)!(n - p)!$ Let I denote the power index of the ith member of a decision-making body. Since there are $n!$ alignments in all, the power index for the ith member is

(1.1)
$$I = C \cdot \frac{(p - 1)!(n - p)!}{n!},$$

where

C = the number of minimal winning coalitions S_p for each p, and
p = the number of members for each S_p coalition.

Example 1.6. In the four-member committee whose permutations are shown in Table 1.2 the minimal winning coalitions S_p for member a are $\{c, d, a\}$, $\{b, d, a\}$, and $\{b, c, a\}$ since there are three S_p's with $p = 3$, $C = 3$. Hence, the power index for member a by (1.1) is

$$I = C \cdot \frac{(p - 1)!(n - p)!}{n!} = 3 \cdot \frac{(3 - 1)!(4 - 3)!}{4!} = 3 \cdot \frac{2 \cdot 1 \cdot 1}{4 \cdot 3 \cdot 2 \cdot 1} = \frac{1}{4}$$

as previously.

Observe that in the above example $C = 3$, not 6. Although the two pre-pivotal positions can be arranged in 3 times 2 equals 6 ways, or permutations, as shown in row 1 of Table 1.2, there are only three S_p's, i.e., $C = 3$, since order is unimportant. In other words, C represents the number of ways that two committee members can be selected from the three b, c, and d available. The number of such selections, called *combinations*, is defined by

(1.2)

$$C(m, r) = \frac{m!}{r!(m - r)!},$$

where

$m =$ the number of nonveto committee members minus one,
$r =$ the number of pre-pivotal nonveto positions.

Since in the above Example 1.6 $m = 3$ and $r = 2$, by (1.2)

$$C(3, 2) = \frac{3!}{2!(3 - 2)!} = \frac{3 \cdot 2 \cdot 1}{2 \cdot 1 \cdot 1} = 3.$$

1.4. Distribution of Voting Power in Certain Decision-Making Bodies.

In order to illustrate the use of the power index formula we shall compute the power distribution in previously introduced decision-making bodies.

Example 1.7. The voting power in the partnership J. B. Gordon in Example 1.2 is distributed as follows:

Case 1: If each partner has one vote, for partner G the minimal winning coalitions S_p are $\{JG\}$ and $\{BG\}$. Since there are two S_p's with $p = 2$, $C = 2.$. The same result may be obtained by applying (1.2). Since $m = 2$ and $r = 1$,

$$C(2, 1) = \frac{2!}{1!(2 - 1)!} = 2.$$

By (1.1) partner G has a power index

$$I = C \cdot \frac{(p - 1)!(n - p)!}{n!} = 2 \cdot \frac{(2 - 1)!(3 - 2)!}{3!} = \frac{1!1!}{3} = \frac{1}{3}.$$

And by the rules of additivity and symmetry the power index of the other two partners is $1 - \frac{1}{3} = \frac{2}{3}$ or $\frac{1}{3}$ for each partner.

Case 2: If partner G is a dictator, then his power index is equal to 1 since he is the pivot in all winning coalitions $\{G\}$, $\{JG\}$, $\{BG\}$, and $\{J, B, G\}$, where the number of members $p = 1$, $p = 2$, $p = 3$, and $C = 1$, $C = 2$, and $C = 1$, respectively. The reader may verify the values of C by applying (1.2) in each case. Substituting in (1.1) for each value of p and C we have

$$I = 1 \cdot \frac{(1 - 1)!(3 - 1)!}{3!} + 2 \cdot \frac{(2 - 1)!(3 - 2)!}{3!} +$$

$$+ 1 \cdot \frac{(3 - 1)!(3 - 3)!}{3!} = \frac{2! + 2 + 2!}{3!} = 1.$$

Case 3: The power index for each partner in a "troika" type of voting arrangement is equal to $\frac{1}{3}$. Since there is only one winning coalition $\{G, J, B\}, p = 3$ and $C = 1$. Hence, the power index for partner B by (1.1) is

$$I = 1 \cdot \frac{(p-1)!(n-p)!}{n!} = 1 \cdot \frac{(3-1)!(3-3)!}{3!} = \frac{2}{6} = \frac{1}{3}.$$

It is the same for each of the other two partners. Why?

The reader may realize that the distribution of voting power in the equal-vote and "troika" cases are identical. But the "troika" partnership is quite dysfunctional since the only possibility for a motion to pass is with unanimous voting.

Case 4: By the doctrine of "mutual agency" each partner in a partnership may be considered almost a "dictator." In such a case we may consider that no decision-making body exists and the power index is not applicable. In fact, the arrangement is quite dysfunctional for group decisions. This latter observation is important in view of the legal provisions in the partnership law already mentioned.

Example 1.8. Consider the stockholders of XYZ Corporation in Example 1.3. Let $n = 10$. We wish to determine the voting power distribution among the stockholders of the corporation.

Answer:

First, we compute the power index for a "small" shareholder. Each "small" stockholder can become pivotal only if he occupies the second voting position following the "large" stockholder in the first position. Hence, there is only one minimal winning coalition with $p = 2$. Since the first of the two voting positions of a minimal winning coalition must be occupied by the "large" stockholder who has a "veto" power for owning 50 percent of the shares, $m = 8$ and $r = 0$. Therefore by (1.2)

$$C(8, 0) = \frac{8!}{0!8!} = 1$$

and by (1.1) the power index for each small stockholder is

$$I = 1 \cdot \frac{(2-1)!(10-2)!}{10!} = \frac{1! \cdot \not{8}!}{10 \cdot 9 \cdot \not{8}!} = \frac{1}{90}.$$

Second, the power index for the "large" stockholder is computed as follows: By the rules of symmetry and additivity all "small" stockowners have an index $9 \cdot \frac{1}{90} = \frac{1}{10}$ and the "large" stockholder $1 - \frac{1}{10} = \frac{9}{10}$.

The power distribution for n stockholders is determined as follows: The "large" shareholder is the pivot in all minimal winning coalitions except when he occupies the first voting position. Since there are $n!$ of them, the "large" stockholder is the pivot in all except $(n-1)!$ of the alignments. Therefore, the power index of the "large" shareholder is

$$(1.3) \qquad I = \frac{n! - (n-1)!}{n!} = \frac{n!}{n!} - \frac{(n-1)!}{n(n-1)!} = 1 - \frac{1}{n}.$$

Since a "small" stockowner can be pivotal only when he occupies the second voting position following the "large" stockholder in the first position, each "small" shareowner is the *pivot* in $(n - 2)!$ alignments. His power index is

(1.4) $$I = \frac{1}{n!}(n - 2)! = \frac{(n-2)!}{n(n - 1)(n-2)!} = \frac{1}{n(n - 1)}.$$

Let $n = 10$. Then by formula (1.3) the "large" stockholder with 50 percent of the shares has an index

$$I = 1 - \frac{1}{n} = 1 - \frac{1}{10} = \frac{9}{10};$$

and by (1.4) any "small" stockowner has an index

$$I = \frac{1}{n(n - 1)} = \frac{1}{90}$$

as found in Example 1.8.

Example 1.9. Compute the power distribution of the ten-member board of directors of Rothmund Enterprises of Example 1.4.

We begin by computing the power index for any one of the nonveto members. For passing a measure six votes are needed including the Big Four. Since in each minimal winning coalition four positions must be occupied by the Big Four and the sixth by the pivot nonveto member, only one position can be permuted among the remaining five nonveto board members. Hence, $m = 5$ since there are six nonveto members. Since of the six pre-pivotal positions only one can be occupied by a nonveto member, $r = 1$. Substituting in (1.2) we have

$$C(5, 1) = \frac{m!}{r!(m - r)!} = \frac{5!}{1!(5 - 1)!} = 5.$$

Substituting $n = 10$, $p = 6$, and $C = 5$ in (1.1), the power index for any nonveto board member is

$$I = C \cdot \frac{(p - 1)!(n - p)!}{n!} = 5 \cdot \frac{5!4!}{10!} = \frac{1}{252}.$$

By the symmetry and additivity rules the power index of all nonveto members is

$$I = 6 \cdot \frac{1}{252} = \frac{1}{42};$$

and of any of the Big Four is

$$I = \frac{1}{4}\left(1 - \frac{1}{42}\right) = \frac{41}{4 \cdot 42} = \frac{41}{168}.$$

Observe that the voting power of a veto member is $\frac{41}{168}/\frac{1}{252}$, or 61.5 times greater than that of a nonveto member.

1.5. Manifest and Real Voting Power. The above index measures the voting power of the members of a decision-making body on the basis of a set of formal or manifest voting rules. One can imagine an urn with balls in it, each representing one of the possible voting alignments which the members of a voting group can form. Each ball bears a number which indicates the pivotal member of the voting alignment. The power index measures the relative frequency with which each member will be drawn in a *large number of trials*. In this sense the power index depicts a probabilistic model where each alignment is as likely to be drawn as any other. Thus, the index does not take into consideration the possible effect which abstentions, leadership, conflict of interests, factionalism, group politics, and other sociological factors may have on voting in a real situation. For example, in a seven-member committee with each member having one vote and simple majority rule, a member's real voting power is much greater than his manifest power of $\frac{1}{7}$ if he is frequently given the opportunity to break ties between two three-member warring factions. In sum, although the power index is a mathematical model of a kind measuring the manifest voting power of members of a deliberating group, it may be used as a first approximation for assessing voting power in a real-world situation.

PROBLEMS

1.1. A committee consists of five members $\{1, 2, 3, 4, 5\}$, each with one vote.
  a) List the power set whose elements are the subsets of the universal set representing the committee.
  b) List the winning, minimal winning, blocking, and losing coalitions (if any) if motions are carried by a simple majority vote.
  c) Compute the voting power of the committee members.

1.2. Let the universal set $\mathcal{U} = \{x, y, z, w\}$ be the set of a decision-making body where members x and y have one vote, z has two votes, and w has four votes. A simple majority vote is needed to carry a measure.
  a) List the elements of the power set $2^{\mathcal{U}}$.
  b) Indicate the subsets of $\mathcal{U}$ which are winning, minimal winning, losing, and blocking coalitions.
  c) List all permutations and find the power distribution of the members.
  d) Suppose member w has the right to veto any measure in addition to having four votes. Does this change in the voting rules affect your answer to questions (*b*) and (*c*)? Explain.

1.3. The Suburban Realty Company is a partnership of three individuals. Decisions are made by a simple majority vote. List all the permutations and compute the voting power of the partners for each of the following voting rules:
  a) One vote for each partner.

b) One, one, and two votes.
c) One, one, and three votes.
d) One, two, and three votes.
e) Two, two, and three votes.

1.4. A decision-making body has n members, each having one vote. Describe the minimal winning, winning, losing, and blocking coalitions:

   *a) If a simple majority wins and n is an even positive integer greater than two.

   b) If a two-thirds majority wins and n is an odd positive integer divisible by three.

*1.5. Every committee member has one vote except the chairman who can vote *only* to break ties. A majority rule decides. Compute the power index for the chairman of the following committees:

   a) A four-member committee, including the chairman.

   b) A five-member committee, including the chairman.

1.6. In a five-member board of trustees each member has one vote, but the chairman has veto power. Decisions are made with a simple majority rule.

   *a) Describe the minimal winning, blocking, and losing coalitions.

   b) Compute the power indices for the board members.

1.7. Allen-Beck-Clark-Price Distributors is a partnership of wholesalers of frozen food. Let the initial letters of the four partners represent the universal set $\mathcal{U}$ and list the elements of the power set $2^{\mathcal{U}}$. Indicate the different types of coalitions which can be formed, write out all permutations, and compute the power distribution of the partners under the following voting rules:

   a) Each partner has a vote.

   b) Partner A can decide without the vote of any other partner.

   c) Each partner has veto power.

   d) Every partner can decide without the vote for any other partner.

1.8. McBee Manufacturing Corporation has 1,000,000 shares of common stock outstanding, each representing one vote. How many shares must a shareholder own in order to have a veto, to be a dictator—

   *a) If a simple majority vote is required to carry a measure?

   b) If a two-thirds majority is necessary for a decision?

1.9. The board of directors of Atlas Steel Corporation consists of eleven members, the "Big Five" with veto power and the "small" members each with one vote. Seven votes are required to carry a motion.

   a) Describe the types of voting coalitions which can be formed.

   b) Compute the power indices for each member.

   c) What international decision-making body has the same membership and identical voting rules?

1.10. Phipps, Furth, and Fuller own all 100,000 outstanding shares of Electronics Corporation of America. A simple majority of shares decides. Compute the distribution of their power if—

   *a) Phipps owns 50,000 shares; Furth, 49,999; and Fuller, 1.

b) Phipps owns 50,000 shares; Furth, 25,000; and Fuller, 25,000.

c) Explain why the power distribution in (*a*) and (*b*) remains the same.

1.11. Consider the case of Example 1.3.

a) Compute the power distribution when *n*, the number of stockholders of XYZ Corporation, is 20, 50, 100, 1000.

b) Explain why the power distribution depends on the number of "small" stockholders and not on the number of shares they own.

1.12. In a five-member committee each member has one vote and a simple majority decides. There are two factions of two committee members each of which always votes down the other's motions.

*a) What is the voting power of the fifth independent member?

b) How does his voting power compare with the power he would have had without the presence of warring factions?

1.13. In a four-member committee two members vote always the same way. If each committee member has one vote and a majority rule is required to carry a motion—

a) What is the team's voting power?

b) Has teaming up increased their power?

*2. TWO-DIGIT NUMBER SYSTEMS; BINARY ARITHMETIC

The introduction of the decimal number system was a laborsaving innovation to the mathematicians of Medieval Europe. Unlike other systems such as the Roman numerals, the Hindu-Arabic notation had two important advantages: any number could be written by using only ten digits, $0, 1, 2, \ldots, 9$, while the positional character of notation greatly facilitated arithmetic operations. We shall see that other number systems can be constructed which have fewer or more than ten digits. Like the introduction of the decimal system these new number systems may be considered great laborsaving devices in the sense that their use by digital computers allows the processing of a vast amount of data in a short period of time. For the purpose at hand we shall concentrate on two-digit number systems, namely, Boolean algebra of (0, 1), modulus 2, and particularly the *binary number system*.

2.1. Boolean Algebra (0, 1). The simplest mathematical system which satisfies the abstract laws of Boolean algebra consists of a set containing two elements. Since $\varnothing$ and $\mathfrak{U}$ must be included in such a set, they constitute the whole set. In other words, we can imagine a power set $2^{\mathfrak{U}}$ where $\varnothing$ and $\mathfrak{U}$ are the only elements.

Substituting 0 for $\varnothing$, 1 for $\mathfrak{U}$, + for $\cup$, and $\cdot$ for $\cap$, the basic operations of this simple system are shown in columns 1–8 of Table 2.1 where *P* and *Q* represent either 0 or 1. The reader may notice that the basic

TABLE 2.1.

Logical Possibilities	Complement		Multiplication			Addition				
	(1)	(2)	(3)	(4)	(5)	(6)	(7)	(8)	(9)	(10)
	P	P'	P	Q	$P \cdot Q$	P	Q	$P+Q$	$P+Q$	$P+Q$
R_4	0	1	0	0	0	0	0	0	0	0
R_3	1	0	0	1	0	0	1	1	1	1
R_2			1	0	0	1	0	1	1	1
R_1			1	1	1	1	1	1	0	10

operations of complement, multiplication, and addition of algebra (0, 1) are identical to the corresponding basic operations of sets. We can easily obtain the operations of Table 2.1 by substituting the symbols 0 for $\notin$ and 1 for $\in$. The row order of the four logical possibilities has been reversed to facilitate later reference.

It is important to realize that all the laws of Boolean algebra shown in Table 4.1, Chapter 1, as well as the theorems which are based on them, hold in this simple system. We can verify any one of them by using the basic operations of (0, 1) algebra.

Example 2.1. We can illustrate this point by deriving the (0, 1) table for the symmetric difference

$$P \triangle Q = (P \cdot Q') + (P' \cdot Q)$$

as shown in Table 2.2. We may observe that, except for the use of different symbols, column 7 of Table 2.2 is identical to column 7 of Table 4.5, Chapter 1.

TABLE 2.2.

(1) P	(2) Q	(3) P'	(4) Q'	(5) $P \cdot Q'$	(6) $P' \cdot Q$	(7) $(P \cdot Q') + (P' \cdot Q)$
0	0	1	1	0	0	0
0	1	1	0	0	1	1
1	0	0	1	1	0	1
1	1	0	0	0	0	0

This correspondence between Boolean algebra and (0, 1) algebra is of great importance. It indicates that upon making the proper changes in notation, any statement which is logically true in the former is also true in the latter system. Furthermore, the symbols 0 and 1 are *undefined values* subject to different interpretation.

Suppose a zero-one numerical interpretation is given to (0, 1) elements of the system, what are the possible ways the operations of multiplication and addition can be performed? The multiplication table can be completely determined as shown in column 5 of Table 2.1 by the two well-known rules of arithmetic, namely, multiplying a number by zero yields zero and multiplying a number by one leaves the number unchanged. Similarly, the rule which says that adding a zero to a number leaves that number unchanged determines all but row R_1 of the addition tables in columns 8–10 of Table 2.1. In order to decide what sum $1 + 1$ will yield we shall consider all possibilities. Since we can use only zero and one, we can form four two-digit numbers: 00, 01, 10, 11. The first two of these numbers are equivalent to 0 and 1, respectively. The only other possibility is number 10 since number 11 or any larger number would cause a discontinuity in the addition table. Hence, if the sum $1 + 1$ is equal to 1, we obtain the addition table in column 8 of Table 2.1 of the (0, 1) arithmetic already discussed. Possibilities 0, and 10 lead to modulus 2 and the binary number system, respectively, which we shall discuss in turn.

2.2. Modulus 2.   This second two-digit number system represents the parity of a positive integer where 0 stands for "even" and 1 for "odd." The basic addition and multiplication tables of the system shown in columns 9 and 5 of Table 2.1, respectively, are reproduced in Table 2.3. In this system an even positive integer, say 20, is represented

TABLE 2.3.

Addition			Multiplication		
+	0	1	·	0	1
0	0	1	0	0	0
1	1	0	1	0	1

by 0 and an odd positive integer, say 21, by 1. The same holds true for the sum or product of any two positive integers. For example, $5 + 7 = 0$ since 12 is an even number and $3 \times 5 = 1$ since 15 is an odd number. In all cases a positive integer of the decimal system is reduced by a multiple of 2 so that its remainder is either 0 or 1. When number 2 is used in this fashion, it is called *modulus*.

Example 2.2.   Frequently modulus 2 is used as a method of detecting errors in coding input data in binary notation for a digital computer.

Consider the simple problem, for instance, of recording the first five positive integers of the decimal system, shown in column 1 of Table 2.4, into the memory unit of a computer. Since computers are constructed of binary elements, i.e., elements having two states, such as *off* and *on*, the decimal numbers must be converted into various combinations of "bits" of information. One such method is converting the decimal numbers into binary as shown in column 2. We shall see shortly how decimal numbers are converted to binary equivalents. In the meantime, observe that each digit in column 2 corresponds to a binary element representing a "bit" of information. Since errors in recording are not detected by this binary code,

TABLE 2.4.

(1) Decimal Number	(2) Binary Number	(3) Parity Bit	(4) Modulus 2 Even Parity
1	0001	1	0
2	0010	1	0
3	0011	0	0
4	0100	1	0
5	0101	0	0

a fifth bit position is added to the code, shown in column 3, in order to make the total number of 1 bit in each binary number even as shown in column 4. Thus, if in the process of recording the five numbers into the memory of a computer a single bit is mistakenly added or dropped for mechanical or other reasons, a 1 bit appears in column 4 indicating that an invalid number has been recorded. This method is known as an *even parity check*. It is left for the reader to construct an *odd parity check*.

There is nothing magic about number 2. Any other positive integer larger than 2 can serve as modulus. Thus, we can develop a special kind of arithmetic, the arithmetic of positive integers modulus M where M is any integer greater than one. Modulus M arithmetic has many practical uses as the following example illustrates.

Example 2.3. The hour hand of a clock is a case of modulus 12 arithmetic with the hours numbered $0, 1, 2, \ldots, 12 \ (= 0)$. If it is now 10 o'clock, 6 hours later the time will be $10 + 6 = 4$ o'clock, since $16 - 12 = 4$. What time will it be 37 hours from now if it is now 6 o'clock? $6 + 37 = 7$ o'clock since $43 - 3(12) = 7$. There is one disadvantage with the use of modulus 12 arithmetic in recording time. In cases such as the last one we cannot easily tell whether the answer 7 refers to A.M. or P.M. hours. Modulus 24 arithmetic which is used by the armed forces of the United States and of other countries overcomes this disadvantage. The answer to the previous question is 19 hours or 7:00 P.M. since $43 - 24 = 19$ with the zero hour at midnight.

Terminating this short diversion from the two-digit system of modulus 2, let us focus our attention on the third and most important two-digit number system.

2.3. Binary Number System.   The third two-digit number system is the so-called binary number system. Like the decimal the binary system is based on a set of characters and positional notation. But instead of the ten characters 0 through 9, of the decimal, the binary is based on a set of two characters, namely, 0 and 1; and instead of base 10 of the decimal, number 2 is used as base by the binary.

Consider the decimal number 16 for example. It can be written as follows:

$$16 = 1 \cdot 10^1 + 6 \cdot 10^0.$$

Observe that the positional value of each digit in 16 is determined by the character of the system and the power of base 10. Thus, the value of the rightmost digital position contains character 6 multiplied by base 10 to the zero power; and the value of the next digital position to the left contains character 1 multiplied by base 10 to the first power.

The following question is now raised: How can we express the decimal number 16 in binary notation? The decimal number 0 corresponds to the binary zero since $0 \cdot 2^0 = 0$, where 0 is the character multiplied by base 2 to the zero power. Similarly, the decimal 1 corresponds to the binary 1 since $1 \cdot 2^0 = 1$, where 1 is the character multiplied by base 2 to the zero power. But the decimal 2 corresponds to the binary 10 since $2 = 1 \cdot 2^1$, where 1 is the character multiplied by base 2 to the first power. Observe that the power of base 2 indicates, as in the decimal system, that character 1 should be moved to the left one digital position. Hence, the binary decimal 2 is 10 since $2 = 1 \cdot 2^1 + 0 \cdot 2^0$. On the same basis the decimal number 16 corresponds to the binary 10000 since

$$1 \cdot 2^4 + 0 \cdot 2^3 + 0 \cdot 2^2 + 0 \cdot 2^1 + 0 \cdot 2^0 = 2^4 = 16.$$

Observe that character 1 is multiplied by base 2 raised to the power of 4 which indicates the number of digital positions that 1 must be moved to the left in the first position. In Table 2.5 we show some decimal numbers converted to binary. Observe that with the exception of

TABLE 2.5.

	Decimal		Binary
(1)	(2)	(3)	(4)
0 =	$0 \cdot 10^0$	$= \; 0 \cdot 2^0 \; =$	0
1 =	$1 \cdot 10^0$	$= \; 1 \cdot 2^0 \; =$	1
2 =	$2 \cdot 10^0$	$= \; *1 \cdot 2^1 \; =$	10
4 =	$4 \cdot 10^0$	$= \; *1 \cdot 2^2 \; =$	100
8 =	$8 \cdot 10^0$	$= \; *1 \cdot 2^3 \; =$	1000
16 =	$1 \cdot 10^1 + 6 \cdot 10^0$	$= \; *1 \cdot 2^4 \; =$	10000
32 =	$3 \cdot 10^1 + 2 \cdot 10^0$	$= \; *1 \cdot 2^5 \; =$	100000
64 =	$6 \cdot 10^1 + 4 \cdot 10^0$	$= \; *1 \cdot 2^6 \; =$	1000000
128 =	$1 \cdot 10^2 + 2 \cdot 10^1 + 8 \cdot 10^0$	$= \; *1 \cdot 2^7 \; =$	10000000
256 =	$2 \cdot 10^2 + 5 \cdot 10^1 + 6 \cdot 10^0$	$= \; *1 \cdot 2^8 \; =$	100000000

*Expressions have been abbreviated by omitting the powers of 2 that result in zeros. For example, expression $1 \cdot 2^3 + 0 \cdot 2^2 + 0 \cdot 2^1 + 0 \cdot 2^0$ is written $1 \cdot 2^3$.

the first two, all decimal numbers are equal to 1 multiplied by the binary base 2 raised to a certain power which determines the number of digital positions 1 should be moved to the left in order to obtain the equivalent binary. Every decimal number can be converted to binary and vice versa by using key conversions such as the ones shown in the table. For example, the decimal 3 corresponds to binary 11 since $3 = 2 + 1$, the decimal 5 to binary 101 since $5 = 4 + 1$, the decimal 6 to binary 110 since $6 = 4 + 2$, the decimal 35 to binary 100011 since $35 = 32 + 2 + 1$. Inversely, the binary number 111 corresponds to decimal 7 since $111 = 2^2 + 2^1 + 1$, the binary 1001 to decimal 9 since $1001 = 2^3 + 1$, the binary 1101 to decimal 13 since $1101 = 2^3 + 2^2 + 1$.

2.4. Binary Arithmetic.   The basic binary addition and multiplication tables shown in columns 10 and 5 of Table 2.1, respectively, are reproduced in Table 2.6. Observe that each operation requires only

TABLE 2.6.

Addition			Multiplication		
+	0	1		0	1
0	0	1	0	0	0
1	1	10	1	0	1

$2 \times 2 = 4$ entries, a great simplification over the decimal system which requires 10×10 or 100 entries. This simplicity in addition and multiplication becomes particularly useful in the design and operation of digital computers. Of course a price is paid for it. For a given number the binary is "longer" than the decimal. Thus, simplicity is obtained at the expense of more digits required to accommodate binary numbers. This conflict creates problems in computer design and operation. Yet the efficiency of the binary system is overwhelming as the following examples on binary addition, subtraction, multiplication, and division illustrate.

Addition is *the* most important of the four basic arithmetic operations since, as we shall shortly see, it can replace subtraction, multiplication, and division.

Example 2.4. Find the sum of the following additions:

a) $8 + 3$:

Decimal	Binary
8	1000
+3	+0011
11	1011

b) $9 + 9$:

Decimal	Binary
	$*\quad*$
9	1001
+9	+1001
18	10010

c) $15 + 1$:

Decimal	Binary
	$****$
15	1111
+01	+0001
16	10000

The digits of the last two binary additions marked with an asterisk have carries. A carry is done exactly as with the addition in the decimal system. The binary answers are the answers we expect to get with decimal arithmetic since $1011 = 2^3 + 2^1 + 1 = 11$, $10010 = 2^4 + 2^1 = 18$, and $10000 = 2^4 = 16$.

Subtraction in the decimal system may require borrowing when a digit with a larger character is subtracted from a digit with a smaller one. This requirement makes subtraction a more complex operation than addition. An easy way of avoiding such a difficulty is a method called *complementing*. We shall illustrate complementing in the decimal system first.

Example 2.5. Subtract 82 from 450.
Answer:

Ordinary Subtraction	Subtraction by Complementing
450	450
− **0**82	+ 917
368	1367
	+ 1
	$\cancel{1}$368

Subtraction by complementing involves the following steps: (*a*) the subtrehend 082 is subtracted from 999 to find its complement 917; (*b*) the complement 917 is added to the minuend 450; (*c*) to the sum 1367 number 1 is added; and (*d*) the correct answer is obtained by ignoring the 1 in the leftmost position of the sum 1368.

Observe that a meaningless zero (in boldface) is placed to the last leftmost full digit of the subtrahend 82 which ordinarily would be ignored; in complementing, however, this zero is necessary for obtaining the correct complement.

The same above procedure is followed in a subtraction by complementing in the binary system.

Example 2.5—*Continued.* Converting the above decimal numbers 82 and 450 to binary equivalents, we have

<table>
<tr><td align="center">Ordinary
Subtraction</td><td align="center">Subtraction by
Complementing</td></tr>
<tr><td align="center">111000010</td><td align="center">111000010</td></tr>
<tr><td align="center">− 001010010</td><td align="center">+110101101</td></tr>
<tr><td align="center">101110000</td><td align="center">1101101111</td></tr>
<tr><td></td><td align="center">+   1</td></tr>
<tr><td></td><td align="center"><s>1</s>101110000</td></tr>
</table>

which is the correct answer since

$$101110000 = 2^8 + 2^6 + 2^5 + 2^4 = 256 + 64 + 32 + 16 = 368 \,.$$

It is important to note that the complement of the binary subtrahend can be easily obtained by replacing 0 by 1 and 1 by 0. Also, observe that, as in the decimal system, meaningless zeros are placed to the leftmost full digit of the subtrahend in order to obtain its correct complement.

When the subtrahend is larger than the minuend, subtraction is accomplished by adding the complement of the *minuend* to the subtrahend. The rest of the procedure remains as described above. The reader will find exercises with the subtrahend larger than the minuend in Problem 2.9 of this section. At any rate the net of the matter is that with base-plus-one complementing subtraction is replaced by addition.

Multiplication in the binary system is identical to decimal multiplication.

Example 2.6. Multiply 31 by 25.
Answer:

<table>
<tr><td align="center">Decimal</td><td align="center">Binary</td></tr>
<tr><td align="center">31</td><td align="center">11111</td></tr>
<tr><td align="center">× 25</td><td align="center">× 11001</td></tr>
<tr><td align="center">155</td><td align="center">11111</td></tr>
<tr><td align="center">62</td><td align="center">00000</td></tr>
<tr><td align="center">775</td><td align="center">00000</td></tr>
<tr><td></td><td align="center">11111</td></tr>
<tr><td></td><td align="center">11111</td></tr>
<tr><td></td><td align="center">1100000111</td></tr>
</table>

The binary answer is correct since

$$1100000111 = 2^9 + 2^8 + 2^2 + 2^1 + 1 = 512 + 256 + 4 + 2 + 1 = 775 \,.$$

Note that when a digit of the binary multiplier in the above example is 1, the multiplicand is simply *copied*. This is a great advantage over decimal multiplication which may involve a carry unless the digit of the decimal multiplier is 1. When a digit of the binary multiplier is 0, the multiplicand is not copied. This latter operation can be replaced by shifting the next copying of the multiplicand one digit to the left for each 0 digit in the multiplier.

Example 2.6—*Continued*. The binary multiplication in Example 2.6 can be done as follows:

```
                            11111
                         ×11001
                         ────────
Copy........................    11111
Shift, shift, shift, and copy   11111
Shift and copy ...............  11111
                         ────────
                        1100000111
```

Observe that adding the partial products together is cumbersome. This disadvantage is overcome with successive adding of the partial products and proper shifting.

Example 2.6—*Continued*. Multiplying 31 by 25 in the binary system can be accomplished as follows:

```
                            11111
                         ×11001
                         ────────
Copy........................    11111
Shift, shift, shift, copy and add..  11111
                         ────────
Partial sum.............    100010111
Shift, copy and add...........  11111
                         ────────
Final sum .............   1100000111
```

as before.

It is important to note that multiplication in the above example has been reduced with proper shifting to repeated addition of the multiplicand.

Division is the operation of finding how many times the divisor can be subtracted from the dividend. Thus, division may be accomplished with repeated subtraction.

Example 2.7. Divide 54 by 15.
Answer:

	Decimal		Binary	
	54		1111 /110110	
	−15	one	−1111	01
	──		──	
	39		100111	
	−15	two	−1111	10
	──		──	
	24		11000	
	−15	three	−1111	11
	──		──	
	9		1001	

Note that since $1 + 1 = 10$ in binary addition, it follows that $10 - 1 = 1$ in binary subtraction. In both the decimal and binary division the quotient is 3 since $11 = 2^1 + 1 = 3$ and the remainder is 9 since $1001 = 2^3 + 1 = 9$.

Since we have already shown that subtraction can be replaced by addition through base-plus-one complementing, division can be also replaced by addition. How this is done will be shown in Section 3 since binary division with base-plus-one complementing requires some knowledge of digital computers. Furthermore, binary division is much simpler than decimal because the binary divisor may be contained only once in each digital position.

2.5. Binary Fractions. Binary division may yield a quotient with fractions. As in the decimal system a "radix point" called binary point is used to separate the whole binary number from a fraction.

Some key conversions of decimal fractions to binary are shown in Table 2.7. Conversion of any decimal fraction to binary may be expressed as a combination of key conversions such as the ones shown in the table.

TABLE 2.7.

	Decimal		Binary
(1)	(2)	(3)	(4)
.5	$= \frac{1}{2}$	$= 1 \cdot 2^{-1}$	.1
.25	$= \frac{1}{4}$	$= 1 \cdot 2^{-2}$	.01
.125	$= \frac{1}{8}$	$= 1 \cdot 2^{-3}$	.001
.0625	$= \frac{1}{16}$	$= 1 \cdot 2^{-4}$	.0001
.03125	$= \frac{1}{32}$	$= 1 \cdot 2^{-5}$	.00001

Example 2.8. Convert the decimal fraction $\frac{7}{8}$ to binary.
Answer:
Since $\frac{7}{8} = \frac{1}{2} + \frac{1}{4} + \frac{1}{8}$, by the key conversions of Table 2.7 we have

$$2^{-1} + 2^{-2} + 2^{-3} = .1 + .01 + .001 = .111 .$$

The reverse process of finding the decimal equivalent of a binary fraction follows the general rules of character and positional notation.

Example 2.9. Find the decimal of the binary number 11.101.
Answer:

$$11.101 = 1 \cdot 2^1 + 1 \cdot 2^0 + 1 \cdot 2^{-1} + 0 \cdot 2^{-2} + 1 \cdot 2^{-3}$$
$$= 2 + 1 + \tfrac{1}{2} + 0 + \tfrac{1}{8}$$
$$= 3\tfrac{5}{8} .$$

2.6. Recapitulation on the Binary Number System. It is important to realize that the foregoing discussion clearly shows the advantages of the binary over the decimal system. The examples on arithmetic operations show the process by which addition replaces all other three basic arithmetic operations. Although this substitution can also be done in the decimal system, basic operations through addition are greatly simplified in the binary system. Copying and successive adding of partial products reduces multiplication to repetitive addition, while shifting cuts the number of additions considerably since half of the digits in the multiplier are likely to be 0's. Finally, complementing reduces subtraction and division to routine binary addition. All these features of the binary system are very important in simplifying the design and facilitating the operation of digital computers.

We have seen that number 2 is the base of binary arithmetic. Any integer greater than one can be used as a base for a new arithmetic system. Thus, we can obtain a number system with the integers 3, 4, 5, and so on as a base. Some systems, in particular the *octal* with base 8 and the *hexadecimal*, with base 16, are used in testing the reliability of digital computers. Like the binary, the octal number system is also used with many computers. Any discussion, however, of these and other related topics must necessarily lie outside the scope of this book.

PROBLEMS

*2.1.   What laws from Table 4.1, Chapter 1, were used in constructing the addition and multiplication tables of (0, 1) algebra? Identify these laws and verify them, using a 0 for $\notin$ and a 1 for $\in$.

*2.2.   How many entries must an addition or a multiplication table have for modulus 3? modulus 4? modulus 10? Construct addition and multiplication tables for modulus 3.

2.3.   In Example 2.2 an even parity check is shown for the first five positive integers by converting these numbers to binary and supplying a parity digit.
*a) Extend this check table to the first sixteen positive integers.
b) Construct an odd parity check for the same integers.

2.4.   Convert the following decimal numbers to their binary equivalents.
*a) 25.
b) 46.
*c) 20.75.
d) $17\frac{15}{32}$.

2.5.   Find the decimal numbers which correspond to the following binary numbers:
*a) 1110110.
b) 0010111.
*c) 11.11.
d) 101010.1111.

2.6.   Add the following binary numbers. Check your answers in the decimal system.
*a) 101 + 101.
*b) 01010 + 10101.
c) 111.101 + 011.010.
d) 1111.11 + 00111.11 + 10111.01.

2.7. Carry out the following additions in the binary system. Check by comparing binary and decimal answers.

*a) 8 + 7.

b) 13 + 20.

*c) 17.5 + 4.25.

d) $25\frac{1}{4} + 5\frac{3}{16}$.

2.8. Subtract the following binary numbers by complementing. Check your answers in the decimal system.

*a) 11011 − 01010.

b) 111111 − 101011.

c) 11011 − 00100.

d) 10111.011 − 01000.100.

2.9. Carry out the following subtractions in the binary system by complementing. Check by comparing binary and decimal answers.

*a) 17 − 7.   e) 25 − 36.

b) 20 − 13.   f) 325 − 442.

*c) 5.75 − 3.25.   g) 2.25 − 5.125.

d) $6\frac{1}{2} - 3\frac{1}{4}$.   h) $6\frac{1}{4} - 8\frac{2}{4}$.

2.10. Do the following binary multiplications by both adding all partial products and by repeated addition of partial products. Check your answers in the decimal system.

*a) 101·111.

b) 0111010·0111.

c) 1111·110001.

d) 11.011·01.101.

2.11. Multiply the following numbers in the binary system by regular addition and by repeated addition of partial products. Check by comparing binary and decimal answers.

*a) 3·5.

b) 27·14.

*c) 0.25·0.5.

d) $2\frac{1}{4}\cdot 4\frac{1}{2}$.

2.12. Divide the following binary numbers by subtracting and check by comparing decimal and binary answers.

*a) 1101 ÷ 10.

b) 01111 ÷ 0101.

*c) 101.01 ÷ 1.01.

d) 101011.110 ÷ 01.11.

2.13. Carry out the following divisions in the binary system by subtracting and check your answers.

*a) 12 ÷ 4.

b) 13 ÷ 3.

*c) 0.75 ÷ 0.25.

d) $2\frac{5}{8} \div 1\frac{1}{8}$.

2.14. Discuss the advantages of the binary system over the decimal with respect to addition, subtraction, multiplication, and division. Is there any serious disadvantage?

2.15. Let $\mathcal{U}$ be the universal set with four elements. Each subset can represent a binary number as follows: The first digit is 1 if and only if the first element is in the subset, the second digit is 1 if and only if the second element is in the subset, and so on.

  a) Show that this process assigns a unique binary number, from 0 to 15, to each subset.

  b) Show that the same result can be obtained by means of a tree diagram where there are four tasks and each task can be performed in two ways, i.e., placing either 0 or 1.

2.16. In the binary number system each digital position can be filled in two different ways, either by a 0 or by a 1. Let n be any number of digits. Then prove that 2^n binary numbers can be formed corresponding to the decimal numbers from 0 to 2^n.

2.17. In the octal number system the number 307 stands for $3 \times 8^2 + 0 \times 8^1 + 7 \times 8^0 = 199$ since the numbers under this system are expressed to the base 8.

  *a) Convert the decimal numbers 1 to 30 to octal equivalents.

  b) Construct tables of addition and multiplication for the octal system.

  c) Multiply the decimal numbers 6×6 in the octal system.

2.18. The following is an excerpt from Rand Corporation, *A Million Random Digits with* 100,000 *Normal Deviates* (Glencoe, Ill.: The Free Press, 1955), pp. 22–23, referring to the use of the table of random numbers:

> "The lines of the digit table are numbered from 00000 to 19999. In any use of the table, one should first find a random starting position. A common procedure for doing this is to open the book to an unselected page at the digit table and blindly choose a five-digit number; this number with the first digit reduced modulo 2 determines the starting line; the two digits to the right of the initially selected five-digit number are reduced modulo 50 to determine the starting column in the starting line."

  a) Following the above instructions, select a random starting position.

  b) From this starting position select 25 random numbers assuming that these numbers represent a random sample from a statistical population numbered 0001–2000.

2.19. In addition to the zero-one interpretation, Boolean algebra (0, 1) can be given a yes-no interpretation. A yes or no response to a specific question may be expressed with a 0 or a 1 binary digit in a specific location. For instance, we can obtain the correct answer to a multiple-choice examination question with four parts by receiving a yes or no answer to two questions of the type required in the parlor game "Twenty Questions." "Is the number of the correct answer less than

3?" If the answer were "yes," we could ask, "Is it less than 2?" And if the answer to our first question were "no," we could ask "It is less than 4?" Thus, the number of the correct answer can be determined from the four logically possible answers or messages 00, 01, 10, 11 where each message contains two *bits of information*, abbreviated from *binary digits*. In other words, the quantity of information contained in each message is the $\log_2 4 = 2$ since the base 2 must be raised to the second power to give 4, the number of possible answers. In general, for n different messages the quantity of information in each message is said to be $\log_2 n$. With these introductory remarks to the modern theory of information developed by communication engineers answer the following questions:

a) How many bits (questions of yes-no type) of information are needed to determine a chosen number from 1 to 8? from 1 to 16? from 1 to 24? Explain how you have arrived at your answer in each case.

b) Consider the following set of eight corporations: United States Steel Corporation (1901), New York Central Railroad Company (1826), American Telephone and Telegraph Company (1885), General Motors Corporation (1916), General Electric Company (1892), E. I. Du Pont de Nemours & Company (1915), Standard Oil Company, N.J. (1882), General Dynamics Corporation (1952), where the year in parentheses indicates the year each firm was established. Find three yes-or-no questions which, if answered in a specific sequence, will enable you to identify any one of the firms.

c) A carefully selected probability sample of 1000 cars showed the following distribution:

	Domestic		Foreign		
	Full Size (1)	Compact (2)	Full Size (3)	Compact (4)	Total (5)
3 years old or less	350	75	50	100	575
More than 3 years old	150	25	100	150	425
Total	500	100	150	250	1000

Construct three yes-or-no questions which can be answered in any sequence, i.e., each question can be answered independently of the answers to the other two questions, and still enables you to identify any one of the eight categories of cars.

d) What is the underlying assumption in the binary messages involved in questions (*a*) and (*b*) above? How could this restriction be removed to place the theory of information closer to real-world situations? (For a short and unsophisticated answer see M. Richardson, *Fundamentals of Mathematics* (rev. ed.; New York: The Macmillan Co., 1958). Pp. 172–74.

*3. BOOLEAN ALGEBRA AND DIGITAL COMPUTERS
(Designing a Hypothetical Computer)

In the preceding section a n.. ..r of Boolean algebra (0, 1) inter-pretations were discussed, namely, zero-one Boolean arithmetic, modulus 2, and the binary number system. We concentrated on the latter system by showing how to convert decimal numbers to binaries and how to perform binary addition, multiplication, subtraction, and division. Furthermore, the efficiency of the binary over the decimal system in performing these basic arithmetic operations was emphasized. Thus, while we have shown another application of Boolean algebra, at the same time we have supplied the required background for the last two sections of Part I.

The basic question to be answered is: "In what respects is Boolean algebra important for the design and operation of digital computers?" In the first place, a digital computer is an ingeniously devised and intri-cate network of switching circuits. But construction of electrical switches is another application of Boolean algebra (0, 1). Circuitry is a device by which the laws of Boolean algebra can be mechanized. In this respect, it can be said that the arithmetic and logical operations of a digital computer rest on the laws of Boolean algebra already explained. In the second place, the "open-closed" stable states of electrical circuits, being the electrical equivalents of false-true, are suitable for an input expressed in terms of a two-digit number system. Hence, a binary code, or a modified version of it, and binary arithmetic become the natural elements for computer operations.

It is not our intention to show the design and operation of a particular or an imaginary digital computer in any degree of completeness. This subject is so vast, as its rich and rapidly growing literature testifies, as to defy comprehensive treatment within manageable proportions. Our aim is much less ambitious. We shall first show how the laws of Boolean algebra are mechanized with electrical switches. Then we shall briefly describe the major parts of an imaginary digital computer by illustrating its design with the construction of an adder only. In the next and final section of Part I we shall show how arithmetic operations are mechan-ized, and we shall introduce a few examples to demonstrate computer programming. All the above topics will be treated to the extent that it is necessary for the reader to acquire a conceptual understanding of the design and operation of digital computers as our last but not least important application of Boolean algebra.

3.1. Mechanization of Boolean Algebra. A network of switches or a circuit is an arrangement of wires and switches which control the flow of electric current between two terminal points. Each

switch has two stable states; it can be either "open," which prevents the flow of current, or "closed," which permits such flow. In fact, the stable states may be considered as another interpretation of Boolean algebra (0, 1), where the "open" state corresponds to 0 or false and the "closed" state to 1 or true. Thus, all the laws of abstract operations of Boolean algebra, shown in Table 4.1, Chapter 1, as well as any logical relation based on them, can be expressed in terms of appropriately constructed switching networks.

How electric circuits are constructed with devices such as relays, electron tubes, diodes, transistors, and cores, is the job of the electrical engineer. Instead, we would like to acquire a working understanding of the process by which the laws of Boolean algebra are mechanized. We shall illustrate this process with schematic presentations which can describe complex circuitry with a minimum of drawing.

The symbols, standard among electrical engineers, which depict the simple circuits for the three basic operations of Boolean algebra ∩ or ·, ', and ∪ or + are shown in Figure 3.1. The *and-circuit* permits the

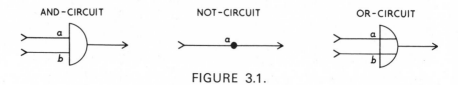

AND-CIRCUIT   NOT-CIRCUIT   OR-CIRCUIT

FIGURE 3.1.

flow of current from left to right if and only if switches a and b are both "closed." In the *not-circuit* the "closed" state of switch a is reversed to the "open" state. Current flows in the *or-circuit* if either switch a or switch b or both switches are "closed."

Using the above basic circuits we can present schematically more complex circuitry which can illustrate the mechanization of any of the laws of Boolean algebra in Table 4.1, Chapter 1.

Example 3.1. Let P and Q be sets with elements 0 and 1 depicting the "open" and "closed" stable states, respectively, of two switches. With the multiplication sign · omitted for convenience, we will illustrate the law of symmetric difference in Figure 3.2. Observe that the symmetric difference circuit requires a combination of all three basic circuits. Furthermore, it permits the flow of current if either P or Q is exclusively in a "closed" state. In other words, current does not flow if P and Q are both either in an "open" or "closed" state. The (0, 1) table of this circuit is shown in column 7 of Table 2.2.

The symmetric difference circuit is basic for the construction of our imaginary digital computer. We shall see this after we discuss systematically the construction of circuits having a given (0, 1) table.

In studying sets we have shown how to obtain membership tables, given a combination of sets. The same process was demonstrated in the preceding section. Given a combination of sets P and Q, where each set represents either 0 or 1, we were able to find the (0, 1) table

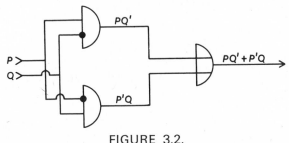

FIGURE 3.2.

which corresponds to that set (cf. Example 2.1). Now, we shall consider the converse problem, namely, given a (0, 1) table, representing "open" and "closed" states of switches respectively, to find one or more sets having the desired table. In order to solve this problem we first construct sets which depict a "closed" state in only one of all logical possibilities. Such basic sets for three switches are shown in Table 3.1. For example,

TABLE 3.1.

"Closed" State Possibility	P	Q	R	Basic Sets
R_8	0	0	0	$P'Q'R'$
R_7	0	0	1	$P'Q'R$
R_6	0	1	0	$P'Q R'$
R_5	0	1	1	$P'Q R$
R_4	1	0	0	$P Q'R'$
R_3	1	0	1	$P Q'R$
R_2	1	1	0	$P Q R'$
R_1	1	1	1	$P Q R$

the state of the basic set $P'Q'R'$ is only possibility R_8, indicating that all three switches are "open," while the state of circuit PQR is only possibility R_1, indicating that all three switches are "closed." The order of rows in Table 3.1 has been reversed to correspond to the regions of a three-set Venn diagram such as the one shown in Figure 3.5, Chapter 1. Then, by combining circuits which these basic sets represent, we can construct more complex circuits having a desired (0, 1) table.

Example 3.2. We wish to construct an electric circuit for recording a secret simple majority vote of a three-member decision-making body. A circuit can be designed so that each member can vote "yes" by closing a switch—pushing a button—and "no" by leaving it open—not pushing a button. A signal light will go on if a majority (two or all three) of the deciding members vote "yes."

Let P, Q, and R be the $(0, 1)$ sets—buttons—corresponding to the three deciding members. Then the complex circuit can be obtained by combining the basic sets which represent the "closed" states R_1, R_2, R_3, R_5 in Table 3.1 as follows:

$$PQR + PQR' + PQ'R + P'QR.$$

A schematic presentation of this circuit appears in Figure 3.3.

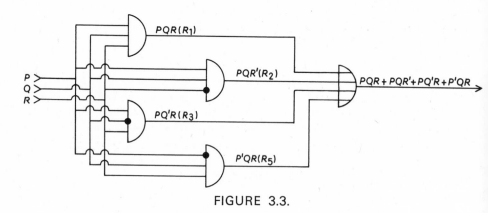

FIGURE 3.3.

It is interesting to note that the symmetric difference circuit is represented by a combination of two basic sets, PQ' and $P'Q$, having two switches instead of three. The reader can very easily construct tables such as Table 3.1 of basic sets for two or more than three switches.

3.2. QUAC—A Hypothetical Digital Computer.

Our "experience" on circuitry design is far from adequate for constructing a digital computer. Yet, it is sufficient for demonstrating the design of an adder, the complex circuit which can perform addition of two binary numbers. We shall assume that all other circuits required for the arithmetic unit and other units are given. The computer we shall describe is unlike any digital computer in existence. It will be an imaginary computer, a model incorporating the standard features of actual computers and sophisticated enough to serve our limited purpose. For lack of a better term we may call our fictitious computer QUAC (Quantitative Analysis Calculator).

Although arithmetic operations can be performed in many ways, our adder will be designed to perform binary arithmetic operations the way such operations have been described in the preceding section.

Consider, for example, the binary addition of the decimal numbers 12 and 10:

$$
\begin{array}{r}
1100 \\
+1010 \\
\hline
\end{array}
$$

Record	0110
Carry	10000

$$
\begin{array}{r}
\hline
\end{array}
$$

Sum	10110

It is important to realize that adding requires two distinct operations—record and carry—which are shown separately. Adding 0 and 0 results in recording 0 and carrying 0, while $0 + 1$ or $1 + 0$ results in recording 1 and carrying 0. But $1 + 1$ leads to recording 0 and carrying 1. Finally, the sum is obtained by shifting carry 1 one digit to the left.

Note that the above addition involves all logical possibilities shown in Table 3.2 where the sets P and Q represent 0 or 1. The record column

TABLE 3.2.

$P + Q$	Record	Carry
$0 + 0$	0	0
$0 + 1$	1	0
$1 + 0$	1	0
$1 + 1$	0	1

corresponds to the (0, 1) table of the symmetric difference (Table 2.2, column 7), and the carry column to the (0, 1) table of multiplication PQ (Table 2.1, column 5). Hence, mechanizing addition requires a switching network which combines a symmetric difference circuit for the record column and an and-circuit for the carry column. Such a complex circuit is shown in Figure 3.4. It is called a *half-adder* because it

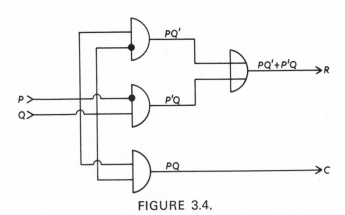

FIGURE 3.4.

performs only half of the task required for adding the two digits of a column. It provides for a carry when addition of a column involves 1's in the digits of both the addend and the augend, but it does not provide for a previous carry. For complete addition two half-adders are needed. Since a *full-adder* circuitry adds only the two digits representing a single column, we must consider two basic modes of mechanical addition for QUAC.

In *serial addition* each column is supplied to a single full adder at different time intervals. Addition is mechanized with two half-adders and a delay as shown in Figure 3.5, where each box represents a half-

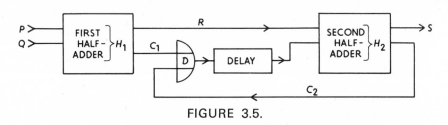

FIGURE 3.5.

adder such as the one shown in Figure 3.4. Serial addition is akin to the typical paper-and-pencil variety. The following example illustrates the process.

> **Example 3.3.** Let 111(7) and 101(5) be the binary numbers fed into the adder in Figure 3.5 at points P and Q, respectively. The process of addition may be described in a sequence of time intervals.
>   1. For $1 + 1$, H_1 records 0 at point R which H_2 records as the sum of the first column at point S. Carry 1 from H_1 at C_1 passes through the or-circuit D and is delayed one time interval.
>   2. For $1 + 0$, H_1 records 1 at R which, together with the delayed carry 1, passes through H_2, resulting in record 0 for the sum of the second column at S and in carry 1 at C_2. Carry 0 from H_1 at C_1 and carry 1 from H_2 at C_2 pass through D, resulting in 1 which is delayed one time interval.
>   3. For $1 + 1$, H_1 records 0 at R which, together with delayed carry 1, passes through H_2, resulting in record 1 for the sum of the third column at S and in carry 0 at C_2. Carry 1 at C_1 from H_1 and carry 0 from H_2 at C_2 pass through D, resulting in 1 which is delayed one time interval.
>   4. The delayed carry 1 passes through H_2 and is recorded as the sum of the fourth column at S.
>   Thus, the sum 1100 is recorded in four successive time intervals.

Since one full-adder is required for adding two numbers of any length, serial addition economizes circuitry. But this is accomplished at the expense of time because each digit must be added consecutively. *Parallel addition*, on the other hand, economizes time at the expense of more circuitry inasmuch as each number digit is added by a separate full-adder. The design of a parallel adder for three-digit numbers is illustrated in Figure 3.6 where each box denoted by H represents a half-adder. We may notice that no delay inhibitor is required, but for adding three-digit numbers five half-adders are needed.

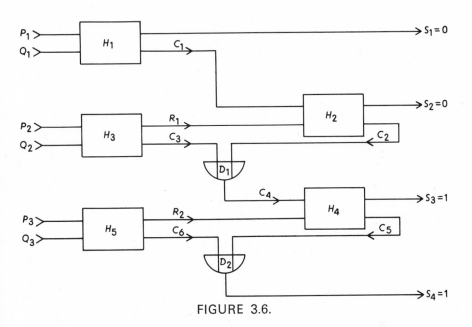

FIGURE 3.6.

Example 3.4. Since, in parallel addition, all digits are added simultaneously, addition of the binary numbers 111(7) and 101(5) cited in Example 3.3 can be explained in terms of digits instead of time intervals.

1. For $1 + 1$ entering the adder at P_1 and Q_1 respectively, H_1 records 0 which becomes the sum of the first column at S_1 and a carry 1 at C_1.

2. For $1 + 0$ entering at P_2 and Q_2 respectively, H_3 records 1 at R_1 which, together with carry 1 at C_1, pass through H_2, resulting in record 0 as the sum of the second column at S_2 and in carry 1 at C_2. Also, from H_3 carry 0 at C_3 and carry 1 from H_2 at C_2 pass through the or-circuit D_1, resulting in carry 1 at C_4.

3. For $1 + 1$ entering at P_3 and Q_3 respectively, H_5 records 0 at R_2 which, together with carry 1 at C_4, pass through H_4, resulting in record 1 as the sum of the third column at S_3 and in carry 0 at C_5. Also, from H_5 carry 1 at C_6 and carry 0 from H_4 at C_5 pass through D_2 to become 1 which is the sum of the fourth column at S_4.

Remember that the above parallel addition is done in a single time interval or a little more which for a high-speed computer represents but a small fraction of a second, as little as 1/100,000 of a second or even less than that, per time interval.

We choose a parallel adder for QUAC because it is more efficient than a serial adder and because it facilitates later illustrations. The adder, together with other circuits, makes up the arithmetic unit, one of the five basic units of QUAC whose block diagram is shown in Figure 3.7.

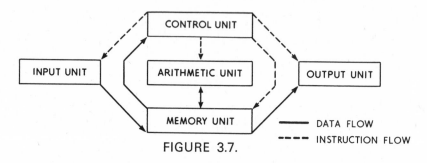

FIGURE 3.7.

—— DATA FLOW
- - - - INSTRUCTION FLOW

Although division of functions among the units differ from machine to machine, for our computer each unit performs the following separate functions. The input unit converts the decimal numbers representing data and instructions to machine language, while the output unit converts results back to the decimals in the form of reports or summaries. The four arithmetic operations—namely, addition, multiplication, subtraction and division—are performed by the arithmetic unit. Finally, the control unit analyzes the instructions already stored in the memory unit in order to dictate the operation to be performed by the other units and the data, or operands, to be used. Thus, while the arithmetic unit performs the four basic arithmetic operations, the control unit does all other logical operations of an instruction sequence. What logical operations a control unit can perform depends on its design. QUAC's control unit is designed to store input data and instructions into the memory unit, carry data from the memory to the arithmetic unit and instruct the latter to perform certain arithmetic calculations, store the results of these calculations back to the memory unit, compare magnitudes, and instruct the output unit to convert results to decimals and print reports.

3.3 Recapitulation. By now it must be apparent to the reader why construction of QUAC is based on Boolean algebra (0, 1). It is much easier to design and build machines with two-stable-state than with ten-stable-state circuitry for the decimal system. A two-stable-state system simplifies the design of equipment and reduces construction cost. Furthermore, because of these features QUAC operates efficiently.

PROBLEMS

3.1. Let P, Q, and R be sets with elements 0 and 1 depicting the "open" and "closed" stable states, respectively, of three switches. Construct a complex circuit for both sides of the following laws of Boolean algebra. Which side of each law requires fewer switches?
*a) $P + (QR) = (P + Q)(P + R)$.
*b) $P(Q + R) = (PQ) + (PR)$.
 c) $(P + Q)' = P'Q'$.
 d) $(PQ)' = P' + Q'$.

3.2. Construct a complex circuit for each set below. Then design another circuit more efficient than the previous one by simplifying the given sets.
*a) $(P + Q)(P + Q')$.
*b) $(PQ) + (PQ') + (P'Q)$.
 c) $[(P'Q') + (Q'R') + (P'Q')]'$.
 d) $P + [(P + Q)R] + [Q(P' + R')]$.

3.3. Let p, q, r and z be propositional statements and P, Q, R, and Z their respective sets with 0 and 1 elements where the "open" or 0 stable state stands for false and the "closed" or 1 stable state for true. Using these sets of switches construct circuits for the following arguments. (*Hint:* Remember that $p \to q = p' \cup q$.)
*a) $[(p \to q) \cap q'] \to p'$.
*b) $[(p \to q) \cap q] \to p$.
 c) $[(p \to q) \cap p'] \to q$.
 d) $[(p \to z) \cap (z \to r) \cap (r \to q)] \to (p \to q)$.

3.4. Using the arguments quoted in Problem 3.3 show that if an argument is valid, then current will always flow through its circuit while this is not the case for a circuit representing an invalid argument.

3.5. Prepare tables of basic sets such as those shown in Table 3.1 for—
 a) Two switches.
 b) Four switches.

3.6. What sets do the following circuits represent?
*a)

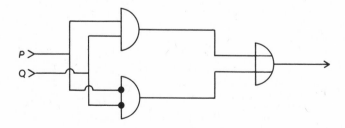

b)

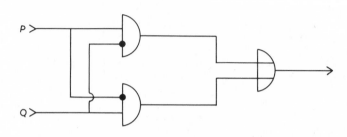

c)

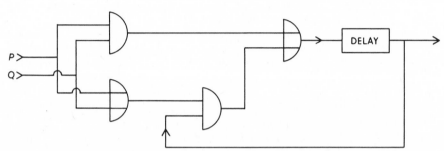

*3.7. The manager of an antique shop would like to install a circuit which will ring a bell when customers enter the store from either or both entrances. Let P and Q represent sets where element 0 stands for the "open" and element 1 stands for the "closed" stable states of the respective switches. Find the required set and design the corresponding complex circuit which will accomplish the desired effect.

3.8. Find the set and design the corresponding complex circuit similar to the one designed in Example 3.2 for a four-member committee when the chairman of the committee has the right to break ties when voting for a motion.

3.9. In order to construct a half-adder, we used the symmetric difference set $PQ' + P'Q$. Show that the following sets are equivalent and design their complex circuity.
**a)* $(P + Q)(P' + Q')$.
b) $(P + Q)(PQ)'$.

3.10. The switches of a simple circuit may be schematically presented as follows:

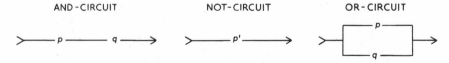

where p = "switch P is closed" and p' = "switch P' is open." Using the new symbols the symmetric difference circuit may be diagrammed like this:

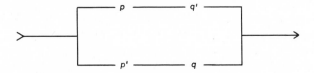

Design complex circuits using this type of symbolism for—
*a) The circuit in Figure 3.3.
 b) Problem 3.6 (a), (b), (c).
 c) Problem 3.7.
 d) Problem 3.8.
 e) The circuit in Figure 3.4.
 f) Problem 3.9 (a), (b).

3.11. Describe the process of serial addition as illustrated in Example 3.3 by adding—
a) 011 and 100.
b) 0111 and 0110.
c) 1011, 0110, and 1111.

3.12. Describe the process of parallel addition as illustrated in Example 3.4 by adding—
a) 011 and 100.
b) 101 and 010.
c) 101, 011, and 111.

*3.13. We have seen that for parallel adding of three-digit binary numbers five half-adders were required. How many half-adders would be necessary for parallel adding of n-digit binary numbers, where n is a positive integer greater than 3?

*4. BOOLEAN ALGEBRA AND DIGITAL COMPUTERS
(QUAC in Operation)

Before illustrating how addition, subtraction, multiplication, and division are mechanized and how QUAC is instructed to perform these operations, we must decide on two important matters, namely, machine language and length of number.

4.1. QUAC's Language and Capacity. Our hypothetical computer is designed to handle inputs expressed in 0 and 1 binary digits, frequently called *bits*. But this arrangement requires conversion of input data from the decimal to some version of 0 and 1 language which QUAC can "understand." In order to increase the efficiency of conversion operations and construct machines capable of handling alphabetic characters, computer designers frequently use codes such as a version of the *binary-coded decimal* or the *alphanumerical*. Use of such coding devices, however, is done at the expense of either more circuitry or slow processing. Although a binary-coded decimal method of conversion may be desirable for business applications which involve a large amount of processing in proportion to input-output volume, QUAC uses pure binary numbers.

The length of a number is equally important for QUAC's operations. A binary number cannot be longer than its storage location in the memory unit. A real digital computer has thousands of storage locations in its memory, each able to hold binary numbers of 36 or more digits of maximum length. In order to facilitate matters in illustrating the mechanization of arithmetic, we shall initially assume that QUAC is built to handle only four-digit binary numbers. But our exposition will hold for a binary number of any desirable length. Later we shall relax this assumption and increase the length of number which QUAC can handle to the extent that this is necessary to accommodate our demonstration in computer programming. In describing how QUAC operates we shall follow the convention and use the term *bit* to denote a binary digit, reserving the term *digit* when referring to the decimal system only.

In recording a number of QUAC's memory the maximum length of four bits is always used by attaching meaningless zeros on the left end of a binary number shorter than this maximum. Since the adder must be capable of handling any number in its memory, addition of two maximum length numbers yields a sum one bit longer than the maximum provided because of the carry from the left-hand column. For example, if the maximum length were fixed at three bits, adding in Example 3.4 would create the so-called *overflow* at point S_4 in Figure 3.6 with the extra bit being lost. In order to prevent overflow, QUAC has one extra storage position in the sum register and special storage capacity other than in the main memory.

4.2. Mechanization of Arithmetic. The most important part in QUAC's arithmetic unit is the parallel adder. This is understandable since we have seen that all four arithmetic operations can be replaced with addition. Furthermore, for mechanizing arithmetic QUAC is equipped with registers which record inputs and outputs of arithmetic operations and counters which control such operations. All these major components of the computer's arithmetic unit are shown in Figure 4.1. The *upper register* is frequently called *storage register* or *distributor* while the *counter* is often called *multiplier-quotient*. The reason for the use of these terms will become apparent as soon as we illustrate how the components of QUAC perform mechanical addition, subtraction, multiplication, and division.

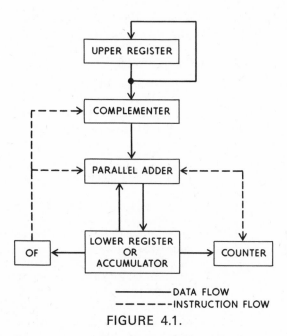

FIGURE 4.1.

Example 4.1. Suppose the control unit of QUAC reads the instruction, stored in the memory unit, to add numbers 0111(7), 0101(5), and 1011(11). *Mechanical addition* involves the following sequence:

0111	U.R.	Lower register (L.R.) is cleared by being filled with zeros and number 0111 to be added (an addend) is recorded in upper register (U.R.).
0000	L.R.	

0101	U.R.	Content of both registers is "dumped" into parallel adder and the sum of 0111 + 0000 is recorded in L.R. while second addend 0101 is placed on U.R.
0111	L.R.	

1011	U.R.	Content of both registers shown in the previous step is "dumped" again into parallel adder and new sum 1100(12) is recorded in L.R. while third addend 1011 is placed on U.R.
1100	L.R.	

OF

1	0000	U.R.	Above-shown content of both registers is again "dumped" into parallel adder and the final sum 10111(23) is recorded in the overflow (OF) and L.R.
	0111	L.R.	

In mechanical addition the complementer shown in Figure 4.1 is bypassed. The lower register is frequently called *accumulator register*, although we shall presently show that it performs other functions besides accumulating sums.

Example 4.2. *Mechanical subtraction* is identical to the base-plus-one complementing already illustrated in Section 2. Let us assume that QUAC is instructed to subtract 1001(9) from 1111(15). Referring again to Figure 4.1, the computer performs the following tasks.

1001	U.R.	The two operands arrive from storage; minuend 1111 is placed on L.R., passing through U.R. and bypassing complementer; subtrahend 1001 is recorded in U.R.
1111	L.R.	

0110	CT	Subtrahend passes through complementer (CT) and its content as well as the content of L.R. are "dumped" into parallel adder.
1111	L.R.	

OF	0000	U.R.	Adding the extra 1 to subtrahend is done automatically. Since there is never a previous carry for the right-hand column of the parallel adder (see Figure 3.6), the carry circuit always supplies a 0 to the right column when straight addition takes place. But this carry is always changed to 1 when a complement is added. Also, the unwanted 1 on the left end of the remainder (sum) is automatically discarded since QUAC prevents it from being recorded on the overflow leaving the correct answer 0110 in L.R.
0	0110	L.R.	

Mechanical parallel multiplication by shifting and adding partial products which QUAC can perform is similar to the arithmetic multiplication already described in Section 2 with one notable exception. Instead of shifting each partial product to the left and adding, QUAC shifts each previous sum to the right and adds. The following illustration shows how multiplication is mechanized.

Example 4.3. The lower register is set at zero while the multiplicand, say 1111 (15), is recorded in the upper register and the multiplier, say 1001(9), in the counter shown in Figure 4.1. The complementer is bypassed. In order to prevent the multiplicand from being lost each time it is added, a recirculation loop, shown in the diagram, rewrites the multiplicand into the upper register. QUAC decides to add the multiplicand by observing through the control circuit (dotted line) whether the right-hand digit of the multiplier in use at a given cycle is 1 or 0. Adding and shifting continues until all the bits of the multiplier have been read off and shifted out of the counter and the final product is recorded in the lower register and the emptied counter. Since all this activity is recorded in the lower register and the counter, the above multiplication is arranged below as QUAC would have solved it.

Lower Register   Counter

0000	1001	Initial content of L.R. and counter (C) as described above.

Lower Register   *Counter*

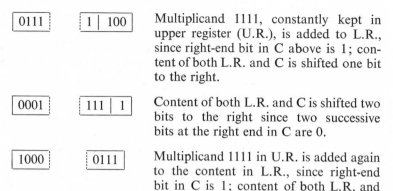

| 0111 | | 1 | 100 | Multiplicand 1111, constantly kept in upper register (U.R.), is added to L.R., since right-end bit in C above is 1; content of both L.R. and C is shifted one bit to the right. |

| 0001 | | 111 | 1 | Content of both L.R. and C is shifted two bits to the right since two successive bits at the right end in C are 0. |

| 1000 | | 0111 | Multiplicand 1111 in U.R. is added again to the content in L.R., since right-end bit in C is 1; content of both L.R. and C is shifted one bit to the right. The so-called *most significant half* of the product appears in L.R. and the *least significant half* in C. |

Mechanical parallel division by shifting is a little more roundabout than the paper-and-pencil division by repeated subtraction illustrated in Section 2. We can best illustrate the steps with an example referring to the diagram in Figure 4.1.

Example 4.4. Suppose QUAC is instructed to divide 1001(9) by 0101(5). Here is the course the computer would follow:

OF

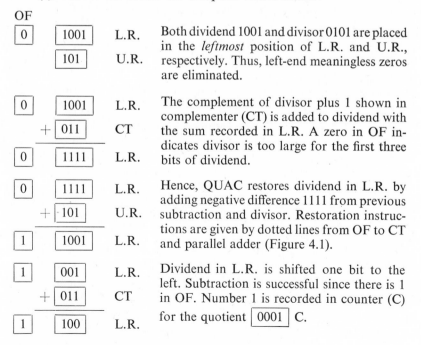

| 0 | | 1001 | L.R. | Both dividend 1001 and divisor 0101 are placed in the *leftmost* position of L.R. and U.R., respectively. Thus, left-end meaningless zeros are eliminated. |
| | | 101 | U.R. | |

0		1001	L.R.	The complement of divisor plus 1 shown in complementer (CT) is added to dividend with the sum recorded in L.R. A zero in OF indicates divisor is too large for the first three bits of dividend.
+	011		CT	
0		1111	L.R.	

0		1111	L.R.	Hence, QUAC restores dividend in L.R. by adding negative difference 1111 from previous subtraction and divisor. Restoration instructions are given by dotted lines from OF to CT and parallel adder (Figure 4.1).
+	·101		U.R.	
1		1001	L.R.	

1		001	L.R.	Dividend in L.R. is shifted one bit to the left. Subtraction is successful since there is 1 in OF. Number 1 is recorded in counter (C)
+	011		CT	
1		100	L.R.	for the quotient	0001	C.

OF

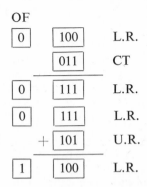

0	100	L.R.	Remaining dividend in L.R. is not shifted since no additional bits are available. Sub-
	011	CT	traction is not successful as the zero in OF indicates.
0	111	L.R.	

0	111	L.R.	QUAC restores previous portion of dividend in L.R. by adding negative difference 111
+	101	U.R.	from previous subtraction and divisor. The remainder 100 in L.R. is positive since there
1	100	L.R.	is a 1 in OF.

Thus, division is completed with the quotient 1 in the counter and the remainder 100(4) in the lower register.

QUAC is equipped to handle negative and fractional binary numbers although no attempt will be made to demonstrate operations involving such numbers.

4.3. A Few Additional Features of QUAC.   Although the arithmetic unit is designed to perform operations, the "brain" of QUAC is the control unit. It reads and carries out the instructions which must be prepared and stored in advance in the memory unit. Each *instruction* consists of two parts, the *code* indicating the operation to be performed and a number, called *address*, indicating the storage location in the memory which contains the operand to be used. Hence, in order to accommodate the instructions for the control unit we shall drop the previously made assumption and lengthen the number of bits which QUAC can store in its memory from four to nine, four bits for the code and five bits for the address. Obviously, QUAC cannot have more than 16 coded operations and not more than 32 storage locations (why?). Most digital computers in existence are one-address, two-address, three-address, or four-address machines. Our QUAC is a single-address machine with capacity far below the capacity of a real computer, but sufficient for our limited purpose of illustrating how QUAC is instructed to perform numerical and logical operations.

It is important to realize that each storage location can be used to record either an instruction or an operand. Therefore, each storage location, called *cell* or *word space*, now being nine bits long can accommodate a binary number of eight bits maximum length. The ninth leftmost bit of a word space is reserved for the sign, 0 for plus and 1 for minus, of the stored operand. Of course, we also assume that the capacity of the arithmetic unit has increased commensurably.

Since instructions are stored in the memory in consecutive order, QUAC's control unit is equipped with a *control register* which selects each instruction in sequence from the memory and brings it to a special complex circuit, the *instruction register*. The latter analyzes each instruction and dictates the operation to be performed as well as the operand to be used. Selection of the specified location in the memory unit is verified by a special circuit, the *equality comparator*, which matches the address number in the instruction with the address number in the memory. This process continues until all instructions have been carried out one by one. Naturally, QUAC's control unit is equipped with additional circuits which are capable of performing more specialized tasks. But their description is not necessary for illustrating computer programming.

4.4. Elements of Computer Programming.

Our exposition of digital computers as an application of Boolean algebra may be considered incomplete if we fail to illustrate how QUAC is instructed to perform numerical and logical operations. This process, called *programming*, involves a *flow chart*, an *instruction routine*, and *coding* the instruction routine in machine language.

A *flow chart* is a graphic and symbolic presentation of the major operational tasks that a computer is required to perform for solving a particular problem.

Example 4.5. Consider the following problem. Given the constants a, b, c, and d, find

$$Q = \frac{(a+b)^3 - 5c}{d}.$$

Observe that this problem requires all four basic arithmetic operations. Normally, no flow charting may be needed for such a trivial problem. If it were drawn, however, it might look like this:

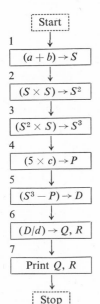

1. Add a and b and assign sum to S.

2. Multiply S times S and assign product to S^2.

3. Multiply S^2 times S and assign product to S^3.

4. Multiply 5 times c and assign product to P.

5. Subtract P from S^3 and assign difference to D.

6. Divide D by d.

7. Print quotient Q and remainder R.

The above simple flow chart consists of two types of components. The basic component is a rectangle or a *box* with solid lines. Each box contains a computation or order as explained. The other type of component is a rectangle with dotted lines, called *terminal*. It is used for starting and stopping the flow chart. The direction of the flow or sequence of computational and logical steps is denoted by arrows. A third type of component will be introduced later.

QUAC's control unit is wired to understand instructions in pure binary numbers. Therefore, before preparing the other two parts of computer programming for our problem we must know the codes of operations or *commands* which QUAC's control unit understands. The commands which QUAC needs to solve the assigned problem are shown below:

Code			Description of Commands
Decimal	Binary		
+0	0000	HLT	= Stop
+1	0001	CLA	= Clear (accumulator) and add
+2	0010	ADD	= Add
+3	0011	SUB	= Subtract
+4	0100	MPY	= Multiply
+5	0101	DIV	= Divide
+6	0110	STQ	= Store counter's content
+7	0111	STA	= Store accumulator's content
−0	1000	PRT	= Print (read output, translate, print)
−1	1001	LDQ	= Load counter
−2	1010	RDS	= Read (read input, translate, store in memory)

The reader may recall that the leftmost of the nine bits in a word space is reserved for the sign of an operand, 0 for plus and 1 for minus. The sign bit is effectively used for coding commands by classifying them into positive and negative. In this manner QUAC can accommodate 16 instead of 8 commands. Additional commands may be added to the above list as they are needed.

The *instruction routine*, the second step in computer programming, consists of listing the instructions required for the computer to carry out the computational and logical steps which are specified in the flow chart.

Example 4.5—*Continued.* In QUAC's memory we reserve addresses from 0 to 22 to store instructions and from 23 to 31 to store data. The instruction routine and the data of our problem are listed in human language as follows:

Storage Address	Instruction and Data	Address
00	RDS = Read number a in	23
01	RDS = Read number b in	24
02	RDS = Read number 5 in	25
03	RDS = Read number c in	26
04	RDS = Read number d in	27
05	CLA = Clear and add number a stored in	23
06	ADD = Add number b stored in	24
07	STA = Store accumulator's sum S in	28
08	LDQ = Load counter with S stored in	28
09	MPY = Multiply by S stored in	28
10	MPY = Multiply by S stored in	28
*11	STQ = Store counter's content S^3 in	29
12	LDQ = Load counter with 5 stored in	25
13	MPY = Multiply by c stored in	26
14	STQ = Store counter's content P in	30
*15	CLA = Clear and add S^3 stored in	29
16	SUB = Subtract P stored in	30
17	DIV = Divide accumulator's content D by d stored in	27
18	STQ = Store counter's quotient Q in	31
19	STA = Store accumulator's remainder R in	28
20	PRT = Print Q stored in	31
21	PRT = Print R stored in	28
22	HLT = Stop	
23	Number a	
24	Number b	
25	Number 5	
26	Number c	
27	Number d	
28	Sum S	
29	Product S^3	
30	Product P	
31	Quotient Q	
28	Remainder R	

Observe that remainder R is stored in memory address 28 thus erasing the sum S previously stored in that address. This is necessary because QUAC's memory has 32 storage locations only, since only the five rightmost bits of word space are reserved for coding an address. Also, in this programming we assumed that products S^3 and P do not require more than an eight-bit counter. Otherwise, either QUAC's counter and word space must be increased or the most significant part of a product will appear in the lower register or accumulator. In the latter case additional commands will be required to handle our problem.

Also, note that command RDS is used for the data of the problem only and not for the computational and logical instructions. This is so because the codes of the latter are already built into QUAC's arithmetic and control units.

Encoding the instruction routine, the third step in computer programming, can be carried out with the codes of the previously given commands.

Example 4.5—*Continued*. In order to facilitate understanding the encoded instruction routine of our problem is presented below in both human and machine language:

Storage Address		Instructions			
Decimal	Binary	Decimal		Binary	
00	00000	−2	23	1010	10111
01	00001	−2	24	1010	11000
02	00010	−2	25	1010	11001
03	00011	−2	26	1010	11010
04	00100	−2	27	1010	11011
05	00101	+1	23	0001	10111
06	00110	+2	24	0010	11000
07	00111	+7	28	0111	11100
08	01000	−1	28	1001	11100
09	01001	+4	28	0100	11100
10	01010	+4	28	0100	11100
11	01011	+6	29	0110	11101
12	01100	−1	25	1001	11001
13	01101	+4	26	0100	11010
14	01110	+6	30	0110	11110
15	01111	+1	29	0001	11101
16	10000	+3	30	0011	11110
17	10001	+5	27	0101	11011
18	10010	+6	31	0110	11111
19	10011	+7	28	0111	11100
20	10100	−0	31	1000	11111
21	10101	−0	28	1000	11100
22	10110	+0		0000	

Note that each instruction is divided into two parts. The first, consisting of four bits, contains the code of a command; the second, consisting of five bits, contains the address where an operand is stored. For example, instruction | 1010 | 10111 | in the first row of the encoded instructions directs QUAC to read— | 1010 | —input number *a*, convert it from decimal to binary, and store it in address— | 10111 |; instruction | 0001 | 10111 | in the sixth row of the encoded instructions directs QUAC to clear the accumulator and add— $\boxed{0001\}$ —operand a stored in address $\boxed{10111}$, and so on.

Of course the above encoded instruction routine represents the programming for finding the value of Q in our problem for any values of a, b, c, d which QUAC can handle. We must show now the encoding when these numbers are specified.

Let $a = 3$, $b = 2$, $c = 10$, and $d = 13$. Those operands expressed in the decimal notation are fed into QUAC's input unit. Command *read* directs QUAC to convert the data into binary numbers and store them in its memory, addresses 23 through 27. The above data will appear in QUAC's memory as shown below:

| Storage Address | | Data | |
Decimal	Binary	Decimal	Binary in Memory
23	10111	$a = 3$	0 | 00000011
24	11000	$b = 2$	0 | 00000010
25	11001	5	0 | 00000101
26	11010	$c = 10$	0 | 00001010
27	11011	$d = 13$	0 | 00001101

Observe how data are recorded in QUAC's memory. Operand 11(3), for example, stored in address 10111(23) occupies eight bits. A zero recorded on the ninth leftmost bit of the word indicates that the operand is a positive real number.

The above-encoded instruction routine is recorded in the indicated storage addresses of the memory. When QUAC is turned on, the counter of the control register is set to address 00000 of the first command. This command is brought to the instruction register. While command $1010(-2)$ is being carried out, the counter of the control register is advanced by one to address 00001 and the control register selects the next command $1010(-2)$. Our problem is solved in a very small fraction of a second. The answers for Q and R are converted to decimal numerals and printed out by QUAC's output unit.

In the above example we deliberately made no effort to economize in word space and machine time. We assumed that the original data stored in the memory should be preserved. Otherwise we could have used the same addresses 23 to 27 to store the results of the instruction routine. Such storing arrangement would have economized on word space at the expense of erasing the original data from the memory. Furthermore, we can economize on machine time by reducing the number of instructions required to solve the problem. By forming the product $5c$ first and then computing S^3 we can have S^3 already in the accumulator when subtracting $5c$, thus eliminating instructions 11 and 15 marked with an asterisk. This new instruction routine is left for the reader as an exercise (Problem 4.7).

4.5. Programming Another Problem.   The above computer programming example solves the assigned problem when $a + b$ is
raised to the third power only. It does not solve the same problem
when $a + b$ is raised to the nth power. This is a new problem requiring
new instructions so that QUAC is in what is called a *loop* which raises
the sum $a + b$ to any specified power.

Example **4.6.** Given the constants a, b, c, and d, find

$$Q = \frac{(a+b)^n - 5c}{d}$$

where n is any positive integer greater than 1.

A flow chart for this problem may look like this:

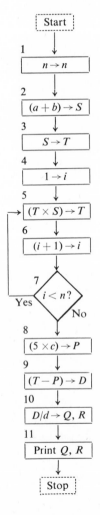

1. Since $a + b$ must be raised to the
   nth power, number n, whatever
   n, is stored.

2. Add a and b and assign sum to S.

3. Assign S to location T.

4. Set 1 into i to initialize count.

5. Multiply T times S and store
   new product in T.

6. Increase i by 1 and store new i.

7. Is i less than n?
   If *yes*, go to 5.
   If *no*, go to 8.

8. Multiply 5 times c and assign
   product to P.

9. Subtract P from T and assign
   difference to D.

10. Divide D by d and assign quo-
    tient to Q and remainder to R.

11. Print quotient Q and remainder
    R.

With the above example we introduce a third type of component of a flow chart called *diamond*. It contains a question to be answered. With the diamond in our example QUAC is instructed to decide whether or not i, the power to which the sum $a + b$ has been raised, is less than the desired nth power. If the answer is yes, QUAC is instructed to repeat steps 5, 6, and 7. This repetitive pattern or *loop* goes on until $i = n$. Then the answer is no, and QUAC is instructed to go to step 8. In sum, our flow chart may consist of three types of components: terminals for starting and ending an instruction routine, boxes for computations, and diamonds for decision points.

The other two steps for programming the above problem, namely, instruction routine and encoding, are left for the reader as an exercise in Problem 4.8.

4.6. More Recent Developments. It must be clear by now that programming is a time-consuming task. This is so partly because of the complexities involved in preparing instructions but principally because of the excess amount of time spent in check-outs in order to secure programming free of errors which otherwise may spell disaster. Recent efforts are concentrated in designing machines which will do their own programming. One such automatic coding system is FOR-TRAN (Mathematical FORmula TRANslating system). This system accepts a problem in a form similar to ordinary mathematical language and automatically prepares the required programming. Another such development aims at automatic programming for commercial data processing. A statement such as "Tabulate amount-of-insurance premium number-of-policies by policy-account branch year plan age" would be translated by a compiler-generator program into a set of machine instructions for a particular computer. Developments such as the above may some day bring about a revolution in computer programming.

Compared with modern digital computers in existence QUAC is a "primitive" machine. Like the first heavier-than-air machine of the Wright brothers compared with modern jetliners, QUAC is not more than a hypothetical prototype of today's highly sophisticated and versatile machines.

There is no way of describing briefly the present and potential uses of digital computers in business and industry. Suffice it to say that electronic computers are already contributing to the more efficient supervision, control, and planning of business operations and to making wiser managerial decisions based more on factual information and less on intuition. Thus Boolean algebra, an abstract mathematical system, has supplied the theoretical basis for the design and operation of practical devices, namely, the digital computers of today, which are increasingly becoming indispensable to management.

PROBLEMS

4.1. Describe addition as illustrated in Example 4.1 for the following binary numbers:

a) 1011, 0010, and 0001.
b) 1001, 0100, and 1010.
c) 1111, 0001, and 1010.

4.2. Describe mechanical subtraction as demonstrated in Example 4.2 for the following numbers:

a) 1001 minus 1000.
b) 1010 minus 0110.
c) 1111 minus 1011.

4.3. Mechanical multiplication has been demonstrated in Example 4.3. Follow the same steps and multiply the following:

a) 1111 times 1111.
b) 1110 times 1010.
c) 1011 times 1110.
d) 0101 times 1111.
e) 1111 times 0101.

4.4. Follow the steps required for mechanical division as shown in Example 4.4 and divide—

a) 1111 by 0101.
b) 1001 by 0011.
c) 1111 by 0100.

4.5. Describe the following mechanical arithmetic operations:

a) $(1010 + 0101) - 0111$.
b) $[(1011 + 0100) - 1001] \times 0010$.
c) $\{[(0011 + 1011) - 1010] \times 0011\} \div 0101$.

4.6. From each of the indicated problems below, prepare the instruction routine and encode the computer programming as illustrated in Example 4.5.

a) Problem 4.1(*a*).   d) Problem 4.4(*a*).
b) Problem 4.2(*a*).   e) Problem 4.5(*a*).
c) Problem 4.3(*a*).

4.7. For computing the value of

$$Q = \frac{(a+b)^3 - 5c}{d}.$$

Prepare a more efficient programming than the one illustrated in Example 4.5.

4.8. Programming the seventh step of the flow chart in Example 4.6 requires the command TRN = "Transfer if the sign of the accumulator is negative,"or in short "If negative, jump." This instruction is placed after QUAC is directed to subtract $i - n$ in step 7 of the flow chart. If the result is negative, the machine is instructed to jump to the appropriate instruction in order to repeat steps 5, 6, and 7; otherwise, QUAC goes on to steps 8, 9, 10, and 11.

Let the code of TRN be -3. Let $a = 3$, $b = 2$, $n = 4$, $c = 100$, and $d = 25$. Lengthen QUAC's counter and word space so that no part of products $(a + b)^n$ and $5c$ appears in the accumulator. Complete the programming of this problem by—

a) Preparing an instruction routine in human language.

b) Encoding this instruction routine in machine language.

4.9. QUAC may be instructed to find and report the number of wage earners in a payroll who are paid at least a given hourly wage rate, or the number of items in an inventory which are priced at least a certain amount. The same instruction routine can be used in other similar problems concerning invoices, accounts receivable or payable, etc.

a) Prepare a flow chart for instructing QUAC to find and report the number of wage earners in a payroll who are paid equal to or more than a given hourly wage rate.

b) Prepare an instruction routine for this problem in human language.

c) Encode this instruction routine in machine language.

(Use the new instruction -3 explained in Problem 4.8 and increase QUAC's counter and word space if necessary.)

4.10. Read references 3, pp. 624–30 and 8, pp. 6–10, at the end of this chapter as well as other sources of information and write a short essay on the history of the development of computers.

4.11. Read references 3, pp. 610–21, and 4, pp. 308–14, at the end of this chapter as well as other sources of information and write a short essay about prospects in the development and use of electronic computers.

4.12. Computers are not used for the development of data processing systems only. They are increasingly utilized in solving business problems such as budgeting, inventory control, returns on investment, forecasting, manufacturing and distribution patterns, and production scheduling. Furthermore, computers are put to work for simulating business situations. One such development is the programming of management games for the purpose of educating executive personnel by simulating the process of decision making.

In a short report give a description of the following management games and discuss their advantages and disadvantages. Information about each game is available in the individual source and also in reference 6 at the end of the chapter.

a) *General Management Simulation.* American Management Association, AMA Academy, Saranac Lake, New York.

b) *Materials Management Simulation II*, American Management Association, AMA Academy, Saranac Lake, New York.

c) *Management Game.* Graduate School of Industrial Administration, Carnegie Institute of Technology, Pittsburgh 13, Pennsylvania.

d) *Management Decision-Making Laboratory.* IBM Data Processing Division, 9415 Western Avenue, Chicago 20, Illinois.

e) *Retail Industry Management Game.* IBM Corporation, 112 East Post Road, White Plains, New York.

f) *Bank Management Game.* McKinsey & Company, Inc., 270 Park Ave., New York, New York.
g) *Marketing Management Simulation.* Remington Rand UNIVAC, 315 Park Avenue South, New York City.
h) *Manufacturing Management Simulation.* Remington Rand UNIVAC, 315 Park Avenue South, New York City.
i) *UCLA Executive Game #3.* Western Management Science Institute, Graduate School of Business Administration, University of California, Los Angeles 24, California.

SUGGESTED REFERENCES

1. ALLENDOERFER, C. B., AND OAKLEY, C. O. *Principles of Mathematics,* pp. 115–21. New York: McGraw-Hill Book Co., Inc., 1955. (**1–3**)

2. GOLDBERG, SAMUEL. *Probability: An Introduction,* pp. 27–28. Englewood Cliffs, N.J.: Prentice-Hall, Inc., 1960. (**1**)

3. GREGORY, R. H., AND VAN HORN, R. L. *Automatic Data-Processing Systems.* San Francisco: Wadsworth Publishing Co., Inc., 1960. (**2–4**)

4. IRWIN, W. C. *Digital Computer Principles.* New York: D. Van Nostrand Co., Inc., 1960. (**2–4**)

5. KEMENY, JOHN G., *et al. Introduction to Finite Mathematics,* pp. 49–53, 74–78, 108–12. Englewood Cliffs, N.J.: Prentice-Hall, Inc., 1957. (**1–3**)

6. KIRBES, J. M., *et al. Management Games.* New York: Reinhold Publishing Corp., 1961. (**4**)

7. MATHEMATICAL ASSOCIATION OF AMERICA, COMMITTEE ON THE UNDER-GRADUATE PROGRAM. *Elementary Mathematics of Sets with Applications* pp. 67–74, 82–87. 1958. (**1–3**)

8. MCCRACKEN, D. D. *Digitial Computer Programming.* New York: John Wiley & Sons, Inc., 1957. (**3, 4**)

9. RICHARDSON, M. *Fundamentals of Mathematics,* pp. 189–92, 196–98. Rev. ed. New York: The Macmillan Co., 1958. (**1–3**)

10. SCHEID, FRANCIS. *Elements of Finite Mathematics,* pp. 36–42, 104–20. Reading, Mass.: Addison-Wesley Co., Inc., 1962. (**2–4**)

PART II

Algebra, Analytic Geometry, and Functions

In Part I we have studied Boolean algebra as a mathematical system. We have seen how the laws of this system can be applied to real-world business situations. But the tools of Boolean algebra fall short of giving "definite" answers to managerial problems. What the algebra of sets and propositions accomplishes, from the viewpoint of making quantitative decisions, is to supply us with the tools of logical analysis. In this respect, set thinking may be considered as the first stage in the decision-making process. Business problems are analyzed; and if their nature requires or permits, they are broken down into a set of mutually exclusive and collectively exhaustive logical courses of action.

After a logical analysis, we must find methods for expressing a managerial problem in mathematical terms and develop techniques for finding an optimal solution to such a problem. How to accomplish this will be our objective in the remainder of this course. For this objective we must understand changes in the internal and external operations of business organizations; we must find ways for expressing such changes in quantitative terms; and we must study variations in quantities, or the so-called variables, such as inventory changes, wage rates, inputs, outputs, prices, sales, and profits. More important than that, we must study the relations among such varying quantities, or the so-called functions. In sum, to serve the process of decision-making we must study the kind of mathematics which we may, for lack of a better term, call the mathematics of varying quantities.

How can data from real-world situations be expressed in abstract algebraic terms? In what sense can algebra as a mathematical system give us empirically meaningful answers? How do analytic geometry and functions bridge the gap between abstract algebraic simplifications and the empirical world? And how can functions be used for planning, controlling, and analyzing the economics of business operations? In order to answer questions such as these we need to study the fundamentals of algebra, analytic geometry, and functions. This is done in the present Part II of the course. From the problem-solving viewpoint, we shall deal with the more specialized subjects of the mathematics of varying quantities, namely, linear programming, calculus, and probability, in the three subsequent parts of this book in that order.

Chapter 5

FUNDAMENTALS OF ALGEBRA
AND ANALYTIC GEOMETRY

ALTHOUGH the reader is likely to be quite familiar with elementary algebra and coordinate geometry, a discussion of the fundamentals of these mathematical systems may be a welcome review to many. But reviewing is neither the principal nor the sole purpose of this chapter. We shall be given the opportunity to establish logical continuity with what preceded and pave the way for what follows.

How can algebra describe an empirical situation? What is an algebraic solution from the mathematical as well as from the empirical standpoints? In other words, how can algebra give us "definite" answers with real-world meaning? Together with a review of basic algebraic operations, an attempt is made in Sections 1 and 2 to answer these questions. Sections 3 and 4 of this chapter deal with the Cartesian coordinate system, the distance formula, graphs, slopes, and the average rate of change. Thus in Chapter 5 we lay down the foundations for more specialized and empirically more meaningful topics.

1. ALGEBRAIC EQUATIONS AND THE REAL WORLD

This and the section which follows deal with algebraic equations in one unknown as a familiar introduction to analytic geometry and functions. Our immediate purpose is twofold. First, we shall explain the process of solving algebraic equations. Second, we shall show how algebra can describe real-world situations by finding algebraic equations and interpreting their solutions. Both of these topics will enable us to clearly understand in what respect algebra can give us definite answers for solving real-world problems. Furthermore, understanding equations will enable us to understand functions.

1.1. The Process of Solving Algebraic Equations. Let us focus our attention on the process of solving an equation involving a single unknown, say x. This process consists of two parts: (1) finding all values of x, called *roots*, which *satisfy* the equation; and (2) verifying that each root satisfies the equation. The first part is called *analysis* and the second is called *check*. Let us consider the following *first-degree* or *linear* equation:

Example 1.1. Solve the equation

$$(5000 + x) + (5000 + 2x) + (5000 + 3x) = 57,000.$$

Analysis:
If $(5000 + x) + (5000 + 2x) + (5000 + 3x) = 57,000$,
    then $6x + 15,000 = 57,000$, by collecting terms;
    then $6x = 42,000$, by transposition;
    then $x = 7000$, by dividing both sides by 6.
Check:
If $x = 7000$,
    then $(5000 + 7000) + (5000 + 14,000) + (5000 + 21,000) = 57,000$,
    then $12,000 + 19,000 + 26,000 = 57,000$,
    then $57,000 = 57,000$,
as required.

Before discussing the process of solving an equation shown above, let us consider a *second-degree* or *quadratic* equation:

Example 1.2. Solve the equation

$$(80 + 2x)(60 - x) = 4800.$$

Analysis:
If $(80 + 2x)(60 - x) = 4800$,
    then $4800 + 120x - 80x - 2x^2 = 4800$, by multiplication;
    then $40x - 2x^2 = 0$, by cancellation of terms;
    then $x^2 - 20x = 0$, by dividing both sides by -2;
    then $x(x - 20) = 0$, by factoring out x;
    then $x_1 = 20$ and
        $x_2 = 0$, since both values satisfy last equation.
Check:
If $x_1 = 20$,
    then $[80 + 2(20)][60 - 20] = 4800$,
    then $(120)(40) = 4800$,
    then $4800 = 4800$,
as required.
    It can be easily seen that the other root $x_2 = 0$ also satisfies the equation.

Observe that in both examples the process of solving an equation involves the application of laws governing algebraic operations, with which we assume the reader to be familiar. Checking is not a redundant operation designed to reassure the insecure reader. It is an integral part of the solution process. Furthermore, the check part of a solution is an application of the *reversibility principle*, namely, that *each step in the solving process must be reversible*. This is an important principle which can be sufficiently illustrated with the following case. It shows that multiplying both sides of an equation by a quantity involving unknowns is not always reversible.

Example 1.3. Solve the equation

$$\frac{2x}{x-2} = \frac{4}{x-2}.$$

Analysis:

If $\dfrac{2x}{x-2} = \dfrac{4}{x-2}$,

   then $2x = 4$, on multiplying by $(x-2)$;
   then $x = 2$, on dividing by 2.

Check:

If $x = 2$,

$$\text{then } \frac{2x}{x-2} = \frac{2 \cdot 2}{2-2} = \frac{4}{0},$$

which does not satisfy the original equation, since division by zero is excluded from the system of rational numbers. The original equation has no roots since the first operation in the analysis is not reversible. Number 2 is the root of the derived equation $2x = 4$, called an *extraneous* root because this equation is not equivalent to the original one.

Thus, the whole process of solving an equation is underlined by the principle of reversibility. For this principle means that each equation must imply the solution and, conversely, each solution must imply the equation; and in the sense that the solution of an algebraic equation is *implied* by the equation, in that sense algebra gives "definite" answers. The process of solving equations is the very same process of deductive reasoning whereby we begin with an equation representing a statement or a hypothesis and on the basis of the abstract laws of algebra we arrive at an implied solution or solutions.

1.2. Finding Algebraic Equations and Interpreting Their Solution. The fact that with algebra we obtain "definite" answers is important in another respect. Neither an equation nor its solution need be empirically meaningful; in other words, whether an equation and its solution have any empirical meaning is not a mathematical problem; it depends on the definition of the real-world situation under consideration. It is worth our while, therefore, to show how to express an empirical situation in terms of an algebraic equation, i.e., how to find an equation, and how to interpret its solution.

Example 1.4. During the last fiscal year the earnings of a partnership amounted to $57,000. The partnership agreement provides that the three partners shall receive $5000 each for their personal services to the firm. The remaining net profit shall be distributed so that partner A receives three times and partner B twice as much as partner C. How much income does each partner realize?

Find Equation:

Let x be the share of profits for partner C. Then the income of partner C will be ($5000 + x$), of B ($5000 + 2x$), and of A ($5000 + 3x$). Hence the equation is

$$(5000 + x) + (5000 + 2x) + (5000 + 3x) = 57,000.$$

Solve Equation:

The analysis and check parts of the solution have already been shown in Example 1.1 where $x = 7000$.

Interpret Solution:

Since C will receive $7000 in addition to the original $5000, partner B will receive $19,000 and partner A $26,000.

Observe that originally the equation and its solution in the above example was an abstract mathematical entity without real-world meaning. It became empirically meaningful as soon as we introduced the above empirical situation. Furthermore, the whole process of solving an empirical problem involves three stages: finding the equation, solving it, and interpreting the solution. Let us further illustrate these three stages.

Example 1.5. The filling station of a heating oil distributor is equipped with a main pump which can fill the tank of an oil truck in 20 minutes. In addition, an auxiliary pump is available which alone fills the tank of an oil truck in 30 minutes. This auxiliary pump is used in emergencies, such as when the main pump is out of order or when there is a waiting line of trucks. How much time does a station gain when both pumps are used together?

Find Equation:

Let x be the number of minutes it takes for both pumps to fill a tank together. Then in one minute both pumps together can fill $1/x$ of a tank. Similarly, in one minute the main pump can fill $\frac{1}{20}$ and the auxiliary $\frac{1}{30}$ of a tank. Therefore, in one minute the portion of a tank which can be filled by the main pump plus the portion of the tank which can be filled by the auxiliary pump must equal the portion of a tank which can be filled by both pumps working together; and the equation is

$$\frac{1}{20} + \frac{1}{30} = \frac{1}{x}.$$

Solve Equation:

If $\dfrac{1}{20} + \dfrac{1}{30} = \dfrac{1}{x}$,

then $3x + 2x = 60$, multiplying by $60x$;

then $x = 12$, by addition and division.

The check part of the solution is left for the reader.

Interpret Solution:
The two pumps working together can fill the tank of an oil truck in 12 minutes. Since it takes 20 minutes for the main pump working alone to do the same job, the filling station will gain 8 minutes if both pumps work together. This is a 40 percent reduction of the time required for the main pump to fill a tank alone.

Example 1.6. A businessman wishes to invest $10,000 in two types of short-term secured loans at 5 percent and 6 percent interest rate. How much should he invest in each type of loan in order to realize $285 semiannually?

Find Equation:
Let x be the amount invested at 5 percent interest rate. Then the annual income from this type of loan will be $0.05x$. Since the remaining investable sum is $10,000 − x$, the annual income from the second type of loan will be $0.06(\$10,000 − x)$. Therefore, the annual income from the first type of loan plus the annual income from the second type of loan must equal the total desired annual income of $285 \times 2 = \$570$; and the equation is

$$0.05x + 0.06(10{,}000 − x) = 570.$$

Solve Equation:
If $0.05x + 0.06(10{,}000 − x) = 570$,
   then $0.05x + 600 − 0.06x = 570$,
   and $x = \dfrac{30}{0.01} = 3000$.

The reader may supply the omitted steps of the analysis and check the solution.

Interpret Solution:
In order to realize $285 semiannually, the businessman should invest $3000 at 5 percent and $7000 at 6 percent interest rate.

Example 1.7. The manager of a real estate firm faces the problem of deciding the monthly rental he should charge for each of the 60 newly built apartment units. His past experience tells him that at $80 rental per month, all apartments units will be occupied, but for each $2.00 increase in rent, one apartment unit is likely to remain vacant. Since service and maintenance costs are higher for occupied than for vacant apartments, he realizes that he can increase his profit margin by raising the monthly rental and still collect the same total rental of $4800. How much rental should he charge and how many apartment units are likely to remain vacant at the higher rent?

Find Equation:
Let x be the number of vacant apartment units. Then the number of occupied apartments will be $(60 − x)$ and the rental for each occupied unit will be ($80 + $2x$). Since the new rent times the number of occupied apartments should equal the total rent of $4800, the equation is

$$(80 + 2x)(60 − x) = 4800.$$

Solve Equation:
This equation has been found to be equivalent to

$$x^2 - 20x = 0$$

and has been solved in Example 1.2 where $x_1 = 20$ and $x_2 = 0$. Here, we shall solve it again using the familiar quadratic formula

$$x = \frac{-b \pm \sqrt{b^2 - 4ac}}{2a}.$$

Since $a = 1$, $b = -20$, and $c = 0$, we have

$$x = \frac{20 \pm \sqrt{400}}{2} = \frac{20 \pm 20}{2}$$

where $x_1 = 20$ and $x_2 = 0$, as previously.

Interpret Solution:
When all apartments are occupied then $x_2 = 0$ and the manager realizes $4800 total rental. However, he can realize the same total rental and increase his profit margin by raising the monthly rental per unit to $120 = [\$80 + \$2(20)]$ when $x_1 = 20$, i.e., when 20 apartment units are vacant.

1.3. Recapitulation.

The above examples illustrate how physical relations among varying quantities can be translated into algebraic equations and a solution be found which has empirical meaning. In each case three stages are involved. First, on the basis of an empirical situation, we form an equation. Second, we solve this equation using algebraic operations. Third, depending on the definition of the empirical situation, we give physical meaning to the results of the solution. In this manner we obtain "definite" answers which have real-world meaning.

It is important to realize, however, that in carrying out the second stage of solving each equation we can forget all about the empirical meaning of the known and unknown quantities. For in solving equations in general, the unknown x may represent a positive, negative, irrational, or imaginary number. On the other hand, in the illustrative examples the unknown x may represent positive numbers or zero only. In addition, knowledge of the empirical situation is needed in order to form each equation and interpret the results, but this knowledge plays no part whatsoever in the actual process of solving each equation. This task is accomplished by a judicious use of abstract laws governing algebraic operations. Thus, algebra may not give us empirically meaningful answers. We shall see that for problems in business and economics, algebraic solutions are rarely meaningful unless they represent zero or positive numbers.

In sum, solving equations is a mathematical problem, while interpreting equations and their solution is an empirical one.

PROBLEMS

For each of the following word Problems 1.1–1.16, (i) find the equation; (ii) solve it; and (iii) interpret the result(s).

*1.1. A train of 90 loaded freight cars must be sent to their destination. Two engines, however, must be used because a single engine is not powerful enough to haul the whole train. Since one engine is three times as powerful as the other and since there are certain scheduling advantages in forming two separate trains, how many freight cars should be assigned to each train?

*1.2. A commercial bank officer contemplates investing $500,000 in two different types of short-term loans to industrial firms—loans without security at 6 percent interest and secured loans at 4.5 percent. He wishes to realize an annual return of 5 percent from his loans and keep the amount invested in unsecured loans to a minimum in order to reduce his risk. If the sum is invested in lots of $1000, how much should the bank officer invest in each type of loan?

1.3. A real estate broker knows that an industrial firm is willing to pay $210,000 for a choice piece of land suitable for building a new plant. How much should the broker pay the owner of the land if he wants to make a 5 percent commission on the owner's selling price?

*1.4. An item costing $20 was marked up to the selling price S. Because the item did not move fast enough it was marked down 30 percent off the selling price, yet the businessman made a 5 percent profit on the original cost. What was the markup selling price?

1.5. A coffee roasting and distributing firm uses two grades of coffee beans to prepare the blend for which the company is well known, grade A costing $0.55 per pound and grade B at $0.35 per pound. Experimental and survey research has shown that the proportions of each grade of coffee need not be kept fixed in order to secure the desired quality of the final product and that price stability of the blended coffee is important for the long-run growth of sales.

  *a) What should be the cost of the blended coffee per pound if its selling price is $0.70 and management thinks that a 40 percent margin on cost is sufficient to cover all roasting and distribution costs and also secure a profit at the expected sales volume?

  *b) For the cost determined in (a), how many pounds of each grade should be used for every 100 pounds of blended coffee?

  c) Find the answers to (a) and (b) assuming that the selling price of the blended coffee is $0.63 per pound.

1.6. A small earth dam can be completed by one earth-moving tractor in 20 workdays and by another tractor in 30 workdays. How long will it take to finish the dam if both tractors are used?

1.7. Worker A finishes an assignment alone in 60 minutes. With the assistance of worker B, however, the assignment is finished in 24 minutes. Which worker is more efficient?

1.8. The sales volume of firm A increases $2000 and of firm B $2500 each month. If firm A has an initial annual sales volume of $420,000 and firm B $360,000, how many months will it take for the sales of firm B to catch up with the sales of firm A?

1.9. A publisher spends $5000 to prepare a book and make the plates for printing it. He also pays $500 for each 100 copies printed. If the book sells for $10 a copy, how many copies must the publisher sell before making a profit?

*1.10. The cost of tooling to manufacture a new mechanical toy made of plastic is $500. It costs an additional $40 for each 100 units produced. If the toy retails for $0.95 per unit, how many toys should be sold for the manufacturer to make a 10 percent profit based on the manufacturing cost?

*1.11. For every $100 invested in secured commercial loans a bank receives $112.36 every two years which represents capital and interest compounded annually. What is the rate of interest?

1.12. For reasons unknown the new management of a store selling electrical appliances is unable to find the original inventory of a certain type of radio as well as its selling price. The record, however, shows that sales revenue amounted to $6000 which is equal to the amount paid to purchase the original inventory, that the radio was sold at $10 profit each, and that 100 of them were still unsold. Find the original inventory and the selling price of this item.

1.13. Clerk A can do an assignment alone in 10 minutes less time than it takes clerk B to do the same assignment alone. If both work together, however, the assignment is done in 12 minutes. How long does it take for each clerk to do the same assignment alone?

*1.14. A rancher can sell 200 steers of average weight 1200 pounds each at a profit of $0.04 per pound. From past experience he knows that each steer gains 40 pounds per week, while his profit is not likely to decrease more than $\frac{1}{10}$ of a cent per pound per week. This time, however, he has reason to believe that if he waits for a while, he might be able to make a larger profit. For how long can he wait before his profit declines below the profit he can realize now?

1.15. When ski conditions are "good" to "excellent" a railroad company runs a special weekend ski train from Boston to a town in the North which is well known for its winter sports facilities. A fare of $10 per person is charged for the round trip under the assumption that at least 200 persons make use of the special service. The economist of the company who studied past records points out that the demand for this type of transport service is quite elastic since the number of passengers is likely to increase by 20 for every $0.50 reduction in the train fare. An increase in the number of passengers, however, creates some additional costs for running the train. Since the manager of the railroad believes that it is to the long-run interest of the carrier to serve the largest group of passengers possible, he decides to absorb these additional costs and reduce the fare as long as gross receipts remain unchanged at $2000 per run. How much should he reduce the train fare and how many passengers are likely to be served then?

1.16. A production run to manufacture 800 units of an important part of an automobile engine costs $3200. For every increase of five units, however, cost is reduced by one cent. How many more units can be produced in each production run for the same initial cost and what would be the cost per unit for this larger production run?

1.17. Select any of the previous Problems 1.1–1.16 and write down the "analysis" and "check" steps of its solution in the form of a valid biconditional argument. Discuss your answer in the light of the proposition that "solving equations is a mathematical problem while interpreting the results is an empirical one."

1.18. Given the analysis step of the following solutions, determine whether the root(s) you are given are the roots of the original equation and explain your answer.

a) Solve $\sqrt{x + 10} = -5$.
   Analysis:
   If $\sqrt{x + 10} = -5$,
      then $x + 10 = 25$, by squaring both sides;
      then $x = 15$.

b) Solve $\sqrt{x - 4} = 4$.
   Analysis:
   If $\sqrt{x - 4} = 4$,
      then $x - 4 = 16$, by squaring both sides;
      then $x = 20$.

c) Solve $x = \dfrac{5}{x - 4}$.
   Analysis:

   If $x = \dfrac{5}{x - 4}$,

      then $x^2 - 4x = 5$, on multiplying both sides by $x - 4$;
      then $x^2 - 4x - 5 = 0$, by transposition;

      then $x = \dfrac{4 \pm \sqrt{16 + 20}}{2}$, by quadratic formula; $x_1 = 5$ and

   $x_2 = -1$.

2. ALGEBRAIC OPERATIONS WITH EQUATIONS

Now that we have established the connection between algebra and the real world, let us examine some of the tools which are part of the mathematical system of algebra. We shall have a quick review of basic rules governing algebraic operations and of methods for solving equations in one unknown.

2.1. Basic Rules Governing Operations with Equations.

In the course of our discussion we have used algebraic operations. Such algebraic manipulations and all proved theorems in algebra are based on laws called *axioms* or *postulates*. Thus ordinary algebra is a mathematical system based on abstract laws similar to the laws of Boolean algebra considered in Part I. For a systematic review of the number system of algebra and its laws, the reader may find it useful to read reference 6 cited at the end of this chapter, especially pp. 55–56. Here, we shall merely summarize the rules of elementary operations with equations most of which have already been used and all of which are based on the *principle of reversibility* of algebraic operations or the *assumption that a solution exists.*

1. *A term may be transferred (transposed) from one side of an equation to the other if and only if its sign is changed.*

    Thus $6x + 15,000 = 57,000$ in Example 1.1 becomes $6x = 57,000 - 15,000$, or $6x = 42,000$, by transposition.

2. *Both sides of an equation may be multiplied or divided by a nonzero constant.*

    Hence, $6x = 42,000$ becomes $x = 7000$ by dividing both sides of the equation by 6 or multiplying them by $\frac{1}{6}$.

3. *If $a^2 = b^2$, then $a = \pm b$.*

    This step, like the previous two, is reversible, since its converse is also true, i.e., if $a = \pm b$, then $a^2 = b^2$. For example, if $x^2 = 4$, then $x = \pm 2$; and if $x = \pm 2$, then $x^2 = (\pm 2)^2 = 4$.

4. *Multiplying or dividing both sides of an equation by a quantity involving unknowns or squaring both members of an equation must be used with caution because they are not always reversible steps.*

We have already illustrated the application of the last rule in Example 1.3. Two additional examples follow.

Example 2.1. Solve $2x^2 = 4x$.
Analysis:
If $2x^2 = 4x$,
  then $x = 2$, on dividing by $2x$.
Check:
If $x = 2$,
  then $2 \cdot 2^2 = 4 \cdot 2$,
  and $8 = 8$.
Although number 2 *is* a root of the original equation, there happens to be another root, namely 0, which has been lost in the process. Hence, dividing both sides of the equation by a quantity such as $2x$ which contains the unknown x is an *irreversible* step.

Example 2.2. Solve $\sqrt{x - 2} = -2$.
Analysis:
If $\sqrt{x - 2} = -2$,

then $x - 2 = 4$, by squaring both sides;
and $x = 6$.
Check:
If $x = 6$,
  then $\sqrt{6 - 2} = -2$,
  then $\sqrt{4} = -2$,
  and $2 \neq -2$,
since the square root sign refers to the *nonnegative* square root of 4. Therefore, the original equation does not have a real root. In this case, squaring both sides of the equation is a nonreversible step.

Generally speaking, if the derived equation contains fewer roots than the given equation such as in Example 2.1, the derived equation is called *defective*. On the other hand, if the derived equation has more roots than the original equation like the case shown in Example 2.2, the derived equation is called *redundant.*

In our later work we shall be given the opportunity to further illustrate the importance of the reversibility principle in algebraic operations. A list of frequently committed wrong operations appears as an exercise for the reader in Problem 2.5.

2.2. Solving Quadratic Equations.   There are three basic methods for solving algebraically a quadratic equation of the form

(2.1)
$$ax^2 + bx + c = 0,$$

where a, b, and c are given constants, $a \neq 0$, and x is an unknown number. These methods are *factoring, completing the square,* and using the *quadratic formula.*

I. Factoring.   A simple factoring operation was employed in solving the second degree equation in Example 1.2. Here, we shall further illustrate how to solve quadratic equations by applying four additional forms for factoring polynomials.

Case 1: $x^2 + 2ax + a^2 = (x + a)(x + a) = (x + a)^2$.

A)   When $a > 0$

Example 2.3. Solve $x^2 + 6x + 9 = 0$.
Analysis:
If $x^2 + 6x + 9 = 0$,
  then $x^2 + 2 \cdot 3x + 3^2 = 0$,
  then $(x + 3)(x + 3) = 0$,
  or $(x + 3)^2 = 0$.
Therefore $x = -3$, which is called the *double root* of the equation.

The check step for the above solution, as well as for subsequent cases, is left for the reader.

B) When $a < 0$

Example 2.4. Solve $2x^2 - 16x + 32 = 0$.
Analysis:
If $2x^2 - 16x + 32 = 0$,
    then $x^2 - 8x + 16 = 0$, on dividing by 2,
    then $x^2 + 2 \cdot (-4)x + (-4)^2 = 0$,
    then $(x - 4)(x - 4) = 0$,
    then $(x - 4)^2 = 0$,
    and $x = 4$.
    a double root as previously.

Case 2: $x^2 - a^2 = (x + a)(x - a)$.

Example 2.5. Solve $x^2 - 16 = 0$.
Analysis:
If $x^2 - 16 = 0$,
    then $(x + 4)(x - 4) = 0$.
Setting each factor equal to zero, we have $(x + 4) = 0$ and $(x - 4) = 0$.
Hence, $x_1 = -4$ and $x_2 = 4$ are the roots of the equation.

Equations of the general form $x^2 - a^2 = 0$, such as $x^2 - 16 = 0$ in the above example, are called *pure quadratic*. They can be solved by transposition and then taking the square root.

Example 2.6. Solve $x^2 - 16 = 0$
Analysis:
If $x^2 - 16 = 0$,
    then $x^2 = 16$, by transposition;
    and $x = \pm 4$, by taking the square root.
The answer is the same as in Example 2.5.

Pure quadratic equations of the general form $x^2 + a^2 = 0$ involve imaginary roots. For example $x^2 + 16 = 0$ has roots $\pm 4i$, where $i = \sqrt{-1}$. Inasmuch as we are interested in the mathematics of varying quantities for solving real-world problems from business and economics, in this course we shall be primarily concerned with algebra in the *real number system*.

Case 3: $x^2 + (b + d)x + bd = (x + b)(x + d)$.

Example 2.7. Solve $x^2 + 6x + 8 = 0$.
Analysis:
If $x^2 + 6x + 8 = 0$,
    then $x^2 + (2 + 4)x + 2 \cdot 4 = 0$,
    then $(x + 2)(x + 4) = 0$.
Hence, $x_1 = -2$ and $x_2 = -4$ are the roots of the equation.

Case 4: $acx^2 + (ad + bc)x + bd = (ax + b)(cx + d)$.

Example 2.8. Solve $6x^2 + x = 12$.
Analysis:
If $6x^2 + x = 12$,
  then $6x^2 + x - 12 = 0$, expressed in standard form;
  then $(3\cdot2)x^2 + [3\cdot3 + 2\cdot(-4)]x + (-4)\cdot3 = 0$,
  where $a = 3$, $c = 2$, $b = -4$, and $d = 3$;
  then $(3x - 4)(2x + 3) = 0$, since $(ad + bc) = 3\cdot3 + (-4)\cdot2 = 1$.
Setting each factor equal to zero, we obtain

$$3x - 4 = 0 \qquad\qquad 2x + 3 = 0$$
$$3x = 4 \qquad\qquad 2x = -3$$
$$x_1 = \frac{4}{3} \qquad\qquad x_2 = -\frac{3}{2},$$

the roots of the equation.

The reader may observe that application of this form of factoring requires some trial and error. The coefficient of x^2 and the constant term of the equation must be expressed in pairs of factors, and a combination of them must be selected for which the sum of the cross products is the coefficient of the middle term.

II. Completing the Square. Consider the polynomial (2.1) of the general form $x^2 + 2ax + a^2$ used in factoring case 1. Note that this polynomial is equal to $(x + a)^2$. Thus we may conclude that an expression of the form $x^2 + 2ax$ can become a perfect square as follows:

$$x^2 + 2ax + \left(\frac{2a}{2}\right)^2 = x^2 + 2ax + a^2 = (x + a)^2,$$

i.e., by adding the square of half the coefficient of x.

Example 2.9. Solve $2x^2 - 7x + 5 = 0$ by completing the square.
Analysis:
If $2x^2 - 7x + 5 = 0$,
  then $2x^2 - 7x = -5$, by transposing 5;
  then $x^2 - \frac{7}{2}x = -\frac{5}{2}$, on dividing by 2;
  then $x^2 - \frac{7}{2}x + (\frac{7}{4})^2 = -\frac{5}{2} + (\frac{7}{4})^2$, by adding $(\frac{7}{4})^2$ to both sides in order to complete the square;
  then $(x - \frac{7}{4})^2 = \frac{9}{16}$, by factoring and addition of common factors;
  then $(x - \frac{7}{4}) = \pm\frac{3}{4}$, by taking the square root;
  then $x = (7 \pm 3)/4$, by transposition and addition of common fractions;
  hence, $x_1 = 2\frac{1}{2}$ and $x_2 = 1$, the roots of the equation.

III. Quadratic Formula. The use of the quadratic formula in Example 1.7 has already been illustrated for solving a second-degree equation of the form $ax^2 + bx = 0$. The following example illustrates the formula's use for solving equations of the form $ax^2 + bx + c = 0$.

Example 2.10. Solve $2x^2 - 7x + 5 = 0$ by the quadratic formula

$$x = \frac{-b \pm \sqrt{b^2 - 4ac}}{2a}.$$

Analysis:
If $2x^2 - 7x + 5 = 0$,

then $x = \dfrac{-(-7) \pm \sqrt{(-7)^2 - 4 \cdot 2 \cdot 5}}{2 \cdot 2}$, where $a = 2$, $b = -7$, and $c = 5$;

$$= \frac{7 \pm \sqrt{9}}{4} = \frac{7 \pm 3}{4},$$

Hence, $x_1 = 2\frac{1}{2}$ and $x_2 = 1$
as previously.

2.3. Solving Equations of Higher Degree.
The quadratic formula guarantees that a second-degree equation can always be solved by expressing the roots of the equation in terms of the coefficients. Formulas exist for finding the roots of third-degree or *cubic* and fourth-degree or *quartic* equations. For algebraic solutions of general cubic and quartic equations the reader is referred to reference 6, pp. 327–31, in this chapter's bibliography. Niels H. Abel (1802–29), a Norwegian mathematician, at the age of 22 proved that it is impossible to write the roots of the general equation of degree higher than four in terms of the coefficients. His proof is a striking example of the unique power of deductive reasoning used in mathematics. It removes once and for all any possibility that someone some day, using inductive reasoning, may find such a formula.

This discovery was not a contradiction to the Fundamental Theorem of Algebra proved in 1799 by the famous German mathematician Karl F. Gauss, which states that every polynomial equation with coefficients from the complex number system has a root in that system. In the first place, we shall show later that the real roots of an equation with real coefficients can be approximated graphically. Furthermore, digital computers made possible the efficient use of numerical methods and procedures for approximately finding the roots of an equation of degree higher than four.

PROBLEMS

2.1. Solve the following equations:

a) $3x - 7 = x + 5$.

b) $3x + 4 = x + 13$.

c) $7x + 20 = 3x + 10$.

d) $2x^2 + 8 = 5x^2 - 19$.

e) $x^2 - 10 = 2x^2 - 55$.

f) $4x^2 - 9 = 9x^2 - 22$.

2.2. Solve and determine whether the roots you have found satisfy the given equation. Indicate whether the derived equation is defective or redundant.

a) $\dfrac{3x}{x-4} = \dfrac{12}{x-4}$.

e) $\sqrt{x^2 - 1} = -1$.

b) $\dfrac{15}{x-3} = \dfrac{3x}{x-3}$.

f) $\sqrt{x^2 - 3} = 3$.

c) $\sqrt{x-3} = -3$.

g) $x - 5 = \sqrt{x-3}$.

d) $\sqrt{x+7} = -5$.

h) $\sqrt{x-4} = \sqrt{x} + 4$.

2.3. Solve and determine whether the roots you have found satisfy the given equation. Indicate whether the derived equation is defective or redundant.

a) $x = \dfrac{30}{x-7}$.

d) $\dfrac{x^2}{(x-5)(x+1)} - \dfrac{5}{(x-5)} = -\dfrac{5}{(x-5)(x+1)}$.

b) $\dfrac{x}{2-x} = \dfrac{2}{x-2}$.

e) $\dfrac{1}{x} + \dfrac{1}{x+1} = \dfrac{1}{x+2}$.

c) $\dfrac{x}{6-x} = \dfrac{3}{x-6}$.

f) $\dfrac{x^2}{(x-2)(x-3)} - \dfrac{2}{(x-2)} = \dfrac{6}{(x-2)(x-3)}$.

2.4. Solve and determine whether the derived equation is defective or redundant.

a) $\sqrt{x^2 + 6x + 33} = 2x + 3$.

b) $\sqrt{10x^2 + 6x + 2} = 3x + 2$.

c) $\sqrt{5x^2 + 4x - 11} = 5 + 2x$.

d) $\sqrt{2x+4} = \sqrt{2x-4} + 2$.

e) $\sqrt{3x+1} = 3 - \sqrt{x-4}$.

f) $\sqrt{3x+4} = 2 - \sqrt{2x-4}$.

2.5. Consider the operations listed below:

a) $\dfrac{3}{0} \neq 0$.

b) $|-5| \neq -5$.

c) $4^2 \cdot 4^3 \neq 16^5$.

d) $a^2 \cdot b^4 \neq (ab)^6$.

e) $a + (2x - y) \neq a + 2x + y$.

f) $x - 5(y + z) \neq x - 5y - z$.

g) $5 - (-2) \neq 5 - 2$.

h) $3a + 5b \neq 8ab$.

i) $4x^{-1} \neq \dfrac{1}{4x}$.

j) $\sqrt{x^2 + y^2} \neq x + y$.

k) $\dfrac{x+y}{x+w} \neq \dfrac{y}{w}$.

l) $\dfrac{1}{x-y} \neq -\dfrac{1}{x+y}$.

m) $\dfrac{x}{y} + \dfrac{z}{w} \neq \dfrac{x+z}{y+w}$.

n) $\dfrac{xa+xb}{x+xc} \div x \neq \dfrac{a+b}{1+c}$.

o) $x\left(\dfrac{a}{b}\right) \neq \dfrac{ax}{bx}$.

p) $\sqrt{-x} \cdot \sqrt{-y} \neq \sqrt{xy}$, where x and y are not both positive numbers.

The sign $\neq$ means that the left-hand side is not equal to the right-hand side. The sign $|x|$ refers to the absolute value of x. The *absolute value* of a number refers to the corresponding positive number; thus the absolute value of -2 is 2 and the absolute value of 2 is 2. The absolute value of zero is zero. Explain any mistakes committed in carrying out the above listed operations and give the correct answer, if any, to each one.

2.6. Solve:

*a) $x^2 - 25 = 0$.   *d) $x^2 + 45 = 0$.

*b) $x^2 + 25 = 0$.   e) $x^2 + 8x + 16 = 0$.

c) $x^2 - 45 = 0$.   f) $x^2 + 2x + 4 = 0$.

2.7. Solve by factoring and check:

*a) $x^2 - x - 6 = 0$.   e) $2x^2 - x - 6 = 0$.

*b) $-x^2 + 5x - 6 = 0$.   f) $5x^2 + 20x + 15 = 0$.

c) $x^2 + 5x + 6 = 0$.   *g) $9x^2 + 12x + 4 = 0$.

d) $x^2 + \frac{5}{6}x + \frac{1}{6} = 0$.   h) $6x^2 - 5x - 6 = 0$.

2.8. Solve by completing the square:

*a) $x^2 + 6x = 0$.   e) $-x^2 + 2x + 6 = 0$.

*b) $x^2 - 8x = 20$.   f) $x^2 - 5x + 6 = 0$.

c) $x^2 - 16x - 36 = 0$.   g) $-2x^2 + 5x + 12 = 0$.

d) $x^2 - 6x - 2 = 0$.   h) $2x^2 = 20 - 18x$.

2.9. Verify your answer to any of the exercises in Problems 2.6 through 2.8, making use of the quadratic formula.

2.10. Solve by factoring:

*a) $x^3 - x = 0$.

*b) $x^3 - 1 = 0$.

*c) $x^4 - 1 = 0$. (*Hint:* let $u = x^2$.)

d) $x^4 - 16 = 0$.

e) $x^3 - 8 = 0$.

f) $(x-2)^4 - 4(x-2)^2 - 5 = 0$. (*Hint:* let $u = (x-2)^2$.)

g) $(x^3 - 1) + (2x^2 + x - 3) = 0$. (*Hint:* Factor each expression in parentheses and extract the common factor.)

2.11. Algebraic equations in one unknown may be written in standard polynomial form as the following general equations indicate:

The general linear equation in x:

$ax + b = 0$ ($a \neq 0$), or $a_0 x + a_1 = 0$ ($a_0 \neq 0$).

The general quadratic equation in x:

$ax^2 + bx + c = 0$ ($a \neq 0$),

  or $a_0 x^2 + a_1 x + a_2 = 0$ ($a_0 \neq 0$). And

The general equation of nth degree in x:
$$a_0x^n + a_1x^{n-1} + a_2x^{n-2} + \ldots + a_{n-1}x + a_n = 0 \ (a_0 \neq 0),$$
where $a, b, a_0, a_1, a_2, \ldots a_{n-1}, a_n$ are constants.
Write each equation given below in standard form and state its degree.
a) $5x^4 + 3x^3 + x^2 - 7 = 5x^2(x^2 + x) - 2x^3 - x + 6.$
b) $2x^3 + 3x^2 - 1 = x^2(2x + 3) - 5x + 7.$
c) $x^2(3x^2 - x) - x(x - 5) + 10 = 3x^4 - 2x^3 - 7x^2 - x + 5.$
d) $x(7x^2 + 3x + 1) = 3x^2 + x - 5.$
e) Write the general equations of your answer to (c) and (d) above.
f) Write the general equations of degree 4 and 5.

2.12. Let the roots of the general quadratic equation $ax^2 + bx + c = 0$ $(a \neq 0)$ be

$$r_1 = \frac{-b + \sqrt{b^2 - 4ac}}{2a} \quad \text{and} \quad r_2 = \frac{-b - \sqrt{b^2 - 4ac}}{2a},$$

a) Then prove that

$$r_1 + r_2 = -\frac{b}{a} \quad \text{and} \quad r_1r_2 = \frac{c}{a}.$$

b) Find the sum and product of the roots without solving:
  i) $x^2 + 2x + 1 = 0.$
  ii) $2x^2 - x - 6 = 0.$
  iii) $15x^2 + x - 2 = 0.$
c) Find r_2 and the value of k when—
  i) $x^2 + 2x + k = 0$ and $r_1 = 3.$
  ii) $2x^2 - kx + 5 = 0$ and $r_1 = 1.$
  iii) $2kx^2 - 3x + 2k = 0$ and $r_1 = 2.$

2.13. a) Let r_1 and r_2 be the roots as defined in Problem 2.12. Then prove that $ax^2 + bx + c = a(x - r_1)(x - r_2)$. (*Hint:* Factor out a in $ax^2 + bx + c$ and substitute for $r_1 + r_2$ and r_1r_2.)
b) Let $r_1 = \frac{1}{3}, r_2 = -\frac{2}{3}$. Then form a quadratic equation with integral coefficients having the given roots: From part (a) above we have

$$a\left(x - \frac{1}{3}\right)\left(x + \frac{2}{3}\right) = 0.$$

Letting $a = 3 \cdot \frac{3}{2}$ and substituting we obtain

$$3\left(x - \frac{1}{3}\right) \cdot \frac{3}{2}\left(x + \frac{2}{3}\right) = 0,$$

$$(3x - 1)\left(\frac{3}{2}x + 1\right) = 0,$$

$$\frac{9}{2}x^2 + \frac{3}{2}x - 1 = 0,$$

$$9x^2 + 3x - 2 = 0.$$

Following the above example, form quadratic equations with integral coefficients having indicated roots:

*i) $2, -3$.

ii) $\frac{1}{2}, -\frac{1}{3}$.

iii) $\pm 2\sqrt{5}$.

iv) $2 \pm \sqrt{3}$.

*v) $3 \pm 3i$.

vi) $1 \pm i\sqrt{5}$.

3. THE TWO BASIC IDEAS OF ANALYTIC GEOMETRY

Until the seventeenth century algebra and Euclidean geometry were studied separately, since it was thought that the former dealt with numbers but the latter with points and lines in space. Analytic or coordinate geometry or Cartesian geometry, named after the French mathematician and philosopher Rene Descartes who introduced it in 1637, marked a turning point in the development of mathematics. On the one hand, it supplied a unified approach to a more systematic study of both subjects. On the other hand, it became part of the foundations on which the calculus was developed.

In this section we shall explain how this union of algebra and geometry was accomplished. For this purpose, we shall first discuss the distance between points on a scaled line and the midpoint formula. Then, we shall explain the two basic ideas (theorems) of Euclidean geometry from which all of plane analytic geometry follows, namely, the Cartesian coordinate system and the distance formula.

3.1. The Distance between Points on a Scaled Line.

Let the scaled straight line in Figure 3.1 be given, where there is one-to-one correspondence between the set of points on the line and the set of

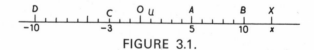

FIGURE 3.1.

real numbers (an idea to be fully explained shortly). The positive direction on the line is determined by a point O with coordinate zero and a point U with coordinate one.

Let X be any point on the line with coordinate x, then the directed line segment from the initial point O to the terminal point X is denoted by $\overline{OX}$. The line segment is _positively_ directed if, and only if, X is to the right-hand side of point O; otherwise it is _negatively_ directed. The _directed distance_ from O to X is the coordinate x whose sign agrees with the designated direction on $\overline{OX}$.

Example 3.1. Given the points $A(5)$, $B(10)$, $C(-3)$, and $D(-10)$ in Figure 3.1, find the directed distance of $\overline{AB}$, $\overline{BA}$, $\overline{AD}$, and $\overline{DA}$.

Solution:

$$\overline{AB} = 10 - 5 = 5; \qquad \overline{BA} = 5 - 10 = -5;$$
$$\overline{AD} = (-10) - 5 = -15; \qquad \overline{DA} = 5 - (-10) = 15.$$

The *absolute value* or the *magnitude* of the real number x is the distance between O and X, or the length of the line segment OX, denoted by $|OX|$. It is defined by

$$|OX| = |x|, \text{ where } |x| = \begin{cases} x \text{ if } x \geqslant 0 \\ -x \text{ if } x < 0. \end{cases}$$

Example 3.2. Given the points $A(5)$ and $B(10)$, find the distance $|AB|$ and $|BA|$.

Solution:

$$|AB| = |10 - 5| = 5,$$
$$|BA| = |5 - 10| = 5.$$

Observe that $|AB| = |BA|$, i.e., the distance or length of the line from point A to point B is 5 since $|10 - 5| = |5 - 10| = 5$; but $\overline{AB} \neq \overline{BA}$ since the directed distance from A to B is $10 - 5 = 5$ units, while the directed distance from B to A is $5 - 10 = -5$.

3.2. The Midpoint Formula.

Closely associated with the distance between two points is the formula for finding the midpoint of a line segment.

Let x' be the coordinate of the midpoint between two different points on a scaled line shown in Figure 3.2 with coordinates x_1 and x_2. Then

$$x' = \frac{x_1 + x_2}{2}.$$

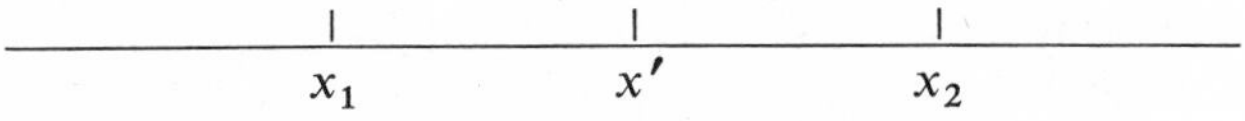

FIGURE 3.2.

Proof:

Case 1:   Let $x_1 < x' < x_2$. Then the distance $x' - x_1$ and $x_2 - x'$ are positive; and since x' is the coordinate of the midpoint, we have

$$x' - x_1 = x_2 - x'$$
$$x' + x' = x_1 + x_2$$
$$2x' = x_1 + x_2$$
$$x' = \frac{x_1 + x_2}{2}$$

as required.

It is left for the reader to prove Case 2, where $x_1 > x' > x_2$.

Example 3.3. Find the coordinate of the midpoint between points $A(5)$ and $D(-10)$ shown in Figure 3.1.

Solution:

Since $x_1 = 5$ and $x_2 = -10$, substituting in the midpoint formula we have

$$x' = \frac{5 + (-10)}{2} = -2.5,$$

The midpoint formula is a geometric interpretation of the arithmetic mean, a statistical measure of central tendency. The reader will find exercises on the simple and weighted arithmetic mean among the problems of this section.

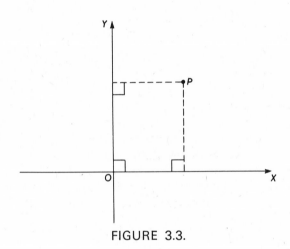

FIGURE 3.3.

3.3. The Rectangular Coordinate System. This first basic idea of plane analytic geometry states that *there is one-to-one correspondence between the set of all points on a given plane and the set of all ordered pairs (x, y) of real numbers.*

Let two straight lines intersect each other at right angles at point O, called the *origin*, on a given plane, shown in Figure 3.3. As a matter of pure convention line X, called the X-axis, is drawn horizontally and line Y, called the Y-axis, vertically. Also, it is important to realize that these lines extend indefinitely in either direction and do not have finite length.

From the geometric standpoint we can locate any point P on the plane by starting from the origin O and moving along the X-axis up to point P_x and then along the line segment P_xP parallel to the Y-axis. Also, we can locate the same point P by following the alternate route OP_yP.

Now, let a real number be assigned to each point on the X-axis. Then to each and every point on this line one and only one number is assigned from the infinite set R of real numbers. In a similar fashion to each and every point on the Y-axis one and only one number is assigned from the set R of all real numbers.

Thus, a point such as P on the plane in Figure 3.3 can be located on the plane shown in Figure 3.4 by the corresponding ordered number pair (x, y); in other words, a point P on the plane has two identities: a capital letter, such as P, representing its *location* and an ordered pair of real numbers, such as (x, y), indicating its *location address*. The x-coordinate of P is called the *abscissa* and the y-coordinate the *ordinate*.

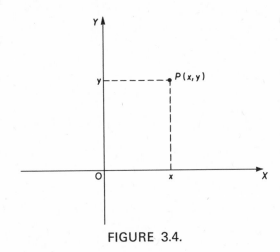

FIGURE 3.4.

This one-to-one correspondence between points and number pairs is called *rectangular coordinate system* in the plane. A plane, together with a coordinate system, is called *Cartesian coordinate plane*, henceforth abbreviated to cc-plane.

Example 3.4. Plot the points $A(4, 3)$, $B(-5, 3)$, $C(-5, -2)$, and $D(4, -2)$ on a cc-plane.
Solution:
The results are shown in Figure 3.5. In each case we locate the given value of x and y on their respective axes and from each such point we draw a line perpendicular to the x- and y-axis, respectively. The designated point is located at the intersection of the two perpendicular lines.

The x and y coordinate axes divide a plane into four regions called *quadrants*, as shown in Figure 3.5. For a point P not lying on the x-axis there are two possibilities for the sign of the coordinate y: $y > 0$ or $y < 0$. Similarly, for a point P not lying on the y-axis there are two possibilities for the sign of the coordinate x: $x > 0$ or $x < 0$. Hence, for a point P not lying on either axis there are four possibilities as shown in Figure 3.5. It is important to remember that since algebraic solutions are rarely empirically meaningful, unless they represent zero or positive numbers, the first quadrant is the most frequently used.

There is another way of understanding this first basic idea of analytic geometry. A pair of real numbers in which one number is distinguished as the first and the other, which need not be different, as the second is called an ordered number pair or an *ordered two-tuple*. For example, (1, 2) is an ordered two-tuple which is different from (2, 1) since the

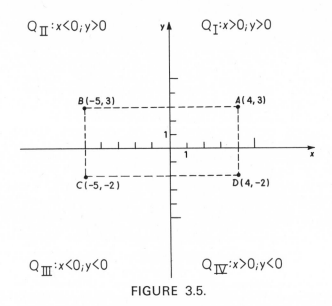

FIGURE 3.5.

order in which the two numbers appear is important. An ordered number pair (for that matter any other object) is quite different from the set {1, 2} which is the same as the set {2, 1} since in listing elements of a set order is immaterial. Let sets $P = \{4, -5\}$ and $Q = \{3, -2\}$ be given. Then $P \times Q$, called the *Cartesian product set* is the set of order two-tuples $\{(4, 3), (4, -2), (-5, 3), (-5, -2)\}$. Note that each element-ordered two-tuple of this set represents the coordinates of a point on a cc-plane as shown in Figure 3.5.

Now consider the infinite set of all real numbers

$$R = \{x | x \text{ any real number}\}.$$

Let R be the set of all real numbers; and let each number of set R be assigned to one and only one point on the X-axis in Figure 3.3. Also, let the numbers of another set R be assigned to the points on the Y-axis on the same one-to-one basis. Then the Cartesian product set $R \times R$ will span the plane in Figure 3.3 so that each ordered two-tuple will correspond to one and only one point on the cc-plane in Figure 3.4.

3.4. The Distance Formula. This is the second basic idea of plane analytic geometry. Let the right triangle PRQ shown in Figure 3.6 be given, where the line segment PQ is its hypotenuse. By the well-known Pythagorean theorem the length of the line segment PQ is

$$|PQ|^2 = |PR|^2 + |QR|^2, \text{ or}$$

(3.1)
$$\boxed{|PQ| = \sqrt{|PR|^2 + |QR|^2}.}$$

Formula (3.1) represents a geometric interpretation of the distance of the line segment PQ.

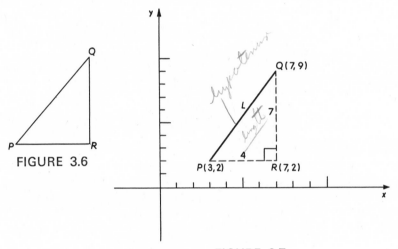

FIGURE 3.6

FIGURE 3.7.

Let PQ be the line segment given above, but now on a cc-plane as shown in Figure 3.7, where $P(3, 2)$ and $Q(7, 9)$. Starting at point P which is 3 units to the right of the y-axis we must move $(7 - 3) = 4$ units to point $R(7, 2)$ in order to be as far to the right of the y-axis as point Q; similarly, from point R which is 2 units above the x-axis we must move $(9 - 2) = 7$ units upward in order to be as far above the x-axis as point Q. Thus, the right triangle PRQ is formed in which the distance L is the hypotenuse and 4 and 7 are the lengths of the sides of the right angle. By formula (3.1) we have

$$|PQ| = \sqrt{|7 - 3|^2 + |9 - 2|^2}$$
$$= \sqrt{65}.$$
$$\approx 8.$$

In general the distance between any two points $P(x_1, y_1)$ and $Q(x_2, y_2)$ on the cc-plane is determined by

(3.2)

$$|PQ| = \sqrt{(x_2 - x_1)^2 + (y_2 - y_1)^2}$$

as shown in Figure 3.8. Formula (3.2) represents an algebraic interpretation of the length of the line segment PQ.

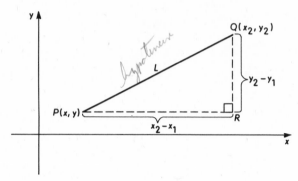

FIGURE 3.8.

In the previous illustration we found the distance of an *oblique* line segment, i.e., a line segment which is neither horizontal nor vertical. Let us illustrate these latter cases.

Example 3.5. Find the distance between $P(-2, 1)$ and $Q(7, 1)$.
Solution:
Substituting $x_1 = -2$, $x_2 = 7$, $y_1 = 1$, and $y_2 = 1$ in formula (3.2) we have

$$|PQ| = \sqrt{[7 - (-2)]^2 + (1 - 1)^2}$$
$$= \sqrt{81}$$
$$= 9.$$

It can be seen in Figure 3.9 that the line segment PQ is horizontal since

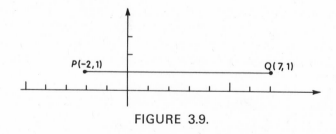

FIGURE 3.9.

$y_1 = y_2 = 1$. Also, it is important to note that the distance $|PQ|$ is a nonnegative magnitude since $\sqrt{[7 - (-2)]^2} = |7 - (-2)|$ by the definition of the square root.

Example 3.6. Find the distance between $P(-2, -3)$ and $Q(-2, 5)$.
Solution:

$$|PQ| = \sqrt{[(-2) - (-2)]^2 + [5 - (-3)]^2}, \text{ by (3.2)}$$
$$= \sqrt{64}$$
$$= 8.$$

The reader may draw the line segment PQ to verify the above answer and find that it is parallel to the y-axis.

3.5. Recapitulation. While the first basic idea of analytic geometry explains the association between the set of points on a plane and the set of ordered two-tuples of real numbers, the distance formula demonstrates how geometry can be interpreted algebraically and how algebra can be interpreted geometrically. The two ideas combined form the basis of analytic geometry which represents a unified approach greatly facilitating the study of both subjects.

PROBLEMS

3.1. In each case, plot the given points A and B on a cc-line and answer the following: (i) determine the directed distance $\overrightarrow{AB}$ and $\overrightarrow{BA}$; (ii) find the length or distance $|AB|$; (iii) explain the difference between these two measurements.

*a) $A(3), B(9)$.
b) $A(4), B(10)$.
*c) $A(6), B(-13)$.
d) $A(5), B(-15)$.
e) $A(-2), B(7)$.
f) $A(-7), B(2)$.
g) $A(5), B(5)$.

*h) $A(-3), B(-3)$.
i) $A(-7), B(-3)$.
j) $A(-3), B(-10)$.
k) $A(0), B(10)$.
l) $A(-7), B(0)$.
m) $A(-8), B(\sqrt{12})$.
n) $A(\sqrt{(-2)^2}), B(\sqrt{0^2})$.

3.2. On a *cc*-line locate two points A and B such that $|AB| = 7$. How many pairs of points can be found on a *cc*-line with each pair involving a line segment with the same length?

3.3. Find the coordinate x' of a midpoint between points A and B with coordinates.

*a) $A(5), B(12)$.
b) $A(10), B(-2)$.
c) $A(-15), B(3)$.
d) $A(-2), B(-5)$.

We have mentioned in the text that the midpoint formula is a geometric interpretation of the arithmetic mean. This formula is used as the basis for Problems 3.4 through 3.8.

Let $x_1, x_2, x_3, \ldots, x_n$ be the coordinates of points $P_1, P_2, P_3, \ldots, P_n$ on a coordinate line, respectively. Then the coordinate

$\bar{x}$ of point $\bar{P}$ is defined as

$$\bar{x} = \frac{x_1 + x_2 + x_3 + \ldots + x_n}{n},$$

where n is a positive integer. Point $\bar{P}$ is a geometric interpretation of *average* or *arithmetic mean*.

3.4. Let $x_1 = \$10,000$, $x_2 = \$7000$, $x_3 = \$12,000$, $x_4 = \$5000$, and $x_5 = \$3000$, representing the annual incomes of five individuals be given. Then using the above formula, find the mean or average income of these individuals.

3.5. Let the nonnegative weights $w_1, w_2, w_3, \ldots, w_n$, not all zero, be placed at points with coordinates $x_1, x_2, \ldots, x_n$ on a coordinate line, respectively. Then the coordinate $\bar{x}_w$ of point $\bar{P}$ is defined as

$$\bar{x}_w = \frac{w_1 x_1 + w_2 x_2 + w_3 x_3 + \ldots + w_n x_n}{w_1 + w_2 + w_3 + \ldots + w_n},$$

where n is a positive integer. Point $\bar{P}$ is called the *centroid or center of gravity* of the system of weights $w_1, w_2, w_3, \ldots, w_n$. This centroid of a system of weights is a geometric interpretation of the *weighted average* or *weighted arithmetic mean*.

During 100 sales days, sales of an item are as follows:

Daily sales x	10	15	25	20
Number of sales days w	30	40	20	10

Using the above formula, find the average units sold per day during the period.

3.6. Using the formula in Problem 3.5, compute the centroid of weights in the following case:

A system of weights 5, 10, 15 is placed at points with coordinates $-10, 5, 20$, respectively. Illustrate the problem by drawing a cc-line and locating all points.

3.7. Given the following data:

Interest rate x	10%	4%	6%
Amount invested w	\$2000	\$4000	\$4000

what is the annual average rate of return for the \$10,000 invested? Use the formula given in Problem 3.5.

3.8. Divide each number of sales days given in Problem 3.5 by the total 100 sales days, thus converting sales days to a relative frequency with total equal to 1. Show that the centroid of weights

$$\bar{x}_w = d_1 x_1 + d_2 x_2 + d_3 x_3 + d_4 x_4,$$

where d_i represents the relative frequency that the ith sales volume occurred.

3.9. Let x_1 and x_2 be the coordinates of two distinct points A and B on a cc-line. Then prove that

*a) $\bar{x} = \dfrac{x_1 + 2x_2}{3}$, if point C with coordinate $\bar{x}$ is two thirds of the distance $|AB|$.

b) In general, if A, B, and C have coordinates x_1, x_2, and $\bar{x}$, respectively, and $\overline{AC}/\overline{AB} = a/b$, then

$$\bar{x} = \frac{(b-a)x_1 + ax_2}{b}.$$

3.10. Let set $A = \{-3, -2, -1, 0, 1, 2, 3\}$ be given. Form the Cartesian product set $A \times A$ and plot the elements of this set on a cc-plane.

3.11. Plot each pair of the following points on a cc-plane and find the distance between them.

*a) (2, 3), (5, 7).   h) (−2, −3), (5, 6).
*b) (0, 0), (8, 2).   i) (−2, 2), (0, 0).
c) (−3, 3), (6, 0).   j) (−3, −3), (5, 5).
d) (0, 0), (−5, 0).   k) (5, 3), (−2, 3).
*e) (−5, 1), (2, −6).   l) (−7, 4), (−7, 3).
f) (−6, −7), (3, 5).   m) (−5, −4), (6, −4).
*g) (−3, −4), (−1, −8).   n) (2, 5), (2, −3).

3.12. What is the y-coordinate of any point on the x-axis? The x-coordinate of any point on the y-axis?

3.13. For each pair of points given in *(a), *(b), (c), (d), *(e), (f), *(g), (h), (i), (j), (k), (l), (m), and (n), of Problem 3.11 indicate the quadrant, if any, in which each point belongs.

3.14. On each quadrant of a cc-plane locate two points P and Q such that $|PQ| = 8$ and the line segment PQ is
  a) Oblique.
  b) Parallel to the x-axis.
  c) Parallel to the y-axis.
  d) How many pairs of such points can be found whose distance between them is the same?

*3.15. If one of the vertices of a square is the point (5, 5) with its center (the point at which its diagonals intersect) at the origin, find the coordinates of the other three vertices.

3.16. Using the distance formula, show that points (3, 2), (7, 9), and (7, 2) are vertices of the right triangle in Figure 3.7.

3.17. Show that

$$\sqrt{(x_1 - x_2)^2 + (y_1 - y_2)^2} = \sqrt{(x_2 - x_1)^2 + (y_2 - y_1)^2}.$$

*3.18. The coordinates (x', y') of the midpoint of a line segment with (x_1, y_1) and (x_2, y_2) as coordinates of its end points are given by

$$x' = \frac{x_1 + x_2}{2}, \qquad y' = \frac{y_1 + y_2}{2}.$$

Find the midpoint of a line segment with coordinates $(2, 3)$ and $(-5, -6)$ at its end points. Draw the line segment on a cc-plane and locate the midpoint.

3.19. Let the positive weights $w_1, w_2, \ldots, w_n$, not all zero, be placed at points $P_1, P_2, \ldots, P_n$ with coordinates $(x_1, y_1), (x_2, y_2), \ldots, (x_n, y_n)$, respectively. Then the centroid of the set of weights is the point $\bar{P}$ with coordinates

$$\bar{x} = \frac{w_1 x_1 + w_2 x_2 + \ldots + w_n x_n}{w_1 + w_2 + \ldots + w_n} \qquad \bar{y} = \frac{w_1 y_1 + w_2 y_2 + \ldots + w_n y_n}{w_1 + w_2 + \ldots + w_n}$$

Find the centroid or weighted average of points $P(3, 2)$, $Q(-5, 6)$, $R(-3, -8)$, and $S(5, -10)$ with weights 1, 2, 3, 4, respectively. Plot the given points as well as the center of gravity on a cc-plane.

3.20. On the basis of the information given in the text *prove* that there is one-to-one correspondence between the elements of the following sets: The set of all points of a given plane and the set of all ordered pairs of real numbers.

4. TWO IMPORTANT PROBLEMS OF ANALYTIC GEOMETRY

Closely associated with the two basic ideas of analytic geometry are two important problems. First, given an equation, sketch its graph, i.e., find the set of points in a cc-plane which satisfy the equation. Second, given a set of points in a cc-plane, find the equation which is satisfied by the coordinates of this set of points.

In this section we shall discuss these two problems in connection with linear equations. First, we shall show how a graph of a given equation may be sketched. Sketching the graph of a given linear equation will give us the opportunity to discuss two subordinate topics of the first important problem of analytic geometry, namely, the slope of a straight line and the average rate of change of a varying quantity. We shall deal only briefly with the problem of finding the equation of a given set of points. The above two important problems of analytic geometry will be taken up again in the following chapter after the introduction of the function concept and functional notation.

4.1. The Graph of a Linear Equation. Let us consider first the graph of a linear equation in one unknown.

Example 4.1. Sketch the graph of

$$5x - 60 = 0$$

Solution:

Let G be the set of points satisfying equation $5x - 60 = 0$ such that

$$G = \{x \,|\, 5x - 60 = 0\}.$$

Then G is a set made up of one point on the x-axis, namely, $x = 12$, representing the graph of the equation on a cc-line. On a cc-plane, however, the same equation represents a relation between the x- and y-coordinates such that

$$G = \{(x, y) | 5x - 60 = 0\},$$

which is satisfied by all points with x-coordinate 12 but *any* y-coordinate. Then G is the set of points forming a straight line in the plane perpendicular to the x-axis at $x = 12$ as shown in Figure 4.1.

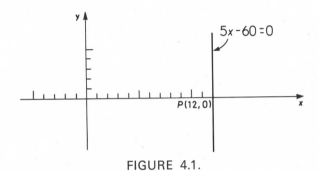

FIGURE 4.1.

Although graphs can be useful in giving a geometrical interpretation of a linear equation, they become particularly important in the analysis of equations in two unknowns. Let us then consider graphs of linear equations in two unknowns whose *general equation* is of the form

(4.1)
$$\boxed{Ax + By + C = 0,}$$

where A, B, and C are constants and where A and B are not both zero.

Example 4.2. Sketch the graph of the following equation:

$$4x - 2y - 5 = 0,$$

where $A = 4$, $B = -2$, and $C = -5$.
Solution:
Any ordered two-tuple (x, y) of real numbers which satisfies the equation is a solution and hence it represents the coordinates of a point on the graph of the equation. Of course we can obtain an infinite number of them since for every value of x there is a corresponding value for y. For instance,

when $x = -3$, then $4(-3) - 2y - 5 = 0$ and $y = -\dfrac{17}{2}$,

when $x = -2$, then $4(-2) - 2y - 5 = 0$ and $y = -\dfrac{13}{2}$,

and so on. A sample of pairs of values (x, y) are given in Table 4.1 called *table of values.*

TABLE 4.1.

x	-3	-2	-1	0	1	$\dfrac{5}{4}$	2	3
y	$-\dfrac{17}{2}$	$-\dfrac{13}{2}$	$-\dfrac{9}{2}$	$-\dfrac{5}{2}$	$-\dfrac{1}{2}$	0	$\dfrac{3}{2}$	$\dfrac{7}{2}$

They represent the coordinates of points which are plotted on a cc-plane in Figure 4.2. A portion of the graph of the given linear equation is

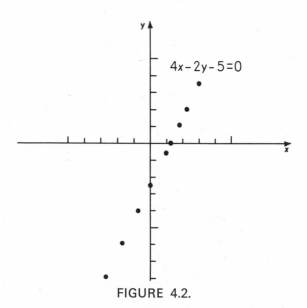

$$4x - 2y - 5 = 0$$

FIGURE 4.2.

obtained by drawing a straight line through these points under the assumption that the infinite points of the graph of the equation lying between as well as beyond the plotted points will lie on this same straight line. Such portion of the graph of the equation is shown in Figure 4.3.

In fact a portion of the graph of a linear equation may be drawn from no more than any two points whose coordinates satisfy the equation. This follows from the well-known axiom of Euclidean plane geometry that *there is one and only one straight line through two given points*. A portion of the graph is then obtained by plotting the two points and drawing a line through them. A third point is often plotted as a check. More frequently than not the selected points are the points where the graph crosses the axes. These points are called *x-intercept* and *y-intercept* of the line.

Example 4.3. Sketch the graph of equation $4x - 2y - 5 = 0$ by finding the x- and y-intercepts.

Solution:
Let $y = 0$, then

$$4x - 2(0) - 5 = 0 \text{, and}$$
$$x = \tfrac{5}{4}.$$

Let $x = 0$, then

$$4(0) - 2y - 5 = 0 \text{, and}$$
$$y = -\tfrac{5}{2}.$$

Hence, the x-intercept is $(\tfrac{5}{4}, 0)$ and the y-intercept is $(0, -\tfrac{5}{2})$.

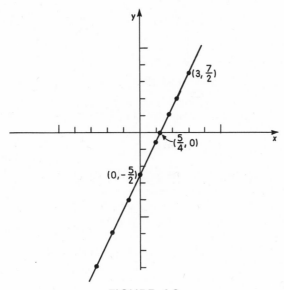

FIGURE 4.3.

Plotting these two points on a cc-plane and drawing a straight line through them we obtain the portion of the graph of $4x - 2y - 5 = 0$ shown in Figure 4.3.

A third point is sometimes plotted as a check.

Let $x = 3$, then

$$4(3) - 2y - 5 = 0 \text{, and}$$
$$y = \tfrac{7}{2}.$$

Thus, point $(3, \tfrac{7}{2})$ may be plotted, as shown in Figure 4.3 as a check.

4.2. The Slope of a Straight Line.

We have seen that straight lines represent graphs of linear equations in two unknowns. Thus, the above problem of sketching the graph of a given linear equation leads to a discussion of the slope of a straight line.

Let $P(x_1, y_1)$ and $Q(x_2, y_2)$ be any two distinct points in a nonvertical

line such as line L shown in Figure 4.4(a). Then the slope of a nonvertical
line L is defined by

(4.2)
$$m = \frac{y_2 - y_1}{x_2 - x_1}.$$

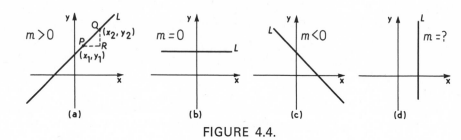

FIGURE 4.4.

Example 4.4. Find the slope of the straight line passing through the
points

$$P(3, 3.5) \text{ and } Q(-3, -8.5).$$

Solution:
Substituting $x_1 = 3$, $y_1 = 3.5$, $x_2 = -3$, and $y_2 = -8.5$ in (4.2), we
have

$$m = \frac{-8.5 - 3.5}{-3 - 3} = 2.$$

It is the slope of the line in Figure 4.3 which is a portion of the graph of
$4x - 2y - 5 = 0$.

The above example raises the following problem: given an equation
of the previously specified (4.1) general form

$$Ax + By + C = 0,$$

find its slope. Solving for y, we obtain

(4.3)
$$y = mx + b,$$

where $m = -A/B$ and $b = -C/B$, the y-intercept. Equation (4.3) is the
slope-intercept form of (4.1).

Example 4.5. Express equation $4x - 2y - 5 = 0$ in form (4.3).
Solution:
If $4x - 2y - 5 = 0$,
then $2y = 4x - 5$
and $y = 2x - 5/2$.
where $m = -A/B = -4/(-2) = 2$ and $b = -5/2$

Observe that the same answer for m was found in Example 4.4 by substituting the coordinates of two points of the graph of the equation in (4.2).

In geometric terms the slope of a line such as line L in Figure 4.4(a) may be defined by

(4.4)
$$m = \frac{\overline{RQ}}{\overline{PR}};$$

in other words, m is the ratio of directed distance $\overline{RQ}$ over the directed distance $\overline{PR}$, the ratio of the vertical rise of line L over its horizontal run. Thus depending on the value of slope m, the graphs of linear equations of form (4.3) may be classified into four categories.

a) When $m > 0$, the graph of equation (4.3) is a straight line such as line L in Figure 4.4(a) where y *increases as x increases*.

b) When $m = 0$, equation (4.3) reduces to $y = b$ whose graph is a line *parallel* to the x-axis such as line L in Figure 4.4(b). In terms of equation (4.2)

$$m = \frac{0}{x_2 - x_1} = 0, \quad \text{since } y_2 - y_1 = 0.$$

c) When $m < 0$, the graph of equation (4.3) is a line such as line L in Figure 4.4(c), where y *decreases* as x *increases*.

d) If the graph of equation (4.3) is a line such as line L in Figure 4.4(d), which is parallel to the y-axis, the slope m is not defined since $x_2 - x_1 = 0$.

In sum, the slope m of a straight line is a number which determines its *direction* and measures its *steepness*:

a) When $m > 0$, the line slants upward to the right;
b) When $m = 0$, the line is horizontal or parallel to the x-axis;
c) When $m < 0$, the line slants downward to the right;
d) A vertical line or a line parallel to the y-axis has no slope;
e) The larger the absolute value of m, i.e., the larger $|m|$ is, the steeper the line.

4.3. The Average Rate of Change.

The slope of a line may be discussed in terms of the rate with which the value of y varies as the value of x varies. In linear equations this rate of change can be easily understood since it is a constant. Yet, it is so important for future discussions as to deserve further study.

Let Δx, read "delta x," denote the *increment* by which the value of x varies. If the variable x is given certain values, then the value of the increment or the quantity Δx is the first difference between successive values of the x variable, as shown in Table 4.2. The y column of the table is obtained by substituting each value of x in $y = 2x - 5/2$, the equation of Example 4.5 (see also Table 4.1), while the Δy column is the incremental difference of y values. Observe that the ratio $\Delta y/\Delta x = 2$ is the value of m of the slope of the straight line shown in Figure 4.3. Thus, we can arrive at the following definition. Let (x, y) be a point on the graph. Change x by the increment Δx and suppose the corresponding change in y is denoted by Δy. Thus $(x + \Delta x, y + \Delta y)$ is another point on the graph. Then the quotient $\Delta y/\Delta x$ is defined to be the *average rate of change* of y with respect to x in the interval from x to $x + \Delta x$.

TABLE 4.2.

x	Δx	y	Δy	$\Delta y/\Delta x$
-3		$-17/2$		
	1		2	$2/1 = 2$
-2		$-13/2$		
	1		2	$2/1 = 2$
-1		$-9/2$		
	2		4	$4/2 = 2$
1		$-1/2$		
	1		2	$2/1 = 2$
2		$3/2$		
	3		6	$6/3 = 2$
5		$15/2$		

This definition is important because it touches upon our next subject, namely, functions. We shall deal with the concept of a function in the first section of the following chapter. In the meantime, the following example illustrates the meaning of the average rate of change in a real-world situation.

Example 4.6. Consider equation

$$y = 2x - \tfrac{5}{2}$$

studied previously. Let x represent sales of a product in units and y dollar profits. Since slope $m = 2$, the average rate of change means that dollar profits change at a rate of $2.00 per product unit sold. In fact, in this example the value of the slope represents the average profit per unit sold for $x > 1$.

4.4. The Equation of a Set of Points. This second important problem of analytic geometry will be studied in detail in Sections 2 and 3 of the following chapter. For the sake of logical continuity, however, we shall peripherally touch upon it by limiting our discussion of it to the following two simple cases:

Case 1: Find the equation of a line, given the coordinates of a point on the line and the slope of the line. Let (x, y) be the coordinates of any point on a line and (x_1, y_1) the coordinates of a *given* point on the same line. Then by (4.2) the slope of a nonvertical line L is

$$m = \frac{y - y_1}{x - x_1}.$$

Multiplying both sides of this equation by $(x - x_1)$ and reversing sides we obtain

(4.5) $$\boxed{y - y_1 = m(x - x_1)}$$

which is the *point-slope* form of the equation of a straight line.

Example 4.7. Find the equation of the line through point $(5, -2)$ and with slope $m = -2$.
Solution:
Substituting the given values in (4.5) we have

$$y - (-2) = -2(x - 5),$$
$$y = -2x + 8.$$

If $(0, y_1)$ is the given point where y_1 is the y-intercept, then (4.5) reduces to

$$y = mx + y_1$$

since $x_1 = 0$. This is the slope-intercept form (4.3) where $y_1 = b$. It represents a special and important variation of the above case.

Example 4.8. Find the equation of the line through point $(0, 8)$ and with slope $m = -2$.
Solution:
Substituting in (4.3), we have

$$y = -2x + 8$$

as previously.

Case 2: Find the equation of a line, given the coordinates of two points on the line.
We have seen that by (4.2) the slope of a nonvertical line L is

$$m = \frac{y_2 - y_1}{x_2 - x_1},$$

where (x_1, y_1) and (x_2, y_2) are the coordinates of two given points. Let (x, y) be the coordinates of *any* point of such a line L. Then by (4.2) we have

$$m = \frac{y - y_1}{x - x_1},$$

where (x_1, y_1) are the coordinates of one of the two given points. But since the slope m of a straight line is a constant, it follows that

(4.6)
$$\frac{y - y_1}{x - x_1} = \frac{y_2 - y_1}{x_2 - x_1}.$$

This is the *two-point form* of the equation of a straight line.

Example 4.9. Find the equation of a straight line passing through the points $P(3, 3.5)$ and $Q(-3, -8.5)$.
Solution:
Substituting $x_1 = 3, y_1 = 3.5, x_2 = -3$, and $y_2 = -8.5$ in (4.6), we have

$$\frac{y - 3.5}{x - 3} = \frac{-8.5 - 3.5}{-3 - 3},$$

$$\frac{y - 3.5}{x - 3} = 2,$$

$$y = 2x - \frac{5}{2}.$$

A portion of the graph of this equation is shown in Figure 4.3.

4.5. Recapitulation of Chapter 5. In reviewing the fundamentals of algebra and analytic geometry in this chapter we have accomplished a number of additional objectives. First, we showed how these two subjects are connected with sets. Second, we drew the distinction between algebraic solutions and the empirical meaning of these solutions in solving real-world problems. Third, we demonstrated how the mathematical systems of algebra and Euclidean geometry can be studied more effectively through the unified approach of analytic geometry. In this connection we have studied a graph of a linear equation, the slope of a straight line, the average rate of change, and the equation of a set of points. In sum, we supplied the basic ideas and tools which will enable us to study functions in particular and the mathematics of varying quantities in general.

PROBLEMS

4.1. For each case below do the following:
  i) Sketch the graph of the equation on a cc-line and a cc-plane.
  ii) Label properly the x-axis.
  a) $6x + 15,000 = 57,000$ in Example 1.1.
  b) $0.05x + 600 - 0.06x = 570$ in Example 1.6.

4.2. Sketch the graph of the following equations on a cc-plane:
  a) $3x - 6 = 0$.   e) $y - 5 = 0$.
  b) $4x - 9 = 0$.   f) $3y - 2 = 0$.
  c) $2x + 8 = 0$.   g) $7y + 14 = 0$.
  d) $5x + 4 = 0$.   h) $5y + 3 = 0$.

4.3. The graph of the equation in Problem 4.1(a) is a point, if plotted on a cc-line, and a straight line parallel to the y-axis, if sketched on a cc-plane. What is the graph or locus of this equation, if sketched on a three-dimensional space? on an n-dimensional space?

4.4. Plot the graph of equation—
a) $3x + 2y - 6 = 0$.
b) $2x - 5y + 7 = 0$.
c) $y = x - 3$.
d) $x + y = 0$.
e) $x - y = 0$.
f) $y = x + 7$.

g) $y = |x|$.
h) $x = |y|$.
i) $y = |x - 2|$.
j) $|x| + |y| = 2$.
k) $|x + y| = 2$.
l) $xy = 0$.

4.5. For each equation—
i) Find the slope by expressing the equation in slope-intercept form (4.3);
ii) Plot the graph of the equation.
*a) $2x + y - 2 = 0$.
*b) $2x + y = 0$.
c) $2x + y + 2 = 0$.
d) $2x + y + 4 = 0$.

e) $y - 2x + 4 = 0$.
f) $y - 2x + 2 = 0$.
g) $y - 2x = 0$.
h) $y - 2x - 2 = 0$.

4.6. Draw a line through the given two points and find its slope.
*a) $(3, 5)$, $(-6, 2)$.
*b) $(2, 6)$, $(-4, -5)$.
c) $(-3, 7)$, $(6, -4)$.
d) $(2, 8)$, $(10, -3)$.

e) $(-5, 2)$, $(6, 2)$.
f) $(-4, -3)$, $(5, -3)$.
g) $(-5, 7)$, $(-5, 3)$.
h) $(3, 6)$, $(3, 2)$.

4.7. Let x in equation $y = -50x + 2000$ represent months and y the average undepreciated dollar value per truck of a fleet of trucks used by a wholesale distributor of fresh fruit and vegetables where $0 \leqslant x \leqslant 40$.
a) Sketch the graph of the equation.
b) Prepare a table such as Table 4.2 for $x = 0, 5, 10, 15, 20, 25, 30, 35$, and 40.
c) Interpret the meaning of the average rate of change $\Delta y / \Delta x$.

4.8. If the selling price of an item is $3.00 per unit, express the relation between sales revenue and quantity sold in an equation form. Sketch the graph of the equation and explain the meaning of the average rate of change $\Delta y / \Delta x$.

4.9. A housewife spends $50 a week on food. Let x represent food of vegetable origin and y food of animal origin in thousands of calories and let the prices per 1000 calories for each type of food be $2.00 and $5.00, respectively.
*a) Find the equation.
*b) Sketch its graph.
c) Find the slope of the line and explain its meaning.
d) If 60 percent of her budget should be allocated to purchasing food of animal origin and 40 percent to food of vegetable origin, how many calories of each type of food could she purchase?

e) If she needs 19,000 calories of food of both kinds to feed her family, use the slope to show how she could allocate her budget to meet the needs of her family.

f) What are the implications of your answers to (*e*) assuming the allocation in (*d*) is considered to meet the minimum nutritional requirements for food of animal origin?

4.10. Let x and y in Problem 4.9 represent the satisfaction or pleasure the members of the family expect to enjoy by eating food of vegetable and animal origin, respectively, and assume that the rate of change is not a constant but changes in a way such that $|\Delta y/\Delta x| < 1$, $|\Delta y/\Delta x| = 1$, and $|\Delta y/\Delta x| > 1$ as x increases.

a) Sketch the graph of such relationship between x and y.

b) Discuss the important implications involved in such a relationship in terms of utility or satisfaction.

4.11. Each group of equations (*a*) through (*e*) and (*f*) through (*j*) below have the same slope but different y-intercepts. Discuss their graphs.

*a) $y = 3x + 3$.   *f*) $y = -x/3 + 3$.
*b) $y = 3x + 1$.   *g*) $y = -x/3 + 1$.
*c) $y = 3x$.   *h*) $y = -x/3$.
d) $y = 3x - 1$.   *i*) $y = -x/3 - 1$.
e) $y = 3x - 3$.   *j*) $y = -x/3 - 3$.

4.12. On the basis of your findings in Problem 4.11 and given the following equations:

i) Express each equation in slope-intercept form (4.3).

ii) Find another equation whose line is parallel to the line of the given equation.

iii) Verify your answer to (ii) by sketching the graphs of both equations.

*a) $3x + 5y + 6 = 0$.

b) $2x - 7y + 2 = 0$.

c) $x/5 + y/2 = 1$.

d) $x/3 - y + 1 = 0$.

4.13. For each point and slope given below:

i) Find the equation using the point-slope form (4.5).

ii) Express the equation in slope-intercept form (4.3).

iii) Sketch the graph of the equation.

*a) $(6, -5)$, $m = 3$.

*b) $(-3, 7)$, $m = -\frac{1}{3}$.

c) $(2, -5)$, $m = -2$.

d) $(-2, -1)$, $m = 5$.

4.14. With given slope and y-intercept,

i) Find the equation using the slope-intercept form (4.3).

ii) Sketch the graph of the equation.

*a) $m = 4$, $(0, -5)$.

*b) $m = 3$, $(0, 3)$.

c) $m = -1$, $(0, 6)$.

d) $m = -6$, $(0, -4)$.

4.15. For each pair of points whose coordinates are given below:
  i) Plot the points on a cc-plane and draw a straight line through these points.
  ii) Find the equation of the line using the two-point form (4.6).
  *a) (2, 5), (−4, 2).   e) (−4, 3), (7, 3).
  *b) (3, 7), (−3, −4).   f) (−7, −5), (6, −5).
  c) (−2, 8), (5, −3).   g) (−8, 3), (−8, 6).
  d) (2, 10), (7, −5).   h) (5, 7), (5, 3).

4.16. For each pair of x- and y-intercepts:
  i) Find the equation using the two-point form (4.6).
  ii) Determine the slope of the line.
  iii) Sketch the graph of the equation.
  *a) (5, 0), (0, 6).
  b) (−3, 0), (0, 7).
  c) (−7, 0), (0, −8).
  d) (4, 0), (0, −2).

4.17. Let $m_1 = 3$ and $m_2 = -\frac{1}{3}$, the slopes of the two groups of equations in Problems 4.11. Then $m_1 \cdot m_2 = -1$.
  a) Show that the line of any equation from the first group is perpendicular to the line of any equation from the second group.
  b) On the basis of the results in (a) write a general statement about the *perpendicularity* or *orthogonality* of two nonvertical lines.
  c) Would you consider your answer to (a) as proof of the statement (theorem) in (b)? Why or why not?

4.18. Suppose your statement in Problem 4.17(b) is a logically true statement, i.e., the theorem is proved, and given an equation from Problem 4.12*(a), (b), (c), (d):
  i) Express each equation in slope-intercept form (4.3).
  ii) Find another equation whose line is perpendicular to the line of the given equation.
  iii) Verify your answer to (ii) by sketching the graphs of both equations.

SUGGESTED REFERENCES

1. COOLEY, H. R., *et al. Introduction to Mathematics*, pp. 78–96. Boston: Houghton Mifflin Co., 1949. **(1)**

2. DAUS, P. H., AND WHYBURN, W. M. *Algebra with Applications to Business and Economics*, pp. 64–77. Reading, Mass.: Addison-Wesley Publishing Co., Inc., 1961. **(1)**

3. NIELSEN, K. L. *College Mathematics*, pp. 1–28. New York: Barnes & Noble, Inc., 1958. **(2–4)**

4. KLINE, MORRIS. *Mathematics: A Cultural Approach*, pp. 271–81. Reading, Mass.: Addison-Wesley Publishing Co., Inc., 1962. **(3)**

5. OAKLEY, C. O. *Analytic Geometry*, pp. 44–59. New York: Barnes & Noble, Inc., 1960. **(4)**

6. RICHARDSON, M. *College Algebra*, pp. 1–79, 184–85. Al. ed. Englewood Cliffs, N.J.: Prentice-Hall, Inc., 1958. (**1, 2**)

7. RICHARDSON, M. *Fundamentals of Mathematics*, pp. 224–36. Rev. ed. New York: The Macmillan Co., 1958. (**3**)

8. ROSE, I. H. *A Modern Introduction to College Mathematics*, pp. 137–61. New York: John Wiley & Sons, Inc., 1960. (**3**)

9. WESTERN, D. W., AND HAAG, V. H. *An Introduction to Mathematics*, pp. 94–114, 174–82. New York: Henry Holt & Co., Inc., 1959. (**2–4**)

Chapter 6

FUNCTIONS AND MANAGERIAL
PLANNING

FUNCTIONS occupy such a pivotal position in the mathematics of varying quantities as to deserve special attention. Since the importance of functions cannot be appreciated unless the concept of a function itself is explained, in Section 1 of this chapter we shall attempt to give a clear understanding of what a function is from the mathematical as well as the empirical standpoints. The remaining part of this chapter is devoted to the application of linear and quadratic functions for managerial decisions and for economic analysis. How linear functions may be derived from empirical data and how they may be used by management for planning and control is the subject matter of Section 2. No less important is Section 3 which consists of a study of the basic properties of quadratic functions and their use in obtaining "definite" answers for management.

1. THE CONCEPT OF FUNCTION; FUNCTIONAL NOTATION

In introducing the concept of a function we shall discuss the following topics. First, we shall define functions, explain the important parts of a function, and introduce functional notation. Second, we shall define and explain inverse functions. Third, we shall establish logical continuity with earlier discussions by showing how functions are related to equations. Fourth, we shall distinguish between functions and relations. Finally, we shall examine some important characteristics of functions.

1.1. Definition. *A function is a rule that associates with each element of a set, called the domain, one and only one element of another set, called the range, thus generating a set of ordered (tuples) so that any two having the same first element also have the same second element.* Let us study this definition of a function carefully.

In the first place, the above definition indicates that each function consists of three distinguishable parts: the *rule*, the *domain*, and the *range*.

Example 1.1. Let the function

(1.1) $y = 50x + 3000$

be given. Then x is the variable over the set

$$X = \{x \in R \mid -\infty < x < \infty\},$$

where R is the infinite set of real numbers. The expression in braces $\{\ \}$ reads "x is an element of set R such that x ranges from minus infinity to plus infinity." Similarly, y is the variable over the set

$$Y = \{y \in R \mid -\infty < y < \infty\}.$$

Set X is the domain and set Y the range of the function. The rule of association or simply the rule of the function is the operation given by the mathematical formula or equation $y = 50x + 3000$. This association can be illustrated with a machine such as the one shown in Figure 1.1, where

DOMAIN

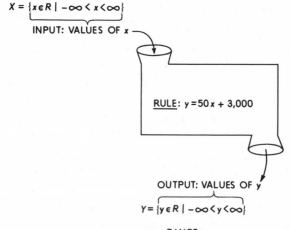

FIGURE 1.1.

the variable x over the set X represents the input and the variable y over the set Y the output. We may observe that whenever a value from the set X is assigned to the variable x, a value for the variable y is determined by the rule "y equals 50 times the value of x plus 3000."

In the second place, the above definition of a function says that from this association between two sets another set is generated whose elements are ordered tuples so that any two such tuples having the same first element also have the same second element.

Example 1.1—*Continued*. Consider again the function

$$y = 50x + 3000.$$

The rule of this function pairs each element from set X, the domain, with one and only one element, from set Y, the range, and generates a new infinite set

$$Z = \{(x, y)|y = 50x + 3000\},$$

whose elements are ordered tuples, which constitutes the function. The following ordered tuples are some of the elements of set Z:

$$(0, 3000), (50, 5500), (100, 8000), (200, 13,000).$$

They are obtained by letting $x = 0$, 50, 100, and 200 in the rule of the function, respectively. The set of points whose coordinates are the elements of set Z represent the graph of the function shown in Figure 1.2. Note that no two ordered tuples of set Z can have the same coordinate x and a different coordinate y.

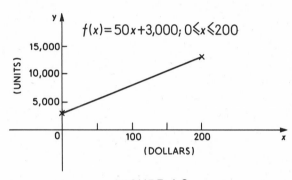

FIGURE 1.2.

Furthermore, the above definition of a function implies more than what has been said so far. When we speak of a function such as function (1.1) we mean that variable y *is the function of or depends on* x; in other words, we consider x to be the *independent* and y the *dependent* variable. This special association may be expressed by

$$y = f(x),$$

where $f(x)$, read "f of x," is the value of function f at x.

Example 1.1—*Continued.* Function (1.1) can be expressed in a proper notational form as

(1.2) $f(x) = 50x + 3000,$

where the left-hand side of (1.2) is merely shorthand notation of the right-hand side.

But in order to understand this special functional association depicted by (1.2), let x be advertising expense in dollars and y sales of an item in units. Then the function f in (1.2) expresses the relationship that sales depend on advertising expense; specifically, sales increase at an average rate of 50 units for every dollar spent on advertising, starting from a sales volume of 3000 units.

Observe that f denotes a function while $f(x)$ denotes the value of function f at a given number x. In addition to f, other letters such as g, h, etc., are used to denote a function.

The notation $y = f(x)$ has the advantage of symbolizing briefly the existence of a special association between x and y. Moreover, it is convenient in designating the particular value of x and the corresponding value of y; by substituting a specific value of x in $f(x)$ the rule of the function f yields the corresponding value of y.

Example 1.2. Consider function (1.2) again,

$$f(x) = 50x + 3000,$$

where x represents advertising expense in dollars and y units sold of an item. The function's rule is "given x, add 3000 to 50 times the given value of x."

Let $x = 100$. Then

$$f(100) = 50(100) + 3000 = 8000.$$

Let $x = a$, where a is any constant. Then

$$f(a) = 50a + 3000.$$

Let $x = a + k$,
where
a = advertising outlay for all previous months,
k = advertising outlay for current month.
Then

$$f(a + k) = 50(a + k) + 3000$$
$$= 50a + 50k + 3000.$$

1.2. Inverse Function. *Given a function f, the set of ordered tuples which are obtained from f by interchanging the first and the second elements in each ordered tuple is called the inverse function. It is denoted by f^{-1}.*

Example 1.3. Let function (1.1), considered previously, be given

$$f(x) = 50x + 3000,$$

where

x	0	50	100	200
$f(x)$	3000	5500	8000	13,000

are some of the ordered tuples representing the coordinates of some points on the graph of function f. Interchanging the first and the second elements of f we obtain

x	3000	5500	8000	13,000
$f^{-1}(x)$	0	50	100	200

which are some of the ordered tuples of the inverse function.

$$f^{-1}(y) = \frac{1}{50} y - 60,$$

where x is a function or depends on y. In order to observe the convention that x always depicts the independent variable, we switch symbols and express the above inverse in proper notational form

(1.3) $$f^{-1}(x) = \frac{1}{50} x - 60.$$

The graph of function (1.3) is shown in Figure 1.3. But now the x variable stands for sales and the y for advertising outlay. This inverse function

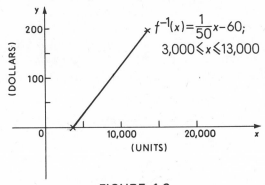

FIGURE 1.3.

means that advertising outlay is a function of or depends on sales volume; and the policy of the company is to spend \$1.00 on advertising for every 50 sold units of the product.

Thus, function (1.3) is the inverse of function (1.2) and vice versa.

Observe that the domain of an inverse function is the range and the range is the domain of the primary function. The inverse of a function may be obtained by solving the primary function for the independent variable.

Example 1.4. The inverse function (1.3) in the previous example is obtained from the primary function

$$y = 50x + 3000.$$

Solving for the independent variable x, we have

$$x = \frac{1}{50} y - 60 ; \text{ and}$$

by interchanging symbols

$$f^{-1}(x) = \frac{1}{50} x - 60,$$

as previously.

The reader may study the graphs of function (1.2) in Figure 1.2 and of function (1.3) in Figure 1.3 to clearly understand the relationship between a function and its inverse.

1.3. Functions and Equations. At this point an important question may be raised: how are functions related to equations? Although the reader may readily find an answer to this question from the definitions of a function and its inverse, it is important to make this point clear.

In Section 4 of the preceding chapter we have studied linear equations in two unknowns of the general form

(1.4)

$$Ax + By + C = 0,$$

where A, B, and C are constants and where A and B are not both zero. From such an equation we may derive two functions by solving it for either of the two variables.

Example 1.5. Consider the equation

$$100x - 2y + 6000 = 0.$$

Case 1: Solving for y, we derive

$$y = 50x + 3000$$

which is function (1.2) studied in Example 1.1.

Case 2: Solving for x, we derive

$$x = \frac{1}{50} y - 60$$

which is the inverse function (1.3) studied in Examples 1.3 and 1.4.

While both the equation and the two derived functions in the above example depict an association between the variables x and y, a very important difference exists between these two mathematical concepts. In the case of a function the association between x and y is a special one, where one of the variables is considered to be the function of or to depend on the other. This special association between x and y need not be present in the case of an equation. Furthermore, the domain of a function may be restricted by the definition of the empirical situation which the function may describe.

Example 1.6. A *portion* of the graph of equation

$$100x - 2y + 6000 = 0$$

is shown in Figure 1.2. The graph of this equation extends indefinitely in either direction of the line segment.

Although in the mathematical sense the domain of the derived function

$$f(x) = 50x + 3000$$

consists of the infinite set of real numbers, it is restricted by the empirical situation as defined in Example 1.1. The domain of the function is the set

$$X = \{x \in R \mid 0 \leqslant x \leqslant 200\},$$

where R is the infinite set of real numbers. The special association between advertising outlay and sales volume expressed by this function may exist only for $0 \leqslant x \leqslant \$200$. The graph of the function is the set of all points within the restricted domain specified above. If the domain of the above function were not restricted, then its graph would be the graph of the equation from which the function is derived.

Similarly, the graph of the derived function

$$f^{-1}(x) = \frac{1}{50}x - 60$$

is shown in Figure 1.3 where its domain is the set

$$X = \{x \in R \mid 3000 \leqslant x \leqslant 13{,}000\},$$

R being the infinite set of real numbers.

It is important to know that deriving functions from linear equations may not always make sense from the empirical point of view. This depends on the definition of the particular problem.

Example 1.7. Consider the equation

$$2y - 4x + 5 = 0.$$

Solving for y we derive the function

$$g(x) = 2x - \frac{5}{2}, \qquad x > 1,$$

where x represents sold units of a product and $y = g(x)$ dollar profits (cf. Example 4.6 in Chapter 5). But the inverse of function g, the function

$$g^{-1}(x) = \frac{1}{2}x + \frac{5}{4}, \qquad x \geqslant 0,$$

may not make empirical sense since in a real-world situation we sell a product first and then we may realize a profit. In other words, a function depicting that sales depend on profits may not make sense empirically.

Furthermore, while deriving functions from linear equations may not present a problem, this process may involve difficulties when nonlinear functions are considered. Also, derived functions may exist even when conversion of nonlinear equations to functions by solving for one variable cannot be carried out. But such cases lie outside the scope of this book.

In general, when a function is derived from an equation, it is said to be given *implicitly* by the equation. Thus, the general equation $Ax + By + C = 0$ defines a function denoted by

(1.5) $$F(x, y) = Ax + By + C = 0,$$

which specifies either variable implicitly in terms of the other. The two functions which can be derived from the above expression may be denoted in their *explicit* form as follows:

$$f(x) = mx + b$$

and

$$g(y) = \frac{y}{m} + a,$$

where one is the inverse function of the other and $m = -A/B$, $b = -C/B$, and $a = -C/A$.

All in all, the graph of a function, unless its domain is unrestricted, usually represents a portion of the graph of the corresponding equation. Moreover, in contrast to equations, functions express not only an association between two variables but they also specify that one variable depends on the other. It is this dependence between variables which makes functions important enough, particularly from the empirical standpoint, to deserve special attention.

1.4. Functions and Relations.   The special association between variables depicted by a function is closely related to another important characteristic of functions. *A function may be a one-way street;* in other words, a function may not have an inverse.

Example 1.8. Consider the equation

$$x^2 - y = 0.$$

Solving for y, we derive the function

$$f(x) = x^2$$

since for every value of x there is one and only one value of y.

But the inverse of function f

$$f^{-1}(x) = \pm \sqrt{x}$$

is not a function since for every value of x there are two values of y. The inverse of the above function f is said to represent a *relation.*

The difference between function f and its relation is illustrated in Figure 1.4. Consider the four ordered tuples of the relation. The first two (1, 1) and $(1, -1)$ have the same first element but a different second element. The same is true with the other ordered tuples $(4, 2)$ and $(4, -2)$ of the relation. But this is not true for the four ordered tuples of the function. The reader may plot the points of the relation and function whose coordinates are given in Figure 1.4 on a cc-plane in order to visualize the above distinction.

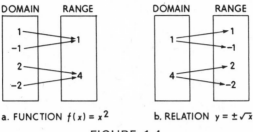

a. FUNCTION $f(x) = x^2$ b. RELATION $y = \pm\sqrt{x}$

FIGURE 1.4.

However, from the above relation we may obtain two functions

$$g(x) = \sqrt{x}, \quad x \geqslant 0,$$

and

$$h(x) = -\sqrt{x}, \quad x \geqslant 0.$$

They represent special cases of the relation.

1.5. Additional Characteristics of Functions.
With regard to the rule of association, the domain, and the range of a function, a number of additional points should be kept in mind.

1. *The domain of a function represents a set which may contain more than one variable, while the range of a function represents a set which can contain one and only one variable.* This is the case of functions involving several variables frequently found in real-world problems, where the dependent variable is the function of several independent variables.

Example 1.9. Consider the function

$$f(x_1, x_2, x_3, x_4) = \$0.10x_1 + \$0.20x_2 + \$0.75x_3 + \$0.80x_4$$

where

x_1 = flour,
x_2 = sugar,
x_3 = butter,
x_4 = chocolate,

and $y = f(x_1, x_2, x_3, x_4)$ the cost of cake mix for a given combination of the four ingredients. In this function the cost of producing cake mix depends on four independent variables. Observe that, instead of using four different letters, letter x is used with subscripts 1, 2, 3, and 4 to denote the four independent variables. This notation is of great convenience in cases such as linear programming where a function may have several independent variables.

2. Neither the domain nor the range of a function need consist of numbers.

Example 1.10. Let the function $y = f(x)$ be given where x is the variable over the set X of consumers of a product and y the variable over the set Y of occupations. Let the rule of the function f be "given a consumer, state his principal or primary occupation." Then neither the domain nor the range of f consists of numbers.

In this book we shall be concerned only with *real valued* functions, i.e., functions whose ranges are subsets of real numbers.

3. Determining the domain and range of a function is important because it may require finding excluded values.

Example 1.11. Consider the function

$$f(x) = \frac{3}{x + 3}.$$

The domain of f is the set of all real numbers except $x = -3$ since division by zero is undefined.

Let function

$$g(x) = x^2$$

be given. The range of g is the set of all nonnegative real numbers.

Excluded values in the domain of a function are related to problems of continuity about which much will be said in Chapter 11, Section 1.

4. Frequently, it is important to distinguish between the mathematical and the empirical domain and range of a function. In differentiating between functions and equations we have pointed out that the domain of a function is usually restricted. Indeed, most functions we shall study in this book have an empirical domain and range of nonnegative integers with the significant part of their graph appearing on the first quadrant, Q_1, of a cc-plane. Furthermore, from the mathematical standpoint the variables of the restricted domain and range of a function are assumed to be infinitely divisible. From the empirical standpoint this divisibility may be neither necessary nor feasible.

Example 1.12. In Example 1.6 we have restricted the domain of function

$$f(x) = 50x + 3000$$

to $0 \leqslant x \leqslant \$200$. From the mathematical standpoint, x may represent cents or smaller fractions of a dollar. But from the empirical standpoint we can hardly, if ever, think about advertising expense in terms of units less than $1.00.

Or consider the function

$$f^{-1}(x) = \frac{1}{50}x - 60,$$

where its domain was restricted to $3000 \leqslant x \leqslant 13{,}000$ units of a product. Whereas we can think of sales in terms of whole units, from the mathematical standpoint we can use values of x representing fractions of a unit. Thus, a function is an idealization of the association between the independent variable(s) and the dependent variable which may be empirically meaningful in terms of whole numbers only.

5. *The notion of a function does not imply the existence of any "cause and effect" relationship.* It is a simple association or correspondence between the independent variable(s) and the dependent variable. However, such causal relationship may not be excluded.

Example 1.13. Consider the function

$$f(x) = 50x + 3000,$$

where x is advertising outlay and $y = f(x)$ sales volume. The function does not imply that changes in advertising outlay *cause* changes in sales volume. Although such a causal effect may not be excluded, the function depicts an association which according to the rule involves the mathematical operation of multiplication and addition.

6. *Depending on the rule of association, functions are classified into algebraic and transcendental.* The most common types of functions are the following:

a) Algebraic functions, i.e., functions whose rule is defined in terms of polynomials such as $2x^2 + 5x + 4$ and fractional expressions such as

$$\frac{5}{x+5} + \frac{2}{x-4}.$$

Such functions may be further classified into *linear* of the form

$$f(x) = a_0 x + a_1, \qquad a_0 \neq 0;$$

quadratic of the form

$$f(x) = a_0 x^2 + a_1 x + a_2; \qquad a_0 \neq 0;$$

or other nonlinear of higher than second degree. Finally, there are other algebraic functions such as *rational.*

For example,

$$f(x) = \frac{x^2 + x - 1}{x + 2}$$

defines a rational function f which has as its domain the set of all numbers except number -2.

b) *Transcendental functions*, i.e., functions whose rule involves logarithmic expressions, like function h defined by

$$h(x) = \log x,$$

or exponents such as the exponential function g defined by

$$g(x) = 2^x,$$

or a trigonometric expression such as the cosine function s defined by

$$s(x) = \cos (x).$$

Some of these functions will be discussed in the sections which follow.

PROBLEMS

1.1. The following linear equations are expressed in implicit form.
   i) Assuming that x is the independent and y the dependent variable, find the function and express it in functional notation.
   ii) Sketch the graph of the function and state the average rate of change of y with respect to x over the interval $1 \leqslant x \leqslant 4$.
   iii) Find the inverse of the function in (i) and express it in functional notation.
   iv) Sketch the graph of the inverse function and state the average rate of change of x with respect to y over the interval $1 \leqslant y \leqslant 4$.
   *a) $F(x, y) = 2x - y = 0$.
   b) $G(x, y) = 4x - 5y + 6 = 0$.
   c) $H(x, y) = 2x + 3y = 0$.
   d) $F(x, y) = 3x + 2y - 3 = 0$.
   e) $G(x, y) = 2x - y + 5 = 0$.

1.2. For each equation in *(a), (b), (c), (d), and (e) of Problem 1.1 do the following:
   i) Prepare a table of values such as Table 4.1 in Chapter 5 for $x = -4$, -3, -2, -1, 0, 1, 2, 3, and 4, assuming that x is the independent variable.
   ii) Sketch the graph of the points you have found in (i) on a cc-plane.
   iii) Interchange the symbols x and y in the table of values in (i) and sketch the graph of the new points on the same cc-plane.
   iv) Are the lines on the cc-plane the graphs of two functions, the one being the inverse function of the other? Explain.

1.3. Each of the following equations represents either the demand for or the supply of a commodity, where p is the price and q the quantity.
   i) Assuming that price depends on quantity, derive the demand or supply function and express it in proper notational form.
   ii) Explain the slope of each function in terms of average rate of

change and indicate whether the function is a demand or a supply function.

iii) Sketch the graph of the function.

iv) Is the assumption that price depends on quantity justified more than the assumption that quantity depends on price? Discuss.

v) If your answer to (iv) is a qualified "yes," derive the inverse of the function in (i), sketch its graph, and discuss its slope.

*a) $2p + 3q = 54$.

b) $5p - 3q - 10 = 0$.

c) $\frac{3}{2}p - q = 3$.

d) $q + \frac{2}{3}p = 9$.

1.4. Assuming that sales volume is a function of advertising outlay and that the amount of advertising expense is determined as a matter of managerial policy by dollar profits, would the inverse function $g^{-1}(x) = \frac{1}{2}x + \frac{5}{4}$ in Example 1.7 make empirical sense? Does it imply a causal relationship? Discuss.

1.5. Express in functional notation the following statements using the symbols in parentheses:

*a) "The price (p) of a commodity depends on the quantity (q) demanded."

b) "The price (x) of a commodity is a function of the quantity (y) supplied."

*c) "Profits (P) depend on fixed costs (F), variable costs (V), and sales revenue (R)."

d) "Population growth (y) is a function of the initial population (x_1), the annual rate of growth (x_2), and time (x_3)."

e) "Corporate taxes (T) are determined by corporate income (I) and the rate (r) of federal corporate tax."

f) "The market price of a bond (B) depends on current interest rates (r)."

g) "The market price of stock (S) depends on corporate earnings (E)."

h) "The purchasing power of the dollar (P) is a function of the cost-of-living index (I)."

1.6. Consider the equation in Problem 4.7 in Chapter 5.

*a) Express it in functional notation form.

*b) Which is the independent and which the dependent variable?

c) Explain the meaning of the slope in terms of average rate of change.

d) Indicate the mathematical and the empirical domain and range of the function.

e) Does the inverse of the function make empirical sense? Why or why not?

1.7. For each of the equations in *(a), (b), (c), and (d) of Problem 1.3:

*a) Sketch the graph of the equation.

b) Indicate its mathematical and empirical domain and range of the function when—

i) Price is the independent variable.

ii) Quantity is the independent variable.

1.8. Consider the tables of values given in (a), (b), (c) and (d) below, where x is the independent variable.

  i) Write the ordered two-tuples given in each table.

  ii) Indicate which table defines a function and which a relation.

  iii) Plot the points given in each table on a cc-plane.

*a)

x	± 1	± 2	± 3	0	± 4
y	1	4	9	0	16

b)

x	1	4	9	0	16
y	± 1	± 2	± 3	0	± 4

*c)

x	0	1	2	3	4
y	0	1	2	3	4

d)

x	2	2	2	2	2
y	0	2	-3	-2	5

1.9. Let x be the independent variable, where $x \geqslant 0$. For each equation—

  i) Indicate whether it is a function or a relation.

  ii) Indicate the domain, range, and state the rule of each in words.

  iii) Sketch the graph of the equation.

*a) $y = x$.

*b) $y^2 = x$.

  c) $y^2 = x^2$.

  d) $y = |x|$.

1.10. Show that $y \geqslant x$ defines a relation.

1.11. Find an example of a function for which neither the range nor the domain is numerical from the following subjects:

  a) Accounting.

  b) Behavioral science.

  c) Economics.

  d) Finance.

  e) Marketing.

  f) Production.

  g) Statistics.

1.12. State the domain and range of each equation:

  *a) $y = 1/x$.

  b) $y^2 = 3x^2$.

  c) $y = \sqrt{4 - x}$.

  d) $y = \dfrac{1}{x - 1}$.

  e) $y = \sqrt{x}$.

1.13. Let the total cost function

$$f(x) = 2x + 5, \quad x \geqslant 0,$$

and let the sales revenue function

$$g(x) = 6x - 10, \quad x \geqslant 0,$$

be given, where x represents output produced and sold.

a) Find algebraically the break-even output of units produced and sold, i.e., the point at which sales revenue equals total cost.

b) Verify your answer to (a) by sketching the graphs of f and g on the same cc-plane.

c) Since profit equals revenue minus cost, find the profit function.

d) Sketch the graph of the profit function and discuss its relation to the break-even point.

1.14. If $f(x) = x^2 - 3x + 6$, find:

*a) $f(0)$.   d) $f(-2)$.

b) $f(1)$.   e) $f(a)$.

c) $f(2)$.   f) $f(m)$.

1.15. If $h(x) = 2^x$, find:

a) $h(0)$.   *d) $h(\frac{1}{2})$.

b) $h(1)$.   *e) $h(-2)$.

*c) $h(2)$.   f) $h(-\frac{1}{2})$.

1.16. If $g(x) = \dfrac{1}{x-1}$, find:

*a) $g(0)$.   d) $g(\frac{1}{2})$.

*b) $g(1)$.   e) $g(2)$.

c) $g(-1)$.   f) $g(g(a))$ simplified.

1.17. If $F(x) = 3x + 2$, find:

a) $F(a)$.

b) $F(x + h)$.

*c) $\dfrac{F(x+h) - F(x)}{h}$ simplified.

1.18. Consider the functions:

$$I = Pnr \text{ and } S = P + I$$

where

I = interest,

P = initial investment,

S = accumulated sum of principal plus interest at the end of the term,

r = annual interest rate,

n = investment period in years.

*a) Derive the simple interest formula from the given functions.

b) What sum will be accumulated from an initial investment of $1000 in 180 days at 4 percent simple annual interest rate?

c) How long would it take for an initial investment of $800 to earn $60 interest at 3 percent simple annual interest rate?

d) What principal would accumulate to $600 in 60 days at 3 percent annual simple interest rate?

1.19. Functions like ordinary numbers can be combined with operations of addition, subtraction, multiplication, and division. For example, let $f(x) = 2x$ and $g(x) = x + 1$. Then

$$h(x) = f(x) + g(x) = 2x + x + 1 = 3x + 1.$$

If $f(x) = x^2 - 1$ and $g(x) = 2x + 1$, find:

a) $f + g$.
b) $f - g$.
c) $f \times g$.
d) f/g.
e) g/f.

2. LINEAR FUNCTIONS: PREDICTION AND CONTROL

In Section 4 of the preceding chapter we briefly dealt with the problem of finding the equation of a given set of points. Now with the function concept well explained we are ready to be concerned with this important problem of analytic geometry again in greater detail.

Here, we shall illustrate how linear functions may be utilized for planning and controlling business operations. First, we shall establish logical continuity with earlier discussions by showing how to find simple linear functions from empirical situations. Then we shall deal with three special | cases: forecasting, break-even analysis, and mathematical models.|

2.1. Finding Functions. In Section 4 of the preceding chapter we have shown how the equation of a straight line can be found by applying simple formulas such as

(2.1)
$$\boxed{y = mx + b}$$

and

(2.2)
$$\boxed{\frac{y - y_1}{x - x_1} = \frac{y_2 - y_1}{x_2 - x_1}}$$

Let us see now how these formulas may be used for deriving functions from real-world situations.

Example 2.1. At the beginning of each month a store is stocked with 300 units of a particular item. If the sales of such an item average 12 units per sales day, find the function which gives the number of units in stock at any given sales day during each month.

Solution:

Let $y = f(t)$ be the number of units in stock and t the number of sales days. Since $t = 0$ when $y = 300$ and since $m = -12$, by formula (2.1) we have

$$f(t) = -12t + 300, \quad 0 \leqslant t \leqslant 25.$$

Question 1: In how many sales days would the store run out of stock?
Answer:
Since running out of stock means that $f(t) = 0$, we have

$$f(t) = -12t + 300 = 0$$

and

$$t = 25 \text{ days.}$$

Question 2: What is the stock level at $t = 12$?
Answer:
Substituting $t = 12$ in function f, we have

$$
\begin{aligned}
f(12) &= -12(12) + 300 \\
&= \quad 156 \text{ units.}
\end{aligned}
$$

Question 3: Suppose an order is placed for additional units of the item as soon as the stock level reaches 60 units, what sales day of the month is a reorder placed?
Answer:
Since reordering is made when $f(t) = 60$, we have

$$f(t) = -12t + 300 = 60$$

and

$$t = 20$$

Hence, reordering is made the 20th sales day of the month.

Example 2.2. Unless otherwise instructed by the central office, the store managers of a chain of five-and-ten stores determine the selling price of an item with a 45 percent markup on cost. Find the function which determines the selling prices of any given item.
Solution:
Let c be the cost of purchasing an item and S its selling price. Then by (2.1) we have

$$
\begin{aligned}
S(c) &= 0.45c + c \\
&= 1.45c.
\end{aligned}
$$

Question 1: If the unit of an item costs \$4.80, what is the unit selling price of the item?
Answer:
Substituting $c = 4.80$ in function S, we have

$$
\begin{aligned}
S(4.80) &= 1.45 \, (4.80) \\
&= 6.96 \text{ dollars.}
\end{aligned}
$$

Question 2: What is the selling price of an item costing \$0.60?
Answer:
Substituting $c = 0.60$ in S, we have

$$S(0.60) = 1.45(0.60) = 0.87 \text{ dollars.}$$

Example 2.3. A retailer sells an item costing \$6.00 for \$9.60 and another item costing \$0.40 for \$0.64. If these two examples represent his general markup policy for determining the selling price of most items in his store, find the function which determines the selling price of an item.

Solution:

Let c be the cost of an item and $y = S(c)$ its selling price. Substituting the coordinates of the given points (6, 9.60) and (0.40, 0.64) in formula (2.2), we have

$$\frac{y - 0.64}{c - 0.40} = \frac{9.60 - 0.64}{6 - 0.40},$$

$$5.60(y - 0.64) = 8.96(c - 0.40),$$

and

$$y = S(c) = 1.60c.$$

Sometimes, especially for functions more complicated than the ones already considered and when approximate answers are as good as exact ones, it is convenient to sketch the graph of the function and read the desired answers from the graph. The reader is invited to sketch the graph of the functions in the above examples on coordinate paper and verify the given answers.

Let us now apply formulas (2.1) and (2.2) to business problems more involved than the above.

2.2. Forecasting. One important application of linear functions is their possible use in predicting or forecasting sales, inventory, cash requirements, assets, receivables, liabilities, and other variables important in the management of business. The following example illustrates the use of linear functions in sales forecasting.

Example 2.4. The marketing research department of Continental Rubber and Tire Company compiled the data shown in Table 2.1. The

TABLE 2.1.

x	43	43.2	44.8	46	47.5	50	53.8	55	56.1	58	61	64	64.5
y	1.5	1.8	2.5	2.8	2.4	3.3	3.2	3.6	4.0	4.2	4.3	4.8	5.4

information represents the experience of 13 years, where x is the yearly passenger car population of the United States in millions and y the corresponding tire sales of the company in millions. The given data are plotted on a cc-plane, as shown in Figure 2.1. The relationship between passenger cars and tire sales is so close that management decides to use this information for forecasting next year's sales. If the passenger car population is expected to reach 68 million next year, find the tire sales function and predict next year's sales.

Solution:

A freehand straight line is fitted to the plotted points representing the given observations. Let two points be given on the straight line with

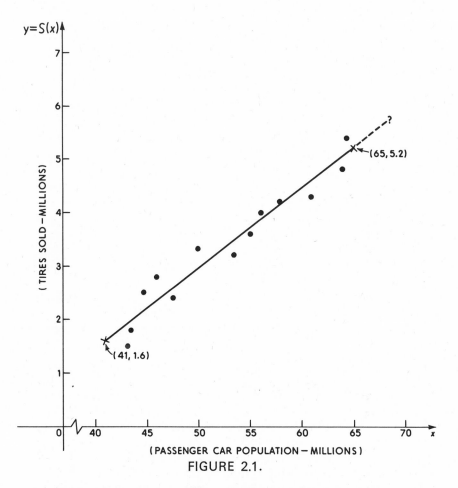

FIGURE 2.1.

coordinates (41, 1.6) and (65, 5.2)—read from a detail chart. Substituting the coordinates of these points in formula (2.2), we have

$$\frac{y - 1.6}{x - 41} = \frac{5.2 - 1.6}{65 - 41},$$

$$24(y - 1.6) = 3.6(x - 41),$$

and

$$y = S(x) = 0.15x - 4,550,000.$$

Since the passenger car population is expected to reach 68 million, substituting $x = 68,000,000$ in S we have

$$S(68,000,000) = 0.15(68,000,000) - 4,550,000$$
$$= 5,650,000.$$

Hence, next year's tire sales are expected to be 5,650,000.

In this case of sales forecast we fitted a line to observed points and used the derived linear function to predict the dependent variable from the available information about the independent variable. Other methods of predicting will be illustrated later. Here, we shall make a few remarks about this type of analysis between two variables.

Since the observed points do not fall exactly on the line but scatter about it, the line, whether fitted by freehand and another more sophisticated method, represents the value of the dependent variable y which is expected to occur on the average, given a value of the independent variable x. Hence, actual sales in Example 2.4 may be larger or smaller than the predicted sales due to this scatter of observations about the line. Under certain conditions such bivariate relationships may involve finding an interval of values instead of a point and then stating how frequently this interval is expected to include the actual value of y for a given value of x. But this is a problem of statistical estimation which lies outside the scope of this book.

Nevertheless, the reader should keep in mind that predicting or forecasting involves the assumption that the forces which are responsible for the observed covariation of x and y will continue to act collectively with the same intensity; that the less scattered the observations are about the fitted line, the more reliable the forecast is likely to be; and that, other things being equal, the longer the forecast period, the less reliable the prediction is likely to be.

2.3. The Break-Even Analysis.   The previous application of linear functions dealt with the prediction of varying quantities. Another application is the break-even analysis which is a valuable control device. For short-run planning where fixed costs are relatively stable, break-even analysis is used to determine the relative profitability of products and the effect of sales composition or mix on profits in general for the period. For long-run planning where most fixed costs are flexible, this analysis determines the point at which sales revenue meets all costs for each product line and therefore provides the means of comparing the profit potential among alternatives. Thus, break-even analysis is used for the purpose of improving the operating efficiency of existing facilities, and planning for expansion. In addition, this type of analysis serves as an effective budgetary control device.

We shall illustrate the use of the break-even analysis in order to determine the profitability of the previously made sales forecast.

> **Example 2.5.** Additional research and comparisons of results from independent methods of prediction convinced the management of the Continental Rubber and Tire Company that the forecast of 5,650,000 tires was a reasonably reliable one for the forthcoming year. However, changes in the cost structure of producing tires required a new break-even analysis in order to determine the profitability of the sales volume for next year.

The accounting department of the firm supplied the information shown in Table 2.2. The major changes in the cost structure were due to the introduction of automation in the production of tires. Automation charges increased fixed costs while gains in labor productivity reduced direct labor costs per unit of output. On the other hand, each tire was expected to sell for $10.

TABLE 2.2.

Fixed Costs (Million Dollars)		Variable Costs per Unit (Dollars)	
Regular overhead	8.6	Materials	3.60
Automation charges	5.3	Direct labor	2.27
Other burdens	1.1	Distribution costs	0.83
Total	15.0	Total	6.70

Given the above data, find the cost and sales functions and prepare a new break-even analysis.

Solution:

Step 1: Find the total cost function.

Let C stand for the total cost function and q for the number of produced tires. Since the variable cost shown in Table 2.2 is $6.70 per tire, $m = 6.70$. Similarly, inasmuch as fixed cost in Table 2.2 is 15 million, $b = 15,000,000$. Substituting in formula (2.1), we have

$$C(q) = 6.7q + 15,000,000.$$

Step 2: Find the sales revenue function.

Let S be the sales revenue function. Then by formula (2.1), we get

$$S(q) = 10q,$$

where $m = 10$ represents selling price and q number of tires sold.

Step 3: Find the break-even sales volume.

The graphs of functions C and S are sketched in Figure 2.2, where the shaded area between the two graphs below the break-even point represent, losses and above that point profits. Since at the break-even point sales revenue must equal total cost, the break-even sales volume q^* is found when

$$S(q) = C(q).$$

Substituting the functions S and C, we obtain

$$10q = 6.7q + 15,000,000$$

and

$$q^* \approx 4,545,454 \text{ tires},$$

far below the expected sales of 5,650,000 tires.

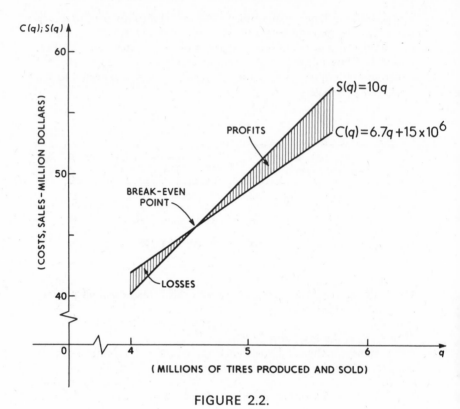

FIGURE 2.2.

Step 4: Find expected profit if next year's sales were as forecast.
Since profit before taxes represents the difference between sales revenue and total cost, the profit function P is defined by

$$P(q) = S(q) - C(q).$$

Substituting functions S and C, we have

$$P(q) = 10q - (6.7q + 15,000,000)$$
$$= 3.3q - 15,000,000,$$

where $m = 3.3$, representing the dollar increment per unit sold which can be used to meet fixed costs, is called the *contributing margin*.
Substituting $q = 5,650,000$, the forecast sales volume, in function P, we have

$$P(5,650,000) = 3.3(5,650,000) - 15,000,000$$
$$= 3,645,000 \text{ dollars profit.}$$

2.4. Mathematical Models for Business Planning.

The use of mathematical models was made increasingly possible with the advent of digital computers and increasingly necessary with the growing needs of business firms for executive action based on systematic analysis of information. Although no formal definition exists, the term *mathematical model* is used in connection with a set of functions or equations which describe in precise terms the interrelation among variables and with which a specific outcome can be determined. The break-even analysis, for example, could be considered as a simple linear mathematical model. Three linear equations show how fixed and variable costs, output, sales revenue, and profit are interrelated and how the profitability under certain conditions can be determined. We shall further illustrate the application of linear functions by introducing a mathematical model for pricing a new product.

Example 2.6. The management of Toy Products, Inc., is planning to market a new mechanical toy for the forthcoming Christmas season. One important problem in marketing a new product is pricing. In the past, prices were determined by management on the basis of production cost estimates and personal judgment. Experience has shown, however, that this pricing method is frequently unsatisfactory. Although the ultimate consumers are not considered to be price conscious, the retailers who handle the products of the firm are price conscious to a considerable degree. The research consultant who is invited to study the problem recommends the following pricing strategy. It is based on a mathematical model which determines the optimum price, i.e., the price which will yield the largest profit on the basis of both a cost function based on production cost estimates and the unit demand function based on information obtained from retailers.

TABLE 2.3.

p	2.90	3.90	4.50	4.90	5.50	5.90	6.75	7.25	8.90
$Q(p)$	6850	6500	5800	5250	4500	4400	3700	2600	600

The data in Table 2.3 were obtained from a survey of retailers, where $Q(p)$ stands for the number of units of the new toy the retailers were willing to buy for each price quotation p. Fixed costs, consisting of regular overhead and tooling for the new toy, amount to $5000. Variable costs, representing material and direct labor, are estimated at $2.00 per unit of output.

On the basis of the above information find the price for the mechanical toy which will yield the largest profit.

Solution:

Step 1: Find the unit demand function.

The data given in Table 2.3 are plotted on a cc-plane, and a freehand straight line is fitted to the points, as shown in Figure 2.3. From the chart we may read points (5.50, 4500) and (10, 0). Let p represent the price and q units of the mechanical toy. Substituting in formula (2.2), we have

$$\frac{q - 4500}{p - 5.50} = \frac{0 - 4500}{10 - 5.50},$$

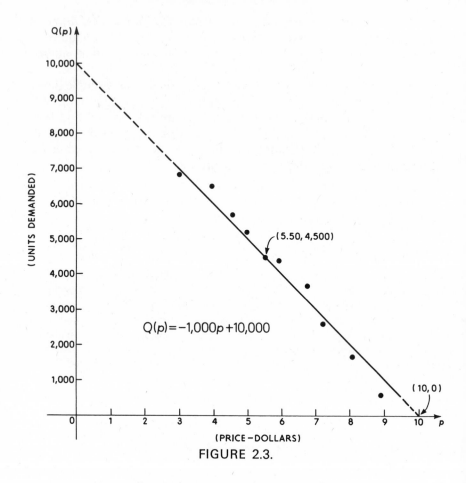

FIGURE 2.3.

$$4.50(q - 4500) = -4500(p - 5.50),$$

and

$$q = Q(p) = -1000p + 10,000.$$

Note that Q is the *unit* demand function where price is the independent and quantity the dependent variable.

Step 2: Find the total cost function.

Let C be such a function. Since fixed costs are expected to be $5000 and variable $2.00 per toy, the cost function by formula (2.1) is

$$C(q) = 2q + 5000.$$

On the basis of functions Q and C we can derive the sales revenue and profit functions. But inasmuch as both are quadratic functions, we shall continue the construction of our model in the next section.

We shall postpone until then additional general remarks about mathematical models.

2.5. Recapitulation. We conclude this section with a few comments on linear functions. In the empirical world varying quantities may and usually do not behave linearly. Under certain conditions, however, the assumption of linearity, as we have seen, may be a reasonably satisfactory approximation to solving problems which actually may involve nonlinear functions.

PROBLEMS

2.1. Sketch the graph of the function and verify the discussion in—
  a) Example 2.1.
  b) Example 2.2.
  c) Example 2.3.

2.2. Sketch the graph of the profit function P in Example 2.5 and verify the fact that $P(q) < 0$, $P(q) = 0$, and $P(q) > 0$ when sales are less than, equal, or greater than the break-even sales, respectively.

2.3. The Confidential Loan Company has the policy of charging a simple discount rate of 1.5 percent per month (t) on negotiated loans.
  a) Find the function which determines the money the borrower receives for each $100 he borrows.
  b) Sketch the graph of the function for $0 \leq t \leq 12$.
  c) If an individual borrows $500 for 6 months, how much does he actually receive?

2.4. A new machine purchased for $10,000 is expected to reduce the cost of every 1000 units of output by $75. Assuming that all cost savings are used to pay for the purchase of the machine:
  a) Find the function which describes the relationship between machine cost and savings.
  b) Sketch the graph of the function.
  c) How many units should be produced to pay for the initial cost of the machine?

2.5. Given the points (1, 2500) and (11, 1500):
  *a) Find the equation of the line passing through the given points.
  *b) Express the equation in slope-intercept form.
  c) Assuming x measures time in months and y the undepreciated value of a machine in dollars, graph the function and interpret the meaning of its slope when the function is defined in the first quadrant only.
  d) What is the original cost of the machine?
  e) How long will it take to depreciate the original cost of the machine?

2.6. Assembly workers in a plant are paid $3.75 per hour. For determining take-home pay, however, 20 percent of the gross pay is deducted for taxes and other withholdings.
  *a) Find the function which determines a worker's take-home pay.
  b) Sketch the graph of the function for $0 \leq h \leq 40$ hours.
  c) What is the take-home pay for a 35-hour workweek?

2.7. The average monthly sales revenue of a retailer is $10,000 dollars and his expenses $9550. If he starts with a net worth of $20,000, and assuming that profits are retained in the business:

*a) Find the function which determines the net value of his business at the end of t months.

b) Find the net worth of the retailer's business when $t = 12$ months.

c) Find the time which is required for the retailer's net worth to reach $35,000.

d) Prepare a table such as Table 4.2 in Chapter 5 for $t = 0, 1, 2, 4, 6, 10,$ and 15 and explain the meaning of $\Delta y/\Delta t$.

2.8. If it costs $4.75 to transport one pound of merchandise 600 miles by air and $19.75, 3000 miles:

*a) Find the function which describes the relationship between cost of air transportation and mileage, assuming that this relationship is linear.

b) Sketch the graph of the function.

c) Prepare a table such as Table 4.2 in Chapter 5 for $x = 0, 100, 200, 300, 1000, 2000,$ and 4000 miles and explain the meaning of $\Delta y/\Delta x$.

2.9. A retailer sells an item costing $5.00 for $7.00 and another item costing $0.40 for $0.56. If these two examples represent his general markup policy in determining the selling price of every item in his store—

*a) Find the function which determines the selling price of an item.

b) Determine the selling price of an item costing $7.50 and another costing $0.73.

c) Sketch the graph of the function and verify your answers to (b) by reading these answers from the graph.

d) Find the inverse of the selling price function and determine the cost of an item selling for $9.90 and of another selling for $0.69.

e) Sketch the graph of the inverse function and verify your answers to (d) by reading the same answers from the graph.

2.10. A railroad company follows the policy of charging $0.50 per mile for moving a carload the first 100 miles over a particular 500-mile route. The carload is transported an additional distance of 100 miles without additional charge, while for the remaining 300 miles of the route there is a freight charge of $0.30 per mile.

*a) Sketch the graph of the relationship between transportation costs and mileage for the entire 500-mile route.

b) Find the function of this relationship.

c) Find the function which determines the transportation cost and the average freight charge per mile for transporting a carload over the entire route.

2.11. In the past the financial needs of Food Consolidated, Inc., a baby food processing company, were estimated in terms of the number of days' sales tied up in an individual item of the balance sheet. Thus, depending on past experience, it was determined that the firm would need 5 days' sales in cash, 25 days' sales in inventory, 40 days' sales in receivables, and so on and so forth. Although under certain conditions this method was dependable for estimating the financial needs of the firm, it was found to be misleading because of market growth factors. The research department of the company suggested that an analysis like the one in Example 2.4 might be a more reliable method than the ordinary technique for both forecasting sales and estimating the financial requirements of the firm. Thereupon, the data shown in the following table were compiled.

a) Plot the population and sales observations for each given year on coordinate paper, fit a freehand straight line to the points, find the function of the fitted line, and forecast next year's baby food sales, given that the baby population in that year is estimated at 4.50 million.

b) Select any one of the other variables from the table and do the following:

i) Plot sales and the selected variable on coordinate paper and fit a freehand straight line to the points.

ii) Find the function of the fitted line and estimate next year's value of the selected variable on the basis of next year's sales forecast you found in (a).

c) Discuss the reliability of the forecasts in terms of the limitations explained in the text.

Data for Sales Forecasting and for Estimating the Financial Requirements of Food Consolidated, Inc.
(Baby Population in Millions; All Other Variables in Millions of Dollars) *

Year (1)	Baby Popula- tion (P) (2)	Sales (S) (3)	Inven- tories (I) (4)	Receiv- ables (R) (5)	Cash Marketable Secur- ities (C) (6)	Current Assets (A) (7)	Current Liabil- ities (L) (8)
1	2.15	36.3	4.0	5.5	3.5	16.5	4.9
2	2.32	53.1	6.5	6.0	9.0	24.0	6.5
3	2.60	65.0	9.8	9.1	7.6	31.8	10.0
4	2.85	74.3	9.2	11.5	11.4	30.5	13.5
5	3.10	85.0	13.0	10.9	9.3	38.0	13.0
6	3.38	97.4	14.7	13.1	7.9	42.3	17.2
7	3.65	108.6	14.9	15.7	15.0	43.8	17.9
8	3.87	128.0	16.8	16.8	10.7	54.5	21.2
9	4.10	139.5	22.0	20.0	15.2	60.2	24.9
10	4.35	157.2	21.2	20.9	17.8	63.0	25.8

*Hypothetical data.

2.12. Assuming that each baby food unit in Problem 2.11 sells for $0.20 fixed costs are $10 million, and variable costs $0.18 per unit produced:

*a) Find the sales, cost, and profit functions.

b) What is the break-even sales volume?

c) What is the break-even sales revenue?

d) Find the realizable profit if next year's actual sales were as forecast.

e) Sketch a break-even chart and verify your answers to (b), (c), and (d).

2.13. An important process in the economic progress of a country is the replacement of human effort with machines. If it costs $15 to move one cubic yard of earth for building a dam by human effort while it costs $5.00 to do the same job with a machine plus a fixed cost of $1000—
a) Find the cost function for human and machine effort.
b) Find the minimum number of cubic yards required for replacing human effort with a machine and discuss the implications of your findings.
c) Sketch the graph of the functions and verify your answer to (b).

2.14. The manager in charge of the dining service on the Silver Arrow, a special train serving two metropolitan areas, collected the following information:

Pullman Reservations	Meals Served
125	280
233	496

Assuming that the above pullman reservations represent the lowest and the highest number of reservations in the past and that the relationship between reservations and meals served is linear—
a) Find the function which describes this relationship.
b) How many meals does the manager expect to serve if there are 175 pullman reservations during a given train run?
c) How precise is your answer to (b)? Discuss.

2.15. In Example 2.5 the management of the Continental Rubber and Tire Company must sell 4,545,454.5 tires to break even. This break-even sales volume, however, as well as expected profits, is determined on the basis of a fixed output of 5.65 million tires. But sales may fall short of the expected volume, and management would like to determine the break-even points for varying outputs. For this purpose $5.65 million of the initial fixed cost of $15 million are considered variable. Thus, for overage, i.e., for produced and unsold tires, there is a cost of $1.00 per tire called *activity variation loss*.
a) Sketch a full scale break-even chart of the original sales revenue and cost functions given in Example 2.5.
b) Let q_s represent the number of tires sold and q_p the number produced. Use the x-axis to measure production volume q_p and activity variation loss (L) where $L = \$5.65$ million when $q_p = 0$ and $L = 0$ when $q_p = 5.65$ million tires. Draw a line parallel to the y-axis at $q_p = 5.65$ million and designate it $q_{p/s}$ scale.
c) If each tire sells for $10, find the cost and profit functions for varying output q_p and sales q_s levels.
d) Find the break-even points when—
   i) $q_p = 5.65$ million tires.
   ii) Losses due to overage are zero.
e) Locate the break-even point where $q_p = q_s$ on the $q_{p/s}$ scale, draw a straight line to connect the initial break-even point and the new break-even point, and verify the fact that this line represents the locus of every $q_{p/s}$ break-even combination when $q_p \geq q_s$.

f) Let q_i represent the beginning inventory of tires in million units and consider the case of underage, i.e., when $q_p < q_s$. Since beginning inventory does not involve activity variation loss, there is a saving of $1.00 for every inventory unit sold. Assuming other conditions remain unchanged, find the cost and profit functions for varying inventory q_i and sales q_s levels.

g) Find the break-even point when gains due to underage are zero.

h) Designate the q_p x-axis as $q_{p/i}$ axis and extend the break-even line you drew in (*e*) up to that point. Verify the fact that this line represents the locus of every $q_{i/s}$ break-even combination when $q_p < q_s$. Designate the area of the chart which represents potential profit for expected sales of 5.65 million tires.

3. QUADRATIC FUNCTIONS: APPLICATIONS

The following topics are covered in this section: quadratic functions and equations; the lowest or highest point and other characteristics of graphs of quadratic functions; the rate of change of the dependent variable with respect to the independent variable; and three cases illustrating the application of quadratic functions in business operations.

3.1. Quadratic Functions and Equations. As in the case of linear functions, there is a close association between quadratic functions and equations. Consider the general quadratic function

(3.1) $$\boxed{f(x) = ax^2 + bx + c,}$$

where *a*, *b*, and *c* are constants and $a \neq 0$. Letting $f(x) = 0$ we obtain the corresponding quadratic equation in *x* of the general form

$$ax^2 + bx + c = 0$$

studied earlier. In fact, *the real, rational, or irrational roots of a quadratic equation in x are the x-coordinates of the points where the graph of the corresponding quadratic function cuts the x-axis.*

Example 3.1. Let function *f* be defined by

$$f(x) = x^2 - x - 2.$$

Sketch the graph of *f* and show the above relationship between the function *f* and its corresponding equation $x^2 - x - 2 = 0$.

Solution:

The values of the function *f* shown in Table 3.1 are obtained by substituting in *f* the various values of the independent variable *x*. For instance let $x = -3$, then

$$f(-3) = (-3)^2 - (-3) - 2 = 10.$$

Plotting the points whose coordinates are given in Table 3.1 on a cc-plane and joining them with a smooth curve, we obtain the graph of the func-

TABLE 3.1.

x	-3	-2	-1	0	$\frac{1}{2}$	1	2	3	4
$f(x)$	10	4	0	-2	$-\frac{9}{4}$	-2	0	4	10

tion in Figure 3.1. It can be seen that the graph of f cuts the x-axis at points $(2, 0)$ and $(-1, 0)$ where x is 2 and -1. But these values of x are also the roots or solutions of the corresponding quadratic equation.

$$x^2 - x - 2 = 0$$

since

$$f(2) = (2)^2 - (2) - 2 = 0$$

and

$$f(-1) = (-1)^2 - (-1) - 2 = 0.$$

This observation suggests that with the aid of sufficiently detailed coordinate paper the graph of a function can be used to estimate approximately the roots of the corresponding quadratic equation with real coefficients.

Example 3.2. Let the function f be defined by

$$f(x) = -x^2 + 6x + 2.$$

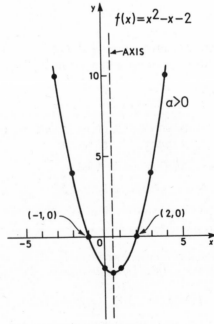

FIGURE 3.1.

Sketch the graph of f and estimate approximately the roots of the corresponding equation

$$-x^2 + 6x + 2 = 0.$$

Solution:

The coordinates of a selected number of points of the graph of f are shown in Table 3.2. The graph of f is sketched in Figure 3.2. It can be seen

TABLE 3.2.

x	-1	0	1	2	3	4	5	6	7
$f(x)$	-5	2	7	10	11	10	7	2	-5

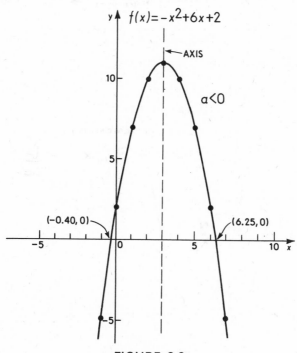

FIGURE 3.2.

that the graph of f cuts the x-axis approximately at points $(-0.40, 0)$ and $(6.25, 0)$. Hence, the roots of the corresponding quadratic equation are approximately

$$r_1 = -0.40 \quad \text{and} \quad r_2 = 6.25.$$

The reader may verify that the roots are

$$r_1 = -0.316625 \quad \text{and} \quad r_2 = 6.316625$$

exactly by solving $-x^2 + 6x + 2 = 0$ with the quadratic formula.

Furthermore, *it can be proved that for a quadratic equation in x with a double root the graph of the corresponding quadratic function is tangent to the x-axis.* Here, we simply illustrate this theorem.

Example 3.3. Consider the function f defined by

$$f(x) = x^2 - 4x + 4.$$

Sketch the graph of function f and show the above relationship between f and its corresponding equation $x^2 - 4x + 4 = 0$.

Solution:

Table 3.3 contains selective values of f and the graph of f is sketched in

TABLE 3.3.

x	-1	0	1	2	3	4	5
$f(x)$	9	4	1	0	1	4	9

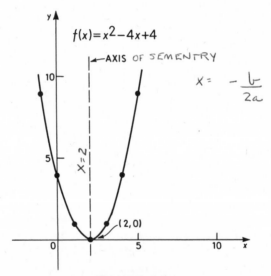

FIGURE 3.3.

Figure 3.3. It can be seen that the graph of f is tangent to the x-axis at $x = 2$. But this value of x is the double root of the corresponding equation since

$$f(2) = (2)^2 - 4(2) + 4 = 0.$$

3.2. The Vertex and Other Characteristics of a Parabola.

The graph of a quadratic function is called a *parabola*. Since quadratic functions are important in later discussions, we shall study their graphs, especially the minimum or maximum point called the *vertex* of the parabola, systematically.

For this purpose we shall analyze the general quadratic function (3.1). Factoring out the coefficient a in (3.1), we have

$$y = a\left[x^2 + \frac{b}{a}x + \frac{c}{a}\right],$$

where $y = f(x)$. Completing the square by adding and subtracting $b^2/4a^2$, we have

$$y = a\left[\left(x^2 + \frac{b}{a}x + \frac{b^2}{4a^2}\right) + \frac{c}{a} - \frac{b^2}{4a^2}\right],$$

and by factoring and adding fractions, we obtain

$$y = a\left[\left(x + \frac{b}{2a}\right)^2 + \frac{4ac - b^2}{4a^2}\right]$$

or

(3.2)
$$y = a\left(x + \frac{b}{2a}\right)^2 - \frac{b^2 - 4ac}{4a}.$$

Now, observe that the value of y in (3.2) depends on the term $(x + b/2a)^2$ which contains variable x; and since the square of a real number is either positive or zero, the smallest value for $(x + b/2a)^2$ is obtained when $x = -(b/2a)$.

a) If coefficient a is positive, the smallest value that y can take occurs when $x = -(b/2a)$.

b) If coefficient a is negative, the largest value that y can take occurs when $x = -(b/2a)$. Hence,

$$x = -\frac{b}{2a} \quad \text{and} \quad y = \frac{4ac - b^2}{4a}$$

are the coordinates of the vertex of a parabola.

The above analysis reveals the following important points about the graph of a quadratic function.

1. The graph of the general quadratic function (3.1) is a parabola with its vertex at

VERTEX

(3.3)
$$x = -\frac{b}{2a} \quad \text{and} \quad y = \frac{4ac - b^2}{4a}.$$

If the coefficient a of (3.1) is positive, then the graph of (3.1) is concave upward or U-shaped, and the vertex is the minimum point on the graph. If a is negative, then the graph of (3.1) is concave downward or inverted U-shaped and the vertex is the maximum point on the graph.

Example 3.4. Consider function f defined by

$$f(x) = x^2 - x - 2.$$

Find the vertex of f and determine whether it represents a maximum or a minimum.

Solution:

Substituting $a = 1$, $b = -1$, and $c = -2$ in (3.3), we have

$$x = -\frac{-1}{2(1)} = \frac{1}{2}$$

and

$$y = \frac{4(1)(-2) - (-1)^2}{4(1)} = -\frac{9}{4}.$$

Hence, the vertex is $(\frac{1}{2}, -\frac{9}{4})$ as shown in Table 3.1.

Since $a > 0$, this vertex is a minimum and the graph of f is concave upward, as shown in Figure 3.1.

The reader can repeat the above analysis for the function given in Example 3.2 in order to verify that the vertex is a maximum with coordinates $(3, 11)$ and the graph of f is concave downward.

2. Sketching the graph of (3.1) may be facilitated by finding the coordinates of the vertex. This is so because the graph of (3.1) is symmetrical with respect to the line at $x = -(b/2a)$, called the *axis of symmetry* of the parabola. The axis of symmetry is the broken line in Figures 3.1, 3.2, and 3.3 which separates each parabola into two halves so that one is the mirror image of the other. The graph of (3.1) may be sketched by finding the vertex, the y-intercept $(0, c)$, and real roots, if any, of the corresponding equation.

Example 3.5. Sketch the graph of f defined by

$$f(x) = x^2 - x - 2.$$

Solution:

In Example 3.4 we have found that the coordinates of the vertex are $(\frac{1}{2}, -\frac{9}{4})$. From the roots of the corresponding equation $x^2 - x - 2$ found in Example 3.1 we obtained the points $(2, 0)$ and $(-1, 0)$ of the graph of f. Letting $x = 0$, $f(0) = -2$ which is the y-intercept of the graph of f at point $(0, -2)$.

The graph of f shown in Figure 3.1, could have been sketched with the coordinates of the above points. However, the coordinates of additional points can be easily obtained, if required, by taking values on one side of $x = \frac{1}{2}$, the x-coordinate of the vertex, *only* at certain intervals and solving for y. For instance, let $x = 3$ then

$$f(3) = (3)^2 - (3) - 2 = 4.$$

Hence, point $(3, 4)$ is a point on the graph of f. The corresponding point on the other side of the axis of symmetry has the same y-coordinate 4 and an x-coordinate -2 because $x = -2$ and $x = 3$ lie equidistant from $x = \frac{1}{2}$ on the x-axis.

3. If the term $b^2 - 4ac$ in (3.2), called the *discriminant*, is a positive number, the graph of (3.1) crosses the x-axis at two distinct points which represent the two roots of the corresponding equation (Figure 3.1); if the discriminant equals zero, the graph of f is tangent to the x-axis at $x = -(b/2a)$ which represents the double root of the corresponding equation (Figure 3.3); if the discriminant is negative, the graph of (3.1) never touches the x-axis and the roots of the corresponding equation are conjugate complex numbers.

3.3 The Instantaneous or Marginal Rate of Change.

Earlier we introduced the average rate of change $\triangle y / \triangle x$, i.e., the rate of change of y with respect to x over a given interval in the case of a linear function. Obviously, we cannot use the average rate of change in the case of a quadratic function since in a second-degree curve y varies with x at a changing rate; in other words, the graph of the general quadratic function (3.1) is a curve no portion of which is a straight line. We are faced, therefore, with the problem of finding the rate of change of y with respect to x *not over a given interval $\triangle x$ but at a given value of x called the instantaneous or marginal rate of change.*

An example from the physical world may amply illustrate this new concept. An object dropped from a high point falls faster and faster as it approaches the surface of the earth. Let y be the distance covered by the falling object in x seconds, then y is a function of x and the speed with which the object falls at a given instant of time is the instantaneous rate of change of y with respect to x. Conceivably, the average speed of the falling object for a given time interval beginning with the given instant will approximate closer and closer the instantaneous speed at that instant for a smaller and smaller time interval.

This approach, however, leads to the limit concept and differential calculus which will be taken up in Part IV. At that time, we shall develop efficient and accurate methods for finding the instantaneous rate of change. In the meantime, we can approximate it graphically since the instantaneous rate of change at a given point of a curve corresponds to the slope of the tangent at that point, as the following example illustrates.

Example 3.6. Let function f be defined by

$$f(x) = \frac{x^2}{100}, \qquad x \geqslant 0,$$

where x represents dollar investment in farming and $y = f(x)$ total wheat production in bushels. Estimate graphically the instantaneous rate of increase in wheat output when investment is $1000.

Solution:

The graph of f is sketched in Figure 3.4 where at point P (1000, 10,000) investment $x = \$1000$ and wheat output $y = 10,000$ bushels. The instantaneous rate of wheat output increase at x may be estimated as follows:

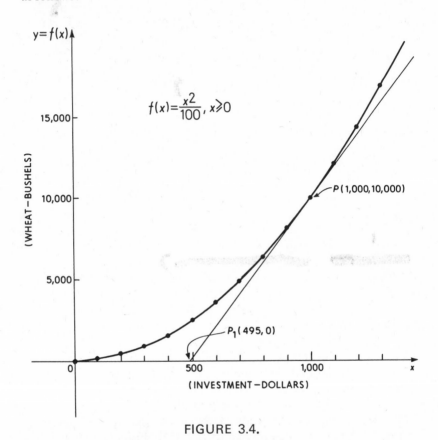

$y = f(x)$

$$f(x) = \frac{x^2}{100}, \ x \geqslant 0$$

15,000

(WHEAT — BUSHELS)

10,000 — P(1,000, 10,000)

5,000

P_1(495, 0)

0   500   1,000 x

(INVESTMENT — DOLLARS)

FIGURE 3.4.

We draw a straight line tangent to the graph of f at point P, as shown in Figure 3.4. This tangent crosses the x-axis at point P_1(495, 0) (coordinates read from the graph). Substituting the coordinates of points P and P_1 in

$$m = \frac{y_2 - y_1}{x_2 - x_1}$$

we have

$$m = \frac{10,000 - 0}{1000 - 495} = 19\frac{81}{101}$$

the slope of the straight line tangent to the graph of f at point P. Hence, the instantaneous or marginal rate of wheat production at $x = \$1000$ investment is approximately $19\frac{81}{101}$ bushels.

It would be unrealistic to assume that wheat production in the above example will increase indefinitely. For a given state in farm technology the employment of additional machinery and labor on limited land will bring about *diminishing returns*, i.e., a slowing down and eventually a decline in total wheat output. Thus, the graph in Figure 3.4 may describe an empirical situation for limited values of investment x. For this empirically meaningful range of x the instantaneous rate of change measures the *marginal efficiency of investment*, i.e., it represents the rate of wheat output at the margin of $1000 investment. This discussion describes a type of analysis, called *marginal*, which is important in understanding managerial decisions. For in many situations a decision may be made on the basis of whether the last "dollar" spent will maximize profits or minimize costs.

3.4. Quadratic Functions in Business Operations.

Business operations may differ widely in their managerial policies and immediate objectives; yet if a business enterprise is to survive and grow in a competitive business world of uncertainty and unpredictability, its long-run objective must be the realization of profit. Thus, situations which require finding an optimum or other important relation among varying quantities are central to a great variety of business operations. We shall illustrate applications of quadratic functions to such empirical situations with three motivating cases.

Case 1: In the preceding section we have shown how with break-even analysis we are able, given the cost and sales revenue functions, to determine the minimum sales volume required for the firm to meet all costs. In a sense, therefore, break-even analysis may be considered an optimization technique. The following example illustrates a case for maximizing profit with a quadratic function.

Example 3.7. Let us consider again the manager of a real estate firm who faces the problem of determining the monthly rental for each of the 60 newly built apartment units (Example 1.7, Chapter 5). At a rental of $80 per month, all apartment units will be occupied. But one apartment unit is likely to remain vacant for each $2.00 increase in rent. Also, an occupied apartment requires $8.00 more per month than a vacant one for service and maintenance.

Find the function which expresses the relationship between gross profit and number of unoccupied apartment units.

Solution:

Let x represent the number of vacant apartment units. Then the rental per occupied apartment is

$$(80 + 2x),$$

the number of occupied apartments are

$$(60 - x),$$

and the extra operational cost for all the occupied apartment units is

$$8(60 - x).$$

Since rental times the occupied apartment minus operational cost equals gross profit, the gross profit function P is

$$P(x) = (80 + 2x)(60 - x) - 8(60 - x);$$

and by multiplying and collecting terms, we have

$$P(x) = -2x^2 + 48x + 4320.$$

Question 1: What is the number of vacant apartments x for which gross profit is largest?
Answer:
Substituting the coefficients $a = -2$ and $b = 48$ of the gross profit function P in

$$x = -\frac{b}{2a}$$

of (3.3), we have

$$x = -\frac{48}{2(-2)} = 12.$$

Since the coefficient a of function P is negative, the vertex of the graph of P is a maximum and $x = 12$ is the number of vacant apartments when profit is largest.
Question 2: What is this maximum gross profit?
Answer:
Substituting the coefficients $a = -2$, $b = 48$, and $c = 4320$ of function P in

$$y = \frac{4ac - b^2}{4a}$$

of (3.3), we have

$$y = \frac{4(-2)(4320) - (48)^2}{4(-2)} = 4608 \text{ dollars.}$$

The empirically meaningful portion of the graph of function P is shown in Figure 3.5 where point V (12, 4608) is the vertex of the parabola. Observe that when no apartment units are vacant gross profit is \$4320. Also gross profit decreases when more than 12 apartment units are vacant. It falls to \$4320 when 24 apartment units become vacant.
Question 3: What is the rental for this optimum?
Answer:
Since the rental for any value of x is $(80 + 2x)$, substituting $x = 12$ we find the optimal rental to be $80 + 2(12) = 104$ dollars.

Case 2: Very frequently finding the profit or the cost function in a business situation may require *fitting* a parabolic curve to empirical data. We shall use our knowledge about quadratic functions to illustrate such a situation.

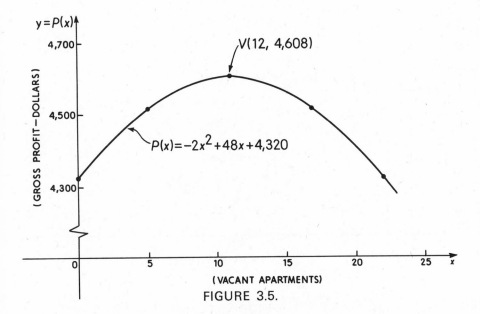

FIGURE 3.5.

Example 3.8. Precision Products, Inc., is producing a machine part for an arsenal of the U.S. Army. Determining the cost of producing an order of parts is time consuming because it varies with the size of each run. The manager in charge of production wants to find a way with which the total cost per run could be quickly approximated. From the records he selects at random 30 runs and plots the average cost of producing a part against the size of each run, as shown in Figure 3.6. He observes that the y-intercept of the curve fitted to the data is about $3000. Also on the basis of the available data the manager observes that a run of 500 parts with $500 cost per part represents a typical minimum average production cost per part.

Given this information, find the total production cost function for a given run.

Solution:
First, find the average cost function per part in a given run.
Step 1: Find coefficient a.

Since the coordinates of the vertex V of the parabola shown in Figure 3.6 are $x = 500$ and $y = 500$, by (3.3) we have

$$x = -\frac{b}{2a} = 500$$

and

$$y = \frac{4ac - b^2}{4a} = 500.$$

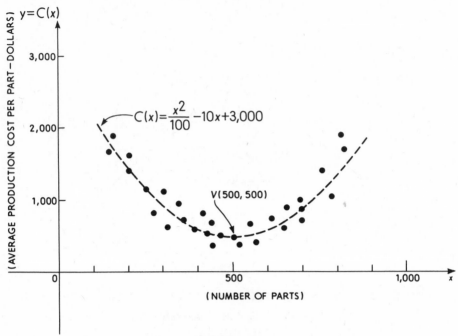

FIGURE 3.6.

Solving the first equation for b, we get
$$b = -1000a.$$
Since the y-intercept of the function is $c = 3000$, substituting in
$$\frac{4ac - b^2}{4a} = 500$$
we have
$$\frac{12{,}000a - b^2}{4a} = 500;$$
and solving for b^2, we get
$$b^2 = 10{,}000a.$$
But $b^2 = (-1000a)^2$, therefore
$$(-1000a)^2 = 10{,}000a$$
$$1{,}000{,}000a^2 - 10{,}000a = 0$$
$$a(1{,}000{,}000a - 10{,}000) = 0$$
and $a = \frac{1}{100}$ since for this value of a the last expression above equals zero.

Step 2: Find coefficient b.

Substituting $a = \frac{1}{100}$ in
$$b = -1000a,$$
we get
$$b = -1000\left(\frac{1}{100}\right) = -10.$$

Step 3: Find average cost function per part.

Since $a = \frac{1}{100}$, $b = -10$, and $c = 3000$, by formula (3.1) the average cost function C is

$$C(x) = \frac{x^2}{100} - 10x + 3000, \qquad 150 \leqslant x \leqslant 850.$$

The empirically meaningful portion of the graph of C is the broken curve in Figure 3.6.

Second, find the total cost function per run.

Since total cost equals average cost times the number of parts produced, multiplying the average cost function C by x, we get

$$T(x) = \left(\frac{x^2}{100} - 10x + 3000\right)x$$

$$= \frac{x^3}{100} - 10x^2 + 3000x, \qquad 150 \leqslant x \leqslant 850.$$

which is the total cost function per run.

With this function the manager was able to find quickly the approximate cost of a run if its size fell within the limits established by experience.

Case 3: The mathematical model for pricing the new mechanical toy which we started in the previous section is another application of quadratic functions to business operations.

Example 3.9. In Example 2.6 of the previous section we found that the unit demand function Q for the new toy is

$$Q(p) = q = -1000p + 10,000$$

and the total cost function C is

$$C(q) = 2q + 5000.$$

We wish to find the profit function in order to determine the price for the toy which yields maximum profit.

Solution:

Step 1: Find the total cost function in terms of the independent variable price p.

Substituting $q = -1000p + 10,000$ in function C, we have

$$C(-1000p + 10,000) = 2(-1000p + 10,000) + 5000$$

and

$$C(p) = -2000p + 25,000.$$

Step 2: Find sales revenue function.

Since sales revenue equals units sold times price, the sales revenue function S is

$$qp = (-1000p + 10,000)p$$

and

$$S(p) = -1000p^2 + 10,000p.$$

Step 3: Find profit function.

Since profit equals sales revenue minus cost, the profit function P is

$$P(p) = S(p) - C(p).$$

Substituting functions S and C, we get

$$P(p) = (-1000p^2 + 10{,}000p) - (-2000p + 25{,}000);$$

and adding common terms, we obtain

$$P(p) = -1000p^2 + 12{,}000p - 25{,}000.$$

The relationship between the sales revenue, cost, and profit functions is shown graphically in Figure 3.7.

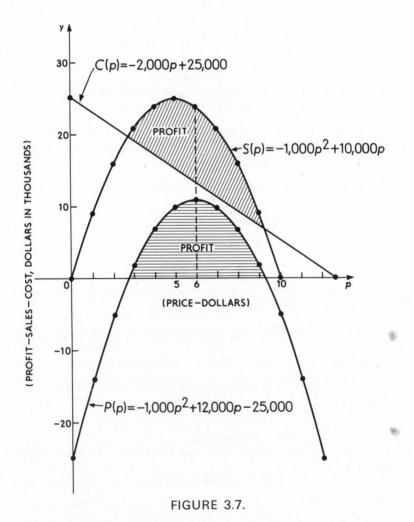

FIGURE 3.7.

Question 1: What is the optimum price p^* for the toy?
Answer:
Substituting the coefficient $a = -1000$ and $b = 12,000$ of function P
in

$$p^* = -\frac{b}{2a}$$

of formula (3.3), we have

$$p^* = -\frac{12,000}{(-2000)} = 6 \text{ dollars.}$$

Question 2: What is the maximum realizable profit for $p^* = \$6$?
Answer:
Substituting $p = 6$ in the profit function P, we have

$$P(6) = -1000(6)^2 + 12,000(6) - 25,000$$
$$= 11,000 \text{ dollars.}$$

Question 3: What is the sales volume for p^*?
Answer:
Substituting $p = 6$ in the unit demand function Q, we obtain

$$Q(6) = -1000(6) + 10,000$$
$$= 4000 \text{ toys.}$$

3.5. General Remarks. Before concluding this section, a few general remarks should be made about mathematical models and optimization. With Example 3.9 we demonstrated how a simple mathematical model consisting of linear and quadratic functions can be used for general business planning. The model enabled us to employ all available information, to synthesize the demand and cost relationships, and to define in precise terms the interrelationship between the key variables of the problem in terms of a closely knit system of equations. Furthermore, using the rules of algebra, we were able to obtain the optimal solution for our problem, i.e., the price which yields the largest profit. More than that, a model such as this can be used to derive a general pricing formula which can be applied to similar situations involving linear demand and cost functions. Thus, since mathematics is a rich reservoir of analytical tools, building models with these tools is a unique and versatile technique for managerial decisions. In fact, the use of mathematical models in business operations is part of the rapidly growing "information technology" which includes data processing systems, mathematical programming, and simulation.

On the other hand, finding the cost-sales revenue relationship for the largest profit may be considered part of the effort of a business firm to economize on scarce resources for profit. But management may have goals which are in conflict with the optimal solutions found through quantitative analysis. In Example 3.7 we found that the real estate manager could realize a maximum gross profit of $4608. This profit, however, could have been obtained by deciding to raise the rental for each apartment unit by $24 to $104, while as many as 12 units were likely to become vacant. Management may feel that such a decision may cause loss of goodwill which may be valued more than the additional realizable profit of $288 (4608 − 4320). Therefore, the real estate manager may decide not to raise the price at all or to compromise by keeping an intermediate rental between $80 and $104. Similarly, the management of Toy Products, Inc., may consider that maximizing sales revenue is more important than maximizing profit. Thereupon, the decision may be made to price the new mechanical toy at $5.00 for a maximum sales revenue of $25,000 instead of $24,000 and a profit of $10,000 instead of the maximum $11,000. In short, optimal solution through quantitative analysis may be in conflict with other managerial goals and therefore must be reconciled with the overall policies of the firm. In this sense, quantitative analysis in most cases is likely to be a suboptimization effort.

PROBLEMS

3.1. Sketch the graph of each of the following functions by finding first the vertex of the parabola as explained in text. AND LET Y=O, FIND ROOTS

*a) $y = x^2 + 25$.   2 *g) $y = -3x^2 + 44x$.

*b) $y = x^2 - 8x + 20$.   *h) $y = -x^2 + 8x - 6$.

c) $y = x^2 - 20x - 101$.   i) $y = -x^2 + 16x - 36$.

d) $y = 2x^2 - 18x + 40$.   j) $y = -x^2 + 30$.

e) $y = 4x^2 - 16x + 16$.   k) $y = -5x^2 + 10x + 7$.

f) $y = 5x^2 + 2x$.   l) $y = -2x^2 + 8x$.

3.2. Discuss the position of the graph of each function in *(a), *(b), (c), (d), (e), (f), *(g), *(h), (i), (j), (k), and (l) of Problem 3.1 with respect to the x-axis in terms of the discriminant $b^2 - 4ac$ of the quadratic formula.

3.3. From the graph of each function in *(a), *(b), (c), (d), (e), (f), *(g), *(h), (i), (j), (k), and (l) of Problem 3.1 verify the fact that the coefficient a of the term x^2 determines the concavity of the graph.

3.4. Estimate graphically the roots of the equation which corresponds to each of the functions in (d), (e), (h), (i), (j), (k), and (l) of Problem 3.1. Verify your estimation by finding the roots of the equation with the quadratic formula.

3.5. Estimate graphically the roots of the following equations:

a) $x^3 + 2x^2 - 5x - 6 = 0$.

b) $2x^3 - 4x^2 - 7x + 12 = 0$.

c) $x^4 + x^3 - x - 1 = 0$.

d) $x^4 + 2x^3 - x^2 + 3 = 0$.

e) $x^5 + 2x^4 - x^3 + 2x^2 - 2 = 0$.

3.6. Estimate graphically the instantaneous rate of change at the indicated values of x for the functions in Problem 3.1.

    *a) $x = 3$, $x = -3$.
    b) $x = 4$, $x = 2$.
    c) $x = 12$, $x = 10$.
    d) $x = 4\frac{1}{2}$, $x = 7$.
    e) $x = 5$.
    f) $x = 2$.
    *g) $x = 7\frac{1}{3}$, $x = 9$, $x = 3$.
    h) $x = 2$, $x = 4$, $x = 6$.
    i) $x = 5$, $x = 8$, $x = 11$.
    j) $x = 2$, $x = -2$.
    k) $x = 1$, $x = 3$.
    l) $x = 2$, $x = 1$, $x = 4$.

3.7. The graph below has a minimum point $A(15, 6)$ and a maximum point $B(27, 16)$. Let m represent the instantaneous rate of change of y over x and x_m the value of the x-coordinate at points A and B. Select values of $x \neq x_m$ and estimate the instantaneous rate of change for each value of x to show that point A is indeed a relative minimum since $m < 0$ for $x < x_m$ and $m > 0$ for $x > x_m$, while point B is indeed a relative maximum since $m > 0$ for $x < x_m$ and $m < 0$ for $x > x_m$.

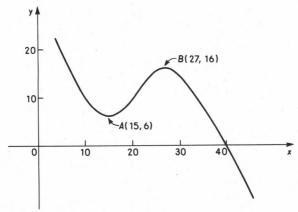

*3.8. Consider Problem 1.14, Chapter 5, and find how long the rancher should wait in order to realize the largest profit.
    a) What is this maximum profit?
    b) Determine the profit per pound and the quantity for the maximum profit.
    c) Sketch the graph of the profit function and verify your answers above graphically.

3.9. Management's goal in Problem 1.15, Chapter 5, was to offer service to the largest possible number of people for the same gross receipts. Let us assume that the manager of the railroad decides to maximize net revenue instead and also to consider the additional costs which amounted to one dollar for each extra passenger.

   a) Determine the fare and the number of passengers for the maximum net revenue.

   b) What is the maximum net revenue?

   c) Verify your answers to (*a*) and (*b*) graphically.

   d) In what sense does management suboptimize in deciding to maximize net revenue?

*3.10. For Problem 1.16, Chapter 5, find the output for which total production cost is highest.

   a) What is the total production cost for this run?

   b) What is the per unit cost of this production run?

   c) Graph the total production cost function.

   d) Find the per unit cost for production runs of 800, 1050, 1300, 1400, 1500, 1750, and 2000 units, and derive the per unit cost function.

3.11. Let the unit demand function be $y = 18 - 2x$, where x represents units demanded and y price. Then the sales revenue function is $S(x) = (18 - 2x)x = 18x - 2x^2$. Also, suppose average cost per unit is $6.00 so that the total cost function $C(x) = 6x$.

   *a) Find the profit function P.

   *b) Determine the quantity and price for which the profit is maximum. Find maximum profit.

   *c) Interpret your answer to (*b*) by sketching in the same diagram the sales revenue S, the total cost C, and the profit P functions.

   d) If price y is the independent variable, then the unit demand function is $x = \frac{1}{2}(18 - y)$ and the total cost function is

$$T(y) = 6x = 6\left[\frac{1}{2}(18 - y)\right] = 54 - 3y.$$

   Find the sales revenue function R and the profit function F.

   e) Determine the quantity and price for the maximum profit. Find maximum profit and verify your answer by sketching the graph of F.

   f) Sketch the graphs of the sales revenue R and total cost T functions in the same diagram and compare your answers to (*e*).

3.12. If the unit demand function is $y = 12 - 3x$, where x represents quantity demanded at price y, and the average cost function is $c = x + 4$—

   a) Find the sales revenue S and total cost C functions.

   b) Find the profit function P.

   c) Determine the quantity and price for the maximum profit. Find maximum profit.

   d) Verify your answer to (*c*) by sketching the graph of the profit function P.

   e) Sketch the S and C functions in the same diagram and compare it with your graphical interpretation of maximum profit in (*d*).

3.13. For each case indicated below:

   i) Approximate the instantaneous or marginal rate of change of the function at the two given values of the independent variable.

ii) Discuss the marginal rates of change you have found in relation to the optimal point of the function.

a) The average cost per part function

$$C(x) = \frac{x^2}{100} - 10x + 3000$$

in Example 3.8 at $x = 200$ and $x = 700$.

b) The profit function

$$P(p) = -1000p^2 + 12{,}000p - 25{,}000$$

in Example 3.9 at $p = 4$ and $p = 7$.

3.14. Given the total cost function

$$T(x) = \frac{x^3}{100} - 10x^2 + 3000x, \quad 150 \le x \le 850,$$

found in Example 3.8—

a) Find the total cost when $x = 700$ and $x = 800$ parts.

b) Explain why the manager may not attempt to find the total cost of a run whose size is beyond the range $150 \le x \le 850$.

3.15. The manager of a coal mine observed that with the *available* mining equipment and other facilities, daily coal output increased by putting more miners to work up to a certain point. He collected the following data where x represents number of miners and y the daily coal output in tons:

x	y	x	y	x	y	x	y	x	y
1	25	11	96	10	96	3	51	4	75
10	104	7	94	5	80	5	72	10	100
3	47	2	33	3	59	8	100	1	28
9	97	4	60	6	82	2	43	8	91
11	102	6	87	4	65	9	103	2	48

a) Plot the given data on a properly scaled cc-plane and draw a free-hand curve through the points.

*b) Given that the y-intercept is zero and the coordinates of the vertex of the parabola are $x = 10$ and $y = 100$, derive the total output-labor quadratic function by finding the a and b coefficients.

c) Estimate graphically the instantaneous rate of y over x for $x = 4, 5,$ and 6, and draw your conclusions about the marginal efficiency of miners.

*d) Suppose the manager has a fixed cost of $2000 daily and pays a daily wage of $20 per miner. Find the total coal output-investment function of his mining operations.

e) Sketch the graph of this function and find the instantaneous rate of change (marginal efficiency of capital) for an investment of (i) $2080; (ii) $2100; (iii) $2120.

f) For what values of x are the labor and investment functions meaningful from the mathematical and empirical standpoints?

3.16. The following data were obtained from 25 production runs where x represents the number of produced units of an item and y the unit production cost per run in dollars:

x	y	x	y	x	y	x	y	x	y
50	1500	19	2620	14	2820	39	1600	66	1610
45	1600	15	2500	57	1430	55	1600	60	1490
35	1800	63	1750	27	2200	50	1600	76	2000
73	2190	70	1800	22	2350	80	2500	35	1990
81	2210	30	2010	43	1400	86	2830	24	1980

a) Plot the given data on a properly scaled cc-plane and draw a free-hand curve through the points.

*b) Given that the y-intercept of the curve fitted to the data is $4000 and the coordinates of the vertex of the parabola are $x = 50$ and $y = 1500$, derive the unit cost function.

c) Estimate graphically the instantaneous rate of change in unit cost for $x = 75, 33$, and 50.

*d) Find the total cost function by multiplying the unit cost function by x and sketch its graph.

e) Estimate graphically the marginal total production cost when $x = 40, 63$, and 100.

f) Discuss the domain and range of the total production cost and unit production cost functions from the mathematical and empirical viewpoints.

*3.17. Fitting a parabolic curve to empirical data can be done with other methods in addition to the one illustrated in the text. One such method is with Lagrange's formula

$$y = y_1 \frac{(x - x_2)(x - x_3)}{(x_1 - x_2)(x_1 - x_3)} + y_2 \frac{(x - x_1)(x - x_3)}{(x_2 - x_1)(x_2 - x_3)}$$

$$+ y_3 \frac{(x - x_1)(x - x_2)}{(x_3 - x_1)(x_3 - x_2)}.$$

Consider the data given in Problem 3.16 and use the coordinates of points $(30, 1800)$, $(50, 1500)$, and $(70, 2000)$ to fit a parabolic curve with the above formula.

3.18. If the unit demand function for the item in Problem 3.16 is

$$p = 152 - 2x,$$

where x is items sold for price p, and the unit cost function is the one found in Problem 3.16(*b*), find the following:

*a) Derive the sales revenue S and profit P functions.

b) Determine the optimum production run size and the maximum profit.

c) Interpret your answer to (*b*) geometrically by sketching the sales revenue and total cost functions.

d) Determine the smallest and largest size of production runs for which the manufacturer breaks even. Verify your answer graphically.

3.19. Let the following function be given:

$$q = ep + b \qquad \text{(unit demand function)}$$
$$C = vq + f \qquad \text{(total cost function)}$$

where

q = sales in units,
p = selling price in dollars,
f = total fixed cost in dollars,
v = variable cost in dollars,
b = unit sales when $p = 0$,
e = the slope of the unit demand function.

a) Express the total cost function C in terms of the independent variable p.

b) Find the sales revenue function S.

c) Find the profit function P.

d) Verify the fact that the functions in (*a*), (*b*), and (*c*) are generalizations of the functions C, S, and P in Example 3.9, respectively.

SUGGESTED REFERENCES

1. ALLENDOERFER, C. B., AND OAKLEY, C. O. *Principles of Mathematics*, pp. 124–81. New York: McGraw-Hill Book Co., Inc., 1955. (**1**)

2. BASS, F. M., *et al.* (eds.). *Mathematical Models and Methods in Marketing*, pp. 3–34. Homewood, Ill.: Richard D. Irwin, Inc., 1961. (**2, 3**)

3. COOLEY, H. R., *et al. Introduction to Mathematics*, pp. 261–306. Boston: Houghton Mifflin Co., 1949. (**1**)

4. DAUS, P. H., AND WHYBURN, W. M. *Algebra with Applications to Business and Economics*, pp. 84–95. Reading, Mass.: Addison-Wesley Publishing Co., Inc., 1961. (**2**)

5. JOHNSON, R. E., AND KIOKEMEISTER, F. L. *Calculus with Analytic Geometry*, pp. 46–57. Boston: Allyn and Bacon, Inc., 1957. (**1**)

6. KLINE, MORRIS. *Mathematics: A Cultural Approach*, pp. 284–93, 318–20, 346–48, 398–402. Reading, Mass.: Addison-Wesley Publishing Co., Inc., 1962. (**1, 3**)

7. LEMKE, B. C., AND EDWARDS, J. D. (eds.). *Administrative Control and Executive Action*, pp. 608–23, 634–44, 777–88. Columbus, Ohio: Charles E. Merrill, Inc., 1961. (**2, 3**)

8. MOORE, G. E. *Algebra*, pp. 66–77. Rev. ed. New York: Barnes & Noble, Inc., 1961. (**3**)

9. RICHARDSON, M. *College Algebra*, pp. 189–95, 457–58. Al. ed. Englewood Cliffs, N.J.: Prentice-Hall, Inc., 1958. (**1, 3**)

10. ———. *Fundamentals of Mathematics*, pp. 275–98. Rev. ed. New York: The Macmillan Co., 1958. (**1**)

11. ROSE, I. H. *A Modern Introduction to College Mathematics*, pp. 18–38. New York: John Wiley & Sons, Inc., 1960. (**1**)

12. WESTERN, D. W., AND HAAG, V. H. *An Introduction to Mathematics*, pp. 182–99. New York: Henry Holt & Co., Inc., 1959. (**1**)

Chapter 7

FUNCTIONS AND THEIR USE IN ECONOMICS AND BUSINESS

SUBJECTS of special interest are covered in this chapter. Supply and demand functions are central to the economic analysis of the firm and the economic theory of value. Hence, Section 1 is a brief but systematic study of such functions. Section 2 deals with growth and decline functions and their application to business situations, especially in the areas of production and marketing. Finally, Section 3 is devoted to the interest formulas and their use for optimal allocation of investable funds.

*1. FUNCTIONS AND THE ECONOMIC "LAWS" OF SUPPLY AND DEMAND

"You can make even a parrot into a learned political economist— all he must learn are the two words 'Supply' and 'Demand'." (see p. 381 of reference 10 at the end of this chapter.) These anonymously quoted remarks point out succinctly the importance of the subject. Determination of price by supply and demand is central to the economic theory of value in particular and to microeconomic analysis in general. Therefore, it behooves us to devote this section to a mathematical analysis of supply and demand functions.

In the past we have talked about supply and demand functions on several occasions. But the treatment was incidental and superficial. In this section we shall have a limited yet systematic discussion of the subject. We shall not be concerned with methods of deriving supply and demand functions from empirical situations. We shall discuss parabolic and hyperbolic demand and supply curves as analytical tools for determining graphically and algebraically the equilibrium price and quantity for a particular commodity.

1.1. Assumptions and Qualifications. The demand and supply schedules are tools which economists employ in order to analyze the interaction between the market price and quantity of a particular

commodity in isolation. Since these analytical tools are abstractions from experience, they involve assumptions which must be explained. Furthermore, the functions which express in equation form the concept of supply and demand schedules are mathematical simplifications. As such they involve a number of qualifications which also should be spelled out.

Lacking the test tube and other sophisticated mechanical means available to physical scientists, economists attempt to simulate the desirable control conditions by assuming that "*other things are equal.*" Thus, we can imagine a market in which the price and quantity of a particular commodity, say wheat, are the only variables. Consumer's incomes, tastes, and preferences, the prices and supplied quantities of substitute goods, as well as market expectations and many other measurable and nonmeasurable variables, remain unchanged.

In addition, we assume that there is "*pure*" or *perfect competition*. The term is defined to include three conditions: the commodity in question is homogeneous so that consumers are unable to distinguish the output produced by a specific supplier from the total market output; the number of consumers and producers is large enough so that the quantity demanded or supplied by any one single individual is not sufficiently large to influence market price; and selling and buying is done in an organized market such as a commodity exchange or auction where demanded and supplied quantities are made known.

Since we are concerned with the most simplified and normal case of supply and demand, we assume that *time* also is not considered. In other words, we shall deal with the so-called *statics* rather than the *dynamics* of the situation.

With the above major assumptions in mind we can accept the idea that at any given instant of time there is a unique schedule of demand and a unique schedule of supply. Let p and q represent price and quantity of a commodity, respectively. We can express the demand and supply schedules graphically as shown in Figures 1.1 and 1.2.

Consider the demand curve in Figure 1.1. If price is raised from p_2 to p_1, the quantity demanded will fall from q_2 to q_1. Inversely, if a larger quantity, say q_2 instead of q_1, is offered, it can be sold at a lower price, say p_2 instead of p_1; in other words, price and quantity demanded are inversely related. Symbolically,

$$q_2 > q_1 \text{ if and only if } p_2 < p_1.$$

In this case we say that *demand is a monotonically decreasing function of price*. The reader can easily verify the fact that with respect to the supply curve in Figure 1.2, price and supplied quantity are directly related, i.e.,

$$q_2 > q_1 \text{ if and only if } p_2 > p_1.$$

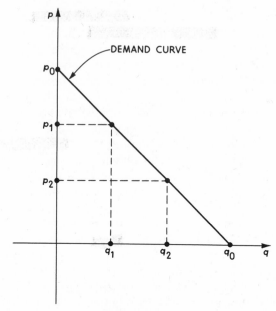

FIGURE 1.1.

Thus, we say that *price is a monotonically increasing function of supplied quantity*.

Another qualification is that *the variables p and q are considered continuous and must be restricted to zero and positive real numbers*. Consider the simplest demand curve, a straight line, such as shown in Figure

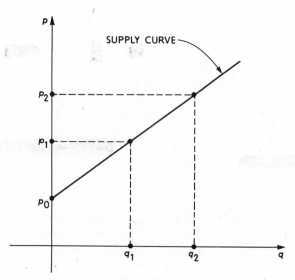

FIGURE 1.2.

1.1. If a commodity is nearly "free" such as water, i.e., if p tends to zero ($p \to 0$), the demanded quantity tends to q_0, which, although finite, may be large. If, on the other hand, a commodity is very scarce such as a rare painting, i.e., if q tends to zero ($q \to 0$), price tends to p_0, which represents the highest price that any consumer is willing to pay for the commodity. Thus, while the mathematical domain and range of the demand function are restricted to

$$0 \le q \le q_0 \quad \text{and} \quad 0 \le p \le p_0,$$

respectively, the empirical counterparts may fall short of the above intervals. For similar reasons the mathematical domain and range of the supply function are restricted to

$$q \geqslant 0 \quad \text{and} \quad p \geqslant 0,$$

respectively, although few of the possible values are likely to be empirically meaningful.

An equally important qualification is that *both the supply and demand schedules are bi-unique, i.e.,* for each demanded or supplied quantity there is one and only one price and for each price there is one and only one supplied or demanded quantity. This restriction is closely associated with the fact that we are concerned with *changes in the quantity demanded or supplied as a result of price change on the same curve* not about an increase in *demand or in supply* which means a shift of the whole curve in question.

Finally, measuring q along a horizontal axis and p along a vertical axis is purely a matter of convention established by economists. From the viewpoint of economic analysis which variable is independent is a matter of further elaboration in economics which is not our concern. This qualification, however, has some bearing on mathematical notation. Demand and supply are expressed in all three functional notation forms.

Example 1.1. Consider the demand equation

$$2p^2 + q - 72 = 0.$$

Any one of the forms

(1.1) $$F(p, q) = 2p^2 + q - 72 = 0$$

(1.2) $$f(q) = \pm\sqrt{36 - (q/2)}$$

(1.3) $$h(p) = 72 - 2p^2$$

can be used to express the same demand function.

It is important to note that (1.1) in Example 1.1 is the *implicit form* of a quadratic equation while the other two are *explicit forms.* According to our previous discussion, form (1.2) is a relation which gives us two functions: $p = \sqrt{36 - (q/2)}$ and $p = -\sqrt{36 - (q/2)}$. Since p cannot be negative, here the former of the two functions is considered only.

With the above assumptions and qualifications on hand we are ready to proceed to our next step.

1.2. Equilibrium of Supply and Demand. Up until this point, we have talked about the unit supply and demand functions separately. For a given quantity we are able to determine at what price producers are willing to sell and consumers to buy that quantity;

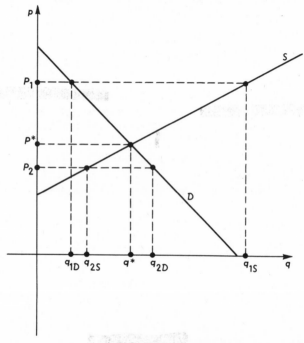

FIGURE 1.3.

or, inversely, for a given price we can tell the quantity that producers are willing to sell and consumers willing to buy. But just what is the level to which price will *actually* settle? And for that price, how much will be produced and consumed?

Neither the supply function nor the demand function alone can give us the answer. But both together can, as shown in Figure 1.3. Let price be at p_1, then producers would be willing to sell quantity q_{1S} which is larger than the quantity q_{1D} consumers would be willing to buy. Price p_1 would not prevail for long since competition among producers would tend to drive the market price down. How far would the price go? Suppose it goes to p_2, then consumers would be willing to buy quantity

q_{2D}. Since the demanded quantity is larger than quantity q_{2S}, which producers are willing to sell, competition among consumers will tend to push the price upward. It is obvious that as long as the supplied quantity does not equal the quantity demanded, price will be unstable. *The only stable price, called equilibrium price, is that at which the quantities supplied and demanded are equal.* In Figure 1.3 the equilibrium price and quantity are p^* and q^*, respectively.

The equilibrium price and quantity can be accurately and efficiently determined by solving the supply and demand functions simultaneously.

Example 1.2. Find the equilibrium price and quantity for the supply function $p = q + 5$ and the demand function $p = -2q + 26$.

Solution:

Since at equilibrium the supply price equals the demand price

$$q + 5 = -2q + 26,$$

solving, we have

$$3q = 21,$$

$$q = 7.$$

Substituting $q = 7$ in the demand function, we get

$$p = -2(7) + 26 = 12.$$

The reader may draw the graph of the supply and demand functions in order to verify graphically that

$$p^* = 12 \text{ and } q^* = 7.$$

1.3. Market Equilibrium with Parabolic Curves. A summary of general types of parabolic demand and supply curves appear in an appendix at the end of this section. Algebraic solutions for determining a market equilibrium price and quantity with parabolic curves may require solving a fourth-degree equation. In such instances, the market equilibrium price and quantity can be approximated graphically. There are three cases, however, which require solving quadratic equations and which we shall study presently.

Case 1 : *When one curve is linear and the other parabolic.*

Example 1.3. The graph of the demand function $p = -3q^2 + 12$ (Table 1.1, type 1(b), in appendix at end of this section) and of a linear supply function $p = 2q + 4$ are shown in Figure 1.4. From the graph we can estimate that equilibrium price and quantity are approximately 1.30 and 6.50, respectively. More accurate answers can be obtained algebraically.

Solution:

$$p = -3q^2 + 12 = 2q + 4,$$

$$-3q^2 - 2q + 8 = 0,$$

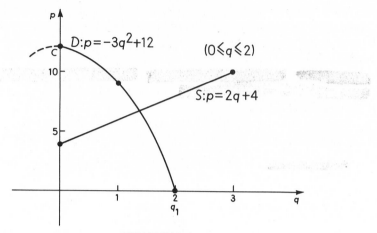

FIGURE 1.4.

$$q^* = \frac{2 \pm \sqrt{4 + 96}}{-6} = \frac{2 \pm 10}{-6} = \frac{4}{3}; \quad \text{and}$$

$$p^* = 2\left(\frac{4}{3}\right) + 4 = \frac{20}{3} = 6\tfrac{2}{3}.$$

Case 2: *When both curves are given with the price defined as a quadratic function of the quantity.*

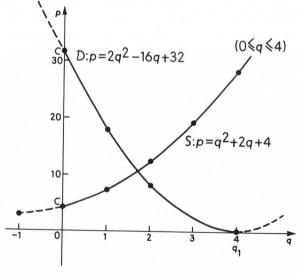

FIGURE 1.5.

Example 1.4. Sketching the graphs of the demand function $p = 2q^2 - 16q + 32$ (Table 1.1, type 2(a), in appendix at end of this section) and the supply function $p = q^2 + 2q + 4$ (Table 1.2, type 1(a), in same appendix) in Figure 1.5, we can easily approximate the equilibrium price at 10.30 and the quantity at 1.70. The exact answers can be found algebraically as follows:

Solution:

$$p = 2q^2 - 16q + 32 = q^2 + 2q + 4,$$
$$q^2 - 18q + 28 = 0,$$
$$(q^2 - 18q \qquad) + 28 = 0,$$
$$(q^2 - 18q + 81) + 28 - 81 = 0,$$
$$(q - 9)^2 = 53, \text{ by completing the square;}$$
$$q = 9 \pm \sqrt{53}$$
$$= 9 \pm 7.28,$$
$$q^* = 1.72; \text{ and}$$
$$p^* = q^2 + 2q + 4 = (1.72)^2 + 2(1.72) + 4 \approx 10.40.$$

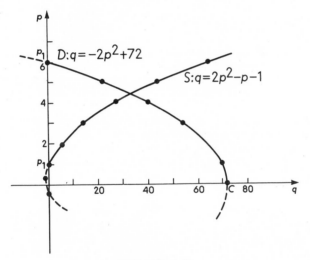

FIGURE 1.6.

Case 3: *When both curves are given with the quantity defined as a quadratic function of price.*

Example 1.5. From the graphs of the demand function $q = -2p^2 + 72$ (Table 1.1, type 3(b), in appendix at end of this section) and the supply function $q = 2p^2 - p - 1$ (Table 1.2, type 2(a), in same appendix) shown in Figure 1.6, we can read an equilibrium price and quantity of about 4.30 and 33.50, respectively. It is left for the reader to check these approximations by finding the exact answers algebraically.

1.4. Hyperbolic Demand Curves and Market Equilibrium. Sometimes the demand price p may be inversely proportional

to the demanded quantity q so that the revenue product c remains constant. A demand curve of this type, called *equilateral hyperbola*, is expressed with an equation of the form

$$p = \frac{c}{q} \quad \text{or} \quad pq = c, \quad a \le q \le b,$$

shown in Figure 1.7, where a and b are both positive. It can be seen that the curve has no intercepts, since if $q = 0$, p is not defined, and if $p = 0$, q is not defined. Furthermore, if q tends to zero, p tends to infinity; and

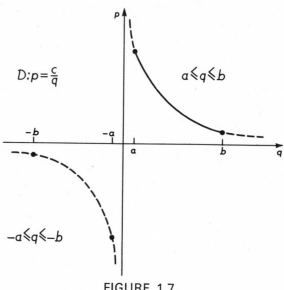

FIGURE 1.7.

if p tends to zero, q tends to infinity. In such a case, the p-axis, where $q = 0$, is called a vertical asymptote and the q-axis, where $p = 0$, a horizontal asymptote. The curve is symmetric with respect to the origin and consists of two parts. Symmetry facilitates sketching the curve since the two parts are identical. Inasmuch as p and q must be restricted to positive numbers, however, we are interested in the part of the curve which lies in the first quadrant of the cc-plane only. Moreover, the absence of intercepts requires that an interval such as $a \le q \le b$ be specified in order to make the demand curve empirically meaningful by excluding very large prices and quantities.

Market equilibrium with hyperbolic demand curves involves two cases which are presently considered.

Case 1 : *When the supply function is linear.* Market equilibrium price and quantity can be easily found graphically and algebraically.

Example 1.6. Given the demand function $pq = 24$ and the supply function $2p - q = 2$, find the equilibrium price and quantity.

Solution:

The graphs of the functions are shown in Figure 1.8. The demand curve is sketched from the points (2, 12), (5, 24/5), and (12, 2) while the supply curve from the points (0, 1) and (12, 7). From the diagram we can estimate that the equilibrium price and quantity are 4 and 6, respectively.

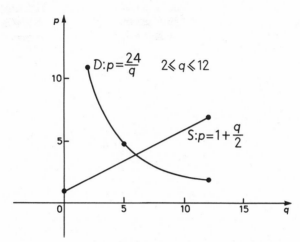

FIGURE 1.8.

Algebraically

$$pq = 24 = \left(1 + \frac{q}{2}\right)q = q + \frac{q^2}{2},$$
$$(q^2 + 2q \qquad) = 48,$$
$$(q^2 + 2q + 1) = 48 + 1, \text{ by completing the square;}$$
$$(q + 1)^2 = 49,$$
$$q^* = 6.$$

Substituting $q^* = 6$ in the supply function, we have

$$p^* = 1 + \frac{6}{2} = 4.$$

Case 2: *When the supply function is quadratic.* A graphical solution can be easily found. An algebraic solution, however, involves a cubic equation which is not considered here.

Example 1.7. The graph of the demand function $p = 45/q$ and the supply function $q = (p^2 - 9)/8$ (Table 1.2, type 2(*c*), in appendix at end of this section) are shown in Figure 1.9.

First Approximation: Suppose $p = 7$ is a close estimate, then $q = 45/7 = 6.43$. For checking we substitute $q = 6.43$ in the supply function and

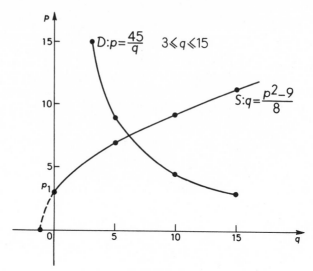

FIGURE 1.9.

find that

$$p = \sqrt{8q + 9}$$
$$= \sqrt{8 \times 6.43 + 9} \approx 7.76.$$

Second Approximation: A closer estimate is made by assuming that $p = 7.5$. Then

$$q = \frac{45}{7.5} = 6,$$

which checks fairly closely with

$$p = \sqrt{8 \times 6 + 9} = 7.55.$$

Thus, the approximate market equilibrium price and quantity are 7.55 and 6, respectively.

Question: How close is this approximation to the exact equilibrium price and quantity?

Answer:

Since $p = 45/q$ and $p = \sqrt{8q + 9}$, then at equilibrium

$$p = \frac{45}{q} = \sqrt{8q + 9}.$$

Substituting $q = 6$, we have

$$\frac{45}{6} = \sqrt{8(6) + 9},$$

$$7.5 \approx 7.549.$$

Thus, $q = 6$ and $p = 7.5$ are fairly close approximations to the exact equilibrium values. More exact solutions may be obtained by repeating the above procedure.

1.5. Concluding Remarks. At the beginning of this section we indicated that the demand and supply functions are mathematical simplifications of abstractions from experience. Yet, the underlying assumptions are not quite unrealistic. For a limited number of farm products such as wheat, cotton, and other cash crops, market equilibrium price and quantity are determined under competitive conditions closely resembling the assumptions of a homogeneous product and a large number of small producers and consumers competing in a nationwide market. From the industrial sector of our economy the stock market may be cited as an example whereby stock prices and quantities are determined under conditions approaching "*pure*" or perfect competition.

Further, economists analyze more complicated and hence more common or realistic situations by modifying or relaxing the assumptions of the original simple "model" of "pure" or perfect competition. One such important case is the so-called monopolistic or imperfect competition, a blending of competition and monopoly, where product differentiation and few sellers modify the initial assumptions. The price and quantity of a great number of services such as of retail stores and products such as toothpaste, cigarettes, electrical appliances, automobiles, and many others are determined under conditions which closely approximate the assumptions of monopolistic or imperfect competition. Another important case is analyzing the relationship of price and quantity with cost of production over time. Three periods are considered: the short-run when supply is fixed; the intermediate-run when firms can increase the supply of a product by producing more of it with the existing plant capacity; and the long-run when plant capacity is given time to expand or contract. Although all these factors and many others may affect price and quantity, they are not in addition to but are included in the forces which determine or act through supply and demand. Thus, economists study the equilibrium price and quantity in the above cases and in many others by changing the shapes or shifting the whole demand and supply curves we have discussed in this section.

APPENDIX: GENERAL TYPES OF PARABOLIC DEMAND AND SUPPLY CURVES

A statistically derived demand and supply curve may be expressed with a parabola whose axis of symmetry is either vertical or horizontal.

There are three general types of parabolic demand curves. Representative forms of each type are shown in Table 1.1. All functions of type 1 represent curves which are concave downward. The graph of one such function, type 1(b), is shown in Figure 1.4. The reader may notice that sketching the graph requires no more than finding the two intercepts c and q_1 and perhaps one or two additional points in between as the case may require.

By contrast the demand functions of type 2 represent curves which are concave upward. The graph of one such function, type 2(a), is shown in Figure 1.5.

TABLE 1.1.

Type	Axis of Symmetry	Example
1. $p = aq^2 + bq + c; a < 0; c > 0$		
a) $b < 0$ $0 \leqslant q \leqslant q_1$	Vertical	$p = -3q^2 - 2q + 12$
b) $b = 0$ $0 \leqslant q \leqslant q_1$	,,	$p = -3q^2 + 12$
c) $b > 0$ $-\left(\dfrac{b}{2a}\right) \leqslant q \leqslant q_1$	,,	$p = -3q^2 + 2q + 12$
2. $p = aq^2 + bq + c; a > 0; c > 0$		
a) $b < 0$ $0 \leqslant q \leqslant q_{1=2}$	Vertical	$p = 2q^2 - 16q + 32$
b) $b < 0$ $0 \leqslant q \leqslant q_1$	,,	$p = q^2 - 9q + 20$
3. $q = ap^2 + bp + c; a < 0; c > 0$		
a) $b < 0$ $0 \leqslant p \leqslant p_1$	Horizontal	$q = -2p^2 - 3p + 72$
b) $b = 0$ $0 \leqslant p \leqslant p_1$	,,	$q = -2p^2 + 72$
c) $b > 0$ $-\left(\dfrac{b}{2a}\right) \leqslant p \leqslant p_1$	,,	$q = -2p^2 + 3p + 72$

Demand curves having an horizontal axis of symmetry are of type 3 where q is a function of p. The graph of function type 3(b) is sketched in Figure 1.6.

TABLE 1.2.

Type	Axis of Symmetry	Example
1. $p = aq^2 + bq + c; a > 0$		
a) $b > 0; c > 0$ $q \geqslant 0$	Vertical	$p = q^2 + 2q + 4$
b) $b = 0; c = 0$ $q \geqslant 0$	,,	$p = q^2$
c) $b < 0; c < 0$ $q \geqslant q_1$	,,	$p = q^2 - 2q - 4$
2. $q = ap^2 + bp + c; a > 0$		
a) $b < 0; c < 0$ $p \geqslant p_1$	Horizontal	$q = 2p^2 - p - 1$
b) $b = 0; c = 0$ $p \geqslant 0$	,,	$q = 2p^2$
c) $b = 0; c < 0$ $p \geqslant p_1$	,,	$q = (p^2 - 9)/8$

There are two general types of parabolic supply curves. Representative variations of them are shown in Table 1.2. Type 1 consists of supply functions which represent curves having a vertical axis of symmetry. The graph of function type 1(a) is sketched in Figure 1.5.

The last group of supply functions, designated type 2 in Table 1.2, represent parabolic curves with a horizontal axis of symmetry. The graph of type 2(*a*) function is sketched in Figure 1.6 and of type 2(*c*) in Figure 1.9.

PROBLEMS

1.1. Sketch the graph of the supply and demand functions given in Example 1.2 and verify graphically that $p^* = 12$ and $q^* = 7$.

1.2. Find algebraically the exact market equilibrium price and quantity of the demand and supply functions in Example 1.5.

*1.3. Consider Example 1.7. Try a third closer approximation to the exact equilibrium price and quantity which may be found with algebra.

1.4. For each case below replace the indicated function and find the new equilibrium price and quantity graphically and, if possible, algebraically.

a) $p = -3q^2 + 12$ in Example 1.3 by—
   * i) $p = -3q^2 - 2q + 12$.
   ii) $p = -3q^2 + 2q + 12$ $(\frac{1}{3} \leqslant q \leqslant q_1)$.
b) $p = 2q^2 - 16q + 32$ in Example 1.4 by—

$$p = q^2 - 9q + 20.$$

c) $q = -2p^2 + 72$ in Example 1.5 by—
   *i) $q = -2p^2 - 3p + 72$.
   ii) $q = -2p^2 + 3p + 72$ $(\frac{3}{4} \leqslant p \leqslant p_1)$.
d) $p = q^2 + 2q + 4$ in Example 1.4 by $p = q^2$.
e) $p = 1 + q/2$ in Example 1.6 by $p = q^2 - 2q - 4$.
f) $q = 2p^2 - p - 1$ in Example 1.5 by —
   *i) $q = 2p^2$.
   ii) $q = (p^2 - 9)/8$.

1.5. For each pair of demand and supply functions—
   i) Estimate the equilibrium price and quantity graphically by assuming that q is the independent variable.
   ii) Verify your answer to (i) by finding the exact values of p and q algebraically.

   *a) D: $p = 20 - 2q$.   S: $p = \frac{2}{3}q + 3$.
   *b) D: $2p + 4q - 44 = 0$.   S: $5p - 10q - 50 = 0$.
   c) D: $p = 4$.   S: $q = 5p - 10$.
   d) D: $2q = 30 - 3p$.   S: $p = 5$.
   e) D: $q = 24 - 3p$.   S: $q = 2p - 1$.
   f) D: $p = 3.3 - 0.3q$.   S: $p = 0.2q + 0.3$.
   g) D: $p = 4.5 - 0.2q$.   S: $q = 0.4p - 0.3$.

1.6. For each pair of demand and supply functions in *(*a*), *(*b*), (*c*), (*d*), (*e*), (*f*), and (*g*), of Problem 1.5—
   i) Sketch their graphs in the same diagram, but with p on the horizontal and q on the vertical axis.
   ii) Verify the fact that equilibrium price and quantity are the same as previously.

254 APPLIED MATHEMATICS: AN INTRODUCTION [Ch. 7]

For each pair of demand and supply functions given in Problems 1.7 through 1.10—
    i) Find the approximate equilibrium price and quantity graphically.
    ii) Verify the results in (i) algebraically.

1.7.   *a)* D: $p = 2(25 - q^2)$.   S: $p = 4q + 2$.
       b) D: $p = -q^2 - 4q + 60$.   S: $2p - 10q - 6 = 0$.
       c) D: $4p + 9q = 40$.   S: $2p - 4q^2 = 1$.
    d) D: $p = -2q^2 - 4q + 240$.   S: $p = q^2 + 2q + 1$.
       e) D: $p = -q^2 + 2q + 48$.   S: $p = q^2 + 3q$ $(1 < q < 8)$.
       f) D: $p + 2q^2 - 72 = 0$.   S: $2p - 4q^2 = 0$.
      g) D: $2p + 2q^2 - 40q = 200$ S: $p = q^2 - 20q + 100$.
          $(10 \leqslant q \leqslant 24)$.

1.8.   *a)* D: $p = q^2 - 10q + 25$.   S: $p = 3q + 2$ $(0 \leqslant q \leqslant 5)$.
       b) D: $2p - 2q^2 + 24q = 70$.   S: $2p - 4q = 6$ $(0 \leqslant q \leqslant 5)$.
       c) D: $p = 2q^2 - 80q + 600$.   S: $2p - 6q^2 = 0$ $(0 \leqslant q \leqslant 10)$.
       d) D: $p = 2(q - 10)^2$.   S: $q^2 - 2p + 1$ $(1 \leqslant q \leqslant 10)$.
       e) D: $p = (q - 20)^2$.   S: $p = 2(q - 10)^2$ $(10 \leqslant q \leqslant 20)$.

1.9.   *a)* $p = \sqrt{25 - q}$ and $p = (2q + 1)/5$.
       b) $q = p^2 - p$ and $q = -2p^2 + 18$.
       c) $q - p^2 + 4p = 4$ and $q + p^2 - 4p = 21$ $(2 \leqslant p \leqslant 7)$.
       d) $q = -2p^2 - 20p + 200$ and $p = -3 + \sqrt{q + 4}$ $(5 \leqslant q \leqslant 200)$.

1.10. *a)* $5p - q = 10$ and $pq = 60$ $(3 \leqslant q \leqslant 24)$.
       b) $q = 32/p$ and $2q - p = 0$ $(2 \leqslant q \leqslant 16)$.

1.11. For each pair of demand and supply functions—
    i) Find the approximate equilibrium price and quantity graphically; then
    ii) Find the third- or fourth-degree equilibrium equation and check your answer to (i) by substituting and solving.
    iii) If not satisfied with your approximation, try a second closer one.
    a) $p = -q^2 - 4q + 60$ and $q = (p^2 - 2p)/400$.
    b) $1000q + 10p - p^2 = 0$ and $p = 2q^2 - 40q + 200$ $(0 \leqslant q \leqslant 10)$.
    c) $q = 25 - p^2 (q \geqslant 1)$ and $40p = q^2 - q$.
    d) $pq = 50$ and $2p^2 - p + 1 - 10q = 0$ $(3 \leqslant q \leqslant 20)$.

1.12. Market equilibrium with linear demand and supply functions can be extended to a number of related commodities. Here, we show how to find the equilibrium prices and quantities of two related commodities. Let the following functions be given:

Demand	*Supply*
a) $q_1 = 6 - 2p_1 + p_2$	*c)* $q_1 = -4 + 4p_1 - p_2$
b) $q_2 = 5 + p_1 - p_2$	*d)* $q_2 = -5 - p_1 + 3p_2$,

where p_1 and p_2 represent the prices while q_1 and q_2 the quantities of the related commodities.

Market equilibrium implies that the demanded quantity equals the supplied quantity.

(1) $q_1 = 6 - 2p_1 + p_2 = -4 + 4p_1 - p_2$ or $6p_1 - 2p_2 = 10$.
(2) $q_2 = 5 + p_1 - p_2 = -5 - p_1 + 3p_2$ or $2p_1 - 4p_2 = -10$.
Solving (1) and (2) simultaneously, we have

$$\left. \begin{array}{r} 6p_1 - 2p_2 = 10 \\ -p_1 + 2p_2 = 5 \end{array} \right\} \qquad \begin{array}{r} 6(3) - 2p_2 = 10 \\ -2p_2 = -8 \end{array}$$

$$\begin{array}{l} 5p_1 = 15 \\ p_1^* = 3 \end{array} \qquad\qquad p_2^* = 4$$

Substituting for p_1 and p_2 in (a) and (b) we get

$$q_1^* = 6 - 2(3) + 4 = 4,$$
$$q_2^* = 5 + 3 - 4 = 4.$$

In order to show that the results are significant, we must solve the demand functions (a) and (b) for p_1 and p_2 and determine whether the equilibrium quantities are within the restricted values as follows:

$$\left. \begin{array}{l} q_1 = 6 - 2p_1 + p_2 \\ q_2 = 5 + p_1 - p_2 \end{array} \right\} \qquad \begin{array}{l} q_1 = 6 - 2p_1 + p_2 \\ 2q_2 = 10 + 2p_1 - 2p_2 \end{array}$$

$$\begin{array}{ll} p_1 = 11 - q_1 - q_2 & p_2 = 16 - q_1 - 2q_2 \\ \text{Hence, } q_2 < 11 \text{ for} & \text{Hence, } q_1 < 16 \text{ for} \\ q_1 = 0 \text{ and positive } p_1. & q_2 = 0 \text{ and positive } p_2. \end{array}$$

On the basis of the above illustration, find the equilibrium prices and quantities for the following sets of functions and show that the results are significant.

	Demand	Supply
*a)	$q_1 = 15 - 4p_1 + 2p_2$	$q_1 = 9$
	$q_2 = 30 + 4p_1 - 6p_2$	$q_2 = 20$
*b)	$q_1 = 5 - p_1 + p_2$	$q_1 = -5 + p_1 + p_2$
	$q_2 = 15 - p_1 - p_2$	$q_2 = -3 - p_1 + 2p_2$
*c)	$p_1 = 5 - q_1 + q_2$	$4p_1 = 9 + 3q_1 - q_2$
	$p_2 = 7 + q_1 - 2q_2$	$2p_2 = 10 + q_2$

1.13. What are the consequences if a tax (t) is imposed on a given commodity or a subsidy (s) is granted? The demand curve will not change. The supply curve will shift upward in the case of a tax and downward in the case of a subsidy.

I. Consider Example 1.2 and assume that an excise tax of 3 monetary units (m.u.) is imposed on each unit of quantity produced, then after taxation—

$$D: p_t = -2q_t + 26. \quad S: p_t = q_t + 5 + 3.$$

A) At equilibrium $p_t^* = 14$ and $q_t^* = 6$.
B) Consumers pay $2(14 - 12)$ and producers $1(12 - 11)$ m.u. in taxes. Consumption drops from 7 to 6.
C) Total revenue $R = 84(6 \times 14)$ m.u.; $18(6 \times 3)$ taxes; $66(6 \times 11)$ net revenue.

II. Suppose a subsidy of 2 m.u. per unit is given, then the original functions can be written as follows:

$$D: p_s = -2q_s + 26. \quad S: p_s = q_s + 5 - 2.$$

A) At equilibrium $p_s^* = 10\frac{2}{3}$ and $q_s^* = 7\frac{2}{3}$.

B) Consumers receive $\frac{4}{3}$ and producers $\frac{2}{3}$ m.u. in subsidies. Consumption increases from 7 to $7\frac{2}{3}$.

C) $R = 81\frac{7}{9}(7\frac{2}{3} \times 10\frac{2}{3})$.

The reader may sketch the appropriate graphs in order to verify the above consequences before attempting to solve the following problems.

For each pair of demand and supply functions—

i) Find the equilibrium price and quantity and sketch the appropriate graph.

ii) Discuss the consequences of the indicated tax and subsidy.

iii) Illustrate the new equilibria on the graph.

a) D: $3p + 6q = 90$. S: $4p - 2q = 10$. Tax, 2. Subsidy, 1.

b) D: $2p + q = 20$. S: $p = 2q + 2.5$. Tax, 3.5. Subsidy, 2.

c) D: $p + 3q^2 = 12$. S: $p - 2q = 4$ as in Example 1.3. Tax, 2.5. Subsidy, 2.

d) D: $pq = 30$. S: $p = 0.2q + 0.8$ $(5 \leqslant q \leqslant 20)$. Tax, 0.20. Subsidy, 0.20.

e) D: $q + 5p = 60$. S: $q = 2p^2 - p - 1$ from Example 1.5. Tax, 1. Subsidy, 1.

[(*Hint:* (1) S: $q = 2(p - 1)^2 - (p - 1) - 1 = 2p^2 - 5p + 2$ or⎤ after
(2) S: $p = \frac{1}{4} + \sqrt{9/16 + q/2} + 1$ ⎬taxation ⎦

(3) S: $q = 2(p + 1)^2 - (p + 1) - 1 = 2p^2 + 3p$ or ⎱ after
(4) S: $p = \frac{1}{4} + \sqrt{9/16 + q/2} - 1$ ⎰subsidy

Solve with (1) and (3) and check with (2) and (4).]

1.14. The slope of a demand or a supply curve is indicative, although not a measure, of its *elasticity*, i.e., the ratio of the *relative* change in quantity to the *relative* change in price. Read the explanations in Problem 1.13, and consider each case below consisting of one demand and two supply functions with different slopes. Let p represent the price of wheat in dollars and q the quantity of wheat in millions of bushels:

i) Find the equilibrium price and quantity for both supply functions.

ii) Find the same assuming that the indicated tax is imposed on both functions.

iii) Sketch the appropriate diagram and discuss the effect which the different slopes (elasticities) of the supply functions have had on the incidence of taxation.

iv) Do steps (ii) and (iii) assuming that a subsidy instead of a tax of an equal amount is granted.

a) D: $p = -0.3q + 6$ $(5 \leqslant q \leqslant 20)$. S: $p = 0.2q + 1$.
S: $p = 0.1q + 2$. Tax, 0.40.

b) D: $pq = 30$ $(5 \leqslant q \leqslant 20)$. S: $p = 0.2q + 1$.
S: $p = 0.1q + 2$. Tax, 0.50.

1.15. What amount of tax should be imposed in order to raise the original equilibrium price of a commodity to a desirable level? Consider the functions in Example 1.3 and assume that we wish to find the tax which will raise the equilibrium price from $6\frac{2}{3}$ to 9, with taxation

$$\text{D: } p_t = -3q_t^2 + 12 \ (0 \leqslant q \leqslant 2) \text{ and S: } p_t = 2q_t + 4 + t,$$

where t stands for the desirable tax. Since $p^* = 9$, we have

$$\begin{aligned} p_t^* = 9 &= -3q_t^2 + 12 = 2q_t + 4 + t \\ -3q_t^2 + 12 &= 9 \qquad 2q_t + 4 + t = 9 \\ q_t^* &= 1 \qquad\qquad t = 5 - 2q_t \end{aligned}$$

Substituting $q_t^* = 1$, we get

$$t = 5 - 2q_t = 5 - 2(1) = 3 \text{ monetary units.}$$

The reader could use the graphs in Figure 1.4 in order to verify the new equilibrium point $(1, 9)$ before attempting to solve the following:
For each problem
i) Find the equilibrium price and quantity.
ii) Find the amount of tax (subsidy) for which the price must be raised (lowered) to the indicated value.
iii) Verify results with a graph.
*a) D: $4p + 4q = 56$. S: $3p - 6q = 6$.
   Find the tax for $p = 11$. Find the subsidy for $p = 8$.
b) D: $p = 2q^2 - 8q + 8$, $(0 \leqslant q \leqslant 2)$. S: $p - 2q = 2$.
   Find the tax for $p = 4$. Find the subsidy for $p = 3$.
c) D: $p + 3q = 30$. S: $p = q^2 + 2q + 1$.
   Find the tax t for $p = 21$. Find the subsidy for $p = 9$.

1.16. Instead of a fixed amount per unit of quantity produced, a tax may represent a fixed rate (usually expressed in percentage terms) imposed on price. Consider Example 1.2 where $p^* = 12$ and $q^* = 7$ and assume that a sales tax (r) of 20 percent is imposed, then

$$\text{D: } p_r = -2q_r + 26 . \quad \text{S: } p_r = (q + 5)(1 + 0.2).$$

A) At equilibrium $p_r^* = 13.5$ and $q_r^* = 6.25$.
B) Equilibrium price without the sales tax is $p = q_r^* + 5 = 6.25 + 5 = 11.25$.
C) Tax at equilibrium is $t = p_r^* - p = 13.5 - 11.25 = 2.25$.
D) Total tax is $T = q_r^* \cdot t = 6.25 \times 2.25 \approx 14.1$.
After you verify the above illustration graphically, for each of the following problems find p^* and q^*, p_r^* and q_r^*, p, t, and T, and sketch the appropriate diagram.
a) D: $10p + 8q = 163$. S: $2p - q = 4$. Tax, 40 percent.
b) D: $pq = 50 \ (5 \leqslant q \leqslant 20)$. S: $4p - q = 4$. Tax, 30 percent.
c) D: $q + 10p = 70$. S: $q = 2p^2 - p - 1$. Tax, 10 percent.

1.17. Instead of specifying the intervals for an equilateral hyperbola demand curve we can use its generalized form

$$(p - k)(q - h) = a^2$$

which becomes

$$p'q' = a^2$$

where $\qquad\qquad p' = p - k, q' = q - h,$ or

$$p = p' + k, q = q' + h,$$

are the equations of *translation of axes*, and where lines $p = k$ and $q = h$ are the asymptotes.

Consider the demand function

$$(p - 2)(q + 2) = 10,$$

where lines $p = 2$ and $q = -2$ are the asymptotes. Writing the given equation in alternative forms

$$p = \frac{10}{q + 2} + 2 = \frac{14 + 2q}{2 + q},$$

we can obtain all the necessary points for drawing the graph of the function.

*a) Let the demand and supply functions be

$$\text{D}: (p - 2)(q + 2) = 10 \qquad \text{S}: p = \tfrac{1}{2}q + 1.$$

Sketch their graphs in one diagram and estimate the equilibrium price and quantity graphically. Verify the results by finding the exact values algebraically.

b) Approximate the equilibrium price and quantity geometrically when

$$\text{D}: (p + 10)(q + 30) = 600. \qquad \text{S}: p = \frac{1}{100}q^2 + 1$$

1.18. Parabolic and hyperbolic curves can be used to describe economic phenomena other than supply and demand. One such case is the so-called *production-possibility* or *production-transformation* curve. At full employment a country utilizing all available productive capacity can produce a given amount of Gross National Product which consists of two representative commodities, "butter" (B) and "guns" (G). The assumption of full employment implies that for a given state of technology and given resources the only way by which a country can increase "butter" is to reduce production of "guns" and vice versa.

For each of the following functions:

a) $G = 90 - \dfrac{B^2}{40}$,

b) $(B - 80)(G - 60) = 1200$,

where G represents "guns in thousands" and B "butter" in millions of pounds do the following:

  i) Find the maximum quantities of "guns" and "butter" that can be produced.

  ii) If the country produces 45 million pounds of "butter," how many "guns" can she produce?

  iii) How many pounds of "butter" should be sacrificed in order to increase production of "guns" in (ii) by 20 percent?

  iv) Discuss the U.S.A. and the Soviet economies in terms of a transformation curve.

Cutting On.

leave out

*2. FUNCTIONS OF GROWTH AND DECLINE

In this section we shall deal with exponential, logarithmic, and certain types of algebraic functions which are particularly suited for expressing growth and decline relationships between varying quantities. Such functions deserve special attention because they are frequently used in business research. This fact will enable us to refer to specific cases from the available literature which deals with applications of mathematics to solving business problems, sometimes called *operations research.*

The characteristics of exponential and logarithmic functions are studied first by means of graphs. Then their use, together with power function of the form $y = ax^b$, is illustrated in three different situations: the sales decay constant, the forecasting of industry demand for a product, and the learning curve.

It is assumed that the reader is familiar with the basic rules of exponents and logarithms as well as with the use of logarithmic tables. Persons who feel the need for reviewing these topics are referred to the suggested bibliography and the exercises among the problems. For the required calculations the tables of reference 11 in this chapter's bibliography have been used. Of course the reader may use any other collection of similar tables.

2.1. Elementary Transcendental Functions and Their Graphs. As explained in Section 1 of Chapter 5, functions whose rule involves exponents such as

(2.1)
$$y = a^x,$$

where x is the independent variable and a is a positive real number different from one, are called exponential functions. The domain of such a function is the set of all real numbers and the range the set of all positive real numbers. Essentially, the graph of an exponential function may be determined by three key points whose coordinates are the two-tuples $(-1, 1/a)$, $(0, 1)$, and $(1, a)$.

Example 2.1. Consider the exponential function

$$f(x) = 2^x,$$

where $a = 2$. The coordinates of the key points of the graph of this function are $(-1, \frac{1}{2})$, $(0, 1)$, and $(1, 2)$ as shown in Figure 2.1. Observe that for positive values of x, y gets larger and larger; and for negative values of x, y, although remaining positive, gets smaller and smaller approaching the x-axis asymptotically. Furthermore, at $x = 0$, $f(x) = 1$ since $2^0 = 1$. In fact, the y-intercept of any exponential function is 1 since $a^0 = 1$ for any number $a \neq 0$.

But the most important property of exponential functions, from the empirical standpoint, is the fact that when the independent variable x changes by a constant amount, the dependent variable y changes by a constant percentage.

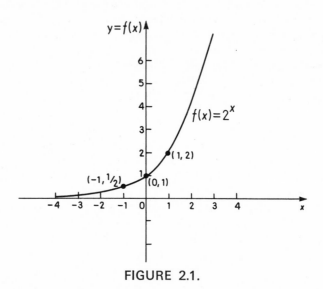

FIGURE 2.1.

Example 2.2. Consider again the exponential function

$$f(x) = 2^x.$$

When x increases by a constant factor 1, say from 1 to 2, 3, 4, etc., y increases by 100 per cent, from 2 to 4, 8, 16, etc. In other words, x increases in an arithmetic progression while y increases in a geometric progression. This relationship is shown graphically in Figure 2.2. The x-axis is on an arithmetic scale where equal distances represent equal absolute amounts of change. The y-axis is on a logarithmic scale where equal distances mean equal rates of change. It is important to notice that the graph of the function is a straight line. This is so because equal absolute changes in x correspond to equal rates or percentage changes in y. Also, inasmuch as the graph of the function approaches asymptotically $y = 0$, the x-axis is drawn at $y = 1$, the y-intercept.

It must be clear by now why exponential functions can be used to express growth or decline relationships between variables.

Furthermore, the arithmetic-logarithmic relationship between x and y indicates *that the inverse of an exponential function is a logarithmic function.* In an exponential function of the general form (2.1), y is obtained by raising the base a to the power x. Since the exponent x is the logarithm of y to the base a, the inverse of (2.1) is the logarithm function $x = \log_a y$; and reversing symbols for the sake of convention, we obtain

(2.2)
$$y = \log_a x.$$

Now the domain of this function is the range and the range the domain of the exponential function (2.1); and the graph of the logarithmic function can be determined by three key points whose coordinates are the two-tuples $(1/a, -1)$, $(1, 0)$, and $(a, 1)$.

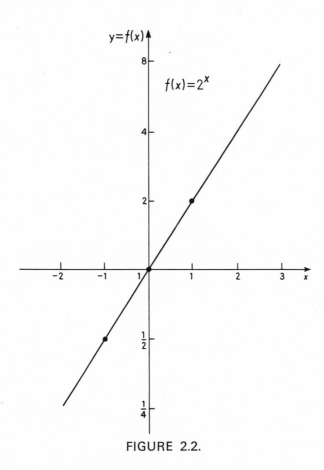

FIGURE 2.2.

Example 2.3. Let the exponential function $y = 2^x$ be given. Then its inverse is the logarithmic function $x = \log_2 y$ which, by reversing symbols, becomes
$$y = \log_2 x.$$

Let $x = 2$, then $y = 1$ since the base 2 must be raised to the first power in order to obtain $x = 2$. Let $x = 1$, then $y = 0$ since $2^0 = 1$. Let $x = \frac{1}{2}$, then $y = -1$ since $2^{-1} = \frac{1}{2}$. These coordinates represent the key points of the graph of the logarithmic function shown in Figure 2.3.

The reader may verify the fact that the graph of the above function is also a straight line if drawn on a paper where the x-axis is logarithmic and the y-axis arithmetic.

In the above examples we used elementary transcendental functions with base 2 for expository purposes. Although any positive real number

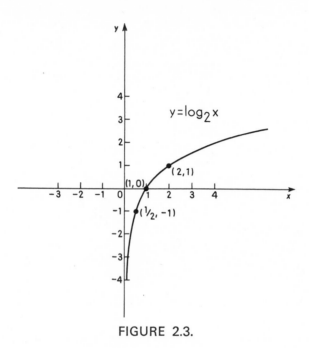

FIGURE 2.3.

other than one can be the base of such functions, the most common exponential function is of the general form

(2.3)
$$y = e^z,$$

where e is the irrational number $2.71828\ldots$ and z the independent variable. Then (2.3) defines the logarithmic function of the general form

(2.4)
$$z = \log_e y = \ln y,$$

where e is the base of natural or Naperian logarithms. Instead of $\log_e$ the equivalent notation $\ln$ is frequently used in mathematics.

Functions of form (2.3) are widely used. Indeed, this form is considered *par excellence the* exponential function. It is frequently denoted by $f(z) = expz$. Before proceeding to the applications of transcendental functions, therefore, it is worthwhile to show how exponential functions with base other than e can be converted to functions with that base.

Let the function $y = a^x$, $a \neq e$, be given. We wish to find the equivalent function $y = e^z$. Since it is given that

$$a^x = e^z,$$

taking the logarithm with base e of both functions, we get

$$x \log_e a = z \log_e e.$$

But $\log_e e = 1$ since $e^1 = e$, and

$$z = x \log_e a$$

Therefore,

(2.5) $$\boxed{y = a^x = e^{x \log_e a}.}$$

The number $\log_e a$ is called the *modulus* of logarithms to the base e with respect to the logarithms to the base a.

Example 2.4. Convert the function $f(x) = 2^x$ into an equivalent one with base e. From a table of natural logarithms

$$z = x \log_e 2 = 0.69315x.$$

Substituting in (2.5), we have

$$y = 2^x = e^{0.69315x}.$$

Converting an exponential function of the form $y = a^x$ to $y = e^z$ may be a matter of great convenience. In the first place, special tables are available which give the value of y for certain values of the domain z of the function. In the second place, the value of the function for a given value of z can be readily approximated from a table of natural logarithms.

Example 2.5. Consider the previously found function

$$y = e^{0.69315x}.$$

Let $x = 5$, then

$$\ln y = 0.69315(5) \ln e = 3.46575$$

since $\ln e = 1$; and from a table of natural logarithms we can read that

$$y = 32.$$

From a table of exponential functions the answer for $x = 3.46$ is 31.817.

Although converting an exponential function to an equivalent function with base 10 would give the same or better computational convenience than the base e, the latter possesses a property which makes functions of form (2.3) particularly important in calculus.

2.2. The Sales Decay Constant. Sales response to promotional effort differs depending on several factors such as the type of

product, the stage a product is in its life cycle, the structural characteristics of the market, competing products, the intensity and length of the
promotional campaign, advertising, promotional media, and others. In
spite of all these factors, and many others, however, extensive experiments have shown that under relatively constant market conditions and
in the absence of promotional effort the sales of a product tend to decrease at a constant yearly rate. Of course, this rate of sales decline was
found to vary considerably among products. But after allowance was
made for seasonal and other short-run variations, the rate of decline
appeared to be constant for a particular product.

The sales decline can be expressed with an exponential function of the
general form

(2.6)
$$S(t) = S(0)e^{-\lambda t},$$

where $S(t)$ represents the rate of sales at time t, $S(0)$ the sales level at
$t = 0$, and λ (lambda) the *sales decay constant*. We may use a concrete
case to illustrate how such an exponential function may be derived from
a set of data.

Example 2.6. In a large-scale test, product A remained unpromoted in
a section of the United States for eight years. Annual average monthly
sales over the period are plotted on a semilogarithmic paper shown in
Figure 2.4. The freehand straight line indicates that an exponential function will fit the data.

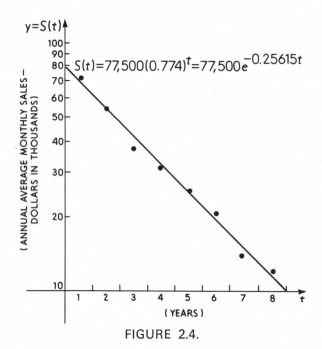

FIGURE 2.4.

Therefore, our immediate problem is to find a method for fitting an exponential function to a set of data. Exponential function (2.6) can be written in general form

(2.7) $$\boxed{y = ab^x.}$$

Taking the logarithm of (2.7), we have

$$\log y = \log a + x \log b.$$

When no base is indicated, the logarithms with base 10, i.e., the system of common logarithms, is implied. Base e or any other base can be used, however, for this purpose. Letting $Y = \log y$, $A = \log a$, and $B = \log b$, we get

(2.8) $$Y = A + Bx.$$

This linear equation means that we may fit a straight line to the points

$$(x_1, Y_1 = \log y_1), (x_2, Y_2 = \log y_2), \ldots, (x_n, Y_n = \log y_n)$$

Example 2.7. Fit a curve of the exponential form (2.7) to the data in the previous example.

Solution:

From Figure 2.4 we select the coordinates of two points on the straight line, say, the annual average monthly sales at the end of the first and the eighth years (1, 60,000) and (8, 10,000), respectively.

Letting $t = x$ and $Y = \log y$, we have

$$(x_1 = 1, Y_1 = 4.7782) \quad \text{and} \quad (x_2 = 8, Y_2 = 4.0000).$$

Substituting the coordinates of these points in the familiar two-point form of a linear equation

$$\frac{Y - Y_1}{x - x_1} = \frac{Y_2 - Y_1}{x_2 - x_1},$$

we have

$$\frac{Y - 4.7782}{x - 1} = \frac{4.0000 - 4.7782}{8 - 1}$$

$$Y = 4.8894 - 0.1112x$$

From (2.8) we get $a \approx 77,500$ and $b \approx 0.774$ since $\log a = 4.8894$ and $\log b = -0.1112 = 9.8888 - 10$. Substituting for a and b in (2.7), we obtain

$$y = 77,500(0.774)^x.$$

It remains for the reader to verify the above exponential function by substituting for $x = 0$, $x = 1$, and $x = 8$. Also, the reader can verify that the above function is equivalent to

$$y = S(t) = 77,500e^{-0.25618t}$$

of form (2.6), where $S(0) = 77,5000$, $\lambda = 0.25618$, and $x = t$. Of course, for curve fitting other methods exist which are more sophisticated than the method applied in the above example. One such method is the method of least squares with curve fitting based on all given points. However, illustrating the application of it lies outside the scope of this textbook.

The sales decay constant λ was used as part of a study of sales response to advertising. The reader may consult reference 12 in the bibliography at the end of this chapter.

2.3 Forecasting Industry Demand for a Product.

Exponential functions of the form (2.7) may be combined with linear functions. We shall present one such case dealing with forecasting industry demand for a product.

> **Example 2.8.** A. C. Nelson Company, a manufacturer of glass containers, has recently encountered a decline in the sale of nonreturnable bottles. The newly introduced plastic and chemical containers by competitors have been cutting into the company's sales to the pharmaceutical, chemical, and cosmetics industries. Worse than that, the malt liquor industry, a large customer of the company, has been increasingly using disposable beer cans instead of nonreturnable bottles.

This situation requires a thorough examination of the company's competitive market position. First, it is necessary to find the sales prospects of the glass containers industry. The next step is to determine the company's competitive position within this industry. A third task involves an analysis of the firm's sales-profit outlook. Finally, on the basis of the findings in the previous areas of research, long-run planning is necessary for managerial action. Such an extensive analysis is a complicated affair which is beyond our limited space. For our immediate objective we shall study the exponential functions for forecasting industry demand for glass containers.

> **Example 2.8** *Continued.* In the light of current developments the research department of the company prepared sales projections based on the demand for the industry's products by individual consumer units such as the liquor, cosmetics, and pharmaceutical industries. Four functions were constructed, each reflecting a different set of market assumptions.
>
> If no changes were made in the existing marketing policies of the firm, industry sales of glass containers in millions of dollars are expected to be
>
> $$S_1(x) = [1 - 0.01(1.20)^n](54 \times 10^6 + 0.0016x),$$
> where
>
> $x =$ national Disposable Personal Income (DPI) in billions of dollars,

$$0.01(1.20)^n = 0 \quad \text{if} \quad x < \$150 \text{ billion,}$$
$$0.01(1.20)^n > 0 \quad \text{if} \quad x \geqslant \$150 \text{ billion,}$$
$$n = \frac{x - (150 \times 10^9)}{10 \times 10^9}.$$

The graph of this function is shown in Figure 2.5. The linear form $(54 \times 10^6 + 0.0016x)$ of $S_1(x)$ represents the expected sales growth of the complete product line, i.e., glass and nonglass containers. On the other hand, the exponential term $[1 - 0.01(1.20)^n]$ expresses expected changes in the proportion of the total market which represents glass containers.

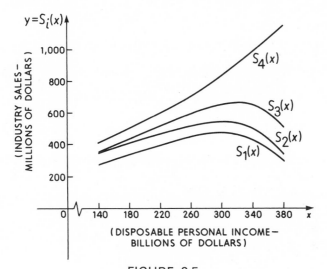

FIGURE 2.5.

At the beginning of the period under study, when $x = \$150$ billion and $n = 0$, nonglass containers represent 0.01 of the total market. When $x > \$150$ billion, however, the market share of nonglass containers is expected to grow exponentially by 20 percent for every $10 billion increase in DPI. Subtracting this market share for nonglass containers from the total sales, we obtain the industry share of sales for glass containers. Since it is assumed that A. C. Nelson Company will continue manufacturing glass containers only, industry sales of the company's market are expected to witness an absolute decline after DPI reaches approximately $300 billion.

Let us assume that our company changes somewhat its marketing policies. New improved types of glass containers are introduced; and a more aggressive promotional effort is made to capture a greater share of the glass containers market currently serviced by the company. Industry sales of the company's market are expected to be

$$S_2(x) = [1.0 - 0.01(1.20)^n] (106 \times 10^6 + 0.0017x),$$

where x, $0.01(1.20)^n$, and n are defined as previously. Under this new set of assumptions the linear part of $S_2(x)$ has changed, the exponential remains as in $S_1(x)$, since nonglass containers will not be manufactured by A. C. Nelson Company. It can be seen that industry sales are likely to have an absolute decline after DPI reaches about $300 billion, though, as shown in Figure 2.5, dollar sales are expected to be larger than under the first set of assumptions.

Under the third set of assumptions, industry sales of the company's market are expected to be

$$S_3(x) = [1.0 - 0.0025(1.25)^n](40 \times 10^6 + 0.0022x),$$

where x, the term $0.0025(1.25)^n$, and n are defined as previously.

Under the fourth set of assumptions sales would be

$$S_4(x) = (1.015)^n (68 \times 10^6 + 0.0024x),$$

where x is defined as previously, and

$$n = 0 \quad \text{if} \quad x \leqslant \$270 \text{ billion},$$

$$n = \frac{x - (270 \times 10^9)}{10 \times 10^9} \quad \text{if} \quad x > \$270 \text{ billion}.$$

After studying functions $S_3(x)$ and $S_4(x)$ and their graph in Figure 2.5, the reader may attempt to discuss the assumptions under which these functions may have been prepared as well as the question of reliability of forecasting in general.

It is evident that the management of A. C. Nelson Company should implement the assumed policies reflected in function $S_4(x)$. But what specific course of action should be taken? This would require the extensive analysis previously mentioned. To find how the above forecasting functions were used as part of such an extensive investigation, see reference 13 in this chapter's bibliography.

2.4. The Learning Curve.
One production tool for predicting labor time requirements and cost per unit of product is the so-called *learning curve*. It is based on the theory that in certain operations the worker learns from experience; and the more often he repeats an operation, the more efficient he becomes. The net result is that direct labor input per unit of product declines. If the rate of improvement is regular enough, the learning curve can be used to predict future reductions in labor requirements and thus becomes a valuable tool for managerial planning and control.

Although learning curves represent power functions of the general form

(2.9)
$$y = ax^b,$$

where $-1 \leqslant b \leqslant 0$ and $a > 0$, we shall see shortly that their curve characteristics are exponential and their derivation requires the use of logarithmic functions.

Example 2.9. Mathewson Electronics Corporation had just completed the assembly of 50 units of a complex new guidance system for missiles. Inasmuch as the company was invited to bid on a new order of 100 additional units, management wanted to know what the assembly labor hours per unit for the new units is likely to be for successful bidding.

The assembly data of 20 units selected at random are plotted on log-log paper as shown in Figure 2.6. Variable x denotes the cumulative

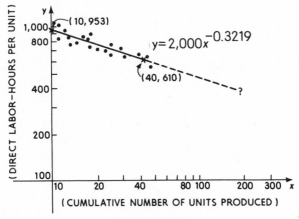

FIGURE 2.6.

number of units produced, i.e., the order each selected unit came out of the assembly line. Variable y represents the average number of direct labor hours required to assemble a cumulative number of units.

One quick approximation of the average labor hours could be readily obtained by extrapolating the free straight-line curve fitted to the data. From the graph of Figure 2.6 we can read that labor hours per unit for 150 units is expected to be about 390. A more precise prediction can be obtained by deriving a power function of the form (2.9).

Taking the logarithm of (2.9), we get

$$\log y = \log a + b \log x.$$

Letting $Y = \log y$, $A = \log a$, and $X = \log x$, we have

(2.10) $$Y = A + bX.$$

Equation (2.10) indicates that we may fit a straight line to the points

$$(X_1 = \log x_1, \, Y_1 = \log y_1), \, (X_2 = \log x_2, \, Y_2 = \log y_2), \ldots,$$
$$(X_n = \log x_n, \, Y_n = \log y_n).$$

Example 2.9—*Continued.* In order to find the man-hours per unit for the new order of 100 guidance-system units, we must do the following:

Step 1: Find a power function $y = ax^b$.

From the graph in Figure 2.6 we can read the coordinates of two points on the straight line such as (10, 953) and (40, 610). For $X = \log x$ and $Y = \log y$, we have $(X_1 = 1.000, \ Y_1 = 2.9791)$ and $(X_2 = 1.6021, \ Y_2 = 2.7853)$. Substituting these logarithms in the two-point form of a linear equation used in Example 2.7, we get

$$\frac{Y - 2.9791}{X - 1.000} = \frac{2.7853 - 2.9791}{1.6021 - 1.000},$$

$$Y = 3.3010 - 0.3219X.$$

From (2.10) we obtain $a = 2000$ and $b = -0.3219$; and substituting a and b in (2.9), we get the power function

$$y = 2000x^{-0.3219},$$

where 2000 is the number of labor hours required to produce the first unit.

Step 2: Find the direct labor hours per unit for assembling 150 units. Let $x = 150$. Then

$$y = 2000(150)^{-0.3219}; \text{ and}$$

$$\log y = \log 2000 + (-0.3219) \log 150$$
$$= 3.3010 - 0.3219(2.1761)$$
$$= 2.6005; \text{ and}$$

$$y = 398 \text{ labor hours, per unit.}$$

Step 3: Find direct labor hours per unit for assembling the new order of 100 units.

Since it was known that 570 labor hours per unit were required for assembling the first 50 units, the labor hours per unit for the new 100 units are found as follows:

Total hours for 150 units: 398×150	59,700
Total hours for first 50 units: 570×50	$-28,500$
Total hours for last 100 units:	31,200
Labor hours per unit for last 100 units:	$\dfrac{31,200}{100} = 312$

Thus the management of Mathewson Electronics Corporation was able to bid for the new contract on the basis of objective and statistically verifiable information.

Observe that functions of the form (2.9) express the man-hours per unit for a *cumulative* number of produced units. Hence, the total man-hours for producing these units is

$$yx = ax^b \cdot x,$$

or

(2.11)
$$g(x) = ax^{b+1}.$$

Example 2.10. Consider the function

$$y = 2000x^{-0.3219}$$

found in Example 2.9. Then the total man-hours production function is

$$g(x) = 2000x^{-0.3219+1} = 2000x^{0.6781}.$$

It is left for the reader to verify the result found in step 3 of Example 2.9 using the above function g.

The term $(b+1)$ in (2.11) is called the *conversion factor*. Multiplying (2.9) by the conversion factor

$$y(b + 1) = (b + 1)ax^b$$

we obtain

(2.12)
$$h(x) = kx^b,$$

where $k = (b + 1)a$, which gives the *rate* of man-hours required to produce the xth unit.

Example 2.11. Consider again the function

$$y = 2000x^{-0.3219}$$

found in Example 2.9. Multiplying this function by the conversion factor $(-0.3291 + 1)$ we obtain

$$h(x) = 1356.2x^{-0.3291}.$$

The reader may use this function to find the man-hours required to produce the 150th unit.

Function (2.12) describes the *rate* of direct labor hours required to produce the xth item. It deserves particular attention. Extensive research in the aircraft industry has shown that, although experience for assembling various categories of air frames such as fighters, bombers, etc., differs somewhat, there is, on the average, a 20 percent reduction in the time required to produce a plane every time production doubles. In other words, the fourth unit requires 80 percent as much direct labor as the second unit, the eighth 80 percent as much as the fourth, and so forth. Since the exponent b is the improvement rate, then

$$2^b = 0.8.$$

Taking the logarithm of both sides, we have

$$b \log 2 = \log 0.8, \quad \text{or}$$

$$b = \frac{\log 0.8}{\log 2} = \frac{-0.0969}{0.3010} = -0.3219.$$

Hence, the graph of function

(2.13)

$$y = ax^{-0.3219}.$$

is called the "80 percent air frame curve." It has become a standard for analyzing procurement, production, and costing problems in the aircraft industry.

The learning-curve technique can be profitably used by other industries such as electronics, home appliances, large-scale residential construction, shipbuilding, machine shops, and generally in cases where assembly or machining costs represent a large portion of the total manufacturing cost. In addition to assembly operations, the method is potentially applicable to other fields such as wage incentive plans and the financing of business operations.

However, extreme caution should be exerted in the collection and analysis of statistical information for deriving a learning curve. Labor savings may be illusory rather than real if improvements are due to shifts in labor input, new tooling, reshuffling of accounting records, and factors other than those attributable to the learning process. For further discussion of the learning curve as a production tool, see reference 1 in this chapter's bibliography.

PROBLEMS

*2.1. Invoke the following rules of exponents

Rule	*Example*
(1) $x^n = x \cdot x, \ldots, x$ (n times)	$x^3 = xxx$
(2) $x^m \cdot x^n = x^{m+n}$	$x^2 \cdot x^3 = x^5$
(3) $(x^m)^n = x^{mn}$	$(x^2)^3 = x^6$
(4) $(xy)^n = x^n y^n$	$(xy)^2 = x^2 \cdot y^2$
(5) $x^{-n} = 1/x^n$	$x^{-3} = 1/x^3$
(6) $x^m/x^n = x^{m-n}$	$x^3/x^2 = x$
(7) $\sqrt[n]{x^m} = x^{m/n}$	$\sqrt{x^3} = x^{3/2}$
(8) $x^0 = 1$	$2^0 = 1$

in order to simplify each of the following expressions:

a) 2^3.

b) 3^2.

c) $3^2 \cdot 3^2$.

d) 5^{-2}.

e) $4^6/4^4$.

f) $\sqrt[3]{2^6}$.

g) $(5^2)^5$.

h) 3^0.

i) $(2 \cdot 5)^3$.

j) $a^4 \cdot a^3$.

k) a^3/a^4.

l) $(x^3/y^5)^2$.

m) $\dfrac{a^3 b^4 c^3}{a^5 b^2 c^3}$.

n) $\sqrt{a^2}$.

o) $(\frac{1}{8})^{-1/3}$.

p) $(\frac{4}{9})^{\frac{1}{2}}$.

q) $(x + y + z)^0$.

r) $5^8 \cdot 5^{-4}$.

*2.2.   Express in logarithmic notation:
a) $10^2 = 100$.
b) $e^5 = 148.41$.
c) $4^2 = 16$.
d) $a^0 = 1$.
e) $5^{-3} = 1/125$.
f) $16^{1/4} = 2$.

*2.3.   Express in exponential notation:
a) $\log_{10} 1 = 0$.
b) $\log_2 64 = 6$.
c) $\log_{10} 0.01 = -2$.
d) $\log_e e = 1$.
e) $\log_{10} 100 = 2$.
f) $\log_4 8 = \frac{3}{2}$.

*2.4.   Evaluate the following:
a) $\log_2 32$.
b) $\log_{10} 0.0001$.
c) $\log_a (a^{10})$.
d) $\log_e 2.718 \ldots$.
e) $\log_{16} 4$.
f) $\log_{81} \frac{1}{3}$.

2.5.   On the basis of the following rules of logarithms
(1) $\log_a (xy) = \log_a x + \log_a y$,
(2) $\log_a (x/y) = \log_a x - \log_a y$,
(3) $\log_a (x^n) = n \log_a x$,
and given $\log_{10} 2 = 0.3010$, $\log_{10} 3 = 0.4771$, and $\log_{10} 5 = 0.6990$,
   i) Find the value of the following without using tables,
   ii) Verify your answer to (i) by looking up a table of common logarithms.
a) $\log_{10} 6$.
b) $\log_{10} 36$.
c) $\log_{10} \sqrt{3}$.
d) $\log_{10} 24$.
e) $\log_{10} (\frac{3}{5})$.
f) $\log_{10} 15/(3\sqrt{2})$.

2.6.   Consider the rules of logarithms in Problem 2.5. Given $\log_e 2 = 0.6932$, $\log_e 3 = 1.0986$, and $\log_e 5 = 1.6094$,
   i) Find the value of each number in (a), (b), (c), (d), (e), and (f) of Problem 2.5 without using tables and assuming that each of them is with base e.
   ii) Verify your answer to (i) by looking up a table of natural logarithms.

2.7.   If N is equal to each of the values indicated below, find:
   i) $\log N$.
   ii) $\ln N$.
*a) 65.
*b) 0.156.
c) 6.85.
d) 0.005.
e) 4000.
f) 15.6.

2.8.   Find the approximate value of N if
   i) $\log N$ is equal to—
*a) 1.1461.
*b) 9.1461 − 10.
c) −2.1549.
   ii) $\ln N$ is equal to—
*a) 2.3026.
*b) 4.6540.
*c) −0.6932.
d) 3.0000.
e) 6.7782 − 10.
f) −3.2218.

d) −5.1160.
e) 5.0106.
f) 9.2103.

2.9. Sketch the graph of $y = \log_2 x$ on a paper, where the x-axis is logarithmic and the y-axis arithmetic. Discuss your graph by comparing it with the graph in Figure 2.2.

2.10. For each of the following exponential functions:
   i) Convert the function into an equivalent one with base e.
   ii) Using the function you found in (i), find $f(2)$.
   *a) $f(x) = 5^x$.   *e) $f(x) = 10^{x+1}$.
   b) $f(x) = 1.20^x$.   *f) $f(x) = 20^{-2x}$.
   c) $f(x) = 0.57^x$.   g) $f(x) = 0.856^{2x+3}$.
   d) $f(x) = 1.015^x$.

2.11. Consider the functions *(a), (b), (c), and (d) given in Problem 2.10.
   i) Convert each function to base 10.
   ii) Use the function found in (i) to find $f(2)$.

*2.12. Given the function $y = 77,500(0.774)^x$:
   a) Find the values of y for $x = 0$, $x = 1$, and $x = 8$.
   b) Convert this function to the base e.
   c) Approximate the values of y for $x = 0$, $x = 1$, and $x = 8$, using the function you found in (b).

2.13. For newly hired workers, the following statistical information was compiled in a machine shop:

t	1	2	3	4	5	6
$E(t)$	95	87	93	81	78	75

where t represents successive workdays and $E(t)$ the number of errors made by an apprentice in a particular machine operation.
   a) Plot the above data on a semilog paper and fit a freehand straight line through the points.
   *b) Let points $(0, 100)$ and $(6, 74)$ be on the drawn line. Derive a function of the form $E(t) = ab^t$.
   c) If the training period lasts 100 workdays, what is the expected number of errors which an apprentice will make during the last day of the period?
   d) Suppose an apprentice is paid $10 a workday and each error costs $0.10 to correct, devise a wage incentive plan which will reward the worker by half of the "savings" that the company expects to realize on the 25th, 50th, 75th, and 100th day of his training.
   e) Do you think that the wage incentive plan in (d) would be a wise plan? Explain why or why not. Suggest an alternative plan and defend it.

2.14. Ten years ago a real estate firm paid $100,000 for a piece of land. If the manager of the firm expects an 8 percent annual return on his investment, what is the price he should ask for the land?

2.15. For the exponential term of the first S_1 and the third S_3 functions in Example 2.8:
   a) Find the coordinates for $n = 1$ and $n = 10$.

*b) Using these coordinates, derive a function of the form $y = ab^x$ and find industry sales when $x = \$250$ billion.

c) Convert the function you found in (b) into one of form $y = ae^z$ and find industry sales when $x = \$250$ billion.

2.16. Consider the fourth function in Example 2.8:

$$S_4(x) = (1.015)^n \cdot (68 \times 10^6 + 0.0024x).$$

a) Find the industry sales when $x = \$370$ billion.

b) Convert the exponential term of the function to the base e and find sales when $x = \$370$ billion.

2.17. Consider the third S_3 and fourth S_4 functions in Example 2.8.

a) Discuss the assumptions upon which these functions may have been based.

b) Indicate the qualifications which should accompany a forecast such as the one provided with these functions (cf. Section 2, Chapter 6).

2.18. Power functions of the form $y = ax^b$ may be used to express other than learning curves. Consider, for example, the following data representing ten years' experience in a southern state:

x	80	82	95	110	105	121	142	142	157	149	150
y	90	75	110	123	95	133	133	138	165	142	160

Variable x represents annual residential housing starts and y sales of residential air conditioners, both in thousands of units.

a) Plot the data on a log-log paper and draw a freehand straight line through the points.

*b) Select the first and the last set from the given pairs of observations and derive a power function.

c) Find the expected number of sales of air conditioners when residential housing starts for a given year are 170 thousand.

d) Because of the time lag between housing starts and air conditioner sales, it is expected that the forecasting in item (c) above is reasonably reliable. Discuss.

2.19. Using the function

$$g(x) = 2000x^{0.6781}$$

found in Example 2.10, verify the result found in step 3 of Example 2.9.

2.20. Using the function

$$h(x) = 1356.2x^{-0.3291}$$

found in Example 2.11, find the rate of man-hours at which the 150th unit of the guidance system will be produced.

2.21. Shnider Machine Company received from the U.S. Army an order for a rough boring operation on 10,000 gun barrels. The contract provides that the order should be completed in five months with 2000 gun barrels delivered each month. The company will receive a total of $1,108,080 payable in equal monthly installments of $220,000 for the first four months and the balance of the sum at the end of the fifth month.

From the previous experience it was known that 100 direct man-hours (machine time) are required for processing the first gun barrel. Also, it was known that operations of this type have a 90 percent rate of learning.

a) Find the average direct labor hours required for processing the 10,000 gun barrels.

b) Use the function $g(x) = ax^{b+1}$, explained in Example 2.10, to find the *total* direct labor hours required to process the 10,000 gun barrels.

c) If a machine operator is expected to work 200 hours a month, determine the number of operators who are required each month for the timely completion of the order.

d) Suppose the contract provides for completion of the order in five months, but it does not specify monthly deliveries; again, assume that each machine operator is expected to work 200 hours a month, but the management of the company wants to employ the same number of machine operators each month. Determine the monthly labor force and the size of monthly deliveries.

e) If the cost of doing the work is measured in terms of direct labor hours and it is $4.00 per hour, determine the monthly net cash flow between cost and reimbursements under the production schedules prepared in case (c) and in case (d) above. In the light of your findings, what changes in the provisions of the contract would you recommend?

f) How much "profit" per hour of direct labor is the company expected to make?

*3. MATHEMATICS OF INVESTMENT AND FINANCE

From the financial standpoint business transactions may be considered as inflows and outflows of funds over time. Funds must be borrowed on *long-term*, a year or longer, basis to replace, improve, or add to existing facilities such as buildings, equipment, and machinery. Funds must, also, be borrowed on *short-term*, less than a year, basis to meet immediate needs such as raw materials or obligations such as payroll. But money has a *time value*, i.e., a dollar today is worth more than a dollar tomorrow, which is expressed in terms of interest charges. Since the use of money bears the cost of interest, management must optimize the employment of investable funds; it must evaluate a wide array of investment opportunities and choose the one which is most profitable.

Optimal allocation of investable funds requires the use of interest formulas. We shall deal with simple interest and present value, compound interest and present value, and with annuity and other uniform payment formulas. Finally, we shall discuss a few special cases in capital budgeting. For the required calculations the interest tables of reference 11 in this chapter's bibliography have been used. But the reader may use any other collection of such tables he wishes.

3.1. Simple Interest and Present Value. Interest may be called the price paid for the use of a sum of money over a period of time. If interest is paid on the originally borrowed sum, but not on the subsequently accrued interest, it is called *simple interest*. Rates of interest are usually stated as percent per annum. For instance, an annual 6 percent interest rate means that for every $100 borrowed for a year, the borrower must pay $6.00.

Let P be the borrowed sum, called *principal*, at a simple interest rate i per year; and let n, called *time* or *term* of the loan, be the number of years or part of it for which the interest is paid. Then I, the amount of interest is defined by

(3.1)
$$I = Pin.$$

Example 3.1. A businessman borrows $2000 at 6 percent simple interest rate per year for 2 years. Find the amount of interest I.
Solution:
Since $P = \$2000$, $i = 0.06$, and $n = 2$,

$$I = 2000(0.06)(2) = 240 \text{ dollars.}$$

Inasmuch as the sum A to be paid at the end of n years, called amount, is the principal P plus the amount of interest I, we have

$$A = P + I$$
$$= P + Pin$$

by (3.1); and

(3.2)
$$A = P(1 + in)$$

Example 3.2. Consider the case in Example 3.1, where $P = \$2000$, $i = 0.06$, and $n = 2$. Substituting in (3.2), we get

$$A = 2000[1 + 0.06(2)]$$
$$= 2000(1.12)$$
$$= 2240 \text{ dollars.}$$

Simple interest is commonly used for short-term loans such as promissory notes which mature in 30, 60, or 90 days. Although special methods are used for determining maturity dates, we shall assume, for the sake of simplifying calculations, that each month consists of 30 days and simple interest is computed on a 360-day per year basis.

Example 3.3. A wholesaler accepts a 90-day $2000 promissory note at 5 percent interest in lieu of a cash payment for goods sold to a retailer. Find the maturity value, or amount A, of the note.

Solution:
Since $P = \$2000$, $i = 0.05$, and $n = 90/360$, substituting in (3.2) we have

$$A = 2000\left[1 + 0.05\left(\frac{90}{360}\right)\right]$$
$$= 2000(1.0125)$$
$$= 2025 \text{ dollars.}$$

In the above examples we wanted to find the amount A, given the principal P, interest rate i, and term of the loan n. In other words, we wanted to find the future value of a present sum of money. Very frequently we may want to find the present value of a sum of money available in the future. In symbols, our problem is to find the value of P given A, i, and n. The appropriate formula can be obtained by solving (3.2) for P, thus

(3.3)
$$P = \frac{A}{1 + in}.$$

Example 3.4. The maturity value of a 120-day interest-bearing promissory note is $1530. If the interest rate is 6 percent per annum, what is the value of the goods purchased?
Solution:
Substituting $A = \$1530$, $i = 0.06$, and $n = 120/360$ in (3.3), we get

$$P = 1530 \cdot \left[\frac{1}{1 + (0.06)\left(\frac{120}{360}\right)}\right]$$
$$= \frac{1530}{1.02}$$
$$= 1500 \text{ dollars.}$$

The present value at simple interest points out the simple fact that money has a time value. This is particularly important, as we shall see, in long-term financing of business operations since their evaluation involves finding the present value of an investment on the basis of an expected stream of future income.

3.2. Compound Interest, Effective Rate, and Present Value.
If the interest payment is added or converted into principal at stated intervals, thereafter earning interest itself, then it is called *compound interest*. A savings account is a typical case where interest is compounded annually or for shorter periods. The time between successive conversions of interest into principal is called the *conversion period*. The original principal plus the compound interest is called the *compound amount*.

Let P be the principal invested at a compound interest rate i per conversion period. Then the compound amount A at the end of the first period will be

$$A_1 = P + Pi = P(1 + i);$$

at the end of the second period A will be

$$A_2 = A_1 + A_1 i = A_1(1 + i)$$
$$= P(1 + i)(1 + i) = P(1 + i)^2$$

since $A_1 = P(1 + i)$; at the end of the third period A will be

$$A_3 = A_2 + A_2 i = A_2(1 + i)$$
$$= P(1 + i)^2(1 + i) = P(1 + i)^3$$

since $A_2 = P(1 + i)^2$; and it is obvious that at the end of the nth period the compound amount will be

$$A = A_{n-1} + A_{n-1} \cdot i = A_{n-1}(1 + i) = P(1 + i)^{n-1} \cdot (1 + i)$$

since $A_{n-1} = P(1 + i)^{n-1}$, or

(3.4)
$$\boxed{A = P(1 + i)^n.}$$

Example 3.5. A manager deposits $2000 with a savings bank. Deposits earn 4 percent interest per annum compounded annually. Assuming no withdrawal or additional deposits, what will the compound amount on deposit be at the end of two years?
Solution:
Substituting $P = \$2000$, $i = 0.04$, and $n = 2$ in (3.4), we get

$$A = 2000(1 + 0.04)^2$$
$$= 2000(1.0816)$$
$$= 2163.20 \text{ dollars.}$$

The interest rate is usually stated as a percent per annum. On the other hand, the conversion period may be equal to a year, but frequently it may be shorter than a year. Thus, depending on the case, interest may be compounded annually, semiannually, or quarterly. When the conversion period is shorter than a year, the interest rate must be divided by the frequency of compounding and n must be multiplied by that frequency. Let f be the number of conversion periods per year. Then the compound interest formula (3.4) becomes

(3.5)
$$A = P\left(1 + \frac{i}{f}\right)^{nf}.$$

Example 3.6. Suppose interest in Example 3.5 is compounded quarterly, find the compound amount.

Solution:

Since $f = 4$, substituting $P = 2000$, $i = 0.04$, and $n = 2$ in (3.5), we get

$$A = 2000\left(1 + \frac{0.04}{4}\right)^{(2)(4)}$$
$$= 2000(1.01)^8 .$$

Using logarithms, we find

$$\log A = \log 2000 + 8 \log(1.01)$$
$$= 3.30103 + 8(0.00432)$$
$$= 3.33559, \text{ and}$$

$$A \approx 2165.65 \text{ dollars.}$$

Instead of logarithms special tables can be used to obtain the same answer as explained later.

From the last two examples we can see that if the interest rate of 4 percent per annum is compounded quarterly, the interest amount is larger than if the same interest rate is compounded annually. The latter case indicates that there is an *effective* annually compounded interest rate greater than 4 percent per annum which is equivalent to the *nominal* 4 percent compounded quarterly. How can this effective rate be found?

Let i be a nominal annual interest rate compounded f times a year. Then for a given principal P the compound amount is given by formula (3.5). Let r be the effective rate compounded annually which is equivalent to the nominal annual rate i compounded f times a year. Then for the same given P, the compound amount is by (3.4),

$$A = P(1 + r)^n .$$

But if r is equivalent to i, then the two compound amounts must be equal. Hence,

$$P(1 + r)^n = P\left(1 + \frac{i}{f}\right)^{nf} .$$

Dividing both sides by P, and taking their nth root, we get

$$1 + r = \left(1 + \frac{i}{f}\right)^f , \qquad \text{and}$$

(3.6)
$$\boxed{r = \left(1 + \frac{i}{f}\right)^f - 1 .}$$

Example 3.7. Consider the case in Example 3.6. Find the effective rate of the interest rate at 4 percent annum compounded quarterly.

Solution:
Substituting $i = 0.04$ and $f = 4$ in (3.6), we obtain

$$r = \left(1 + \frac{0.04}{4}\right)^4 - 1$$
$$= (1.01)^4 - 1$$
$$= 1.0406 - 1$$
$$= 4.06 \text{ percent.}$$

It is important to note that the effective rate depends on the nominal rate i and the number of conversion periods f. It is independent of the principal P and the compound amount A.

The effective rate of interest can be a useful guide for comparing alternative investment opportunities. Also, the effective interest rate compounded continuously is used in studying the theoretical aspects of finance. Unfortunately, however, space limitations compel us to divert our attention elsewhere.

As in the case of simple interest the present value of a sum of money available in the future at a compound interest rate can be easily obtained from formula (3.4). Since the compound amount A is given and we want to find its present value P, solving (3.4) for P we get

(3.7)
$$P = \frac{A}{(1 + i)^n} = A(1 + i)^{-n}.$$

Example 3.8. At the end of the year Bacchus Beverages Company must pay the Industrial Machinery Corporation $2000 against the unpaid balance for the cost of new bottle sterilizing and filling machinery. If a bank pays 4 percent per annum interest compounded quarterly on deposits, how much should the company deposit at the beginning of the year so that the accumulated amount on deposit will meet the company's obligation?

Solution:
Substituting $A = \$2000$, $i = 0.04$, $n = 1$, and $f = 4$ in (3.7), we get

$$P = \frac{2000}{\left(1 + \frac{0.04}{4}\right)^4}$$
$$= \frac{2000}{(1.01)^4}$$
$$= \frac{2000}{1.0406}$$
$$\approx 1921.96 \text{ dollars.}$$

Both the compound interest formula (3.4) and the present value formula (3.7) deal with cases which involve a single payment. These formulas, together with other formulas to be explained shortly, are shown in Table 3.1. The expressions in brackets are called *investment*

TABLE 3.1.

Formula No.	Description	Formula
(3.4)	Single payment at compound interest	$A = P[(1 + i)^n]$
(3.7)	Present value of a single payment—discount	$P = A\left[\dfrac{1}{(1 + i)^n}\right]$
(3.10)	Future value of uniform payments—amount of an annuity	$A = p\left[\dfrac{(1 + i)^n - 1}{i}\right]$
(3.11)	Uniform payments for capital accumulation—sinking fund	$p = A\left[\dfrac{i}{(1 + i)^n - 1}\right]$
(3.12)	Present value of uniform payments—present value of an annuity	$P = p\left[\dfrac{(1 + i)^n - 1}{i(1 + i)^n}\right]$
(3.13)	Uniform payments for capital recovery—amortization	$p = P\left[\dfrac{i(1 + i)^n}{(1 + i)^n - 1}\right]$

factors. Special tables are available which give the value of an investment factor for a certain range of values of i and n. Such tables will be used for subsequent calculations.

3.3 Future and Present Values of Equal Periodic Payments.

Many business transactions involve a series of equal payments made at regular intervals of time. Such a series of uniform payments are frequently called annuities, although the *payment period* may be less than a year. Personal financing such as installment credit usually involves annuities of shorter than a year duration with simple interest. This time, however, we wish to find the *amount* which would be accumulated at the end of n periods from n periodic payments if each payment were invested at a given compound interest rate.

Let p be the periodic payment made at the *end* of each period, i the compounded interest rate per conversion period, and n the number of conversion periods. Then the amount from the last, i.e., nth payment just being made, will be equal to p since it has earned no interest; the payment before the last, i.e., the $(n - 1)$th payment, will be equal to $p(1 + i)$ by (3.4); and the payment before that will be equal to $p(1 + i)^2$, and so on. Finally, the first payment made at the end of the first period will be equal to $p(1 + i)^{n-1}$. Thus, the compound amount will be

$$(3.8) \qquad A = p + p(1 + i) + p(1 + i)^2 + \ldots + p(1 + i)^{n-1}.$$

Multiplying both sides of (3.8) by $1 + i$, we get

(3.9) $A(1 + i) = p(1 + i) + p(1 + i)^2 + p(1 + i)^3 + \ldots + p(1 + i)^n$.

Subtracting (3.8) from (3.9), we obtain

$$A(1 + i) - A = p(1 + i)^n - p.$$

Factoring and solving for A, we finally have

$$A[(\cancel{1} + i) - \cancel{1}] = p[(1 + i)^n - 1], \text{ and}$$

(3.10) $$A = p\left[\frac{(1 + i)^n - 1}{i}\right],$$

as shown in Table 3.1.

Example 3.9. Instead of paying a lump sum of $1921.96, the manager of Bacchus Beverages Company in Example 3.8 chooses to pay $493 quarterly. Would the compound amount from the four quarterly deposits be sufficient to meet his $2000 obligation?

Solution:

Since $p = 493$, $i = 0.04/4 = 0.01$ and $n = 4$, substituting in (3.10), we get

$$A = 493\left[\frac{(1.01)^4 - 1}{0.01}\right]; \text{ and}$$

from the amount of annuity factor table, we have

$$A = 493(4.0604)$$
$$\approx 2001.78 \text{ dollars.}$$

In the above case p, i, and n were known and we wanted to find the compound amount A. More frequently than not, we know the amount A which must be accumulated at a given i and n and we wish to find what the periodic payment p would be. Solving (3.10) for the unknown p in terms of the other variables, we obtain

(3.11) $$p = A\left[\frac{i}{(1 + i)^n - 1}\right]$$

as shown in Table 3.1. The accumulated capital A is called a *sinking fund*. The case in Example 3.9 could be very easily changed into a sinking fund problem by asking what the quarterly payments should be for accumulating $2000 at the end of the year. However, leaving the solution of this problem to the reader, let us consider another case.

Example 3.10. Mr. E. L. Aramian, manager of Aramian Reliable Products, wants to establish a sinking fund of $200,000 in five years for expanding the plant capacity of his company. The Old Yankee Trust

Company, specializing in handling investment portfolios, advised him that Mr. Aramian's annual deposits with the Trust could earn, under the most conservative investment policy, 5.5 percent compounded per annum. How much from the earnings of his firm should Mr. Aramian contribute to the fund annually in order to accumulate $200,000 in five years?

Solution:

Substituting $A = 200,000$, $i = 0.055$, and $n = 5$ in (3.11), we have

$$p = 200,000 \left[\frac{0.055}{(1.055)^5 - 1} \right], \text{ and}$$

taking the reciprocal from the table of the amount of annuity factors, we obtain

$$p = 200,000 \left(\frac{1}{5.581} \right)$$
$$\approx 35,835.88 \text{ dollars.}$$

So far we have considered the cases when we wanted to find the amount A given the annuity p or the annuity p given the amount A. Our next problem is to find the present value of an annuity. In other words, given a series of equal future sums, what is their present worth if these sums were invested at a given compound interest rate? Let P represent the present value of a future amount A of an annuity. Then, if P were invested at compound i interest rate, A is given by (3.4). Also, let p represent an annuity. Then the future amount A of this annuity is given by (3.10). Hence,

$$P(1 + i)^n = p \left[\frac{(1 + i)^n - 1}{i} \right], \text{ and}$$

(3.12)
$$P = p \left[\frac{(1 + i)^n - 1}{i(1 + i)^n} \right] = p \left[\frac{1 - \frac{1}{(1 + i)^n}}{i} \right] = p \left[\frac{1 - (1 + i)^{-n}}{i} \right]$$

as shown in Table 3.1.

Formula (3.12) may be used to evaluate different investment opportunities open to management, thus assisting in the optimal allocation of investable funds. The cost of each investment opportunity may be compared with the present value of the expected series of annual future earnings from such an investment.

Example 3.11. In the regular course of business Ace Contract Machining Company realizes an 8 percent net return on tooling and other incidental costs from a contract. From a recent contract the company expects to realize $10,000 annually for five years. However, accepting the contract requires an expense for retooling and other costs amounting to $35,000. Should management bid on the new contract?

Solution:
We must find the present value of $10,000 annual net return compounded at 8 percent annually for five years. Substituting in (3.12), we get

$$P = 10,000\left[\frac{(1.08)^5 - 1}{0.08(1.08)^5}\right], \text{ and}$$

from the appropriate factor table, we obtain

$$P = 10,000(3.99271)$$
$$\approx 39,927.10 \text{ dollars.}$$

Since the present value P of the contract is greater than $35,000, management should bid on the new contract.

Finally, we may want to find the annuity p for paying back a borrowed sum P earning a given compound interest. This is a uniform payments plan for repaying borrowed capital, otherwise called *amortization*. Since we are given the present value of an annuity and we want to find the annuity itself, solving (3.12) for p we obtain

(3.13)
$$\boxed{p = P\left[\frac{i(1 + i)^n}{(1 + i)^n - 1}\right],}$$

as shown in Table 3.1.

Example 3.12. Earnings after taxes (cost savings or profits) from a new machine are expected to be $4500 per year. The machine costs $20,000 and after five years has no resale or scrap value. A loan can be made for this amount payable in five equal annual installments at 6 percent per annum on the unpaid balance of the loan. Should management buy the machine?
Solution:
We must find the annual payment p which will amortize the $20,000 long-term loan. Substituting in (3.13), we have

$$p = 20,000\left[\frac{0.06(1.06)^5}{(1.06)^5 - 1}\right], \quad \text{and}$$

from the appropriate factor table, we get

$$p = 20,000\ (0.237396)$$
$$\approx 4747.92 \text{ dollars.}$$

Unless other benefits are expected, the new machine should not be purchased since the expected annual earnings are not sufficient to pay for the amortization of the borrowed capital.

3.4. Special Cases in Capital Budgeting. The basic investment formulas in Table 3.1 can be used for handling capital budgeting problems more sophisticated than the ones already considered. Four such cases follow.

Case 1 : *Machinery, equipment, and other capital goods usually have a resale or salvage value.* This value must be included in evaluating an investment. Thus the present value of an investment in capital goods is equal to the sum of the present value of annual returns plus the present resale or salvage value of such goods. Combining formulas (3.12) and (3.7), we get

(3.14)
$$P = p\left[\frac{(1 + i)^n - 1}{i(1 + i)^n}\right] + S\left[\frac{1}{(1 + i)^n}\right],$$

where S represents resale or salvage value and all other symbols are defined as previously.

Example 3.13. We may assume that the new machine in Example 3.12 is purchased with cash and at the end of five years it has $1800 resale value. Also, let us assume that the company would earn a 6 percent return if the $20,000 spent on the machine were invested elsewhere. Substituting in (3.14) and using the appropriate factor tables, we have

$$P = 4500\left[\frac{(1.06)^5 - 1}{0.06(1.06)^5}\right] + 1800\left[\frac{1}{(1.06)^5}\right]$$

$$= 4500\,(4.212364) + 1800(0.747258)$$

$$\approx 18{,}955.64 + 1345.06$$

$$\approx 20{,}300.70 \text{ dollars.}$$

The new machine should be purchased since the present value of its earnings after taxes and its present salvage value exceeds its cost.

Case 2 : *More frequently than not, expected net annual returns from an investment are not equal.* In such a case formula (3.12) cannot be used. We can use formula (3.7), however, to find the present value of each annual return and of the resale price separately and add the results to find the present value of an investment, i.e.,

(3.15)
$$P = \sum_{j}^{n} \frac{A_j}{(1 + i)^j} + \frac{S}{(1 + i)^n},$$

where $\sum$(sigma) represents the sum of the present value of annual returns $A_j, j = 1, 2, 3, \ldots, n,$ and all other symbols are defined previously.

Example 3.14. The total earnings after taxes from the new machine in Example 3.12 were $22,500 distributed evenly over a period of five years.

Let us assume now that these earnings are distributed unevenly as shown below:

Year j	Earnings A_j	Factor $(1+0.06)^{-n}$	Present Value $A_j(1+0.06)^{-n}$
1............	3000	0.94340	2830.20
2............	3000	0.89000	2670.00
3............	4500	0.83962	3778.29
4............	6000	0.79210	4752.60
5............	6000	0.74726	4483.56
	22,500	$\sum_{j=1}^{n=5} \dfrac{A_j}{(1+0.06)^j} =$	18,514.65

Multiplying annual earnings by the present value factor $(1+0.06)^{-n}$ and summing the products we get \$18,514.65. Adding the present value of the resale price \$1345.06, we get $P = \$19,859.71$. Since this present value of the machine is less than its cost of \$20,000, the new machine should not be purchased.

Case 3: *Constructing or renting a factory building is another important capital budgeting problem.* In problems of this sort we must compare the cost of constructing the building with the present value of the rentals and resale price of the building.

Example 3.15. The management of a company can either construct a factory building for \$1,250,000 or rent an equivalent one with a 25-year lease for an annual rental of \$100,000 payable at the beginning of each year and an option to purchase the building for \$130,000 at the expiration of the contract. If the company expects to earn 8 percent per year after taxes from other investment opportunities, should management construct or rent an equivalent factory building?

This problem is similar to the problem in Case 1, but with one important difference. Periodic payments of rentals are made at the beginning, not at the end, of each year. Thus, formula (3.14) must be modified to

$$(3.16) \qquad \boxed{P = p\left[1 + \frac{(1+i)^n - 1}{i(1+i)^n}\right] + (S - p)\left[\frac{1}{(1+i)^n}\right],}$$

where the present value of rentals was increased by p and the purchase option was reduced by the same rental p before being evaluated.

Example 3.15—*Continued.* Substituting for the values given above in formula (3.16) and using the factor tables, we get

$$P = 100,000\left[1 + \frac{(1.08)^{25} - 1}{0.08(1.08)^{25}}\right] + (130,000 - 100,000)\left[\frac{1}{(1.08)^{25}}\right]$$
$$= 100,000(11.6747762) + 30,000(0.146)$$
$$= 1,171,857.62 \text{ dollars.}$$

Management should decide to rent rather than construct a factory building of its own.

Case 4: *Finally, tax advantages from depreciation of capital goods are important in capital budgeting.* Corporations pay a federal income tax on their *reported* earnings. At present this tax is at a constant rate of 52 percent of reported earnings in excess of $25,000 a year. Since depreciation charges reduce reported earnings, corporation taxes are proportionately reduced. For instance, a reduction of reported earnings by $100,000 for depreciation purposes results in a $100,000(0.52) = $52,000 reduction in the tax paid. While the $100,000 reduction in reported earnings does not affect actual cash earnings, the $52,000 saved in taxes increases cash earnings by that amount.

The principal depreciation methods allowed by the Internal Revenue Service for assets with lives of three or more years are (*a*) straight line, (*b*) sum-of-the-years'-digits, and (*c*) double declining balance. Their respective formulas are

$$(3.17) \quad (a)\ A_j = \frac{I}{n}; \quad (b)\ A_j = \frac{n-j+1}{n(n+1)} 2I; \quad (c)\ A_j = \frac{2I}{n}\left(1 - \frac{2}{n}\right)^{j-1},$$

where A_j represents the amount to be depreciated in the jth year, n the number of years, I the cost of investment, and $j = 1, 2, \ldots, n$. For convenience we shall designate them depreciation methods A, B, and C, respectively. Since under method C the undepreciated balance never becomes zero, the corporation is allowed to switch to method A any year before the nth year.

The crucial question is how do we evaluate an opportunity, say of investing in a machine? Such an investment is likely to be profitable if the present value of expected earnings after taxes plus the tax savings on the present value of depreciation exceeds the cost of the investment.

Example 3.16. In Example 3.14 we have found that the new machine should not be purchased since the present value of the machine is less than its cost. This is particularly so if we assume no resale value with the present value of this machine being only $18,514.65. Now with the tax savings from the present value of depreciation added to the above figure we shall reach the decision to purchase the machine. Our problem is to find an optimal depreciation method.

Since the present value of the machine was estimated for a five-year period, the depreciation years $n = 5$. The $20,000 spent on the machine (resale or salvage value assumed to be zero) is depreciated below under all three methods:

Year (1)	Method A (2)	Method B (3)	Method C k = 3 (4)	Method C k = 4 (5)	Method C k = 5 (6)
1............	$4000	$6667	$8000	$8000	$8000
2............	4000	5333	4800	4800	4800
3............	4000	4000	2400	2880	2880
4............	4000	2667	2400	2160	1728
5............	4000	1333	2400	2160	2592
	$20,000	$20,000	$20,000	$20,000	$20,000

Under method C three different approaches are considered. We switch to method A in the third, fourth, and fifth year.

The next step is to find the present value of each yearly depreciated amount at a rate of 6 percent per annum using formulas (3.12) for method A and (3.7) for all other methods and sum the annual amounts as shown below:

Method	Present Value of Depreciation
A.........................	$16,849
B.........................	17,503
C, $k = 3$	17,529
C, $k = 4$	17,562
C, $k = 5$	17,543

The present value of taxes saved is 0.52 times the present value of depreciation under each method. Although management might decide to purchase the machine under any depreciation method, the optimal one is method C with switching to method A in the fourth year since

$$17,562(0.52) + 18,514.65 = 27,646.69 \text{ dollars}$$

exceeds the $20,000 cost of the machine by the largest amount.

In fact, method A is *never* optimal. (Why?) On the other hand, method B under certain conditions may be optimal. Although a firm is not allowed to choose a different depreciation method each year, it is permitted under method C to switch to method A.

One final word of caution should be said about two important points. In the first place, evaluation of investment opportunities is based on expected earnings and costs which are assumed that they will be realized with certainty. Hence such evaluations depend on whether the estimation of such expectations will be correct. In the second place, it should not be forgotten that optimal allocation of investable funds with formulas, as all quantitative techniques, is in fact a suboptimization effort. Such an optimal allocation must be reconciled with the other monetary as well as nonmonetary aspects of business operations.

PROBLEMS

3.1. For each case below find the amount A when principal P, simple interest rate per annum i, and term of the loan n are as follows:
*a) $P = \$10,000$, $i = 5.5$ percent, $n = 5$ years.
b) $P = \$100,000$, $i = 4.5$ percent, $n = 90$ days.
c) $P = \$5000$, $i = 9$ percent, $n = 120$ days.

3.2. Given an amount A, simple interest rate per annum i, and term of the loan n, find principal or present value P in each case below:
*a) $A = \$8640$, $i = 4$ percent, $n = 2$ years.
b) $A = \$9045$, $i = 4$ percent, $n = 45$ days.
c) $A = \$10,000$, $i = 9$ percent, $n = 120$ days.

3.3. Solve formula (3.1) in the text for i and in each case find i when I, P, and n are as follows:
*a) $I = \$625, P = \$5000$, and $n = 2.5$ years.
b) $A = \$9800, P = \$8000$, $n = 3$ years.
c) $P = \$4000$, $A = \$4060$, $n = 90$ days.

3.4. Solve formula (3.1) in the text for n and in each case find n when I, P, and i are as follows:
*a) $I = \$600$, $P = \$6000$, $i = 5$ percent.
b) $A = \$11,500$, $P = \$10,000$, $i = 6$ percent.
c) $P = \$1000$, $A = \$1020$, $i = 8$ percent.

3.5. In each case use logarithms to find compound amount A when P, n, and i are given. Verify your answer by referring to a factor $(1 + i)^n$ table.
*a) $P = \$100,000, i = 5$ percent per annum compounded annually, $n = 10$ years.
b) $P = \$10,000, i = 8$ percent per annum compounded quarterly, $n = 10$ years.
c) $P = \$10,000, i = 6$ percent per annum compounded monthly, $n = 8$ years.

3.6. Observing that formula (3.4) in Table 3.1 can be written $A/P = (1 + i)^n$, we can use the A/P ratio to approximate the value of i when A, P, and n are given. For example, when $A/P = 1.1025$ and $n = 2$ from a factor $(1 + i)^n$ table, we find that $i = 0.05$. Using this trial-and-error method find the approximate value of i when—
*a) $A = \$185,194, P = \$100,000$, and $n = 14$.
b) $A = \$35,816.94, P = \$20,000$, and $n = 10$.
c) $A/P = 4.05877$, and $n = 20$.

3.7. Find the effective annual rate when the nominal rate per annum is—
*a) $i = 6$ percent compounded monthly.
b) $i = 8$ percent compounded quarterly.
c) $i = 9$ percent compounded semiannually.

3.8. Use logarithms to find the present value P when A, n, and i are given. Verify your answer by referring to a factor $(1 + i)^n$ table.

*a) $A = \$13,382.26$, $n = 5$ years, and $i = 6$ percent per annum compounded annually.

b) $A = \$1,989.79$, $n = 10$ years, and $i = 7$ percent per annum compounded semiannually.

c) $A = \$25,000$, $n = 12$ years, and $i = 8$ percent per annum compounded quarterly.

3.9. A new machine is purchased for \$26,000. Profits after taxes from other investments open to the management of the firm are expected to be 8 percent per year. Should management purchase the machine—

*a) If profits after taxes from the machine are expected to be \$9000, \$8000, \$7000, and \$6000 during the four years of the machine's life and if the machine is worthless at the end of the fourth year?

*b) If, in addition to profit in (a), the machine has a resale price of \$2000 at the end of the fourth year?

c) If, in addition to resale price, maintenance and repair costs, not originally deducted from profits, are expected to be \$100, \$200, \$300, and \$400 at the end of each of the four years?

d) Verify your answer to (c) above by finding the present value of the difference of yearly profits and maintenance-repair costs.

3.10. Let machine A be purchased under terms explained in Problem 3.9(b) with one difference. It is sold at the end of the fifth year for \$2000 during which profits after taxes from the machine are expected to be \$5000. Machine B differs from machine A only with respect to the annual profits after taxes which are expected to be \$5000, \$6000, \$7000, \$8000, and \$9000. Explain why machine A should be preferred. Then support your explanation by finding the present value of both machines.

3.11. At end of each year a manager invests \$1000 in stocks of a mutual no load investment fund. If capital gains and dividends are expected to yield a rate of 6 percent per annum and if all earnings are reinvested annually, what would his equity be in (a) 10 years? (b) 20 years? (c) 30 years?

3.12. A bond issue of \$1,000,000 with a 15-year maturity for an industrial corporation provides that the firm contribute annually a sum of money which, if invested at 4.5 percent per annum compounded annually, would accumulate to a fund sufficient to retire the bond issue at the end of the 15th year. What should be the corporation's annual contribution to the fund?

3.13. Observing that formula (3.12) in Table 3.1 can be written

$$\frac{P}{p} = \left[\frac{(1 + i)^n - 1}{i(1 + i)^n} \right],$$

we can use the P/p ratio to find the approximate value of i called the internal *rate of return* when P, p, and n are known. See example for a similar case in Problem 3.6. This method can be used to evaluate the relative profitability of an investment in terms of the internal rate of return.

New equipment costing $15,600 is expected to increase profits after taxes by $6000 annually for three years.

*a) What is the approximate internal rate of return on this investment, if the equipment is worthless at the end of the third year?

b) What is the approximate internal rate of return on this investment if, during the fourth year, profits after taxes were only $3000 and the company sold the equipment for $3000 at the end of the year?

3.14. Let machine A be purchased under terms explained in Problem 3.9(b). Machine B costs the same, and total profits are expected to be the same as for machine A. But profits from machine B are expected to be $7500 each year, and its resale price at the end of the fourth year is $3000. At 8 percent expected rate of return from alternative investments, which machine should be purchased?

3.15. A firm has a 20-year mortgage of $100,000 on its plant at 5.5 percent interest per annum on the unpaid balance of the mortgage. What should the firm's annual payments be for amortizing this mortgage?

3.16. In Example 3.13 we wanted to find P given p, S, i, and n. Frequently we may want to find the level of cost savings or profits after taxes p which will be sufficient to pay for the cost of the machine. This is a kind of a break-even point where the present value of the machine minus the cost of the machine C equals zero, i.e.,

$$P - C = p\left[\frac{1 - (1 + i)^{-n}}{i}\right] + S(1 + i)^{-n} - C = 0.$$

a) Using the above expression show that the break-even level of cost savings or profits after taxes

$$p = (C - S)\left[\frac{i(1 + i)^n}{(1 + i)^n - 1}\right] + Si$$

b) Use the data in Example 3.13 where $C = \$20,000$, $S = \$1800$, $i = 0.06$, and $n = 5$ to find this break-even value. Since earnings after taxes from the machine are expected to be $4500 a year, should the machine be purchased?

3.17. Let p be the unknown variable in Example 3.15 where $P = \$1,250,000$, $S = \$130,000$, $i = 0.08$, and $n = 25$. What is the value of p? Compare its value with the rental of $100,000 per year and decide whether management should construct a factory building or rent an equivalent one.

3.18. Consider Example 3.16 in Case 4.

a) Verify the annual depreciation allowances and their present value under various depreciation methods.

b) Let S be the resale or salvage value of an asset, then the three depreciation formulas in the text become

$$(A) \ A_j = \frac{I - S}{n}; \quad (B) \ A_j = \left[\frac{n - j + 1}{n(n + 1)}\right]2(I - S); \quad (C) \ A_j = \frac{2I}{n}\left(1 - \frac{2}{n}\right)^{j-1}.$$

The depreciation formula for method C remains unchanged. However, at the kth year where we can switch to method A we must subtract the salvage value S from the undepreciated balance of the asset and allocate the difference equally among the remaining years, so that the sum of the depreciation changes does not exceed $I - S$. Let $S = \$2000$ in Example 3.16. Which depreciation method is optimal?

3.19. The assets of a business firm may be evaluated on the basis of their original cost, their replacement cost, or the present value of their current earnings. Although all methods have their limitations, the latter is a better measure of the economic value of an asset than the former two. The present value method is called *capitalization*. It assumes that the series of annual earnings from assets will continue indefinitely into the future, i.e., n approaches infinity. Then as n approaches infinity formula (3.12) reduces to $P = p/i$ since the term $1/(1 + i)^n$ in (3.12) approaches zero. Using the capitalization formula $P = p/i$ solve the following problems.

a) The normal annual net earnings after taxes of AAA Foods, a firm operating a chain of supermarkets, are $300,000. If, in this type of business, a rate of 6 percent is considered a normal rate of return on investment, what is the market value of the company's assets?

b) The earnings of a common stock have been $20 per share. If money invested in common stocks is expected to bring a rate of 5 percent return per year, what is the market value of this stock?

SUGGESTED REFERENCES

1. ANDRESS, F. J. "The Learning Curve as a Production Tool," *Harvard Business Review*, Vol. XXXII, 1 (1954), pp. 87–97. Reprinted in LEMKE AND EDWARDS. *Administrative Control and Executive Action*, pp. 352–61. Columbus, Ohio: C. Merrill Books, Inc., 1961. **(2)**

2. COMMITTEE ON BUSINESS MATHEMATICS, *College Business Mathematics*, pp. 125–59, 191–256. New York: Pitman Publishing Corp., 1960. **(3)**

3. COOLEY, H. R., *et al. Introduction to Mathematics*, pp. 300–306. Boston: Houghton Mifflin Co., 1949. **(1)**

4. BIERMAN, H., AND SMIDT, S. *The Capital Budgeting Decision*. New York: The Macmillan Co., 1960. **(3)**

5. DAUS, P. H., AND WHYBURN, W. M. *Introduction to Mathematical Analysis with Applications to Problems of Economics*, pp. 1–31. Reading, Mass.: Addison-Wesley Publishing Co., Inc., 1958. **(1)**

6. HOWELL, J. E., AND TEICHROEW, D. *Mathematical Analysis for Business Decisions*, pp. 187–205. Homewood, Ill.: Richard D. Irwin, Inc., 1963. **(3)**

7. JOHNSON, R. W. *Financial Management*, pp. 129–57. Boston, Mass.: Allyn and Bacon, Inc., 1959. **(3)**

8. KEMENY, JOHN G., *et al. Finite Mathematics with Business Applications*, pp. 312–46. Englewood Cliffs, N.J.: Prentice-Hall, Inc., 1962. **(3)**

9. RICHARDSON, M. *College Algebra*, pp. 391–420, 477–81. Al. ed. Engle-wood Cliffs, N.J.: Prentice-Hall, Inc., 1958. (**2, 3**)

10. SAMUELSON, P. A. *Economics: An Introductory Analysis*, pp. 367–95. 3d ed. New York: McGraw-Hill Book Co., Inc., 1955. (**1**)

11. *Standard Mathematical Tables*, pp. 1–45, 171–85, 434–75. Cleveland, Ohio: Chemical Rubber Publishing Co., 1959. (**2, 3**)

12. VIDALE, M. L., AND WOLFE, H. B. "An Operations-Research Study of Sales Response to Advertising," *Operations Research*, Vol. V., No. 3, (June, 1957), pp. 370–81. Reprinted in F. BASS *et al. Mathematical Models and Methods in Marketing*, pp. 357–77. Homewood, Ill.: Richard D. Irwin, Inc., 1961. (**2**)

13. WEINBERG, R. S. "Multiple Factor Break-Even Analysis," *Operations Research*, Vol. IV, No. 2 (April, 1956), pp. 152–86. Reprinted in F. BASS *et al. Mathematical Models and Methods in Marketing*, pp. 52–100. Homewood, Ill.: Richard D. Irwin, Inc., 1961. (**2**)

PART III

Fundamentals of Linear Programming

In Section 3 of Chapter 6 we have shown how to optimize in certain business situations with quadratic functions. Essentially, optimization consisted of finding the maximum profit or the minimum cost subject to a single restricting function. Such cases fall within the traditional approach of marginal economic analysis. *Linear programming is another optimization method; but unlike the former cases, it deals with problems which for lack of a better term may be called* allocation problems. *This new quantitative method of analysis shows how to allocate scarce resources, such as materials, money, or time, and how to do such an allocation in the best possible way subject to more than one restricting condition, i.e., inequalities and/or equations.*

Linear programming may be presented with a great deal of mathematics or with virtually no mathematics at all. Here, we shall follow a middle road. The empirical aspects of linear programming are presented with minimal mathematical sophistication consistent with the treatment of previous subjects.

Although the reader will not become an expert in linear programming by studying this part of the text, he will acquire some insight into the mathematics of this specialized subject. More than that, he will be able to understand and appreciate the potentialities and limitations of linear programming so that he may be able to recognize real-world situations where linear programming may be applied, assist or participate in the initial stages of the formulation of a linear programming problem, evaluate and interpret the results, and apply such results with confidence. Last but not least, he may be able to grow into the subject by studying more sophisticated treatments of linear programming than the one on hand.

Chapter 8, the first of Part III, deals with the fundamental concepts of linear programming. The algebra of linear programming is the subject matter of Chapter 9. Finally, the two basic computational methods of linear programming, namely, the simplex and transportation, occupy Chapter 10.

Chapter 8

THE A, B, C OF LINEAR PROGRAMMING

OUR PRIMARY purpose in this chapter is to show the process rather than the computational methods for solving linear programming problems. In other words, we shall show how to formulate a linear programming problem and express it in mathematical terms, how to solve it by means of graphs or with ordinary algebra, what the solution means in empirical terms, and under what conditions linear programming can be used to solve business problems.

1. LINEAR PROGRAMMING WITH GRAPHS

Although graphs are not proper tools for solving real-world linear programming problems, they are very effective in giving a conceptual understanding of the process itself. For this purpose we shall first review briefly inequalities which are necessary for expressing a linear programming problem in mathematical terms. This topic is followed by a motivating yet simple example in linear programming which raises the need for studying systems of inequalities and their graphs. The section concludes with another example further illustrating linear programming with graphs.

1.1. Inequalities and Their Graphs. Statements in which one expression is *greater than* ($>$), *less than* ($<$), *greater than or equal to* ($\geqslant$), *and less than or equal to* ($\leqslant$) *another expression are called inequalities*. Here, we are concerned with the so-called conditional inequalities, i.e., inequalities which are not true for all possible values of the variables involved. For example, inequality $x + 5 \geqslant 8$ is conditional since it is true for $x \geqslant 3$ and not true for $x < 3$.

Two inequalities such as $x_1 + x_2 \leqslant 80$ and $x_1 + 2x_2 \leqslant 100$ are said to have the *same sense* since the signs of inequality point in the same direction. Contrastingly, inequalities such as $x_1 + x_2 \leqslant 80$ and $x_1 + x_2 \geqslant 80$ are said to have *opposite senses*. Inequalities such as all the above cited are called *weak* inequalities while inequalities such as $x_1 + x_2 < 80$, $x_1 + 2x_2 < 100$, and $x_1 + x_2 > 80$ are called *strict* or *strong* inequalities.

The following properties (theorems) of inequalities are presented without proof:

1. *The sense of an inequality is not changed if the same real number is added to, or subtracted from, both sides. For example,*

since $7 > 6,$
                     $7 + 2 > 6 + 2$ or $9 > 8;$
and
                     $7 - 2 > 6 - 2$ or $5 > 4.$

2. *The sense of an inequality is not changed if both sides are multiplied or divided by the same positive number. For instance,*

since $8 > 4,$
                     $8 \times 2 > 4 \times 2$ or $16 > 8;$
and
                     $\dfrac{8}{2} > \dfrac{4}{2}$ or $4 > 2.$

3. *The sense of an inequality is reversed if both sides are multiplied or divided by the same negative number. That is,*

if $6 > 3,$

then $6(-3) < 3(-3)$ or $-18 < -9;$
and
                     $\dfrac{6}{-3} < \dfrac{3}{-3}$ or $-2 < -1.$

Inequalities in one unknown are solved much the same way equations are solved.

Example 1.1. Find the values of x_1 for which $x_1 + 12 \leqslant 5 + 2x_1.$
Analysis: If $x_1 + 12 \leqslant 5 + 2x_1$, then by doing the following operations on both sides of the inequality we have

$$-x_1 + 12 \leqslant 5, \qquad \text{by adding } -2x_1;$$
$$-x_1 \leqslant -7, \qquad \text{by adding } -12;$$
$$x_1 \geqslant 7, \qquad \text{by multiplying by } -1.$$

Check:
Letting $x_1 = 7$, then

$$7 + 12 \leqslant 5 + 2(7) \text{ or } 19 = 19.$$

Letting $x_1 = 8$, then

$$8 + 12 \leqslant 5 + 2(8) \text{ or } 20 < 21$$

as well as for any value of x_1 greater than 7 since the analysis steps are reversible.

Again, in direct analogy to the graph of an equation *the graph of an inequality is the set of all points whose coordinates satisfy the inequality.*

Example 1.1—*Continued.* Sketch the graph of $x_1 + 12 \leqslant 5 + 2x_1$.
Solution:
Step 1: Sketch the graph of the corresponding equation

$$x_1 + 12 = 5 + 2x_1.$$

Since $x_1 = 7$ is the solution to this equation, its graph on a cc-plane is the set of points with coordinates $x_1 = 7$ and any x_2-coordinate. The straight solid line at $x_1 = 7$ in Figure 1.1 is a portion of the graph of this equation.

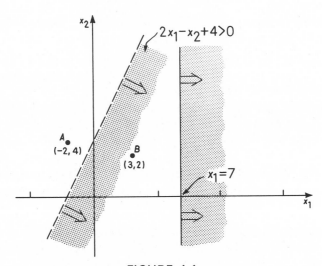

FIGURE 1.1.

Step 2: Sketch the graph of $x_1 + 12 \leqslant 5 + 2x_1$.
Since we have found that $x_1 \geqslant 7$ is the solution to this inequality, its graph is the set of points with coordinates $x_1 \geqslant 7$ and any x_2-coordinate. A portion of this graph is the shaded area shown in Figure 1.1. It is the infinite set of points *on* or to the right-hand side of the line at $x_1 = 7$.

Example 1.2. Sketch the graph of $2x_1 - x_2 + 4 > 0$.
Solution:
Step 1: Sketch the graph of the corresponding equation $2x_1 - x_2 + 4 = 0$.
Since $2x_1 - x_2 = -4$, $x_1 = -2$ when $x_2 = 0$, and $x_2 = 4$ when $x_1 = 0$.
Hence, the graph of the equation cuts the x_1- and x_2-axis at points $(-2, 0)$ and $(0, 4)$, respectively. The broken straight line shown in Figure 1.1 is a portion of the graph of the equation.
Step 2: Find the graph of inequality $2x_1 - x_2 + 4 > 0$.
We must find the set of points whose coordinates satisfy the inequality. This can be easily done by selecting the coordinates of two points, one from each side of the line representing the graph of the corresponding equation, and then finding which one satisfies the inequality.

Let point $A(-2, 4)$ be given. Then the inequality is not satisfied since

$$2(-2) - 4 + 4 < 0 \text{ or } -4 < 0.$$

Let point $B(3, 2)$ be given. Then the inequality is satisfied since

$$2(3) - 2 + 4 > 0 \text{ or } 8 > 0.$$

We may repeat the above process by arbitrarily selecting the coordinates of additional points; but two points are sufficient to determine which of the two half-planes represent the graph of an inequality. Thus, the graph of the above inequality is the set of points to the right-hand side or below the broken line *but not on the line.* A portion of this graph is the shaded area shown in Figure 1.1.

Observe that for a graph of a strong inequality such as $2x_1 - x_2 + 4 > 0$ in Figure 1.1 the boundary line is *broken* in order to indicate the fact that the points on this line *do not satisfy* the strong inequality. On the other hand, for the graph of a weak inequality such as $x_1 \geqslant 7$ in Figure 1.1 the boundary line is *unbroken* in order to indicate that the points on this line *satisfy* the weak inequality.

1.2. An Allocation Problem for Maximizing Profit.
Let us now consider the following motivating linear programming problem.

Example 1.3. Quality Baking Company produces two kinds of cookies which sell for $0.50 and $0.70 per dozen with direct (variable) cost of $0.30 and $0.40, respectively. The bakery has no difficulty in selling all the cookies it can produce. The problem that management faces is a different one. There are only 10 hours of labor available, and oven capacity is limited to 80 dozen cookies. For making one dozen cookies it takes 0.1 hours of labor for cookies of the first kind and 0.2 hours for cookies of the second kind. It takes an equal amount of time to bake either kind of cookies. How can management allocate the limited resources of labor and oven capacity in a way which will secure the highest possible net return?

Finding the optimum allocation of limited resources is equivalent to finding how the two kinds of cookies will share these limited resources so that the net return will be maximized. In other words, in this as well as in other linear programming problems we are looking for an output combination, called *product mix*, which will maximize net returns subject to satisfying the restrictions imposed by the limited resources. Our first step is to express this problem in precise mathematical terms.

Example 1.3—*Continued.* Let x_1 and x_2 represent dozens of cookies of the first and second kind, respectively. Then the total labor time for producing x_1 cookies plus the total labor time for producing x_2 cookies must be equal to or less than ($\leqslant$) the 10 available hours of labor, i.e.,

$$0.1x_1 + 0.2x_2 \leqslant 10 \text{ or}$$
$$(1) \quad x_1 + 2x_2 \leqslant 100,$$

on multiplying by 10.

Similarly, the oven capacity required for baking x_1 cookies plus x_2 cookies should be equal to or less than ($\leqslant$) the 80 dozen cookies of oven capacity, i.e.,

$$(2) \quad x_1 + x_2 \leqslant 80.$$

The net contribution to fixed cost (for sales below the break-even point) or to profits (for sales above the break-even point) is \$0.50 − \$0.30 = \$0.20 for each dozen of x_1 cookies and \$0.70 − \$0.40 = \$0.30 per dozen for x_2 cookies. Since all produced output is sold, we may assume that sales are above the break-even point and net returns are profits before taxes. The function which maximizes profit may be denoted by

$$f_{max} = f(x_1, x_2) = 0.2x_1 + 0.3x_2.$$

The problem may be summarized as follows:

$$f_{max} = 0.2x_1 + 0.3x_2,$$

subject to
$$(1) \quad x_1 + 2x_2 \leqslant 100,$$
$$(2) \quad x_1 + x_2 \leqslant 80,$$
$$(3) \quad x_1 \geqslant 0,$$
$$(4) \quad x_2 \geqslant 0,$$

which means "find the maximum value of function f whose x_1 and x_2 values satisfy the restricting inequalities"—inequalities (3) and (4) being self-explanatory since no negative output is empirically meaningful.

In linear programming terminology the function to be maximized, such as the one in this case, or minimized, as we shall see in a later case, is called the *objective function*. The restricting inequalities, such as (1) through (4) in the above example, and/or equalities when a case requires it are called *restraints*.

Now that our allocation problem has been expressed in mathematical terms we must find the product mix which will maximize the objective function. In order to give an intuitive understanding of the mechanics involved in solving linear programming problems we shall solve our problem graphically. In Section 2 we shall solve the same problem algebraically.

Example 1.3—*Continued.* The first step for a graphical solution is to find the set of points (x_1, x_2) on a cc-plane which simultaneously satisfy all restraints. Let S_1 be the set of points lying on or below the straight line of equation $x_1 + 2x_2 = 100$ in Figure 1.2 and satisfying the corresponding linear inequality (1). Then

$$S_1 = \{(x_1, x_2) | x_1 + 2x_2 \leqslant 100\}$$

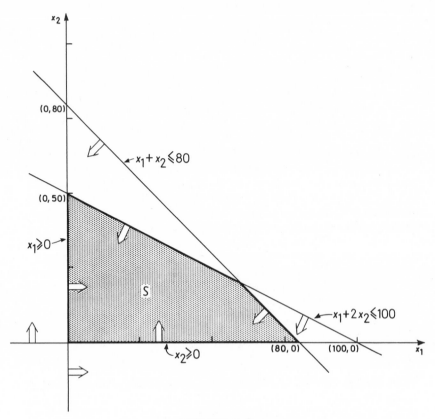

FIGURE 1.2.

Similarly, let S_2 be the set of points whose coordinates satisfy inequality (2). Then

$$S_2 = \{(x_1, x_2) | x_1 + x_2 \leqslant 80\}.$$

Also, let S_3 and S_4 be the sets of points whose coordinates satisfy inequalities (3) and (4), respectively. Then

$$S_3 = \{(x_1, x_2) | x_1 \geqslant 0, \text{ any } x_2\text{-coordinate}\}$$
$$S_4 = \{(x_1, x_2) | x_2 \geqslant 0, \text{ any } x_1\text{-coordinate}\}.$$

Let S be the set representing the intersection of the above sets. Then

$$S = S_1 \cap S_2 \cap S_3 \cap S_4 = \{(x_1, x_2) | x_1 + 2x_2 \leqslant 100 \text{ and } x_1 + x_2 \leqslant 80$$
$$\text{and } x_1 \geqslant 0 \text{ and } x_2 \geqslant 0\}$$

must be the set of points, the shaded polygon in Figure 1.2, whose coordinates satisfy all the restraints of the problem.

A set, such as the set S in the above example, is called the set of *feasible solutions* of a given problem. A feasible solution which maximizes or minimizes the objective function is called *an optimal feasible solution*.

Example 1.3—*Continued.* The second step for a graphical solution of our problem is to find the optimal feasible solution which maximizes the objective function. In other words, from the infinite set of points S we are looking for a point whose coordinates—the product mix (x_1, x_2)—yield the largest profit. One such point is the origin. But when $x_1 = 0$ and $x_2 = 0$, the objective function in Figure 1.3 yields

$$f'_{max} = 0.2(0) + 0.3(0) = 0 \text{ dollars.}$$

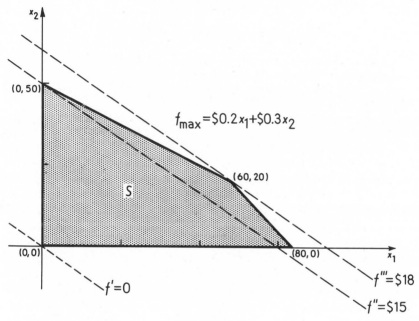

FIGURE 1.3.

Obviously, dollar profits are higher the farther the objective function moves from the origin—the minimum feasible solution. At point $(0, 50)$ the objective function yields

$$f''_{max} = 0.2(0) + 0.3(50) = 15 \text{ dollars.}$$

With this product mix, available labor is fully utilized since

$$1(0) + 2(50) = 100,$$

but oven capacity is not since

$$1(0) + 1(50) = 50 < 80.$$

The only way to produce x_1 cookies is to reduce production of x_2 cookies. Would such substitution be worthwhile? From equation $x_1 + 2x_2 = 100$, which corresponds to inequality (1) of the problem, it can be easily seen that a unit of labor can produce twice as many x_1 cookies as x_2 cookies. Hence, the profit of producing two dozen x_1 cookies, $0.2(2) = \$0.40$, is greater than the profit of producing a dozen x_2 cookies, $0.3(1) = \$0.30$.

Thus, substituting production of x_1 for x_2 cookies would yield larger profits until point (60, 20), read from a sufficiently detailed graph, is reached. Would any further substitution of x_1 for x_2 cookies yield larger profits? The answer is no. This is so because beyond that point since the same oven capacity is required to produce either x_1 or x_2 cookies, the profit of producing one dozen x_1 cookies, \$0.2(1) = \$0.20, is less than the profit from one dozen x_2 cookies, \$0.3(1) = \$0.30. Therefore, the product mix of 60 dozen x_1 cookies and 20 dozen x_2 cookies represents the optimal feasible solution with a maximum profit of

$$f'''_{max} = 0.2(60) + 0.3(20) = 18 \text{ dollars.}$$

It is interesting to note that at this optimal solution both available labor and oven capacity are fully utilized.

Instead of point (0, 50) the reader can reach the same conclusion by testing point (80, 0) first.

The above example leads to a number of important points. First, in obtaining the above optimal solution we tested the objective function at points (0, 0), (0, 50), and (60, 20). A point, such as these points of the feasible solutions set S, which does not lie between any two other points of S, is called an *extreme point* of S. Second, it is important to realize the extreme point (60, 20) which represents the optimal solution is also the common solution to the system of equations which correspond to inequalities (1) and (2) of our problem; but this need not always be the case. Depending on the objective function, the optimal solution could be an extreme point other than point (60, 20). Third, the net of the matter is that *finding the optimal solution of a linear programming problem requires testing the objective function at each of the extreme points of the feasible solutions set S*. A computational method, such as this step-by-step iterative procedure, for solving a problem in a finite number of steps is called an *algorithm*.

1.3. Sets of Feasible Solutions. The above example raises the need for a study of sets of points which satisfy a system of inequalities and equations.

A straight line separates the cc-plane into three mutually exclusive and collectively exhaustive subsets of points whose union is the set of all points on the cc-plane. Consider the graph of equation $x_1 + x_2 = 80$ in Figure 1.4. The cc-plane is separated into the set of points S_1 which lie on the line, i.e.,

$$S_1 = \{(x_1, x_2) | x_1 + x_2 = 80\} ;$$

the set of points S_2 above that line, i.e.,

$$S_2 = \{(x_1, x_2) | x_1 + x_2 > 80\} ;$$

and the set of points S_3 below that line, i.e.,

$$S_3 = \{(x_1, x_2)|x_1 + x_2 < 80\}.$$

Let R_2 be the set representing the union of the above sets. Then

$$R_2 = S_1 \cup S_2 \cup S_3.$$

which contains all the points of the cc-plane.

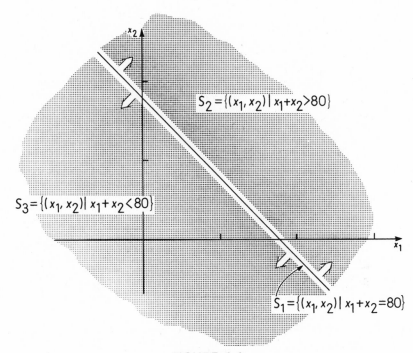

FIGURE 1.4.

Set S_1 in Figure 1.4 is the *boundary* of sets S_2 and S_3. A set which does not contain any portion of its boundary is called an *open set*. Sets S_2 and S_3 are open sets. The half space which each of them represents is called *open half space* since it is defined by a strict or strong inequality. A set which contains its boundary is called a *closed set* and the corresponding half space *closed half space* since it is defined by a weak inequality. Let sets S_4 and S_5 be defined as follows:

$$S_4 = S_1 \cup S_2 = \{(x_1, x_2)|x_1 + x_2 \geqslant 80\} \text{ and}$$

$$S_5 = S_1 \cup S_3 = \{(x_1, x_2)|x_1 + x_2 \leqslant 80\}.$$

Then such sets are closed sets.

Since the sets S_1, S_2, and S_3 in Figure 1.4 are mutually exclusive, their intersection cannot possibly represent a set of feasible solutions since

$$S_1 \cap S_2 \cap S_3 = \varnothing.$$

In such a case, the inequalities whose points represent sets S_2 and S_3 are said to be *inconsistent*. However, the intersection of half spaces may be a set other than the null set, yet the objective function *may* not have a maximum value.

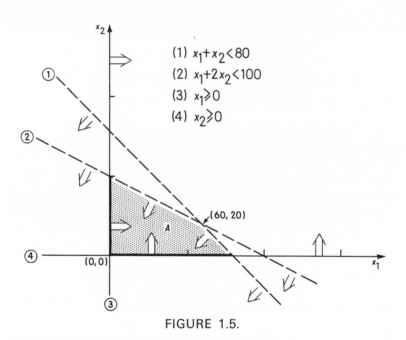

(1) $x_1 + x_2 < 80$
(2) $x_1 + 2x_2 < 100$
(3) $x_1 \geqslant 0$
(4) $x_2 \geqslant 0$

(60, 20)

(0, 0)

FIGURE 1.5.

Example 1.4. Let set A of feasible solutions, the shaded area in Figure 1.5, be given. Although similar to the set in Figure 1.1, the objective function

$$f_{\max} = 0.2x_1 + 0.3x_2$$

of our allocation problem has no maximum since the set A is an open set at point (60, 20). The objective function has a minimum value, however, since the set A is closed at point (0, 0).

The reader can very easily convert the set A in the above example to a set for which the objective function has neither a minimum nor a maximum value by changing the weak inequalities (3) and (4) to strong inequalities.

The set of feasible solutions may be bounded. *A set of points in a cc-plane is bounded if all the points of the set lie inside some circle with center at the origin; otherwise, the set is unbounded.*

Example 1.5. Set A in Figure 1.5 is an open, but a bounded, set. Set B in Figure 1.6, on the other hand, is an unbounded set. An objective function over such a set has no maximum value although it may have a minimum one.

The reader will find additional cases of unbounded or open sets among the problems of this section.

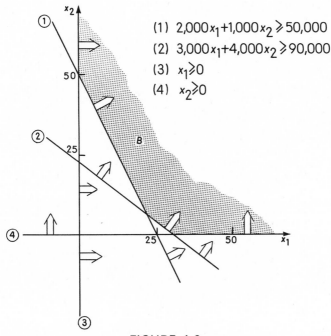

(1) $2{,}000x_1 + 1{,}000x_2 \geqslant 50{,}000$

(2) $3{,}000x_1 + 4{,}000x_2 \geqslant 90{,}000$

(3) $x_1 \geqslant 0$

(4) $x_2 \geqslant 0$

FIGURE 1.6.

A set of feasible solutions may be a bounded and a closed set, yet finding the maximum or the minimum value of the objective function may present difficulties because of the presence of redundant inequalities.

Example 1.6. Suppose Quality Baking Company has 160 pounds of cookie mix and that one pound of cookie mix is required to produce either x_1 or x_2 cookies. The points whose coordinates satisfy the new inequality $x_1 + x_2 \leqslant 160$ make up the closed half space designated (1) shown in Figure 1.7, together with the set of feasible solutions S of the original problem. Inequality (1) is redundant since the set of points which simultaneously satisfy inequalities (1) and (2) is the set of points which satisfy inequality (2) alone. In other words, cookie mix is not a limited resource for this problem. Graphically, inequality (1) contributes nothing to the problem and can be ignored.

Algebraically, linear programming problems such as the one already considered in the above example represent cases of the so-called *degeneracy* with which we shall deal later.

We have seen that a set of feasible solutions in a cc-plane can be a polygon. It can also be a line segment or a point. For example, the solution set in Figure 2.1 in the following section is the dark segment of

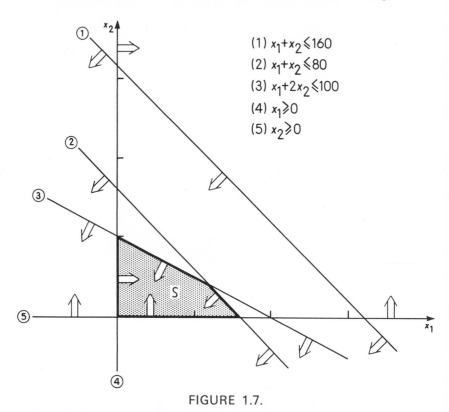

(1) $x_1 + x_2 \leqslant 160$

(2) $x_1 + x_2 \leqslant 80$

(3) $x_1 + 2x_2 \leqslant 100$

(4) $x_1 \geqslant 0$

(5) $x_2 \geqslant 0$

FIGURE 1.7.

line (1). Also, we have seen that a maximum or a minimum can exist when the solution set is open or unbounded. The point which the reader should remember is that if a set of feasible solutions is both bounded and closed, an objective function over this set *will* have a maximum and a minimum value.

1.4. An Allocation Problem for Minimizing Cost.

We conclude this section with a linear programming problem for minimizing the cost of advertising.

Example 1.7. The manager of AAA Department Stores, Inc., considers advertising possibilities of the new collection of gifts for the forthcoming

Christmas. A full page advertisement costs \$60 in newspaper A and \$50 in newspaper B per weekday issue. Among the subscribers of the newspapers the manager expects that for every issue 2000 additional readers will notice the advertisement if it appears in newspaper A and 1000 if it appears in newspaper B. Among the nonsubscribers, however, the number of readers who will notice the advertisement increases to 3000 and 4000 per issue, respectively. In order to break even, the manager feels that a campaign should reach a combined readership of at least 50,000 subscribers and at least 90,000 nonsubscribers. How many daily advertisements should the manager place in each newspaper in order to minimize the cost of newspaper space?

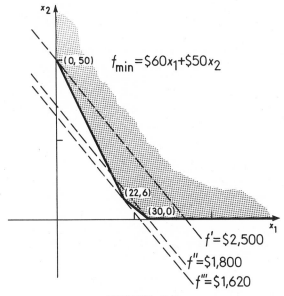

FIGURE 1.8.

Solution:

Let x_1 be the number of daily advertisements to be placed with newspaper A and x_2 with newspaper B. Then the problem in mathematical terms is

$$f_{min} = 60x_1 + 50x_2,$$

subject to

(1) $2000x_1 + 1000x_2 \geqslant 50,000$
(2) $3000x_1 + 4000x_2 \geqslant 90,000$
(3) $x_1 \geqslant 0,$
(4) $x_2 \geqslant 0.$

The set of feasible solutions is shown in Figure 1.6. For convenience this set is reproduced in Figure 1.8. We shall find the optimal feasible solution which minimizes the objective function with the following algorithm.

At point (0, 50) the cost of newspaper space is

$$f'_{min} = 60(0) + 50(50) = 2500 \text{ dollars.}$$

With this "product" mix the minimum requirements for the subscribing readers are exactly met since

$$2000(0) + 1000(50) = 50,000.$$

On the other hand, the requirements for the nonsubscribing readers are overfulfilled since

$$3000(0) + 4000(50) = 200,000 > 90,000.$$

From inequality (1) we can see that the cost of an advertisement per thousand of subscribing readers is less if placed with newspaper A than with newspaper B since

$$x_1 = \frac{60}{2} = 30 \text{ dollars} \quad \text{and} \quad x_2 = \frac{50}{1} = 50 \text{ dollars}.$$

Therefore, the cost for space will be lower if we substitute x_1 for x_2 newspaper space until point (22, 6), read from a detailed graph, is reached. Below that point further substitution would result in higher costs. Why? The reader may verify that placing advertisements to 22 issues in newspaper A and to 6 in newspaper B would meet exactly the minimum readership requirements. With this "product" mix the cost will be

$$f''_{min} = 60(22) + 50(6) = 1620 \text{ dollars}$$

which is the minimum for the problem.

Instead of point (0, 50), the reader can reach the same conclusion by starting the algorithm from point (30, 0) where the cost is $1800.

1.5. Recapitulation. With graphs we were able to conceptualize, introduce the basic terminology, and illustrate the process of solving linear programming problems. Although solutions for problems in two unknowns can be obtained from sufficiently detailed graphs, precise solutions, especially for problems in more than two unknowns, require the tools of algebra which are considered next.

PROBLEMS

1.1. For what values of x are the following inequalities true? Sketch the graph of each.

*a) $2x_1 - 3 < 0$.
*b) $2x_1 - 3 \leqslant 0$.
c) $3x_1 - 6 > 0$.
d) $3x_1 - 6 \leqslant 0$.
e) $5x_1 - 1 \leqslant x_1 + 11$.
f) $5x_1 - 1 < x_1 + 11$.

*g) $\frac{2x_1 - 3}{3} \geqslant \frac{2 - x_1}{2}$.

h) $\frac{2x_1 - 3}{3} < \frac{2 - x_1}{2}$.

*i) $x_1^2 \leqslant 9$.
j) $x_1^2 \geqslant 4$.

1.2. Sketch each inequality and indicate—
    i) The coordinates of a point which satisfy the inequality.

ii) The coordinates of a point which does not satisfy the inequality.

iii) Whether the graph of the inequality is an open or a closed half space.

*a) $2x_1 + x_2 \geqslant 7$.

b) $2x_1 + x_2 \leqslant 10$.

*c) $3x_1 - 2x_2 + 6 > 0$

d) $x_1 + x_2 - 8 < 0$.

e) $x_1 + x_2 \leqslant 1$.

f) $x_1 + x_2 > 1$.

*1.3. From the inequalities in Problem 1.1 or 1.2 give the following examples:

a) A pair of inequalities with the same sense.

b) A pair of inequalities with opposite senses.

c) A strong or strict inequality.

d) A weak inequality.

1.4. For each pair of inequalities—

i) Sketch their graphs in the same cc-plane.

ii) Find the set of points which satisfy both inequalities and express it in set notation form.

iii) Indicate whether each pair is a case of a redundant inequality, inconsistent inequalities, or neither.

*a) $x_1 + 2x_2 - 4 \leqslant 0$ and $x_1 + 2x_2 - 12 \leqslant 0$.

b) $x_1 + 2x_2 - 4 \geqslant 0$ and $x_1 + 2x_2 - 12 \leqslant 0$.

c) $x_1 + 2x_2 - 4 \leqslant 0$ and $x_1 + 2x_2 - 12 \geqslant 0$.

1.5. For each pair of inequalities—

i) Sketch their graphs in the same cc-plane.

ii) Find the set of common solutions (if any) and express it in set notation form.

*a) $2x_1 + x_2 - 2 \geqslant 0$ and $4x_1 + 2x_2 - 4 \geqslant 0$.

*b) $2x_1 + x_2 - 2 \geqslant 0$ and $4x_1 + 2x_2 - 4 \leqslant 0$.

c) $2x_1 + x_2 - 2 > 0$ and $4x_1 + 2x_2 - 4 < 0$.

d) $2x_1 + x_2 - 2 \geqslant 0$ and $4x_1 + 2x_2 - 4 > 0$.

1.6. For each system of linear inequalities and equations below—

i) Sketch their graphs in the same cc-plane.

ii) Find the set of feasible solutions.

iii) Select one point in the set of feasible solutions and another point outside this set and verify the fact that the coordinates of the first point satisfy while the coordinates of the second point do not satisfy all restraints.

iv) Indicate whether the set of feasible solutions is bounded and/or closed.

v) Express the solution set in set notation form.

*a) $x_1 + x_2 - 5 \leqslant 0$, b) $x_1 + x_2 - 5 \leqslant 0$,
     $2x_1 - x_2 - 7 \leqslant 0$, $2x_1 - x_2 - 2 \geqslant 0$,
     $x_1 \geqslant 0$, $x_1 \geqslant 0$,
     $x_2 \geqslant 0$. $x_2 \geqslant 0$.

c) $x_1 + x_2 - 10 \leqslant 0,$
$2x_1 - x_2 + 2 \geqslant 0,$
$x_1 \geqslant 0,$
$x_2 \geqslant 3.$

d) $x_1 + 3x_2 - 12 \geqslant 0,$
$x_1 + 3x_2 - 24 < 0,$
$x_1 \geqslant 0,$
$x_2 \geqslant 0.$

e) $x_1 + 2x_2 - 6 \geqslant 0,$
$x_1 - 2x_2 - 4 \leqslant 0,$
$x_1 \geqslant 0,$
$x_2 \geqslant 0.$

f) $x_1 + x_2 - 6 \geqslant 0,$
$x_1 + 4x_2 - 24 \leqslant 0,$
$x_1 + x_2 - 3 \geqslant 0,$
$x_1 \geqslant 0,$
$x_2 \geqslant 0.$

*g) $3x_1 - 2x_2 + 5 \geqslant 0,$
$x_1 + x_2 \leqslant 8,$
$x_1 - 3x_2 + 6 = 0,$
$x_1 \geqslant -\frac{13}{7},$
$x_2 \geqslant 0.$

h) $3x_1 - 2x_2 + 5 \leqslant 0,$
$x_1 + x_2 - 10 \leqslant 0,$
$x_1 - 4x_2 + 8 = 0,$
$x_1 \geqslant -\frac{4}{10},$
$x_2 \geqslant 0.$

Find the optimal feasible solution of the objective function in Problems 1.7–1.10 graphically. (Use sufficiently detailed coordinate paper.)

*1.7. Maximize the objective function

$$f_{max} = 5x_1 + 2x_2;$$

subject to restraints of Problem 1.6(a).

1.8. Maximize the objective function

$$f_{max} = -x_1 + 3x_2;$$

subject to restraints of Problem 1.6(b).

1.9. Minimize the objective function

$$f_{min} = x_1 + 5x_2;$$

subject to restraints of Problem 1.6(e).

*1.10. Minimize the objective function

$$f_{min} = x_1 + 2x_2;$$

subject to restraints of Problem 1.6(g).

1.11. Write down how you can arrive at the optimal feasible solution in—
a) Example 1.3, starting from the extreme point (80, 0) of the solution set.
b) Example 1.7, starting from the extreme point (30, 0) of the solution set.

1.12. Using the same restraints but the objective function indicated below, solve each problem and verify the fact that the optimal feasible solution need not be the unique solution of the system of equations of the problem.
*a) The problem in Example 1.3 when—
(1) $f_{max} = \$0.30x_1 + \$0.20x_2.$
(2) $f_{max} = \$0.10x_1 + \$0.30x_2.$

b) The problem in Example 1.7 when—
(1) $f_{min} = \$20x_1 + \$60x_2$.
(2) $f_{min} = \$60x_1 + \$30x_2$.

*1.13. During periods of slack activity Apex Manufacturing Company makes two different models of carving knives, model E, the Efficient, and model S, the Silver Beauty. For the forthcoming week, production scheduling indicates that machine A will be free for 8 hours and machine B for 12 hours. To make 1 unit of model E requires 1 hour of machine A and 3 hours of machine B, while 1 unit of model S requires 2 hours of machine A and 2 hours of machine B. If the company makes \$5.00 from model E and \$6.00 from model S per unit sold, what is the most profitable output combination? Find how many knives of each kind should be produced by means of a graph.

*1.14. Suppose the second kind of cookies in Example 1.3 are chocolate covered. There are 6 pounds of chocolate mix available, and it takes 0.2 pounds of chocolate mix to make a dozen cookies. If the other conditions of the problem remain unchanged, what is the most profitable product mix? Approximate the optimal solution graphically. Are all the available quantities of the ingredients fully utilized?

1.15. Farm Supplies Company features a new animal feed which consists of two cereals, A and B. Each pound of cereal A contains 1.2 ounces of protein, 0.2 ounces of fat, and 0.1 ounces of carbohydrates. Each pound of cereal B contains 0.4 ounces of protein, 0.4 ounces of fat, and 0.8 ounces of carbohydrates. Each sack of the new animal feed should contain at least 36 ounces of protein, 16 ounces of fat, and 14 ounces of carbohydrates. If a pound of cereal A costs \$0.03 and cereal B \$0.05, what is the optimal product mix which minimizes cost?
a) Find the optimal solution graphically.
b) What is the weight of each sack of the new feed?
c) How much does a pound of the new animal feed cost?
d) How many ounces of protein, fat, and carbohydrates does each sack of new feed contain?

1.16. Consider the Quality Baking Company case with the following data:

	x_1	x_2	Total Requirements
Labor	0.5	0.6	7.4 hours
Oven capacity	1.0	2.0	22.0 dozen cookies
Cookie mix	4.0	1.0	44.0 pounds

If the company makes \$0.05 profit per dozen of x_1 cookies and \$0.08 per dozen x_2 cookies, what is the most profitable mix?
a) Find the optimal solution by means of a graph.
b) Which of the available quantities of ingredients is not fully utilized?

1.17. The Mesabi Coal Company operates two coal mines with different production capacities. The management of the company has the following data on the daily coal output in tons:

Quality	Mine A	Mine B
High grade	8	2
Medium grade	3	3
Low grade	4	10

The company has made an agreement with a steel plant to provide every week 44 tons of high-grade, 30 tons of medium-grade, and 64 tons of low-grade coal. How many days should the company operate each mine in order to meet its contractual obligations with the steel plant most economically and what grade(s) of coal would be over-produced—

a) If the cost of running mine A is \$120 and mine B \$160 per day?
b) If the cost of running mine A is \$160 and mine B \$120 per day?
c) If it costs \$120 per day to run either mine?
d) Illustrate the above conditions (*a*)–(*c*) with a graph.
e) Find the average cost per ton of coal for each mine in condition (*a*) for the produced quantities of coal.

2. LINEAR PROGRAMMING WITH ORDINARY ALGEBRA

Although no formula is available which can be used to calculate the solution of a linear programming problem, solving simultaneous linear equations is related to the available iterative methods of solving such problems. In the first place, the coordinates of the optimal feasible solution may and usually do represent the common solution to the linear equations of the problem. In the second place, studying systems of linear equations is necessary in order to understand vector and matrix analysis of the algorithmic process involved in solving linear programming problems.

In this section we shall solve linear programming problems involving systems of equations in two or three unknowns with ordinary algebra. In doing so we shall be given the opportunity to discuss in general systems of linear equations. We shall conclude the section with a brief account of the limitations and potentialities of linear programming.

2.1. Linear Programming Problems in Two Unknowns.

Both allocation problems in the preceding section involve two equations in two unknowns. We shall solve these problems as well as another one with three equations in two unknowns with the tools of ordinary algebra. We shall use two methods with which the reader may be already familiar, namely, elimination of one of the unknowns by *substitution* or by *multiplication and addition*.

Example 2.1. Consider the Quality Baking Company case. For solving the company's problem with algebra we must find the coordinates of all the extreme points of the solution set S and test the objective function at all such points. This task is simplified, however, in view of the earlier discussion of the case, especially the graph in Figure 1.2. We may observe that the intersection of the equations which correspond to inequalities $x_1 + 2x_2 \leqslant 100$ and $x_1 + x_2 \leqslant 80$ represents the optimal feasible solution. Thus, we can obtain this solution by solving the set of linear equations

(2.1) $$x_1 + 2x_2 = 100,$$

(2.2) $$x_1 + x_2 = 80.$$

Solving (2.1) for x_1 and substituting its value in (2.2), we have

$$x_1 = 100 - 2x_2,$$
$$100 - 2x_2 + x_2 = 80, \text{ and}$$
$$x_2 = 20;$$

substituting $x_2 = 20$ in (2.1), we obtain

$$x_1 + 2(20) = 100, \text{ and}$$
$$x_1 = 60,$$

the optimal solution as previously.

Example 2.2. The problem of AAA Department Stores Inc., can be solved in a similar fashion. The intersection of the equations which correspond to inequalities $2000x_1 + 1000x_2 \geqslant 50,000$ and $3000x_1 + 4000x_2 \geqslant 90,000$ in Example 1.7 graphed in Figures 1.6 and 1.8, represents the optimal feasible solution. It can be found by solving the set of equations

(2.3) $$2000x_1 + 1000x_2 = 50,000,$$

(2.4) $$3000x_1 + 4000x_2 = 90,000.$$

Subtracting 4 times equation (2.3) from (2.4), and dividing by 100, we have

$$-5x_1 = -110, \text{ and}$$
$$x_1 = 22;$$

substituting $x_1 = 22$ in (2.4), we get

$$3000(22) + 4000x_2 = 90,000,$$
$$4x_2 = 90 - 66, \text{ and}$$
$$x_2 = 6;$$

the optimal solution found graphically.

In both cases above our task of solving each problem with algebra was simplified by previous graphical solutions. However, since any other extreme point of the solution set may be an optimal feasible solution, solving a problem with algebra requires finding the coordinates of *all* extreme points and testing the objective function at all such points. We illustrate this procedure by solving the following problem with ordinary algebra.

Example 2.3. The manager of BB Iron Works Company received an order to produce a number of pipes which require the use of material A costing $3.00 and material B costing $8.00 per unit. For each pipe no more than 12 units of material A and at least 16 units of material B must be used. While each unit of A weighs 4 pounds and each unit of B weighs 6 pounds, the final product must weigh exactly 120 pounds. How many units of each raw material should be used in order to produce the ordered pipes most economically? And what is the cost of each pipe?

Solution:

Let x_1 represent units of material A and x_2 units of material B. Then the problem can be expressed mathematically as follows:

$$f_{min} = 3x_1 + 8x_2$$

subject to

(2.5) $$4x_1 + 6x_2 = 120,$$

(2.6) $$x_1 \leqslant 12,$$

(2.7) $$x_2 \geqslant 16.$$

We can easily find that the system of equations which corresponds to (2.5), (2.6), and (2.7) has no common solution. We must refer to the restraining inequalities themselves.

Step 1: We must determine the feasible solutions set and its extreme points.

The set of feasible solutions must be a segment of the graph of the straight line $4x_1 + 6x_2 = 120$ for which the other two restraints (2.6) and (2.7) are satisfied. Since we are looking for a minimum optimal solution, this feasible solutions set must lie between the minimal values of x_1 and x_2 for which (2.6) and (2.7) are satisfied. The minimum value of $x_1 = 0$. Substituting $x_1 = 0$ in (2.5), we have

$$4(0) + 6x_2 = 120, \text{ and}$$
$$x_2 = 20.$$

The minimum value of $x_2 = 16$. Substituting $x_2 = 16$ in (2.5), we obtain

$$4x_1 + 6(16) = 120, \text{ and}$$
$$x_1 = 6.$$

Hence the feasible solutions set is the line segment of the graph of $4x_1 + 6x_2 = 120$ for which $0 \leqslant x_1 \leqslant 6$ and the extreme points are the two points of this segment, namely (0, 20) and (6, 16).

Step 2: We must test the objective function at these two extreme points.

Substituting the product mix specified by the extreme point (0, 20) in the objective function we get

$$f'_{min} = 3(0) + 8(20) = 160 \text{ dollars.}$$

Substituting the product mix specified by the other extreme point (6, 16) in the objective function, we have

$$f''_{min} = 3(6) + 8(16) = 146 \text{ dollars.}$$

Since there are no other extreme points to consider and since $f''_{min} = $146 < f'_{min} = 160, the optimal product mix should consist of 6 units of x_1 or material A and 16 units of x_2 or material B at the lowest possible cost of \$146 per pipe. The reader may visualize the above algebraic solution by consulting the diagram in Figure 2.1.

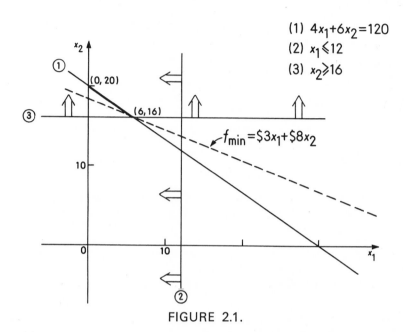

(1) $4x_1 + 6x_2 = 120$
(2) $x_1 \leqslant 12$
(3) $x_2 \geqslant 16$

FIGURE 2.1.

2.2 Systems of Linear Equations in Two Unknowns.

The above three examples clearly point out the need for a study of systems of two or more linear equations in two unknowns.

We have found that each system of two equations in two unknowns in Examples 2.1 and 2.2 have one common solution. Such equations are called *independent*.

Two equations in two unknowns which have infinitely many common solutions are called *dependent*.

Example 2.4. Equations

(2.8) $4x_1 + 6x_2 = 120,$

(2.9) $2x_1 + 3x_2 = 60,$

are dependent, since one is a multiple of the other. Multiplying (2.8) by $-\frac{1}{2}$, we get

(2.8′) $-2x_1 - 3x_2 = -60,$

(2.9′) $2x_1 + 3x_2 = 60,$

which by addition yields

$$0 = 0.$$

The reader may sketch the graphs of (2.8) and (2.9) in the same cc-plane to verify the fact that they represent the same straight line. Thus, the infinite set of solutions of one equation is the solution set of the other equation and vice versa.

Two equations in two unknowns which have no common solution are called *inconsistent*.

Example 2.5. Consider equations

(2.10) $$x_1 + x_2 = 160,$$

(2.11) $$x_1 + x_2 = 80,$$

which correspond to the inequalities (1) and (2) in Figure 1.7, respectively. They are inconsistent since adding -1 times (2.11) to (2.10), we get

$$0 = 80.$$

The reader may observe that the lines of the equations are parallel, i.e., they have the same slopes but different intercepts.

Equation (2.5) and equations corresponding to inequalities (2.6) and (2.7) in Example 2.3 are inconsistent since they have no common solution. So are the three equations which correspond to the inequalities (1), (2), and (3) in Figure 1.7. In general, a system of more than two equations in two unknowns is usually inconsistent. Under special circumstances, however, such a system may be *consistent*, i.e., it may have at least one common solution.

Example 2.6. Consider equations

(2.12) $$2x_1 + 3x_2 = 180,$$

(2.13) $$x_1 + 2x_2 = 100,$$

(2.14) $$x_1 + x_2 = 80.$$

Solving any two of the three equations simultaneously, we find that their common solution $x_1 = 60$ and $x_2 = 20$ is a solution to the third equation. This solution can be very easily verified graphically.

All told, solving simultaneously two or more equations in two unknowns means finding the set of points whose coordinates satisfy all equations. We have seen that this solution set may (*a*) contain a single element when there is a unique solution, (*b*) be an infinite set when there are infinitely many solutions, or (*c*) be the empty set when there is no solution. In the last two cases the system of equations is said to be *degenerate*.

2.3. Linear Programming in Three Unknowns. Let us
now study a linear programming problem in three-dimensional space. We shall solve it algebraically and demonstrate this solution with graphs.

Example 2.7. Let us assume that quality Baking Company produces three kinds of cookies x_1, x_2, and x_3 and management's problem in mathematical terms is

$$f_{max} = 0.2x_1 + 0.3x_2 + 0.2x_3,$$

subject to

(1) $x_1 + 4x_2 + 2x_3 \leqslant 80$ oven capacity (dozen cookies)
(2) $0.2x_1 + 0.1x_2 + 0.2x_3 \leqslant 9.5$ hours of labor
(3) $2x_1 + 3x_2 + x_3 \leqslant 90$ pounds of cookie mix,
(4) $x_1 \geqslant 0$
(5) $x_2 \geqslant 0$
(6) $x_3 \geqslant 0$.

What is the product mix which yields the maximum profit?

In solving this problem we shall demonstrate a new method, called the *diagonalization method*. It consists of performing two basic operations on a set of linear equations: (*a*) dividing an equation by a number; and (*b*) subtracting a multiple of one equation from another equation. Such operations are called *elementary row operations*.

Example 2.7—*Continued*. Solve the following system of linear equations

(2.15) $x_1 + 4x_2 + 2x_3 = 80,$

(2.16) $2x_1 + x_2 + 2x_3 = 95,$

(2.17) $2x_1 + 3x_2 + x_3 = 90,$

which correspond to inequalities (1), (2), and (3) of our linear programming problem, respectively.

Solution:

Subtracting 2 times equation (2.15) from equations (2.16) and (2.17), we get

(2.15′) $x_1 + 4x_2 + 2x_3 = 80,$

(2.16′) $0 - 7x_2 - 2x_3 = -65,$

(2.17′) $0 - 5x_2 - 3x_3 = -70.$

Dividing (2.16′) by -7, we obtain equation $x_2 + \frac{2}{7}x_3 = \frac{65}{7}$. Subtracting 4 times this equation from (2.15′) and adding 5 times the same equation to (2.17′), we have

(2.15″) $x_1 + 0 + \frac{6}{7}x_3 = \frac{300}{7},$

(2.16″) $0 + x_2 + \frac{2}{7}x_3 = \frac{65}{7},$

(2.17″) $0 + 0 - \frac{11}{7}x_3 = -\frac{165}{7}.$

Dividing (2.17″) by $-\frac{11}{7}$, we get equation $x_3 = 15$. Subtracting $\frac{6}{7}$ times this equation from (2.15″) and $\frac{2}{7}$ times the same equation from (2.16″), we finally obtain

(2.15‴) $x_1 + 0 + 0 = 30$,

(2.16‴) $0 + x_2 + 0 = 5$,

(2.17‴) $0 + 0 + x_3 = 15$,

which represents the unique solution to the original set of equations. Of course, this unique solution is one of the several extreme points of the feasible solutions set; and to find which extreme point is the optimal we must employ the algorithm of testing the objective function at all such extreme points. This is a time-consuming task; and one of the advantages of existing linear programming techniques, as we shall see later, is to make this task easier. In the meantime, since our purpose is to show the connection between linear programming problems and systems of linear equations, we shall assume that this algorithm is carried out, and we find that the above unique solution to the set of equations is indeed the optimal solution to our linear programming problem.

Substituting this optimal product mix in the objective function, we get a maximum profit of

$$f_{max} = 0.2(30) + 0.3(5) + 0.2(15) = 10.50 \text{ dollars.}$$

For a geometrical representation of the above problem, *first* we must show graphically the set of feasible solutions.

Example 2.7—*Continued.* Inequalities $x_1 \geqslant 0, x_2 \geqslant 0$, and $x_3 \geqslant 0$ representing restraints (4) through (6) in our linear programming problem define the first octant of a three-dimensional space shown in Figure 2.2. The reader can visualize the first octant by looking at a windowless corner of a room from the room's center. Such a center may correspond to point A in Figure 2.2. Point $(0, 0, 0)$ where the planes representing the surfaces of the floor and the two walls of the corner is the origin of the three-dimensional space; the x_1- and x_3-coordinates are the lines where the plane representing the floor surface cuts the planes representing the right-hand side and the left-hand side wall surfaces respectively, while the x_2-coordinate is the line where the surfaces of the two walls meet. Although an octant corresponds conceptually to a quadrant, it must be understood that a three-dimensional space has eight, not four, octants.

In a three-dimensional space the graph of an equation is a plane and the graph of an inequality a half-space sometimes called *subspace*. In order to find the subspace representing the graph of a linear inequality we proceed in a manner analogous to finding the half-plane of an inequality in a cc-plane, i.e., by first finding the graph of the corresponding equation. For instance, the subspace of inequality $x_1 + 4x_2 + 2x_3 \leqslant 80$ representing restraint (1) in our problem is obtained by finding the graph of $x_1 + 4x_2 + 2x_3 = 80$. Letting x_2 and x_3 equal zero, $x_1 = 80$. Hence, the x_1-intercept is point $(80, 0, 0)$, as shown in Figure 2.2. Letting x_1 and x_3

equal zero, then $x_2 = 20$. Hence, point $(0, 20, 0)$ is the x_2-intercept plotted in the diagram in Figure 2.2. Similarly, point $(0, 0, 40)$ is the x_3-intercept since $x_3 = 40$ if $x_1 = 0$ and $x_2 = 0$. Connecting these points with straight lines we obtain the triangle shown in Figure 2.2, which represents a

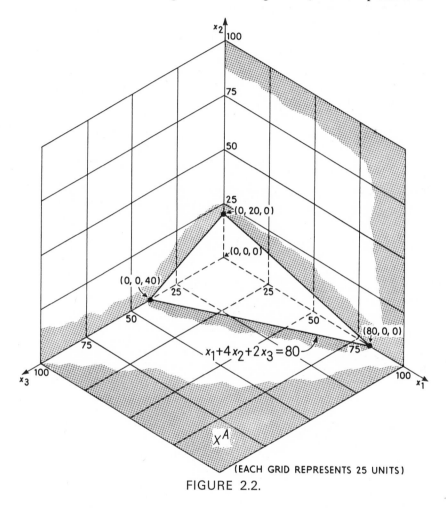

(EACH GRID REPRESENTS 25 UNITS)

FIGURE 2.2.

portion of the *plane* of the equation. The points *on* or *beneath* this plane satisfy inequality $x_1 + 4x_2 + 2x_3 \leqslant 80$ and form a portion of its graph or subspace.

The subspaces of inequalities $2x_1 + x_2 + 2x_3 \leqslant 95$ and $2x_1 + 3x_2 + x_3 \leqslant 90$, representing restraints (2) and (3) in our problem, are obtained in the same manner. The portion of the graphs of inequalities (1), (2), and (3) in the first octant, together with the restraints (4) through (6), form the bounded and closed set S of feasible solutions of our problem, shown as a shaded solid in Figure 2.3. This set S of feasible solutions is called *polyhedron*. Each point inside or on the surface of the polyhedron, defined by three coordinates (x_1, x_2, x_3)—an ordered three-tuple, satisfies all restraints of our problem.

Our *next* task is to find the plane of the objective function which yields the maximum profit.

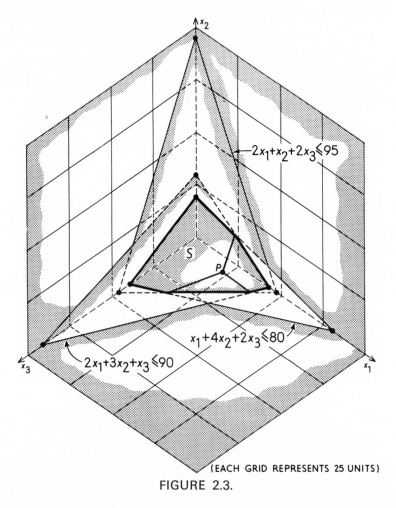

(EACH GRID REPRESENTS 25 UNITS)

FIGURE 2.3.

Example 2.7—*Continued.* Of course, in our particular case this plane can be easily found from the above algebraic solution of the problem where $f_{max} = \$10.50$. However, for the sake of illustrating this case graphically, we shall consider different planes in space for which the objective function is a given amount of dollars, i.e.,

$$f_{max} = 0.2x_1 + 0.3x_2 + 0.2x_3 = \text{ dollars.}$$

For $f'_{max} = \$6$ the plane of the objective profit function is the one close to the origin as shown in Figure 2.4. It can be easily seen that dollar profits increase as the plane of the objective function moves away from the origin. Combining Figures 2.3 and 2.4, the reader can visualize that

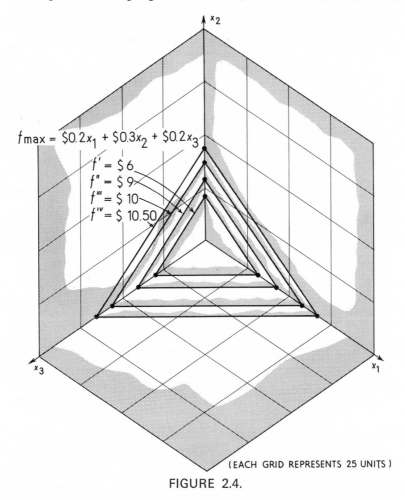

$f_{max} = \$0.2x_1 + \$0.3x_2 + \$0.2x_3$

$f' = \$6$
$f'' = \$9$
$f''' = \$10$
$f^{IV} = \$10.50$

(EACH GRID REPRESENTS 25 UNITS)

FIGURE 2.4.

the plane where $f^{IV}_{max} = \$10.50$ yields the maximum profit. With this profit the plane of the objective function touches the polyhedron S of feasible solution at the extreme point P (30, 5, 15). This is the optimal feasible solution with a product mix of 30 dozen x_1, 5 dozen x_2, and 15 dozen x_3 cookies. This product mix maximizes profits because for any other position of the plane closer to the origin profits will be smaller than \$10.50, while for any other position of the plane yielding larger than this profit no product mix will satisfy all restraints.

Again the optimal solution above need not be the unique solution to the system of equations of the problem. It was arranged that way for purposes of exposition. Otherwise, for finding an optimal solution we had to test the objective function at the other six extreme points (not counting the point at the origin) of the polyhedron set. In real-world problems which may involve several unknowns the process of testing the objective function becomes an almost impossible task without the iterative methods discussed in Chapter 10.

2.4. Systems of Linear Equations in Three Unknowns.

In solving the above linear programming problem we have demonstrated how a system of three equations having a unique solution can be solved with the diagonalization method. As in the case of systems of two equations, systems of three linear equations exist which have infinitely many common solutions or no unique solution. The reader will find such systems among the problems in this section.

Here, we shall consider the case of two equations in three unknowns.

Example 2.8. Solve the system

(2.18) $$x_1 + 4x_2 + 2x_3 = 80,$$

(2.19) $$2x_1 + 3x_2 + x_3 = 90.$$

Solution:
Subtracting 2 times (2.18) from (2.19) we get

(2.18′) $$x_1 + 4x_2 + 2x_3 = 80,$$

(2.19′) $$0 - 5x_2 - 3x_3 = -70.$$

Dividing (2.19′) by -5, we obtain $x_2 + \frac{3}{5}x_3 = 14$.
Subtracting 4 times equation (2.19″) from (2.18′), we have

(2.18″) $$x_1 + 0 - \frac{2}{5}x_3 = 24,$$

(2.19″) $$0 + x_2 + \frac{3}{5}x_3 = 14.$$

The system has infinitely many solutions since the variables x_1 and x_2 can be expressed in terms of the third variable x_3 as follows:

(2.18‴) $$x_1 = \frac{2}{5}x_3 + 24,$$

(2.19‴) $$x_2 = -\frac{3}{5}x_3 + 14,$$

where the value of x_3 can be chosen arbitrarily. For example, letting

$$x_3 = 5, \quad \text{then } x_1 = 26 \text{ and } x_2 = 11;$$
$$x_3 = 10, \text{ then } x_1 = 28 \text{ and } x_2 = 8; \text{ and}$$
$$x_3 = 15, \text{ then } x_1 = 30 \text{ and } x_2 = 5; \text{ etc.}$$

The reader may check by substituting the above solutions into the original equations (2.18) and (2.19). Furthermore, since these equations are equations (2.15) and (2.17) of Example 2.7, the reader may sketch their graphs to verify the fact that their simultaneous solution set is the infinite set of points on a line in a three-dimensional space.

In general, a system of two equations in more than two unknowns is dependent, i.e., it has infinitely many solutions, as the above example illustrates. Under special circumstances, however, which we shall not examine, such a system may be inconsistent, having no common solution.

Although the diagonalization method of solving simultaneously a system of linear equations may be more time consuming than ordinary methods, it has certain important advantages. Methods of ordinary algebra work only for systems of equations which have solutions. Furthermore, even for systems having common solutions, ordinary methods may not give us all possible solutions. The diagonalization method is infallible. It always works for determining whether a system of linear equations has at least one common solution and for writing all such solutions if they exist. In other words, it is a *canonical* procedure since it can be applied to any system of linear equations. More important than that, this procedure is suitable for both computations by hand and with digital computers.

Our findings about simultaneous solutions of systems of linear equations in two and three unknowns can be easily generalized to systems with m equations and n unknowns, where m and n are any positive integers. For such systems we can distinguish the following general possibilities:

1. *If $m = n$, the system may have a unique solution, infinitely many common solutions, or no common solution.*
2. *If $m > n$, the system is usually inconsistent and has no common solution.* Under special circumstances, however, it may have at least one common solution.
3. *If $m < n$, then usually the system has infinitely many common solutions,* although under special circumstances it may be inconsistent, having no common solution.

2.5. Limitations and Applications. Like all quantitative methods of analysis, linear programming has a number of limitations. Some of them are *internal* in the sense that they stem from the underlying assumptions of the linear programming "model" itself. Other limitations are *external* in the sense that they are imposed by the nature of the problem rather than the "model."

One basic internal limitation is the assumption of *certainty*, i.e., all relationships among the variables of the problem are assumed to be known, certain, or exact rather than probable. In the original Quality

Baking Company case, for example, we assumed that profits are certain to be $0.30 per dozen of x_2 cookies for the entire range of the feasible output. Thus, we examined the profit returns under certainty by not assuming that profits per dozen cookies will vary depending on the probable sales volume. In fact, all the "models" which have been discussed so far and which are to be discussed in Part IV are "models" under certainty.

Another fundamental limitation is the assumption of *linearity*. Every term in the objective function and the restraints of a linear programming problem is of the first degree. Relationships among the variables of a linear programming problem are assumed to be strictly proportional. For example, in the original Quality Baking Company for producing one dozen of x_1 cookies we needed 6 minutes of available labor time, while 12 minutes of labor time were necessary for producing one dozen of x_2 cookies. The rate of substitution was a constant one to two for the entire range of the feasible output.

For certain source-to-destination linear programming problems, otherwise called "transportation" problems, an additional limitation stems from the assumption that all *rates of substitution* between the variables of the problem must be *one to one*. For example, in the original Quality Baking Company case the rate of substitution between x_1 and x_2 for oven capacity is one to one. However, neither this case nor all other cases we have considered are "transportation" problems since not all rates of substitution are one to one. The "transportation" problem case will be discussed in Section 2 of Chapter 10.

Although in principle problems with thousands of variables can be programmed, the required *computational load* may be a limiting factor. For problems involving a large number of variables a digital computer must do such a stupendous amount of computations that the time required to solve such a problem is prohibitive. Furthermore, linear programming dealing with manufacturing of products which require different production time for each machine operation can indicate the minimum cost product mix for utilizing the available limited machine capacity. In such problems another external limitation appears, however, if *scheduling* requires that certain operations must be performed before or after other operations.

Neither the internal nor the external limitations are entirely insurmountable. The limitations arising from the assumptions of certainty and linearity can be overcome partly by using the linear programming "model" as a reasonable approximation to real-world problems which nearly but not exactly meet these assumptions and partly by other available techniques. Limitations due to computational load may be overcome by reducing the number of variables to the most essential ones for the problem or by splitting the problem into parts of manageable proportions. Finally, scheduling problems may be handled separately.

Notwithstanding these limitations, linear programming is used in a great variety of cases in industrial as well as in general business operations. Thus, linear programming techniques have been and are increasingly applied not only to problems such as finding the most economical product mix, to job assignment and capacity allocation problems, to production scheduling, to purchasing and distribution problems, but also to financial budgeting and costing of funds problems and recently to such areas as advertising where quantification of variables is difficult though not impossible. In spite of present and potential uses, however, the reader may keep in mind that linear programming, like all quantitative methods of analysis, is a suboptimization effort. Before implementing, an optimal solution obtained with linear programming must be reconciled with the overall managerial objectives of the firm.

PROBLEMS

2.1. For each system of linear equations—
  i) Find all the solutions with one of the ordinary methods and with the diagonalization method and check (when possible).
  ii) Indicate whether the equations of the system are independent, dependent, or inconsistent.
  iii) Sketch the graph of each equation in the same cc-plane.

*a) $2x_1 - 4x_2 = 3,$
    $x_1 + 5x_2 = 4.$

d) $2x_1 + x_2 = 5,$
   $4x_1 + 2x_2 = 15.$

b) $4x_1 - 5x_2 = 8,$
   $x_1 + 3x_2 = 2.$

e) $3x_1 + 5x_2 = 3,$
   $x_1 + \frac{5}{3}x_2 = 1.$

*c) $x_1 + 3x_2 = 12,$
    $x_1 + 3x_2 = 24.$

f) $x_1 + 2x_2 = 9,$
   $3x_1 - 4x_2 = 7.$

2.2. For each system of linear equations—
  i) Find all the solutions with one of the ordinary methods and with the diagonalization method and check (when possible).
  ii) Indicate whether the equations are consistent or inconsistent.
  iii) Sketch the graph of each equation in the same cc-plane.

*a) $x_1 + x_2 = 10,$
    $2x_1 - x_2 = -2,$
    $x_2 = 3.$

*d) $x_1 + 2x_2 - 12 = 0,$
    $2x_1 + x_2 - 12 = 0,$
    $x_1 + x_2 - 8 = 0.$

b) $x_1 + x_2 - 6 = 0,$
   $x_1 + 4x_2 - 24 = 0,$
   $x_1 + x_2 - 3 = 0.$

e) $x_1 + 2x_2 - 11 = 0,$
   $4x_1 + 3x_2 - 29 = 0,$
   $2x_1 + 4x_2 - 22 = 0,$
   $8x_1 + 6x_2 - 58 = 0.$

c) $3x_1 - 2x_2 + 5 = 0,$
   $x_1 + x_2 - 10 = 0,$
   $x_1 - 4x_2 + 8 = 0.$

2.3. For each system of linear equations—
  i) Find all the solutions by the diagonalization method and check (when possible).

ii) Indicate whether the equations are consistent or inconsistent.

*a) $2x_1 + 3x_2 + x_3 = 13,$
$x_1 + x_2 + 4x_3 = 12,$
$3x_1 + x_2 + 2x_3 = 10.$

c) $2x_1 + 3x_2 + x_3 = 13,$
$x_1 + x_2 + 4x_3 = 12,$
$3x_1 + x_2 + 2x_3 = 0.$

b) $2x_1 + 3x_2 - x_3 = 9,$
$3x_1 - x_2 + 2x_3 = 11,$
$x_1 + 2x_2 + 3x_3 = 20.$

d) $3x_1 - 2x_2 - x_3 = 5,$
$2x_1 - 3x_2 = 3,$
$5x_2 - 2x_3 = 4.$

2.4. Find all the solutions of the following systems of equations, check when possible, and indicate whether each system is consistent or inconsistent.

a) $2x_1 + 6x_2 + 4x_3 = 12,$
$3x_1 + 9x_2 + 6x_3 = 18.$

b) $x_1 + 2x_2 + 3x_3 = 6,$
$x_1 + 2x_2 + 3x_3 = 12.$

*c) $2x_1 - x_2 + x_3 + x_4 = 2,$
$3x_1 - 2x_2 + x_3 + 4x_4 = 3,$
$x_1 + x_2 - x_3 + 2x_4 = 4.$

2.5. Using the same restraints but the objective function indicated below, solve the problem in Example 2.3 and verify the fact that the optimal feasible solution is other than the one found previously.

*a) $f_{min} = \$8x_1 + \$2x_2,$
b) $f_{min} = \$4x_1 + \$6x_2.$

*2.6. Sketch the graphs of equations (2.18) and (2.19) in Example 2.8 and verify that the set of their common solutions is the infinite set of points on a line in a three-dimensional space.

2.7. Solve algebraically using the diagonalization method the following linear programming problems of the previous section.

*a) Problem 1.7.
b) Problem 1.8.
c) Problem 1.9.

2.8. Verify algebraically and graphically that the unique solution to the system of equations in Example 2.6 is $x_1 = 60$ and $x_2 = 20$.

2.9. The system of three equations in two unknowns in Example 2.6 was solved by solving simultaneously the equation of the system pairwise. Use this method to solve Problem 1.10 of the previous section. Verify your answer graphically.

2.10. Solve the following linear programming problems of the previous section algebraically.

a) Problem 1.13.
b) Problem 1.14.
c) Problem 1.15.
d) Problem 1.16.

*2.11. Given the cost function $f_{min} = \$5x_1 + \$3x_2 + \$4x_3,$

subject to $2x_1 + 3x_2 + x_3 \geqslant 13,$
$x_1 + x_2 + 4x_3 \geqslant 12,$
$3x_1 + x_2 + 2x_3 \geqslant 10,$
$x_i \geqslant 0 \; (i = 1, 2, 3).$

a) Find the minimum cost product mix algebraically.

b) Sketch the graph of the set of feasible solutions and indicate whether it is bounded and closed.

*2.12. Given the profit function

$$f_{max} = \$10x_1 + \$6x_2 + \$3.5x_3,$$

subject to

$$2x_1 + 3x_2 - x_3 \leqslant 9,$$
$$3x_1 - x_2 + 2x_3 \leqslant 11,$$
$$x_1 + 2x_2 + 3x_3 \leqslant 20$$
$$x_i \geqslant 0 \quad (i = 1, 2, 3)$$

a) Find the maximum profit product mix algebraically.

b) Sketch the graph of the solution polyhedron and indicate whether it is bounded and closed.

2.13. Given the cost function

$$f_{min} = \$5x_1 + \$3x_2 + \$4x_3,$$

subject to

$$2x_1 + 3x_2 + x_3 \geqslant 13,$$
$$x_1 + x_2 + 4x_3 \geqslant 12,$$
$$2x_1 + 2x_2 + 8x_3 \geqslant 24,$$
$$x_i \geqslant 0 \, (i = 1, 2, 3).$$

a) Find the minimum cost product mix algebraically.

b) Sketch the graph of the set of feasible solutions and indicate whether it is bounded and closed.

2.14. Given the profit function

$$f_{max} = \$10x_1 + \$6x_2 + \$3.5x_3,$$

subject to

$$2x_1 + 3x_2 - x_3 \leqslant 9,$$
$$x_1 + 2x_2 + 3x_3 \leqslant 20$$
$$x_i \geqslant 0 \quad (i = 1, 2, 3)$$

a) Find the maximum profit product mix algebraically.

b) Sketch the graph of the solutions set and indicate whether it is bounded and closed.

*2.15. Assume that Apex Manufacturing Company in Problem 1.13 of the previous section makes a super Deluxe model D in addition to the other two carving knives and the linear programming problem is:

$$f_{max} = \$5x_1 + \$6x_2 + \$7x_3,$$

subject to

$$x_1 + 2x_2 + 3x_3 \leqslant 11,$$
$$3x_1 + x_2 + x_3 \leqslant 10,$$
$$x_1 + 4x_2 + x_3 \leqslant 15,$$
$$x_i \geqslant 0 \quad (i = 1, 2, 3).$$

a) How many knives from each kind should be produced in order to maximize profit? Solve algebraically.

b) Sketch the graph of the feasible solutions set.

2.16. Let us consider the new animal feed of Farm Supplies Company again in Problem 1.15. In addition to A and B, the company uses a third cereal C which costs $0.08 per pound. The cost of cereal A remains at $0.03 per pound while the cost of cereal B is reduced to $0.04 per pound. The minimum requirements for each sack of the animal feed are 38 ounces of protein, 24 ounces of fat, 31 ounces of carbohydrates, and 30 ounces of salt. Each pound of cereal contains the following ingredients in ounces:

Ingredients	Cereal A	Cereal B	Cereal C
Protein 1.2	0.4	0.2
Fat.........................0.2	0.4	0.8
Carbohydrates 1.0	0.2	0.5
Salt 0.1	0.6	1.0

a) Find the product mix which will meet the minimum requirements most economically.

b) What is the weight of each sack of the new animal feed?

c) How much does a pound of it cost?

d) Does the product mix contain more than the minimum requirements of any ingredient? Indicate which ingredient (if any) and how much of it.

e) Sketch the feasible solutions set. Is it bounded and closed?

2.17. Let daily output in tons of the Mesabi Coal Company operations be as follows:

Coal Grade	Mine A	Mine B	Mine C	Output Requirements
G_1 8	2	1	48
G_2 3	5	2	49
G_3 2	2	2	30
G_4 6	4	6	80
G_5 2	5	2	45

How many days should the company operate each mine in order to produce the required quantities of coal most economically, and what grade(s) of coal would be overproduced—

a) If the cost of running mine A is $120, mine B $160, and mine C $200 per day?

b) If the cost for mine A is $200, mine B $160, and mine C $120 per day?

c) If the cost is $120 per day for each of the three mines?

d) What is the average cost per ton of coal for each mine in case (*a*) for the produced quantities of coal? (*Hint:* Solve simultaneously the first three and the last three equations which can be derived from above data.)

SUGGESTED REFERENCES

1. BOULDING, K. E., AND SPIVEY, W. A. *Linear Programming and the Theory of the Firm*, pp. 29–33, 61–65. New York: The Macmillan Co., 1960. (**1**)

2. HENDERSON, A., AND SCHLAIFER, R. "Mathematical Programming; Better Information for Better Decision Making," pp. 117–21, in *Statistical Decision Series of Harvard Business Review*, April, 1959. (**2**)

3. KEMENY, JOHN G., *et al. Finite Mathematical Structures*, pp. 359–63. Englewood Cliffs, N.J.: Prentice-Hall, Inc., 1959. (1)

4. ———. *Introduction to Finite Mathematics*, pp. 205–10, 249–66. Englewood Cliffs, N.J.: Prentice-Hall, Inc., 1957. (1, 2)

5. RICHARDSON, M. *College Algebra*, pp. 139–47, 359–62, 382–90. Al. ed. Englewood Cliffs, N.J.: Prentice-Hall, Inc., 1958. (1, 2)

6. STOCKTON, R. S. *Introduction to Linear Programming*, pp. 7–42. Boston: Allyn and Bacon, Inc., 1960. (1)

7. VAZONYI, A. *Scientific Programming in Business and Industry*, pp. 171–93. New York: John Wiley & Sons, Inc., 1958. (2)

8. WESTERN, D. W., AND HAAG, V. H. *An Introduction to Mathematics*, pp. 114–22. New York: Henry Holt & Co., Inc., 1959. (1)

Chapter 9

THE ALGEBRA OF LINEAR
PROGRAMMING

IN THE PRECEDING chapter we gave an intuitive understanding of the process of solving linear programming problems with graphs and ordinary algebra. But neither of these tools is capable of enabling one to obtain a sufficient understanding of the mathematics of linear programming.

In this chapter we shall present the basics of the algebra of linear programming. Section 1 is an introduction to the algebra of vectors and Section 2 to the algebra of matrices. These two topics of modern linear algebra are discussed sufficiently so that the reader may be able to accomplish the following: acquire some understanding of the mathematical aspects of linear programming, appreciate the computational methods of linear programming which are presented in the following chapter, and be able to study some of the mathematical literature on the subject.

*1. THE ALGEBRA OF VECTORS AND LINEAR PROGRAMMING

The mathematical concept of a vector arose from the need to give physical quantities such as forces and velocities a geometric representation. But vectors have much wider and varied applications than their original physical interpretation suggests. Vector operations represent a unique mathematical system which we shall discuss briefly after defining vectors and introducing the necessary notation. Then, we shall establish the connection between vectors and systems of linear equations and demonstrate the use of vector analysis in solving linear programming problems.

1.1. Vectors: Definitions and Notation. From the geometric standpoint vectors are lines with direction and length. In this respect there is a close connection between vectors and directed distances discussed in Chapter 5.

Example 1.1. Consider the one-dimensional Cartesian coordinate space in Figure 1.1. The directed distance $\overline{AB} = 10 - 5 = 5$. The vector corresponding to $\overline{AB}$ can be imagined as an arrow starting at point A and ending at point B. Let $\overrightarrow{AB}$ be such a vector. Then

$$\overrightarrow{AB} = [(5), (10)],$$

where coordinate (5) specifies the *initial point* and coordinate (10) the *end point*. Similarly, the vector corresponding to the directed distance $\overline{DC} = (-10) - (-4) = -6$ is specified by

$$\overrightarrow{DC} = [(-4), (-10)],$$

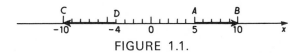

FIGURE 1.1.

Observe that a directed distance is the algebraic difference between the coordinates of the end and initial points, while the corresponding vector is specified by the coordinates of such points themselves. Vectors such as $\overrightarrow{AB}$ and $\overrightarrow{DC}$ in the above example with an arbitrary initial point, not necessarily zero, are called *free vectors*. The reader can easily transfer the concept of a free vector in Euclidean space of two, three, or greater dimensions. The initial and ending points of a free vector in any Euclidean space are specified by the coordinates representing such points.

Here, we shall be concerned with *origin vectors*, i.e., vectors with initial point at the origin. Since the initial point of an origin vector, hereafter to be called simply vector, is fixed, such a vector is uniquely determined by the coordinate(s) of the end point only.

Example 1.2. Consider the vectors

$$(1, 0), (0, 1), (2, 3), \text{ and } (3, 2).$$

We can represent these vectors geometrically with arrows starting from the origin of a cc-plane and terminating at the specified points as shown in Figure 1.2.

Again the above vector concept can be easily generalized for spaces of greater than two dimensions. Thus, we can arrive at the following definition: *A vector in Euclidean n-space is an ordered n-tuple of real numbers.* The elements of the n-tuple are called the *components* of the vector.

An important characteristic of a vector is the number of its components. Vectors in general are denoted by lowercase letters such as p, q, t, s, u, v and described in terms of the number of their components. A vector is called a *row vector* if its components are arranged in a row and a *column vector* if they are arranged in a column.

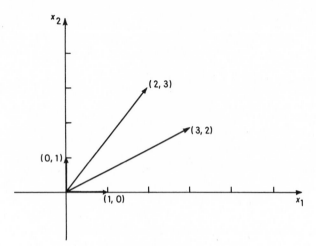

FIGURE 1.2.

Example 1.3. Consider the vectors $p = (5, -3)$; $s = (3, -2, -7)$; $u = (u_1, u_2, u_3, \ldots, u_n)$ and

$$
q = \begin{pmatrix} -5 \\ 6 \end{pmatrix}; \quad t = \begin{pmatrix} 1 \\ -2 \\ 4 \end{pmatrix}; \quad v = \begin{pmatrix} v_1 \\ v_2 \\ v_3 \\ \cdot \\ \cdot \\ \cdot \\ v_m \end{pmatrix}.
$$

Vector p is a two-component row vector and q a two-component column vector. Vectors s and t are a three-component row and column vectors, respectively. Finally, vector u is an n-component row vector and vector v an m-component column vector, where n and m are any positive integers.

General vectors such as u and v above are of special importance from the notational viewpoint. The components of each such vector are denoted by a letter with a subscript, a positive integer called *index*, which specifies their position in the ordered n- or m-tuple. In order to refer to an unspecified component of a row vector, we speak of the jth component. Let u be such a row vector. Then u_j denotes the jth component of vector u, where $j = 1, 2, 3, \ldots, n$. Similarly, for referring to any unspecified component of a column vector we speak of the ith component. Let v be such a column vector. Then v_i denotes the ith component of vector v, where $i = 1, 2, 3, \ldots, m$. Thus, this notation facilitates reference to a general vector with a given number of components.

Example 1.4. If we speak of a row vector with components $u_j (j = 1, 2, 3)$, we mean the three-component row vector

$$
u = (u_1, u_2, u_3).
$$

And if we speak of a column vector with components $v_i (i = 1, 2, 3)$, we mean the three-component column vector

$$v = \begin{pmatrix} v_1 \\ v_2 \\ v_3 \end{pmatrix}.$$

The above notation will be helpful in the section on matrices.

A vector having the number 1 as one of its components and all other components zero is called a *unit vector*. Finally, the origin in space is considered to represent a vector called the *zero or null vector*.

Example 1.5. Consider the vectors

$$p = (0, 1, 0); \; q = \begin{pmatrix} 1 \\ 0 \\ 0 \end{pmatrix};$$

$$o = (0, 0, 0); \; o = \begin{pmatrix} 0 \\ 0 \\ 0 \end{pmatrix}.$$

Vectors p and q are three-component unit row and column vectors, respectively. Vectors o are three-component zero vectors.

Vector equality: Two vectors are said to be equal if and only if (a) both vectors are row or both column vectors having the same number of components, and (b) their corresponding components are equal.

Example 1.6. Let the following vectors be given:

$$p = (2, 3), \quad q = \begin{pmatrix} 2 \\ 3 \end{pmatrix} \quad s = (3, 2), \quad t = (2, 3).$$

Then $p = t$; but $p \neq q, q \neq s$, and $s \neq t$.

The above definition of vector equality is more restrictive than necessary for the algebra of vectors, but consistent with matrix algebra in Section 2.

It is important to realize that the basic idea of one-to-one correspondence of analytic geometry holds true in the case of vectors. There is one-to-one correspondence between the set of all points on a given plane and the set of all two-component row or column vectors. In fact, for an Euclidean space of given dimensions there corresponds a set of row vectors of the same dimensions which is called a *Euclidean vector space*. This is an observation of fundamental importance since such space represents a mathematical system consisting of laws which govern vector operations.

1.2. Important Vector Operations. For our limited purpose we shall discuss and illustrate the following operations with vectors.

I. Addition: Two or more vectors are added if and only if all vectors
(a) are row or column vectors and (b) have the same number of components.
The sum is a row or column vector whose first component is the sum of the
first components of the added vectors, the second component is the sum of
the second components of the added vectors, etc.

Example 1.7.   Add the vectors

$$p = (0, 2) \text{ and } q = (3, 0).$$

Solution:

$$p + q = (0, 2) + (3, 0) = (0 + 3, 2 + 0) = (3, 2).$$

Add the vectors

$$r = \begin{pmatrix} -5 \\ 2 \\ 8 \end{pmatrix}, s = \begin{pmatrix} 1 \\ -6 \\ -4 \end{pmatrix}, \text{ and } t = \begin{pmatrix} 7 \\ 3 \\ -3 \end{pmatrix}.$$

Solution:

$$r + s + t = \begin{pmatrix} -5 \\ 2 \\ 8 \end{pmatrix} + \begin{pmatrix} 1 \\ -6 \\ -4 \end{pmatrix} + \begin{pmatrix} 7 \\ 3 \\ -3 \end{pmatrix} = \begin{pmatrix} (-5) + 1 + 7 \\ 2 + (-6) + 3 \\ 8 + (-4) + (-3) \end{pmatrix} = \begin{pmatrix} 3 \\ -1 \\ 1 \end{pmatrix}.$$

II. Scalar multiplication: Let k be any real number called scalar. Then
multiplying k times any vector v is defined by component-wise multi-
plication of k times the components of v.

Example 1.8.   Multiply kp where

$$k = 2 \text{ and } p = (1, 0).$$

Solution:

$$kp = 2(1, 0) = ((2) \cdot (1), (2) \cdot (0)) = (2, 0).$$

Let k be any real number and v any m-component column vector.
Multiply kv.

Solution:

$$kv = k \begin{pmatrix} v_1 \\ v_2 \\ v_3 \\ \cdot \\ \cdot \\ \cdot \\ v_m \end{pmatrix} = \begin{pmatrix} kv_1 \\ kv_2 \\ kv_3 \\ \cdot \\ \cdot \\ \cdot \\ kv_m \end{pmatrix}.$$

Observe that scalar multiplication, i.e., multiplication of a vector by a
scalar, results in a vector having as many components as the original
vector.

III. Subtraction: Let p and q be two row or two column vectors having
the same number of components. Then for subtracting q from p vector q is
multiplied by the scalar −1 and then the two vectors are added by
using rule I, above.

Example 1.9. Subtract vector

$$q = (2, 3, 5)$$

from vector

$$p = (5, 4, 3).$$

Solution:

Step 1: Multiply q by scalar -1.

$$(-1)q = (-2, -3, -5).$$

Step 2: Add vector from step 1 to vector p.

$$p + (-1)q = (5, 4, 3) + (-2, -3, -5) = (3, 1, -2).$$

Note that in subtraction, like in addition, both vectors must be either row or column vectors, and they must have the same number of components.

IV. Inner multiplication: Let u be an n-component row vector and v an m-component column vector, where m = n. Then the product uv, called inner product is defined as follows:

$$uv = (u_1, u_2, u_3, \ldots, u_n) \begin{pmatrix} v_1 \\ v_2 \\ v_3 \\ \cdot \\ \cdot \\ \cdot \\ v_m \end{pmatrix}$$
$$= u_1 v_1 + u_2 v_2 + u_3 v_3 + \ldots u_n v_m$$
$$= k.$$

The product uv is undefined if u and v have a different number of components, i.e., if $m \neq n$.

Example 1.10.   Multiply pq where

$$p = (2, 4, -3) \text{ and } q = \begin{pmatrix} -1 \\ 3 \\ -5 \end{pmatrix}.$$

Solution:

$$pq = (2, 4, -3) \begin{pmatrix} -1 \\ 3 \\ -5 \end{pmatrix}$$
$$= (2)(-1) + (4)(3) + (-3)(-5)$$
$$= -2 + 12 + 15$$
$$= 25.$$

It is important to realize that inner multiplication, i.e., multiplication of two vectors, results in a scalar. In the above example inner multiplication results in the scalar 25. Also, for inner multiplication the following conditions must exist: (*a*) each vector must have the same number of components; (*b*) one vector must be a row and the other a column vector; and (*c*) we write the row vector first and the column vector second.

The above operations, with inner multiplication and vector equality slightly modified, together with other laws of vector operations, represent the mathematical system of Euclidean vector space.

Explaining the laws of vector space lies beyond the scope of this book. Instead, we shall explain linear combinations of vectors and their relation to solving systems of linear equations and linear programming problems.

1.3. Combinations and Independent Vectors. Since there is one-to-one correspondence between points and vectors in Euclidean space, in looking for solutions to systems of linear equations we are in fact looking for the corresponding solution vectors. But in order to show this important relationship we must first explain linear combinations of vectors, linearly dependent vectors, and linearly independent vectors.

I. Linear Combinations of Vectors: Let P_1, P_2, and P_0 be a set of any vectors in a cc-plane. Then vector P_0 is called a *linear combination* of P_1 and P_2 if

(1.1)
$$\boxed{k_1 P_1 + k_2 P_2 = P_0 \,;}$$

where k_1 and k_2 are some scalars. (The general small letter vector notation is abandoned in order to be consistent with subsequent special topics).

Example 1.11. Let P_1 and P_2 be two given vectors where

$$P_1 = \binom{2}{3} \quad \text{and} \quad P_2 = \binom{3}{2}.$$

Also, let $k_1 = 1$ and $k_2 = -1$.

Then by (1.1), we get

$$(1)\quad \binom{2}{3} + (-1)\binom{3}{2} = \binom{2+(-3)}{3+(-2)} = \binom{-1}{1} = P_0.$$

Vector P_0 is called a linear combination of P_1 and P_2 since it can be obtained by scalar multiplication and addition of these vectors.

II. Linearly Dependent Vectors: Let P_1 and P_2 be a set of any two vectors in a cc-plane. Then such vectors are said to be *linearly dependent* if they satisfy some equation of the form

(1.2)
$$\boxed{k_1 P_1 + k_2 P_2 = Z \,,}$$

where the scalars k_1 and k_2 are not both zero and Z is the zero vector.

Example 1.12. Let P_1 and P_2 be vectors such that

$$P_1 = \begin{pmatrix} 2 \\ 1 \end{pmatrix} \quad \text{and} \quad P_2 = \begin{pmatrix} 4 \\ 2 \end{pmatrix}.$$

Also, let $k_1 = 2$ and $k_2 = -1$.
Then by (1.2) we have

$$2\begin{pmatrix} 2 \\ 1 \end{pmatrix} + (-1)\begin{pmatrix} 4 \\ 2 \end{pmatrix} = \begin{pmatrix} 0 \\ 0 \end{pmatrix} = Z.$$

Since the above scalar multiplication and vector addition yields the zero vector when k_1 and k_2 are not zero, vectors P_1 and P_2 are linearly dependent.

Dependency of vectors may be also explained in another way. Two vectors are linearly dependent if one can be expressed as a scalar multiple of the other.

Example 1.13. Consider again vectors

$$P_1 = \begin{pmatrix} 2 \\ 1 \end{pmatrix} \quad \text{and} \quad P_2 = \begin{pmatrix} 4 \\ 2 \end{pmatrix}.$$

Let $k = 2$. Then

$$kP_1 = 2\begin{pmatrix} 2 \\ 1 \end{pmatrix} = \begin{pmatrix} 4 \\ 2 \end{pmatrix} = P_2.$$

Let $k = \frac{1}{2}$. Then

$$kP_2 = \frac{1}{2}\begin{pmatrix} 4 \\ 2 \end{pmatrix} = \begin{pmatrix} 2 \\ 1 \end{pmatrix} = P_1.$$

III. Linearly Independent Vectors: Let P_1 and P_2 be a set of any two vectors in a cc-plane. Then such vectors are said to be *linearly independent* when they have the property that some equation of the form (1.2) is satisfied *if and only if* k_1 and k_2 are both zero.

Example 1.14. Let P_1 and P_2 be vectors such as

$$P_1 = \begin{pmatrix} 2 \\ 3 \end{pmatrix} \quad \text{and} \quad P_2 = \begin{pmatrix} 3 \\ 2 \end{pmatrix}.$$

These vectors are linearly independent because it is impossible to find a linear combination which satisfies (1.2) unless k_1 and k_2 are both zero. In other words, P_1 and P_2 are linearly independent because it is impossible to express the one as a scalar multiple of the other.

In fact, the above examples suggest that the largest number of linearly independent vectors in a cc-plane is two; and any two such vectors are called *basis* vectors since any other vector is a linear combination of a set of basis vectors. In other words, two basis vectors in a cc-plane represent the smallest spanning set of vectors and any set of more than two vectors is linearly dependent.

Example 1.15. Although any two linearly independent vectors in a cc-plane could be a basis, let us assume for the sake of exposition that our basis consists of the linearly independent unit vectors

$$P_1 = \begin{pmatrix} 1 \\ 0 \end{pmatrix} \quad \text{and} \quad P_2 = \begin{pmatrix} 0 \\ 1 \end{pmatrix}.$$

Then a cc-plane is the set of all linear combinations

$$x_1 P_1 + x_2 P_2,$$

where x_1 and x_2 are scalars.

Let $x_2 = 0$; and let x_1 vary over the set of real numbers R. Then by scalar multiplication $x_1 P_1$ we can obtain the vectors representing all the points on the x_1-axis of a cc-plane.

Let $x_1 = 0$; and let x_2 vary over the set of real numbers R. Then by scalar multiplication $x_2 P_2$ we can obtain the vectors representing all the points on the x_2-axis of a cc-plane.

Let x_1 and x_2 vary over the set of nonzero real numbers. Then with scalar multiplication and vector addition $x_1 P_1 + x_2 P_2$ we can obtain the vectors representing all the points of a cc-plane which do not lie on the axes.

The above discussion can be easily generalized for an n-dimensional Euclidean space, where n is any positive integer greater than 2.

1.4. Vectors and Systems of Linear Equations. The concepts expressed by the vector equations (1.1) and (1.2) have prepared the ground for discussing solutions of linearly independent, linearly dependent, nonhomogeneous, and homogeneous systems of linear equations.

A system of linear equations is said to be *linearly independent* if the coefficient vectors of the system are linearly independent.

Example 1.16. Consider the system of equations

$$x_1 + 2x_2 = 100,$$
$$x_1 + x_2 = 80.$$

It can be written as an equation of scalar multiplication and addition of vectors

$$x_1 \overset{P_1}{\begin{pmatrix} 1 \\ 1 \end{pmatrix}} + x_2 \overset{P_2}{\begin{pmatrix} 2 \\ 1 \end{pmatrix}} = \overset{P_0}{\begin{pmatrix} 100 \\ 80 \end{pmatrix}}$$

and by (1.1)

$$x_1 P_1 + x_2 P_2 = P_0.$$

This system of equations is called linearly independent because its coefficient vectors P_1 and P_2 are linearly independent. The reader may recall that the above system of linear equations corresponds to the restraining inequalities of the original profit maximizing linear programming problem of Quality Baking Company. In solving this problem we injected vectors $(0, 0)$, $(0, 50)$, and $(60, 20)$ representing extreme points of the solutions set into the objective function. We found that the optimal solution vector is $(60, 20)$ which is also the unique solution to the above linearly independent system of equations. It represents the values of the scalars x_1 and x_2 for which the above vector equation is satisfied since

$$60 \begin{pmatrix} 1 \\ 1 \end{pmatrix} + 20 \begin{pmatrix} 2 \\ 1 \end{pmatrix} = \begin{pmatrix} 100 \\ 80 \end{pmatrix}.$$

A system of linear equations is said to be *linearly dependent* if the coefficient vectors of the system are linearly dependent. Such a system may have infinitely many solutions.

Example 1.17.   Consider the system of equations

$$x_1 + 4x_2 + 2x_3 = 80,$$
$$2x_1 + 3x_2 + x_3 = 90.$$

This system is linearly dependent since the coefficient vectors of the system are linearly dependent. Thus, substituting $x_1 = -\frac{2}{3}$, $x_2 = 1$, and $x_3 = -\frac{5}{3}$ in the vector equation of the form (1.2)

$$x_1 P_1 + x_2 P_2 + x_3 P_3 = Z,$$

we have

$$\left(-\frac{2}{3}\right)\begin{pmatrix} 1 \\ 2 \end{pmatrix} + 1 \begin{pmatrix} 4 \\ 3 \end{pmatrix} + \left(-\frac{5}{3}\right)\begin{pmatrix} 2 \\ 1 \end{pmatrix} = \begin{pmatrix} 0 \\ 0 \end{pmatrix} = Z.$$

The system has infinitely many solutions as shown in Example 2.8 of the preceding chapter.

Also, a linearly dependent system of equations may be inconsistent with no common solution.

Example 1.18.   Consider equations

$$x_1 + x_2 = 160,$$
$$x_1 + x_2 = 80.$$

Since the coefficient vectors are linearly dependent, this system is linearly dependent. Substituting $x_1 = 1$ and $x_2 = -1$ in the vector equation form (1.2)

$$x_1 P_1 + x_2 P_2 = Z,$$

we get

$$1 \begin{pmatrix} 1 \\ 1 \end{pmatrix} + (-1) \begin{pmatrix} 1 \\ 1 \end{pmatrix} = \begin{pmatrix} 0 \\ 0 \end{pmatrix} = Z.$$

We have seen in Example 2.5 of the previous chapter that this system of equation has no common solution.

A set of linear equations with constant terms other than zero is called a *nonhomogeneous* system of equations. Thus, all the sets of linear equations in Examples 1.16 through 1.18 are nonhomogeneous systems of equations. A nonhomogeneous system of m linear equations in n unknowns may be written as follows:

(1.3)
$$
\begin{aligned}
a_{11}x_1 + a_{12}x_2 + \cdots + a_{1n}x_n &= b_1 \\
a_{12}x_1 + a_{22}x_2 + \cdots + a_{2n}x_n &= b_2 \\
&\ \ \vdots \\
a_{m1}x_1 + a_{m2}x_2 + \cdots + a_{mn}x_n &= b_m,
\end{aligned}
$$

where

   m and n are any integers,
   $x_j(j = 1, 2, \ldots, n)$ are scalars,
   a_{ij} is the coefficient of the ith row and the jth column,
   b_i is the constant term of the ith equation.

The general form of the nonhomogeneous system of linear equations can be expressed in vector equation form

(1.4)
$$ x_1 P_1 + x_2 P_2 + \ldots + x_n P_n = P_0 $$

where $P_j(j = 1, 2, \ldots, n)$ are m-component column vectors such that

$$
P_1 = \begin{pmatrix} a_{11} \\ a_{21} \\ \vdots \\ a_{m1} \end{pmatrix}, \
P_2 = \begin{pmatrix} a_{12} \\ a_{22} \\ \vdots \\ a_{m2} \end{pmatrix}, \ldots, \
P_n = \begin{pmatrix} a_{1n} \\ a_{2n} \\ \vdots \\ a_{mn} \end{pmatrix}
$$

and P_0 is the m-component column vector of constants. The vector of unknown scalars $X = (x_1, x_2, \ldots x_n)$ which satisfies (1.3) is called the *solution vector*. Vector $X = (60, 20)$ is the only solution vector of the system of equations in Example 1.16; vector $X = (26, 11, 5)$ is one of the infinitely many solution vectors of the system of equations in Example 1.17; while the system of equations in Example 1.18 has no solution vectors.

A set of linear equations where all constant terms are zero is called a *homogeneous* system of equations. Thus, the nonhomogeneous system (1.3) can be converted to a corresponding homogeneous system of m equations in n unknowns by letting all b_i constants ($i = 1, 2, \ldots, m$) be equal to zero. This general form of the homogeneous system of equations can be expressed in vector equation form

(1.5)
$$ x_1 P_1 + x_2 P_2 + \ldots + x_n P_n = Z, $$

where x_j are scalars, P_j are m-component column vectors defined earlier, and Z is an m-component zero column vector. A system of homogeneous equations has at least one solution, namely, when the components of the solution vector X are all zero. Such a solution is called *trivial*.

Example 1.19.   From Example 1.16 we can obtain

$$x_1 + 2x_2 = 0,$$
$$x_1 + x_2 = 0,$$

by substituting zero for each constant term. Observe that this homogeneous system which has been obtained from a linearly independent nonhomogeneous system has only a trivial solution, i.e., only the solution vector $X = (0, 0)$ satisfies the system.

But in addition, a system of homogeneous equations may have a solution when some component of vector X is not zero. Such a solution is called *nontrivial*.

Example 1.20.   Substituting zero for each constant in the system of equations given in Example 1.17 we obtain the homogeneous system

$$x_1 + 4x_2 + 2x_3 = 0,$$
$$2x_1 + 3x_2 + x_3 = 0.$$

We have seen in Example 1.17 that this system has a nontrivial solution since the solution vector $X = (-\frac{2}{3}, 1, -\frac{5}{3})$ satisfies the system. Note that this homogeneous system has been obtained from a linearly dependent nonhomogeneous system of equations.

Thus, there is an important relationship between homogeneous and nonhomogeneous systems of linear equations. From a given system of homogeneous equations we can obtain an infinite number of nonhomogeneous systems by simply changing the zero vector of the former into a nonzero of constants. Moreover, as we shall see later, if the given homogeneous system has a trivial solution only, then each of the corresponding nonhomogeneous systems is an independent system with a unique solution; and if the given homogeneous system has a nontrivial solution, then each of the corresponding nonhomogeneous systems may be a dependent system with infinitely many solutions or an inconsistent with no common solution.

1.5. Vectors and Linear Programming.   We have seen that we can solve linear programming problems by finding the optimal solution with an algorithm. Let us see now how this is done with vectors.

In actual computational methods of a maximizing problem each inequality is converted into an equality by using a *positive slack* variable. (Minimizing problems and problems involving equalities will be discussed later.)

Example 1.21.   Consider the original problem of Quality Baking Company where

(1.6) $f_{max} = 0.2x_1 + 0.3x_2,$

subject to

$$x_1 + 2x_2 \leqslant 100$$

(1.7) $$x_1 + x_2 \leqslant 80$$

(1.8) $$x_j \geqslant 0 \, (j = 1, 2).$$

For each inequality in (1.7) there is a number $x \geqslant 0$ such that when added to the left-hand side each inequality is converted into an equality. Thus,

(1.9) $$f_{max} = 0.2x_1 + 0.3x_2 + 0x_3 + 0x_4,$$

subject to

$$x_1 + 2x_2 + x_3 + 0x_4 = 100$$

(1.10)

$$x_1 + x_2 + 0x_3 + x_4 = 80$$

(1.11) $$x_j \geqslant 0 \, (j = 1, 2, 3, 4),$$

where slack x_3 converts the first inequality and slack x_4 the second inequality into equations. Observe that x_3 and x_4 have zero coefficients in the second and first equations of (1.10), respectively, and zeros in (1.9) so that, although an important part of the final solution, they do not contribute to the optimal solution in the objective function.

In vector form (1.10) can be written as

(1.12) $$x_1 \binom{1}{1} + x_2 \binom{2}{1} + x_3 \binom{1}{0} + x_4 \binom{0}{1} = \binom{100}{80} \quad \text{or}$$

(1.13) $$x_1 P_1 + x_2 P_2 + x_3 P_3 + x_4 P_4 = P_0 \qquad \text{(by 1.4)}$$

In general, a maximizing problem involving m inequalities in n unknowns can be written as follows:

(1.14) $$f_{max} = c_1 x_1 + c_2 x_2 + \ldots + c_n x_n,$$

subject to

$$a_{11}x_1 + a_{12}x_2 + \ldots + a_{1n}x_n \leqslant b_1$$
$$a_{21}x_1 + a_{22}x_2 + \ldots + a_{2n}x_n \leqslant b_2$$
$$\cdot \qquad \cdot \qquad \cdots \qquad \cdot \qquad \cdot$$

(1.15) $$\cdot \qquad \cdot \qquad \cdots \qquad \cdot \qquad \cdot$$

$$\cdot \qquad \cdot \qquad \cdots \qquad \cdot \qquad \cdot$$
$$a_{m1}x_1 + a_{m2}x_2 + \ldots + a_{mn}x_n \leqslant b_m$$

(1.16) $$x_j \geqslant 0 \, (j = 1, 2, \ldots, n),$$

where c_j, a_{ij}, and $b_i (i = 1, 2, \ldots, m)$ are known constants. Introducing the required m slack variables the above general maximizing problem is converted to

(1.17) $$f_{max} = c_1 x_1 + c_2 x_2 + \ldots + c_n x_n + 0x_{n+1} + 0x_{n+2} + \ldots + 0x_{n+m},$$

subject to

$$a_{11}x_1 + a_{12}x_2 + \ldots + a_{1n}x_n + x_{n+1} + 0x_{n+2} + \ldots + 0x_{n+m} = b_1$$
$$a_{21}x_1 + a_{22}x_2 + \ldots + a_{2n}x_n + 0x_{n+1} + x_{n+2} + \ldots + 0x_{n+m} = b_2$$

(1.18)

$$a_{m1}x_1 + a_{m2}x_2 + \ldots + a_{mn}x_n + 0x_{n+1} + 0x_{n+2} + \ldots + x_{n+m} = b_m$$

(1.19) $\quad x_j \geqslant 0 \ (j = 1, 2, \ldots, n, n+1, n+2, \ldots, n+m).$

In vector form (1.18) can be written as

$$(1.20) \quad x_1 \begin{pmatrix} a_{11} \\ a_{21} \\ \cdot \\ \cdot \\ \cdot \\ a_{m1} \end{pmatrix} + x_2 \begin{pmatrix} a_{12} \\ a_{22} \\ \cdot \\ \cdot \\ \cdot \\ a_{m2} \end{pmatrix} + \ldots + x_n \begin{pmatrix} a_{1n} \\ a_{2n} \\ \cdot \\ \cdot \\ \cdot \\ a_{mn} \end{pmatrix} + x_{n+1} \begin{pmatrix} 1 \\ 0 \\ \cdot \\ \cdot \\ \cdot \\ 0 \end{pmatrix} +$$

$$+ x_{n+2} \begin{pmatrix} 0 \\ 1 \\ \cdot \\ \cdot \\ \cdot \\ 0 \end{pmatrix} + \ldots + x_{n+m} \begin{pmatrix} 0 \\ 0 \\ \cdot \\ \cdot \\ \cdot \\ 1 \end{pmatrix} = \begin{pmatrix} b_1 \\ b_2 \\ \cdot \\ \cdot \\ \cdot \\ b_m \end{pmatrix}$$

(1.21) $\quad x_1 P_1 + x_2 P_2 + \ldots + x_n P_n + x_{n+1} P_{n+1} + x_{n+2} P_{n+2} + \ldots +$
$$+ x_{n+m} P_{n+m} = P_0 \qquad \text{(by 1.4)}$$

System (1.18) has an important interpretation. The number of n original unknowns represents an n-dimensional *initial space*. The $n + m$ normal and slack unknowns represent an $n + m$ dimensional space. It is called the *solution space* since the solution vector $X = (x_1, x_2, \ldots, x_n, x_{n+1}, \ldots, x_{n+m})$ is a point in this space. Finally, the m equations represent an m-dimensional space called *requirements space* since m restraints specify the requirements of the problem. The problem in Example 1.21 involves a two-dimensional initial and requirements spaces and a four-dimensional solution space. On the other hand, for a maximizing problem with three inequalities in two unknowns the dimensions of the spaces are two, three, and five, respectively.

System (1.18) is related to another important point in linear programming. It can be proved that such a system of linear equations has a solution with at least n of the unknowns in the solution vector being zero. The remaining unknowns may or may not be zero. Such a solution is called a *basic* solution. In sum, there is a solution to a linear programming problem of m equations in n unknowns which is a basic solution to the corresponding system (1.18).

Thus, if a linear programming problem has an *optimal* solution, such a solution will be found among the *basic* solutions of the solution space;

and the process of finding such an optimal solution to the problem by actual computational methods consists of searching for a set of values of the solution vector X which represents a basic solution. This process is equivalent to testing the objective function at extreme points of the solution set in the initial space.

Example 1.22.   Let us consider the Quality Baking Company problem in Example 1.21. This problem was expressed in vector form as follows:

(1.12) $$x_1 \begin{pmatrix} 1 \\ 1 \end{pmatrix} + x_2 \begin{pmatrix} 2 \\ 1 \end{pmatrix} + x_3 \begin{pmatrix} 1 \\ 0 \end{pmatrix} + x_4 \begin{pmatrix} 0 \\ 1 \end{pmatrix} = \begin{pmatrix} 100 \\ 80 \end{pmatrix} \text{ and}$$

(1.13) $$x_1 P_1 + x_2 P_2 + x_3 P_3 + x_4 P_4 = P_0.$$

Using the above expressions as a starting point we may solve the problem with the following algorithm.
Initial Solution:
The solution vector $X_1 = (0, 0, 100, 80)$ represents the extreme point of the solution set at the origin. It satisfies the vector equation (1.13) since

(1.22) $$P_0 = 0P_1 + 0P_2 + 100P_3 + 80P_4.$$

Injecting, however, vector X_1 into the objective function

$$f_{max} = 0.2x_1 + 0.3x_2 + 0x_3 + 0x_4$$

yields zero profits since

$$f'_{max} = 0.2(0) + 0.3(0) + 0(100) + 0(80) = 0 \text{ dollars}.$$

We must test another extreme point. Since there can be no more than two among the four P_j vectors with nonzero coefficients in (1.22), we must substitute either vector P_1 or P_2 for a linear combination of the basis vectors P_3 and P_4 of the initial solution. In other words, we must find how many units of P_3 and P_4 will be replaced by *one* unit of either P_1 or P_2.
First Iteration:
Let P_2 be the substitute vector. Then
Step 1: Express P_2 as a linear combination of P_3 and P_4.

$$P_2 = aP_3 + bP_4$$

$$\begin{pmatrix} 2 \\ 1 \end{pmatrix} = a \begin{pmatrix} 1 \\ 0 \end{pmatrix} + b \begin{pmatrix} 0 \\ 1 \end{pmatrix}.$$

Thus, $a = 2$, $b = 1$, and

$$P_2 = 2P_3 + 1P_4.$$

Step 2: Find amount of P_2, i.e., the quantity of x_2 cookies, which should be injected into the objective function.
Let scalar k be such an amount. Then

$$kP_2 = 2kP_3 + kP_4, \text{ and}$$

(1.23) $$kP_2 - 2kP_3 - kP_4 = 0.$$

Adding (1.23) to the right-hand side of (1.22) does not change the equality since (1.23) equals zero. Thus,

$$P_0 = 0P_1 + 0P_2 + 100P_3 + 80P_4 + kP_2 - 2kP_3 - kP_4,$$

and

(1.24) $P_0 = 0P_1 + kP_2 + (100 - 2k)P_3 + (80 - k)P_4.$

Since the maximum value of k for which no scalar in (1.24) becomes negative is 50, substituting for $k = 50$ and collecting terms, we get

(1.25) $P_0 = 0P_1 + 50P_2 + 0P_3 + 30P_4,$

which is a new feasible solution with $X_2 = (0, 50, 0, 30)$ as the solution vector.

Step 3: Find profit.

Injecting vector X_2 into the objective function, we get

$$f''_{max} = 0.2(0) + 0.3(50) + 0(0) + 0(30) = 15 \text{ dollars.}$$

Second Iteration:

The same steps are followed for P_1 without explanation.

Step 1:

$$P_1 = aP_2 + bP_4$$
$$\binom{1}{1} = a\binom{2}{1} + b\binom{0}{1}.$$

Thus, $a = \frac{1}{2}$, $b = \frac{1}{2}$ and

$$P_1 = \tfrac{1}{2}P_2 + \tfrac{1}{2}P_4.$$

Step 2: Let k be a scalar. Then

$$kP_1 = \frac{k}{2}P_2 + \frac{k}{2}P_4 = 0,$$

(1.26) $2kP_1 - kP_2 - kP_4 = 0.$

Adding (1.26) to (1.25), we get

$$P_0 = 0P_1 + 50P_2 + 0P_3 + 30P_4 + 2kP_1 - kP_2 - kP_4,$$

(1.27) $P_0 = 2kP_1 + (50 - k)P_2 + 0P_3 + (30 - k)P_4.$

Substituting for $k = 30$ in (1.27), we have

(1.28) $P_0 = 60P_1 + 20P_2 + 0P_3 + 0P_4,$

a new feasible solution with solution vector

$$X_3 = (60, 20, 0, 0).$$

Step 3: Injecting X_3 into the objective function, we obtain

$$f'''_{max} = 0.2(60) + 0.3(20) + 0(0) + 0(0) = 18 \text{ dollars,}$$

the maximum profit as before.

Observe that the above vector analysis consists of moving from one set of basis vectors to another. This iterative process is essentially the process of the *simplex algorithm* or the *simplex method,* an important computational technique of linear programming which we shall discuss after the section on matrices.

PROBLEMS

1.1. Sketch the following free vectors on a cc-plane.
  a) [(3, 0), (7, 0)].
  b) [(2, 5), (6, −7)].
  c) [(−3, 5), (−5, 1)].
  d) [(−5, −1), (−1, −5)].

1.2. Suppose the initial and the end points of each free vector in *(a), *(b), (c), and (d) of Problem 1.1 represent separate origin vectors,
  i) Write each vector in proper notation.
  ii) Sketch each vector on a cc-plane.

1.3. Given the following vectors, indicate whether each vector equality is correct and explain why.

$$p = \begin{pmatrix} 1 \\ 0 \end{pmatrix}, q = (1, 0), r = \begin{pmatrix} 2 \\ 5 \\ 3 \end{pmatrix}, t = (1, 0), v = \begin{pmatrix} 2 \\ 5 \\ 3 \end{pmatrix}.$$

  a) $p = q$.   *f)* $q = t$.
  b) $p = r$.   g) $q = v$.
  c) $p = t$.   h) $r = t$.
  d) $p = v$.   * i) $r = v$.
  e) $q = r$.   j) $t = v$.

1.4. Add each pair of row vectors and present such addition of vectors geometrically.
  a) $p = (3, 0), q = (0, 7)$.
  b) $p = (−2, 5), q = (5, 6)$.
  c) $p = (−3, −6), q = (3, 6)$.

1.5. Write in proper notation the following vectors:
  a) A row vector with components $u_j (j = 1, 2, \ldots, 6)$.
  b) A column vector with components $v_i (i = 1, 2, \ldots, 5)$.

1.6. Given the column vectors

$$u = \begin{pmatrix} 2 \\ 3 \\ 1 \end{pmatrix}, v = \begin{pmatrix} 2 \\ -1 \\ 0 \end{pmatrix}, w = \begin{pmatrix} 0 \\ -2 \\ 2 \end{pmatrix},$$

  compute
  a) $3u$.   e) $u − v + w$.
  b) $−v$.   f) $2u + v − w$.
  c) $3u − v$.   g) $u − 2v − 2w$.
  d) $u + v$.   h) $u − 2v + 3w$.

1.7. Given the vectors $u = (5, −3, 2), v = (2, 4, −1), w = (0, 1, 3)$, compute (a), (b), *(c), (d), (e), (f), (g), and (h) as specified in Problem 1.6.

1.8. Compute the following sums, if possible; otherwise explain why addition is not possible.

*a) $\begin{pmatrix} 2 \\ 1 \end{pmatrix} + \begin{pmatrix} -3 \\ 2 \\ 5 \end{pmatrix}$.

b) $(3, -1, -2) + (5, 2, 1)$.

c) $(6, 2, 5) + \begin{pmatrix} 1 \\ 1 \end{pmatrix}$.

1.9. Find the answer to the following operations given the vectors

$$p = (1, -2, 1) \qquad u = (2, 0, 3)$$

$$q = \begin{pmatrix} -1 \\ 3 \\ -2 \end{pmatrix} \qquad v = \begin{pmatrix} 0 \\ -1 \\ 2 \end{pmatrix}$$

*a) $pq - uv$.

b) $(p - u)(2q - v)$.

c) $3pq - 2[u(3q + v)]$.

d) $k[(p - u)(q - v)]$.

1.10. Compute the following inner products, if possible; otherwise explain why inner multiplication is not possible.

*a) $\begin{pmatrix} 3 \\ 5 \end{pmatrix}(2, 2)$.

b) $k(1, 5, 6)\begin{pmatrix} 1 \\ 0 \\ 1 \end{pmatrix}$.

c) $(2, 3, 1, 0)\begin{pmatrix} 0 \\ 0 \\ 0 \\ 0 \end{pmatrix}$.

1.11. Show that each set of vectors below is linearly dependent by expressing the first vector of each set as a linear combination of the others.

a) $P_1 = \begin{pmatrix} 3 \\ 5 \end{pmatrix}, P_2 = \begin{pmatrix} 6 \\ \frac{4}{10} \\ 4 \end{pmatrix}$.

*b) $P_1 = \begin{pmatrix} 1 \\ 2 \end{pmatrix}, P_2 = \begin{pmatrix} 5 \\ 3 \end{pmatrix}, P_3 = \begin{pmatrix} 4 \\ 7 \end{pmatrix}$.

c) $P_1 = \begin{pmatrix} -1 \\ 1 \\ 4 \end{pmatrix}, P_2 = \begin{pmatrix} 3 \\ -5 \\ -1 \end{pmatrix}, P_3 = \begin{pmatrix} -5 \\ 7 \\ 9 \end{pmatrix}$.

d) $P_1 = \begin{pmatrix} 2 \\ -3 \\ 8 \end{pmatrix}, P_2 = \begin{pmatrix} -1 \\ 2 \\ 3 \end{pmatrix}, P_3 = \begin{pmatrix} 3 \\ 1 \\ -5 \end{pmatrix}, P_4 = \begin{pmatrix} 1 \\ -5 \\ 2 \end{pmatrix}$.

1.12. If any one of the following sets of vectors is linearly dependent, find a linear combination that equals zero. Otherwise, explain why a given set is linearly independent.

*a) $P_1 = \begin{pmatrix} 1 \\ 2 \end{pmatrix}, P_2 = \begin{pmatrix} 5 \\ 10 \end{pmatrix}$.

c) $P_1 = \begin{pmatrix} 3 \\ 5 \\ 5 \end{pmatrix}, P_2 = \begin{pmatrix} 5 \\ 1 \\ 0 \end{pmatrix}, P_3, = \begin{pmatrix} 0 \\ 2 \\ 0 \end{pmatrix}$.

*b) $P_1 = \begin{pmatrix} 3 \\ 4 \end{pmatrix}, P_2 = \begin{pmatrix} 5 \\ 7 \end{pmatrix}$.

d) $P_1 = \begin{pmatrix} 2 \\ 3 \end{pmatrix}, P_2 = \begin{pmatrix} 7 \\ 11 \end{pmatrix}, P_3 = \begin{pmatrix} 3 \\ 5 \end{pmatrix}$.

1.13. Form the Cartesian product set of $x_1 \times x_2$ such that $x_1 = \{-2, -1, 0, 1, 2\}$ and $x_2 = \{-2, -1, 0, 1, 2\}$ and plot each element of the product set on a cc-plane. Let the basis vectors $P_1 = \begin{pmatrix} 1 \\ 0 \end{pmatrix}$ and $P_2 = \begin{pmatrix} 0 \\ 1 \end{pmatrix}$ be given. Show that each element of the Cartesian product set $x_1 \times x_2$ is a linear combination of $x_1 P_1 + x_2 P_2$.

1.14. For each system of linear equations of Section 2 of the preceding chapter indicated below—

    i) Write the corresponding system of homogeneous equations.

    ii) Verify the relationship between solutions of the given system and trivial or nontrivial solutions of the corresponding system of homogeneous equations.

  *a) Example 2.2, equations (2.3) and (2.4).

  *b) Example 2.3, equations (2.5), (2.6), and (2.7).

  *c) Example 2.4, equations (2.8) and (2.9).

  d) Example 2.5, equations (2.10) and (2.11).

  e) Example 2.6, equations (2.12), (2.13), and (2.14).

  f) Example 2.7, equations (2.15), (2.16), and (2.17).

  g) Example 2.8, equations (2.18) and (2.19).

1.15. For each linear programming problem of Chapter 8 indicated below—

    i) Introduce the necessary slack variables and express it in the form (1.17) through (1.19).

    ii) Indicate the dimensions of the initial, requirements, and solution spaces.

  *a) Example 2.7.

  b) Problem 1.13.

  c) Problem 1.14.

  d) Problem 1.16.

1.16. Solve the linear programming problems of Problem 1.15 above, using the vector analysis procedure illustrated in Example 1.22 of the text.

1.17. Let u and v be any column (row) vectors having the same number of m (n) components. Then, using the laws of ordinary algebra, show that—

  *a) $o + u = u$,

  b) $u + 0v = u$,

  c) $u_i = 2v_i$, if $4v - 2u = o$,

    where o is an $m(n)$-component zero vector.

1.18. Let $x_1 = \begin{pmatrix} 1 \\ 2 \end{pmatrix}$ and $x_2 = \begin{pmatrix} -2 \\ 1 \end{pmatrix}$. Then compute the following vectors and illustrate each vector addition geometrically.

  *a) $x_1 + x_2$.   d) $-2x_1 - x_2$.

  b) $\frac{1}{2}x_1 + \frac{1}{2}x_2$.   e) $\frac{1}{3}x_1 + \frac{3}{5}x_2$.

  c) $2x_1 - x_2$.   f) $3x_2 - 2x_1$.

1.19. Three stock market traders, 1, 2, 3, made the following transactions during a day:

$$s_1 = (10, 15, 20), \; s_2 = (\; 5, 22, 35), \; s_3 = (40, 35, 12),$$
$$d_1 = (25, 30, 19), \; d_2 = (15, 17, 21), \; d_3 = (15, 25, 27),$$

where $s_i (i = 1, 2, 3)$ represents the number of shares of three common stocks sold by the traders at the opening of the stock market and $d_i (i = 1, 2, 3)$ the number of shares of the same three stocks bought by the three traders at the close of the same day. Let vectors

$$P_s = \begin{pmatrix} 5 \\ 10 \\ 15 \end{pmatrix} \text{ and } P_d = \begin{pmatrix} 7 \\ 10 \\ 12 \end{pmatrix}$$

be the prices of the sold and bought stocks per share, respectively, in dollars.

a) Find the total volume of sold and bought shares for each stock.

*b) Find how much profit or loss each trader realized.

c) If profits and losses were the only criteria and if the above transactions are representative of the total transactions of the day, would you say that the stock market was bullish or bearish?

1.20. A free vector perpendicular to the boundary and pointing toward the interior of a closed half space is called *normal*. From each extreme point of the feasible solution set of problems indicated below draw the normals to each half space. Let P_1 and P_2 represent two such normals, then the space spanned by $k_1 P_1 + k_2 P_2$ where $k_1 + k_2 = 1$ is called a *cone*. Verify graphically the fact that the normal to the objective function at each extreme point will lie outside the cone spanned by the normals of the restraints except at the extreme point representing the optimal solution to the linear programming problem.

*a) Example 1.3, Figure 1.3, Chapter 8.

b) Example 1.7, Figure 1.8, Chapter 8.

1.21. Let $P_1, P_2, \ldots, P_n$ be a linearly dependent set of n vectors. Then prove that at least one vector (element) of this set is a linear combination of the others.

*2. MATRIX ALGEBRA AND LINEAR PROGRAMMING

Another mathematical system which may help us acquire an understanding of some theoretical and notational aspects of linear programming is the algebra of matrices. First, we shall introduce the necessary definitions and notation. Second, we shall illustrate basic operations with matrices and discuss briefly matrix algebra as a mathematical system. After these fundamental topics we shall focus our attention on the dual of a linear programming problem and the rule for inverting a square matrix. Finally, we shall demonstrate the importance of the inverse of a matrix in solving systems of equations and establish the relation between matrix algebra and linear programming.

2.1. Matrices: Definitions and Notation.

A rectangular array of numbers such as

$$A = \begin{pmatrix} a_{11} & a_{12} & \cdots & a_{1n} \\ a_{21} & a_{22} & \cdots & a_{2n} \\ \cdot & \cdot & \cdots & \cdot \\ \cdot & \cdot & \cdots & \cdot \\ \cdot & \cdot & \cdots & \cdot \\ a_{m1} & a_{m2} & \cdots & a_{mn} \end{pmatrix},$$

where a_{ij} are real numbers and m and n positive integers, is called a *matrix*. In general, matrices are denoted by capital letters such as A, B, C, U, V, I, and others. It is important to note that a matrix such as A can be looked at as a collection of m n-component row vectors or of n m-component column vectors. Thus, like vectors, a matrix is described in terms of the number of its rows and columns, otherwise called the *order* of a matrix. So the order of matrix A is $m \times n$ (m by n).

Example 2.1. Consider the matrices

$$A = (2, 4, -3); \qquad B = \begin{pmatrix} 2 \\ 1 \\ -5 \\ 3 \end{pmatrix}; \qquad C = \begin{pmatrix} 1 & 2 \\ 1 & 1 \end{pmatrix};$$

$$D = \begin{pmatrix} 1 & 4 & 2 \\ 2 & 3 & 1 \end{pmatrix}; \qquad E = \begin{pmatrix} 2 & 3 \\ 1 & 2 \\ 1 & 1 \end{pmatrix}; \qquad 0 = \begin{pmatrix} 0 & 0 & 0 \\ 0 & 0 & 0 \\ 0 & 0 & 0 \end{pmatrix}.$$

The order of matrix A is 1×3 while B is a 4×1, C a 2×2, D a 2×3, E a 3×2, and 0 a 3×3 matrices. Observe that in describing the order of a matrix the first number denotes the number of rows and the second the number of columns.

A matrix is called *square* if $m = n$, i.e., if it has the same number of rows and columns. Matrix C in Example 2.1 is a square matrix since $m = n = 2$. Also, matrix 0, called the *zero* matrix, is a 3×3 square matrix. An important square matrix is the *identity* or *unit* matrix which has the number 1 as elements for its *principal* or *main* diagonal (the diagonal from the upper left-hand side to the lower right-hand side corner) and zeros elsewhere.

Example 2.2. Consider the identity matrices

$$\begin{pmatrix} 1 & 0 \\ 0 & 1 \end{pmatrix}, \quad \begin{pmatrix} 1 & 0 & 0 \\ 0 & 1 & 0 \\ 0 & 0 & 1 \end{pmatrix}, \quad \begin{pmatrix} 1_{11} & 0 & \cdots & 0 \\ 0 & 1_{22} & \cdots & 0 \\ \cdot & \cdot & \cdots & \cdot \\ \cdot & \cdot & \cdots & \cdot \\ \cdot & \cdot & \cdots & \cdot \\ 0 & \cdot & \cdots & 1_{mn} \end{pmatrix}.$$

The first is the identity matrix for two-space, the second for three-space, and the third for n-space where $m = n$. An identity matrix is denoted by the letter I. Note that for each space there is one and only one identity matrix.

Let A be an $m \times n$ matrix, then the $n \times m$ matrix which is obtained from A by making the rows of A into columns and the columns into rows is called the *transpose* of A denoted A^T.

Example 2.3. Let

$$B = (2, 1, -5), \text{ then } B^T = \begin{pmatrix} 2 \\ 1 \\ -5 \end{pmatrix}.$$

Let

$$D = \begin{pmatrix} 1 & 4 & 2 \\ 2 & 3 & 1 \end{pmatrix}, \text{ then } D^T = \begin{pmatrix} 1 & 2 \\ 4 & 3 \\ 2 & 1 \end{pmatrix}.$$

In general let

$$A = \begin{pmatrix} a_{11} & a_{12} & a_{13} \\ a_{21} & a_{22} & a_{23} \\ a_{31} & a_{32} & a_{33} \end{pmatrix}, \text{ then } A^T = \begin{pmatrix} a_{11} & a_{21} & a_{31} \\ a_{12} & a_{22} & a_{32} \\ a_{13} & a_{23} & a_{33} \end{pmatrix}.$$

Observe that for a square matrix such as A its transpose A^T can be obtained by rotating A around its principal diagonal.

Matrix Equality. *Two or more matrices are equal if and only if* (a) *they have the same order, and* (b) *their corresponding components are equal.* Since matrix equality is analogous to vector equality we shall let the reader supply his own examples.

2.2. Basic Operations with Matrices. As in the case of vectors we shall consider the following important matrix operations: addition, subtraction, scalar multiplication, and matrix multiplication.

I. Addition: *Two or more matrices are added if and only if all of them have the same order. The sum is a matrix of the same order with each component being the sum of the corresponding components of the added matrices.*

Example 2.4. Let the matrices

$$A = \begin{pmatrix} 2 & 1 & -2 \\ 3 & -5 & 6 \end{pmatrix} \text{ and } B = \begin{pmatrix} 1 & -3 & 5 \\ 0 & 4 & -2 \end{pmatrix}$$

be given. Find $A + B$.
Solution:

$$A + B = \begin{pmatrix} 2 & 1 & -2 \\ 3 & -5 & 6 \end{pmatrix} + \begin{pmatrix} 1 & -3 & 5 \\ 0 & 4 & -2 \end{pmatrix} = \begin{pmatrix} 3 & -2 & 3 \\ 3 & -1 & 4 \end{pmatrix}.$$

II. Scalar Multiplication: *Let k be any real number. Then multiplying k times any matrix A is defined by component-wise multiplication of k times the components of A.*

Example 2.5. Let $k = 3$ and let matrix

$$A = \begin{pmatrix} 1 & 4 & 2 \\ 2 & 3 & 1 \end{pmatrix}.$$

Find kA.

Solution:

$$kA = 3\begin{pmatrix} 1 & 4 & 2 \\ 2 & 3 & 1 \end{pmatrix} = \begin{pmatrix} 3 & 12 & 6 \\ 6 & 9 & 3 \end{pmatrix}.$$

III. Subtraction: *Let A and B be two matrices of the same order. In order to subtract B from A we first multiply B by scalar -1 and then add the two matrices "algebraically" component by component.*

Example 2.6. Let matrices

$$A = \begin{pmatrix} 2 & 1 & -2 \\ 3 & -5 & 6 \end{pmatrix} \text{ and } B = \begin{pmatrix} 1 & -3 & 5 \\ 0 & 4 & -2 \end{pmatrix}.$$

Subtract B from A.

Solution:

Step 1. Find $(-1)B$.

By scalar multiplication, we have

$$(-1)B = (-1)\begin{pmatrix} 1 & -3 & 5 \\ 0 & 4 & -2 \end{pmatrix} = \begin{pmatrix} -1 & 3 & -5 \\ 0 & -4 & 2 \end{pmatrix} = -B.$$

Step 2. Find the difference A minus B.

Adding A and $-B$, we get

$$A + (-B) = \begin{pmatrix} 2 & 1 & -2 \\ 3 & -5 & 6 \end{pmatrix} + \begin{pmatrix} -1 & 3 & -5 \\ 0 & -4 & 2 \end{pmatrix} = \begin{pmatrix} 1 & 4 & -7 \\ 3 & -9 & 8 \end{pmatrix}.$$

IV. Matrix Multiplication: *Let U be an $m \times p$ matrix and V a $p \times n$ matrix. Then the product matrix $C = UV$ is an $m \times n$ matrix whose components are defined as*

$$c_{ij} = (u_{i1}, u_{i2}, \ldots, u_{ip})\begin{pmatrix} v_{1j} \\ v_{2j} \\ \vdots \\ v_{pj} \end{pmatrix} = u_{i1} \cdot v_{1j} + u_{i2} \cdot v_{2j} + \ldots + u_{ip}\, v_{pj},$$

where

$$(i = 1, 2, \ldots, m)$$
$$(j = 1, 2, \ldots, n).$$

Example 2.7. Let matrices

$$U = \begin{pmatrix} 1 & 3 & 2 \\ 1 & -2 & -3 \end{pmatrix} \text{ and } V = \begin{pmatrix} 5 & -3 \\ 1 & 2 \\ 4 & 0 \end{pmatrix}.$$

Find the product matrix $C = UV$.

Solution:

$$C = UV = \begin{pmatrix} 1 & 3 & 2 \\ 1 & -2 & -3 \end{pmatrix} \begin{pmatrix} 5 & -3 \\ 1 & 2 \\ 4 & 0 \end{pmatrix}$$

$$= \begin{pmatrix} (1)(5) + (3)(1) + (2)(4) & (1)(-3) + (3)(2) + (2)(0) \\ (1)(5) + (-2)(1) + (-3)(4) & (1)(-3) + (-2)(2) + (-3)(0) \end{pmatrix}$$

$$= \begin{pmatrix} 5 + 3 + 8 & -3 + 6 + 0 \\ 5 - 2 - 12 & -3 - 4 - 0 \end{pmatrix}$$

$$= \begin{pmatrix} 16 & 3 \\ -9 & -7 \end{pmatrix}.$$

Observe that for matrix multiplication: (*a*) the number of columns in U must be equal to the number of rows in V; (*b*) the product matrix $C = UV$ has the same number of rows as matrix U and the same number of columns as matrix V; and (*c*) the ijth component of the product matrix is the inner product of the ith row of U and the jth column of V.

Example 2.8. Let matrices

$$A = \begin{pmatrix} 1 & 0 \\ -3 & 5 \\ 2 & -4 \end{pmatrix} \text{ and } B = \begin{pmatrix} 2 & 0 \\ -1 & 3 \end{pmatrix}.$$

Find the product matrix $C = AB$.
    Solution:

$$C = AB = \begin{pmatrix} 1 & 0 \\ -3 & 5 \\ 2 & -4 \end{pmatrix} \begin{pmatrix} 2 & 0 \\ -1 & 3 \end{pmatrix}$$

$$= \begin{pmatrix} 2 & 0 \\ -11 & 15 \\ 8 & -12 \end{pmatrix}.$$

Multiplying a 3×2 matrix A by a 2×2 matrix B yields a 3×2 matrix C. It is important to realize that the product matrix BA is not defined since B has 2 columns and A has three rows.

2.3. The Laws of Matrix Algebra.

Let A, B, and C be any matrices, 0 the zero matrix, and I the identity matrix, all of suitable order. Then the laws shown on the left-hand side column of Table 2.1, together with the operations of matrix addition and multiplication, represent the mathematical system of matrix algebra. Observe that there is a close analogy between the laws of matrix algebra and the laws of ordinary algebra shown on the right-hand column of the table where a, b, c are real numbers and 0 is the number zero. Thus, most laws of matrix algebra can be proved by invoking the corresponding laws of ordinary algebra. This task, however, is beyond the scope of this book.

The reader can verify the above laws of matrix algebra by solving the available problems at the end of this section.

Nonetheless, two important differences between the two systems of algebra should be noted. The first is that the commutative law 7b of ordinary algebra does not hold *in general* for the corresponding law 7a of matrix algebra. In Example 2.8 we have found the product matrix AB and pointed out that the product matrix BA is not defined. The

TABLE 2.1.

MATRIX ALGEBRA	ORDINARY ALGEBRA
A. *Laws governing addition*	
1a. $A + B = B + A$	1b. $a + b = b + a$
2a. $A + (B + C) = (A + B) + C$	2b. $a + (b + c) = (a + b) + c$
3a. $A + 0 = A$	3b. $a + 0 = a$
4a. $A + (-A) = 0$	4b. $a + (-a) = 0$

B. *Laws governing multiplication* (assume that all matrices are square of order $n \times n$)

5a. $A(B + C) = AB + AC$	5b. $a(b + c) = ab + ac$
6a. $ABC = A(BC) = (AB)C$	6b. $abc = a(bc) = (ab)c$
7a. $AB \neq BA$, in general.	7b. $ab = ba$
8a. $AI = IA = A$	8b. $a1 = 1a = a$
9a. $AA^{-1} = I$	9b. $aa^{-1} = 1$
10a. $A0 = 0$	10b. $a0 = 0$

second point is that the reciprocal of a real number as denoted by a^{-1} (law 9b) is defined for all real numbers except zero, while the inverse of a matrix A denoted by A^{-1} (law 9a) is not defined for all square matrices $A \neq 0$. In other words, not all square matrices have an inverse. We shall explain the inverse after the following important topic.

2.4. The Dual of a Problem. It can be shown that for a given problem called the *primal* there arises another problem called the *dual* of the original problem. The dual of a maximizing primal is a minimizing problem and the dual of a minimizing primal is a maximizing problem. Furthermore, if the primal has a solution, then the dual must also have a solution, and if the primal does not have a solution, then neither does the dual. Since the dual of the dual is the original problem, either problem can be considered the primal and the other the dual.

Although proving the duality theorem is beyond the scope of this book, showing the relationship between primal and dual problems and interpreting the latter may be important from the empirical viewpoint.

Example 2.9. Consider the problem of Quality Baking Company.

$$f_{max} = 0.2x_1 + 0.3x_2$$

subject to

$$x_1 + 2x_2 \leqslant 100,$$
$$x_1 + x_2 \leqslant 80,$$
$$x_i \geqslant 0 \ (i = 1, 2).$$

Suppose management would like to know the productivity of the available labor and oven capacity for producing the optimal product mix $x_1 = 60$ and $x_2 = 20$ dozen cookies found earlier. Let u_1 be the productivity value per unit of labor ($\frac{1}{10}$ of an hour) and u_2 the productivity value per unit of oven capacity (capacity for one dozen cookies). Then for producing one dozen x_1 cookies the one unit of labor time required times its unit value u_1 plus the one unit of oven capacity required times its unit value u_2 should be worth at least the profit of \$0.20 to be realized from the sale of the produced x_1 cookies, i.e.,

$$u_1 + u_2 \geqslant 0.20.$$

Similarily, for producing one dozen x_2 cookies the two units of labor times its unit value u_1 plus the one unit of oven capacity times its unit value u_2 should be worth at least the profit \$0.30 for one dozen of sold x_2 cookies, i.e.,

$$2u_1 + u_2 \geqslant 0.30.$$

Now the productivity value of labor and oven capacity can be thought of as costs which management would like to make as small as possible so that the 100 unit of labor times its unit cost u_1 plus the 80 units of oven capacity times its unit cost u_2 should be minimum. Hence,

$$f_{min} = 100u_1 + 80u_2.$$

The above dual problem and its primal are conveniently summarized below.

Primal	*Dual*
$f_{max} = 0.2x_1 + 0.3x_2,$	$f_{min} = 100u_1 + 80u_2$
subject to $x_1 + 2x_2 \leqslant 100$	subject to $u_1 + u_2 \geqslant 0.20$
$x_1 + x_2 \leqslant 80$	$2u_1 + u_2 \geqslant 0.30$
$x_i \geqslant 0 \ (i = 1, 2)$	$u_i \geqslant 0 \ (i = 1, 2)$

The reader may sketch the graph and solve the dual problem to find that $u_1 = \$0.10$, $u_2 = \$0.10$, and $f_{min} = \$18$. Thus, the productivity value of labor is \$1.00 per hour and of oven capacity \$0.10 per dozen of cookies. Economists call such values *shadow* prices. They are inferred prices having no relation to actual market prices. Also, observe that the minimum cost of the dual equals the maximum profit of the primal, i.e., $f_{min} = f_{max}$, where the term profit assumes a special meaning.

The structural similarities and differences between primal and dual problems can be more easily seen if both are expressed in matrix form.

Let A be the matrix of coefficients, B the matrix of constants, X the matrix of unknowns of the restraints, and C the matrix of coefficients of the objective function of a maximizing primal problem. Then the primal and its dual can be expressed as follows:

Primal	Dual
$f_{\max} = CX$	$f_{\min} = B^T U$
subject to $AX \leqslant B$	subject to $A^T U \geqslant C^T$
$X \geqslant 0$	$U \geqslant 0$,

where A^T, B^T, and C^T of the dual are the transpose matrices of A, B, and C of the primal, respectively.

Example 2.10. In matrix form the Quality Baking Company primal and its dual given in Example 2.9 can be written as follows:

Primal

$$f_{\max} = (0.20 \ , 0.30) \begin{pmatrix} x_1 \\ x_2 \end{pmatrix},$$

subject to

$$\begin{pmatrix} 1 & 2 \\ 1 & 1 \end{pmatrix} \begin{pmatrix} x_1 \\ x_2 \end{pmatrix} \leqslant \begin{pmatrix} 100 \\ 80 \end{pmatrix}$$
$$\begin{pmatrix} x_1 \\ x_2 \end{pmatrix} \geqslant 0,$$

Dual

$$f_{\min} = (100 \ , 80) \begin{pmatrix} u_1 \\ u_2 \end{pmatrix}$$

subject to

$$\begin{pmatrix} 1 & 1 \\ 2 & 1 \end{pmatrix} \begin{pmatrix} u_1 \\ u_2 \end{pmatrix} \geqslant \begin{pmatrix} 0.20 \\ 0.30 \end{pmatrix}$$
$$\begin{pmatrix} u_1 \\ u_2 \end{pmatrix} \geqslant 0,$$

where

$$A = \begin{pmatrix} 1 & 2 \\ 1 & 1 \end{pmatrix} \qquad A^T = \begin{pmatrix} 1 & 1 \\ 2 & 1 \end{pmatrix}$$

$$B = \begin{pmatrix} 100 \\ 80 \end{pmatrix} \qquad B^T = (100 \ , 80)$$

$$C = (0.20 \ , 0.30) \qquad C^T = \begin{pmatrix} 0.20 \\ 0.30 \end{pmatrix}$$

$$X = \begin{pmatrix} x_1 \\ x_2 \end{pmatrix} \qquad U = \begin{pmatrix} u_1 \\ u_2 \end{pmatrix}.$$

We can further illustrate the empirical importance of the dual with a minimizing problem.

Example 2.11. Suppose the management of AAA Department Stores Inc., in Example 1.7 of the previous chapter wishes to assign value to each reader who notices the advertisement. Assigning such a value may help management in determining the retail prices of the advertised Christmas gifts. Furthermore, since each reader who notices the advertisement is a prospective buyer, management would like to make such a value as large as possible. Let u_1 be the value assigned to each subscribing reader and let u_2 be the value assigned to each nonsubscribing reader who notices the newspaper advertisement. Then the original minimizing problem and its dual are as follows:

Primal	*Dual*

$f_{min} = 60x_1 + 50x_2,$ $f_{max} = 50,000u_1 + 90,000u_2$

subject to   subject to

$$2000x_1 + 1000x_2 \geqslant 50,000 \qquad\qquad 2000u_1 + 3000u_2 \leqslant 60$$
$$3000x_1 + 4000x_2 \geqslant 90,000 \qquad\qquad 1000u_1 + 4000u_2 \leqslant 50$$
$$x_i \geqslant 0 \ (i = 1, 2) \qquad\qquad\qquad u_1 \geqslant 0 \quad (i = 1, 2)$$

It is left for the reader to sketch the graph of the dual problem and solve it to verify that $u_1 = \$0.018$, $u_2 = \$0.008$, and $f_{max} = \$1620$.

In addition to being a useful analytical tool the dual of a primal linear programming problem offers certain practical advantages. Sometimes solving the dual instead of the primal problem may save time and expense by substantially reducing the prodigious amount of computational work which is required for solving large linear programming problems. Furthermore, the solution of the dual may be used to check the solution to the primal problem.

2.5. The Inverse of a Square Matrix.

Let A be a square matrix of the order $n \times n$. Then if there exists another square matrix A^{-1} of the same order such that $A^{-1} \cdot A = I$ matrix A^{-1} is called the inverse of A. It should be noted that the inverse A^{-1} means neither $\dfrac{1}{A}$ nor $\dfrac{I}{A}$.

If A is a square matrix having an inverse A^{-1}, then such an inverse matrix is unique and satisfies the relation

(2.1)
$$\boxed{A^{-1} \cdot A = AA^{-1} = I.}$$

Example 2.12. Consider the coefficient matrix

$$A = \begin{pmatrix} 1 & 2 \\ 1 & 1 \end{pmatrix}$$

of the original Quality Baking Company problem and let its inverse

$$A^{-1} = \begin{pmatrix} -1 & 2 \\ 1 & -1 \end{pmatrix}$$

be given. Verify relation (2.1).
Solution:

$$A^{-1} \cdot A = \begin{pmatrix} -1 & 2 \\ 1 & -1 \end{pmatrix} \cdot \begin{pmatrix} 1 & 2 \\ 1 & 1 \end{pmatrix} = \begin{pmatrix} 1 & 0 \\ 0 & 1 \end{pmatrix} = I;$$

and

$$AA^{-1} = \begin{pmatrix} 1 & 2 \\ 1 & 1 \end{pmatrix} \cdot \begin{pmatrix} -1 & 2 \\ 1 & -1 \end{pmatrix} = \begin{pmatrix} 1 & 0 \\ 0 & 1 \end{pmatrix} = I.$$

From relation (2.1) it can be easily seen that for a square matrix A there is one and only one inverse, if it exists.

Theorem 2.1. Let A be an $n \times n$ square matrix having a *left inverse* B such that $BA = I$ and a *right inverse* C such that $AC = I$. Then we wish to prove that $B = C$.

Proof: Since $BA = I$ and $AC = I$, we have

$$BA = AC$$
$$BAC = ACC \quad \text{multiplying by } C$$
$$B(AC) = (AC)C \quad\quad\quad \text{[by 6a]}$$
$$BI = IC \quad \text{by hypothesis}$$
$$B = C \quad\quad\quad\quad \text{[by 8a]}$$

If a square matrix such as A has an inverse, it is said to be *invertible* or *nonsingular*; if A has no inverse it is said to be *singular*. Not all matrices are invertible as the following theorem proves.

Theorem 2.2. Let two nonzero square matrices A and B of the same order be given such that $AB = 0$, the zero matrix. Then neither matrix A nor matrix B are invertible.

Proof: Suppose A^{-1} exists. Then

$$AB = 0 \quad \text{by hypothesis}$$
$$A^{-1}AB = A^{-1}0 \quad \text{multiplying by } A^{-1}$$
$$IB = 0 \quad\quad\quad \text{[by 2.1 and 10a]}$$
$$B = 0 \quad\quad\quad \text{[by 8a]}.$$

But this is contrary to the hypothesis that $B \neq 0$. Hence, A cannot have an inverse.

It is left for the reader to prove that matrix B is also not invertible.

Example 2.13. Let the nonzero matrices

$$A = \begin{pmatrix} -1 & 1 \\ 2 & -2 \end{pmatrix} \text{ and } B = \begin{pmatrix} 2 & 2 \\ 2 & 2 \end{pmatrix}$$

be given. Show that $AB = 0$.

Solution:

$$AB = \begin{pmatrix} -1 & 1 \\ 2 & -2 \end{pmatrix}\begin{pmatrix} 2 & 2 \\ 2 & 2 \end{pmatrix} = \begin{pmatrix} 0 & 0 \\ 0 & 0 \end{pmatrix} = 0.$$

Also, it can be proved that if a matrix A is not invertible, then there are infinitely many nonzero matrices B such that $AB = 0$. It is important to realize that matrices A and B in the above example each represent the coefficients of a homogeneous system of equations with nontrivial solutions. Thus, the invertibility of a matrix is intimately related to solving systems of linear equations as we shall presently see.

2.6. The Inverse of a Matrix and Systems of Equations. The process of finding the inverse of a square matrix, called

inversion, may be carried out by the following method, called Gaussian. It is but one of the many algorithms for finding A^{-1}. Let A be an invertible or nonsingular matrix and I its corresponding identity matrix. Then A^{-1} is found by performing elementary row operations on

(2.2) $(A|I)$

called *tableau* in order to transform it into tableau

(2.3) $(I|A^{-1})$.

Example 2.14. Consider again the coefficient matrix of the original profit maximizing problem of Quality Baking Company.

$$A = \begin{pmatrix} 1 & 2 \\ 1 & 1 \end{pmatrix}.$$

By (2.2), we have the tableau

(2.4) $(A|I) = \begin{pmatrix} 1 & 2 & | & 1 & 0 \\ 1 & 1 & | & 0 & 1 \end{pmatrix}.$

Find A^{-1} by transforming (2.4) into tableau of the form (2.3).
Solution:
Subtracting the first from the second row in (2.4), we get

(2.4′) $\begin{pmatrix} 1 & 2 & | & 1 & 0 \\ 0 & -1 & | & -1 & 1 \end{pmatrix}.$

Multiplying the second row by -1, we have

(2.4″) $\begin{pmatrix} 1 & 2 & | & 1 & 0 \\ 0 & 1 & | & 1 & -1 \end{pmatrix}.$

Finally, subtracting 2 times the second from the first row, and replacing the first row with the results, we obtain

(2.4‴) $\begin{pmatrix} 1 & 0 & | & -1 & 2 \\ 0 & 1 & | & 1 & -1 \end{pmatrix} = (I|A^{-1}),$

where A^{-1} is the inverse of the given matrix A.

It is important to note that if A is a square matrix of coefficients of a system of linear equations, finding whether A is invertible is equivalent to finding whether the system has a unique solution; *for the system of equations with no solution or infinitely many solutions has a noninvertible matrix of coefficients.* For such a system it would be impossible to transform tableau $(A|I)$ into $(I|A^{-1})$. Cases with noninvertible matrix A will be found among the problems of this section. Also, the reader should not fail to realize the relation which exists between invertibility of matrix A and linearly independent vectors of a homogeneous system of equations.

The net of the matter is that if A^{-1} exists, then the system of equations has a unique solution which can be found from such an inverse. Let the system of equations

(2.5) $AX = B$

be given, where A is an $n \times n$ coefficient matrix, X an $n \times 1$ matrix of unknowns, and B an $n \times 1$ matrix of constants. If A^{-1} exists, then we have

$$A^{-1} \cdot A X = A^{-1} \cdot B \qquad \text{on multiplying (2.5) by } A^{-1}$$
$$(A^{-1} \cdot A)X = A^{-1} \cdot B \qquad \text{[by 6a]}$$
$$IX = A^{-1} \cdot B, \text{ and} \qquad \text{[by 9a]}$$
(2.6) $$X = A^{-1} \cdot B \qquad \text{[by 8a]}.$$

The last expression indicates that we can find the unique solution of (2.5) by multiplying A^{-1} times B.

Example 2.15. Let the inverse

$$A^{-1} = \begin{pmatrix} -1 & 2 \\ 1 & -1 \end{pmatrix}$$

of the coefficient matrix A of the Quality Baking Company problem be given, where the matrix of constants

$$B = \begin{pmatrix} 100 \\ 80 \end{pmatrix}.$$

Find solution matrix X.
   Solution:
   Substituting in (2.6) for B and A^{-1}, we get

$$X = \begin{pmatrix} x_1 \\ x_2 \end{pmatrix} = \begin{pmatrix} -1 & 2 \\ 1 & -1 \end{pmatrix} \cdot \begin{pmatrix} 100 \\ 80 \end{pmatrix} = \begin{pmatrix} 60 \\ 20 \end{pmatrix},$$

which is the unique solution to that problem.

Furthermore, knowing the inverse of A, we can solve *any* set of linear equations having A as the matrix of coefficients but different matrix of constants B.

Example 2.16. Let the following four systems of equations be given

$$B$$

	(a)	(b)	(c)	(d)
$x_1 + 2x_2 =$	$\begin{pmatrix} 50 \\ 10 \end{pmatrix}$;	$\begin{pmatrix} 20 \\ 70 \end{pmatrix}$;	$\begin{pmatrix} 30 \\ 90 \end{pmatrix}$;	$\begin{pmatrix} 80 \\ 60 \end{pmatrix}$.
$x_1 + x_2 =$				

All four systems have as a coefficient matrix the matrix A of the Quality Baking Company problem with values of B matrix designated (a) through (d).
Find the solution to each system.

Solution:
Multiplying the inverse of A

$$A^{-1} = \begin{pmatrix} -1 & 2 \\ 1 & -1 \end{pmatrix}$$

found previously times each value of B, we get the following solutions to the four systems

$$\begin{array}{cccc} (a) & (b) & (c) & (d) \\ x_1 = \begin{pmatrix} -30 \\ 40 \end{pmatrix}; & \begin{pmatrix} 120 \\ -50 \end{pmatrix}; & \begin{pmatrix} 150 \\ -60 \end{pmatrix}; & \begin{pmatrix} 40 \\ 20 \end{pmatrix}. \end{array}$$

The reader may verify the above results by checking.

Inversion of a square matrix may be accomplished in several ways. One such important method is with determinants. Since, however, our purpose is to illustrate the connection between the inverse of a matrix and the solution of a system of equations rather than to discuss different methods of inversion, the subject of determinants lies outside the scope of this book. We shall confine ourselves to showing the relation between the above procedure of solving a system of equations and a linear programming problem.

2.7. Matrix Algebra and Linear Programming.
In the previous section we have seen how the iterative process of solving a linear programming problem is carried out with vector analysis. Let us see now how the same process, which basically is the process of the simplex method itself, is carried out with elementary row operations on matrices.

From the viewpoint of operations on matrices the diagonalization method demonstrated in Section 2 of the previous chapter consists of performing elementary row operations on the matrix A of coefficients and the matrix B of constants of a system of equations. We can combine the procedure of this method with the procedure of inverting a matrix into one operation by performing elementary operations on tableau

$$(2.7) \qquad (A|I|B)$$

in order to transform it into a tableau

$$(2.8) \qquad (I|A^{-1}|X).$$

Example 2.17. Let us consider tableau (2.4) in Example 2.14 and include matrix B of constants of the original Quality Baking Company problem. Now by tableau (2.7) we have

$$(2.9) \qquad (A|I|B) = \begin{pmatrix} 1 & 2 & 1 & 0 & 100 \\ 1 & 1 & 0 & 1 & 80 \end{pmatrix}.$$

Transform (2.9) into tableau of the form (2.8).

Solution:
Repeating the elementary row operations shown in Example 2.14 on (2.9), we get

$$(2.9')\qquad = \begin{pmatrix} 1 & 2 & 1 & 0 & 100 \\ 0 & -1 & -1 & 1 & -20 \end{pmatrix}$$

$$(2.9'')\qquad = \begin{pmatrix} 1 & 2 & 1 & 0 & 100 \\ 0 & 1 & 1 & -1 & 20 \end{pmatrix}$$

$$(2.9''')\qquad = \begin{pmatrix} 1 & 0 & -1 & 2 & 60 \\ 0 & 1 & 1 & -1 & 20 \end{pmatrix}$$

$$= (I\,|\,A^{-1}\,|\,X).$$

The above procedure is identical to the one followed in the diagonalization method for solving a system of equations. There is only one difference. The required elementary row operations are performed on the identity matrix I as well as the matrix A of detached coefficients. For this reason tableaus (2.7) and (2.8) are sometimes called *tableaus of detached coefficients.*

Example 2.18. Consider the following system of linear equations:

$$\begin{aligned} x_1 + 4x_2 + 2x_3 &= 80, \\ 2x_1 + x_2 + 2x_3 &= 95, \\ 2x_1 + 3x_2 + x_3 &= 90. \end{aligned}$$

It corresponds to the restraining inequalities of the modified Quality Baking Company problem in Example 2.7 of the previous chapter.

Solve this system by transforming tableau of the form (2.7) into tableau of the form (2.8).
Solution:
By (2.7), we have

$$(2.10)\qquad (A\,|\,I\,|\,B) = \begin{pmatrix} 1 & 4 & 2 & 1 & 0 & 0 & 80 \\ 2 & 1 & 2 & 0 & 1 & 0 & 95 \\ 2 & 3 & 1 & 0 & 0 & 1 & 90 \end{pmatrix}.$$

The repeated elementary row operations below are indicated on the right-hand side of each tableau. For instance, $R_2 - 2P_1$ in (2.10') means that the second row is obtained by subtracting from the second row in (2.10) two times the first row. The first row denoted by P_1 is called the *pivotal* row since it remains unchanged and is used to transform the other rows.

$$(2.10')\qquad = \begin{pmatrix} 1 & 4 & 2 & 1 & 0 & 0 & 80 \\ 0 & -7 & -2 & -2 & 1 & 0 & -65 \\ 0 & -5 & -3 & -2 & 0 & 1 & -70 \end{pmatrix}\begin{matrix} P_1 \\ R_2 - 2P_1 \\ R_3 - 2P_1 \end{matrix}$$

$$(2.10'')\qquad = \begin{pmatrix} 1 & 4 & 2 & 1 & 0 & 0 & 80 \\ 0 & 1 & \frac{2}{7} & \frac{2}{7} & -\frac{1}{7} & 0 & \frac{65}{7} \\ 0 & -5 & -3 & -2 & 0 & 1 & -70 \end{pmatrix}(-\tfrac{1}{7})R_2 = P_2$$

$$(2.10''') \quad = \begin{pmatrix} 1 & 0 & \frac{6}{7} & -\frac{1}{7} & \frac{4}{7} & 0 & \frac{300}{7} \\ 0 & 1 & \frac{2}{7} & \frac{2}{7} & -\frac{1}{7} & 0 & \frac{65}{7} \\ 0 & 0 & -\frac{11}{7} & -\frac{4}{7} & -\frac{5}{7} & 1 & -\frac{165}{7} \end{pmatrix} \begin{matrix} R_1 - 4P_2 \\ P_2 \\ R_3 + 5P_2 \end{matrix}$$

$$(2.10^{iv}) \quad = \begin{pmatrix} 1 & 0 & \frac{6}{7} & -\frac{1}{7} & \frac{4}{7} & 0 & \frac{300}{7} \\ 0 & 1 & \frac{2}{7} & \frac{2}{7} & -\frac{1}{7} & 0 & \frac{65}{7} \\ 0 & 0 & 1 & \frac{4}{11} & \frac{5}{11} & -\frac{7}{11} & 15 \end{pmatrix} (-\frac{7}{11})R_3 = P_3$$

$$(2.10^{v}) \quad = \begin{pmatrix} 1 & 0 & 0 & -\frac{5}{11} & \frac{2}{11} & \frac{6}{11} & 30 \\ 0 & 1 & 0 & \frac{2}{11} & -\frac{3}{11} & \frac{2}{11} & 5 \\ 0 & 0 & 1 & \frac{4}{11} & \frac{5}{11} & -\frac{7}{11} & 15 \end{pmatrix} \begin{matrix} R_1 - \frac{6}{7}P_3 \\ R_2 - \frac{2}{7}P_3 \\ P_3 \end{matrix}$$

$$= (I|A^{-1}|X).$$

The reader may verify that $AA^{-1} = I$.

In our next section we shall see that the vector analysis of the previous section and the matrix analysis in this section describe the iterative procedure involved in the most important computational technique for solving linear programming problems, namely, the simplex method.

PROBLEMS

2.1. Indicate the order of the following matrices:

$$*A = (2); \quad *B = (1, 0, -2); \qquad C = \begin{pmatrix} -3 \\ 4 \\ 1 \end{pmatrix};$$

$$I = \begin{pmatrix} 1 & 0 & 0 \\ 0 & 1 & 0 \\ 0 & 0 & 1 \end{pmatrix}; \qquad D = \begin{pmatrix} -1 & 2 & 0 \\ 3 & -4 & 5 \end{pmatrix}.$$

2.2. Find the transpose of each matrix in $*A$, $*B$, C, I, and D of Problem 2.1.

2.3. Find an example of a pair of equal matrices of order
   a) 2×3.
   b) 3×4.
   *c) $m \times n$.

2.4. Given the following matrices, compute the indicated sum, if possible; otherwise, explain why matrix addition is not possible.

$$E = \begin{pmatrix} 4 & 1 & 7 \\ -2 & 0 & -8 \\ 3 & 5 & 2 \end{pmatrix}; \quad F = \begin{pmatrix} 1 & 4 \\ 3 & -6 \\ -2 & 7 \end{pmatrix}; \quad G = \begin{pmatrix} 5 & -1 & -2 \\ 6 & 4 & -4 \\ -7 & 10 & -3 \end{pmatrix};$$

$$H = \begin{pmatrix} 0 & 1 & 4 \\ -2 & -6 & -3 \end{pmatrix}; \quad J = \begin{pmatrix} 0 & 0 & 0 \\ 1 & 2 & 3 \\ 2 & 3 & 1 \\ 3 & 1 & 2 \end{pmatrix}; \quad K = \begin{pmatrix} 1 & -1 & 3 & -1 \\ 2 & -2 & 2 & -2 \\ 3 & -3 & 1 & 3 \end{pmatrix}.$$

   *a) $E + F$.
   *b) $G + E$.
   c) $H + K$.
   d) $J + K$.

2.5. Given the matrices I and D in Problem 2.1 and E, G, and H in Problem 2.4, perform the following operations:
a) $2D - 3H$.
b) $2E + kI$.
c) $E - 2G$.

2.6. Verify the product matrix AB in Example 2.8.

2.7. Given the matrices in Problem 2.1, compute the following, if possible; otherwise, explain why matrix multiplication is not possible.
a) BC.
b) IC.
c) CI.
d) DI.
e) ID.

2.8. The matrices given in Problem 2.4 are of order 3×3, 3×2, 3×3, 2×3, 4×3, and 3×4, respectively. Find the order of:
a) EF. d) GFH.
b) EG. e) $HGEK$.
c) JK. f) $KJGFH$.

2.9. Express the following linear programming problems in matrix form shown in Example 2.10.
a) The AAA Department Stores, Inc., in Example 2.11.
b) The BB Iron Works Company in Example 2.3 of the previous chapter.
c) The Quality Baking Company in Example 2.7 of the previous chapter.

2.10. Let the following matrices be given:

$$A = \begin{pmatrix} 1 & -2 & 4 \\ 3 & 1 & -1 \end{pmatrix}; B = \begin{pmatrix} -1 & 4 & -3 \\ -3 & -2 & 5 \end{pmatrix}; C = \begin{pmatrix} 1 & -2 & 3 \\ -3 & 2 & -1 \end{pmatrix};$$

and 0, a 2×3 zero matrix. Verify the following laws of matrix addition.
a) $A + B = B + A$.
b) $A + (B + C) = (A + B) + C$.
c) $A + 0 = A$.
d) $A + (-A) = 0$.

2.11. Let the following matrices be given:

$$A = \begin{pmatrix} 1 & -2 & 4 \\ 3 & 1 & -1 \\ 2 & -3 & 2 \end{pmatrix}; B = \begin{pmatrix} -1 & 4 & -3 \\ -3 & -2 & 5 \\ -2 & 5 & -6 \end{pmatrix}; C = \begin{pmatrix} 1 & -2 & 3 \\ -3 & 2 & -1 \\ 2 & -1 & 3 \end{pmatrix};$$

0, a 3×3 zero matrix; and I, a 3×3 identity matrix. Verify the following laws of matrix multiplication.
a) $A(B + C) = AB + AC$.
b) $ABC = A(BC) = (AB)C$.
c) $AB \neq BA$.
d) $AI = IA = A$.
e) $A0 = 0$.

2.12. Sketch the graph and solve each dual problem below by the diagonalization method shown in Example 2.18.
a) The dual problem in Example 2.9.
b) The dual problem in Example 2.11.

2.13. For each linear programming problem from the preceding chapter find the dual, interpret it, and solve it by the diagonalization method.
*a) Problem 1.13.
b) Problem 1.14.
*c) Problem 1.15.
d) Problem 2.15.
e) Problem 2.16.

2.14. In Example 2.18 verify that $AA^{-1} = I$.

2.15. Supply a verbal proof of Theorem 2.1.

2.16. Consider Theorem 2.2 and prove that matrix B is also not invertible.

2.17. Let the following matrix be given:

$$A = \begin{pmatrix} -1 & 1 & -1 \\ 2 & -2 & 2 \\ -3 & 3 & -3 \end{pmatrix}.$$

a) Find one nonzero matrix B such that $AB = 0$.
b) Show that A and B matrices each represent a set of linearly dependent row vectors.
c) Show that matrices A and B each represent the coefficients of a homogeneous system of linear equations with nontrivial solutions.

2.18. For each system of equations from Section 2, Chapter 8, indicated below:
i) Using the diagonalization method shown in Example 2.18 find the inverse of the coefficient matrix and the solution of each system if possible.
ii) If A^{-1} exists, verify the fact that $A^{-1}A = I$.
iii) Assume a different set of constants for matrix B and show that $X = A^{-1}B$ is the solution matrix for the new system of equations having the same coefficient matrix.
*a) Problem 2.3(a).
b) Problem 2.3(b).
c) Problem 2.3(c).
d) Problem 2.3(d).
e) Problem 2.4(a).
f) Problem 2.4(b).
*g) Problem 2.4(c).

2.19. Express each of the following linear programming problems from the preceding chapter in matrix form shown in Example 2.10 and solve it by the diagonalization method shown in Example 2.18. Show that $A^{-1}A = I$.
*a) Problem 1.13.
b) Problem 1.14.

368 APPLIED MATHEMATICS: AN INTRODUCTION [Ch. 9]

*c) Problem 1.15.
d) Problem 2.15.
e) Problem 2.16.

2.20. Find the components of the following product matrices in Problem 2.4.
*a) Third row and second column of EF.
*b) Third row and first column of EG.
c) First row and last column of JK.
d) Last row and last column of GFH.

2.21. Consider Problem 1.19 of the previous section and express the number of shares sold and bought in two 3×3 matrices. Find the profit or loss matrix by proper matrix multiplication and subtraction.

2.22. The following list represents the price of selective items of two supermarkets:

	Store A	Store B
Dozen eggs	$0.60	$0.62
Quart of milk	0.25	0.24
Pound of butter	0.85	0.82
Dozen oranges	0.45	0.48
Pound of hamburger	0.75	0.69

A housewife plans to buy 2 dozen eggs, 5 quarts of milk, 3 dozen oranges, 3 pounds of hamburger, and 1 pound of butter.
*a) Which store is less expensive?
*b) Suppose the housewife considers it worthwhile to buy the least expensive items from each store. How much should she pay for purchasing the above items?
Form a 5×3 matrix of prices and find your answers to (a) and (b) with proper matrix multiplication.

2.23. We have mentioned that one important method of inverting a matrix is with determinants. Consider a system of two linear equations in two unknowns.

$$a_{11}x_1 + a_{12}x_2 = c_1,$$
$$a_{21}x_1 + a_{22}x_2 = c_2.$$

The determinant of the coefficient matrix A, denoted by $|A|$, is

$$|A| = \begin{vmatrix} a_{11} & a_{12} \\ a_{21} & a_{22} \end{vmatrix} = a_{11}a_{22} - a_{21}a_{12}.$$

It can be proved that the inverse of the coefficient matrix

$$A^{-1} = \frac{1}{a_{11}a_{22} - a_{21}a_{12}} \begin{pmatrix} a_{22} & -a_{12} \\ -a_{21} & a_{11} \end{pmatrix}$$

if and only if $|A| \neq 0$.
Consider Example 2.14, where $A = \begin{pmatrix} 1 & 2 \\ 1 & 1 \end{pmatrix}$. Then substituting, we have

$$A^{-1} = \frac{1}{(1)(1) - (1)2} \begin{pmatrix} 1 & -2 \\ -1 & 1 \end{pmatrix} = (-1)\begin{pmatrix} 1 & -2 \\ -1 & 1 \end{pmatrix} = \begin{pmatrix} -1 & 2 \\ 1 & -1 \end{pmatrix}$$

as found earlier.

For cases below:
i) Find the inverse of the coefficient matrix using the above method; otherwise, explain why the inverse does not exist.
ii) If an inverse exists, find the solution to the system of equations using the matrix for $X = A^{-1}B$.
*a) Problem 1.13 of the previous chapter.
b) Example 2.4 of the previous chapter.

SUGGESTED REFERENCES

1. BIERMAN, HAROLD, et al. *Quantitative Analysis for Business Decisions*, pp. 218–41. Homewood, Ill., Richard D. Irwin, Inc., 1961. (1, 2)

2. BOULDING, K. E., AND SPIVEY, W. A. *Linear Programming and the Theory of the Firm*, pp. 1–17, 36–89. New York: The Macmillan Co., 1960. (1, 2)

3. DORFMAN, ROBERT, et al. *Linear Programming and Economic Analysis*, pp. 1–80. New York: McGraw-Hill Book Co., Inc., 1958. (2)

4. HADLEY, G. *Linear Algebra*. Reading, Mass., Addison-Wesley Publishing Co., Inc., 1961. (1, 2)

5. KEMENY, JOHN G., et al. *Finite Mathematical Structures*, pp. 240–45, 359–72. Englewood Cliffs, N.J., Prentice-Hall, Inc., 1959. (2)

6. ———. *Finite Mathematics with Business Applications*, pp. 229–68. Englewood Cliffs, N.J.: Prentice-Hall, Inc., 1962. (1, 2)

7. MATHEMATICAL ASSOCIATION OF AMERICA, COMMITTEE ON THE UNDER-GRADUATE PROGRAM. *Modern Mathematical Methods and Models: Volume I Multicomponent Methods*, pp. 35–65. 1959. (1, 2)

8. SCHWARTZ, JACOB T. *Introduction to Matrices and Vectors*. New York, McGraw-Hill Book Co., Inc., 1961.

Chapter 10

COMPUTATIONAL METHODS OF LINEAR PROGRAMMING

WE HAVE already mentioned that there is no algebraic formula for calculating the solution of a linear programming problem. All available methods are iterative. In the first section of this chapter we shall deal with the general computational method of linear programming, namely, the simplex method. The special transportation method will be demonstrated in the second and last section of Part III.

*1. THE SIMPLEX METHOD

We shall demonstrate the general simplex method with a maximizing problem, a minimizing problem, and a degeneracy problem. Although the simplex algorithm can be used to solve real-size linear programming problems, we shall use the simple examples of the previous sections in order to maintain continuity and avoid the prodigious amount of computation which otherwise may be required.

The simplex algorithm or method, developed by George B. Dantzig in 1947, is an iterative computational procedure for solving linear programming problems. The important theoretical aspects of the method have already been discussed with vector and matrix algebra. Computations are carried out in the solution space starting with the initial zero feasible solution and moving from one basic solution to another in a finite number of iterations. In matrix form the computational procedure of the simplex method is in fact equivalent to transforming the initial tableau of detached coefficients $(A|I|B)$ into tableau $(I|A^{-1}|X)$ as illustrated in Examples 2.17 and 2.18 of the preceding chapter.

On the other hand, the computational procedure of the simplex method has certain important features which are not found in vector and matrix analysis. In the first place, alternatives to the initial zero solution are evaluated and the most favorable is selected. Thus, successive iterations are improved solutions leading to the desired result.

Second, the simplex algorithm supplies the tests for determining whether it is necessary to go on, whether there is no solution to the problem, or whether an optimal feasible solution has been found. Finally, the method works almost always, even in the case of degeneracy.

In solving a linear programming problem by the simplex method we must prepare an initial solution by expressing the problem in the form of a tableau of detached coefficients $(A|I|B)$. This requires two conditions. First, the original set of restraints must be converted to a set of linear equations by the addition of slack variables. Second, an initial solution must be introduced by the addition of artificial variables.

1.1. A Maximizing Problem.

We shall use an illustrative case in order to point out the above important features of the simplex method and, at the same time, show the computational steps of the method.

Example 1.1. Consider the original Quality Baking Company maximizing problem

$$(1.1) \qquad f_{\max} = 0.2x_1 + 0.3x_2,$$

subject to

$$(1.2) \qquad \begin{aligned} x_1 + 2x_2 &\leqslant 100, \\ x_1 + x_2 &\leqslant 80. \end{aligned}$$

The first condition in preparing an initial solution to this problem requires the addition of a positive slack variable to each inequality in (1.2) as follows:

$$\begin{aligned} x_1 + 2x_2 + x_3 &= 100, \\ x_1 + x_2 + x_4 &= 80. \end{aligned}$$

In the above system, x_3 and x_4 are the required slack variables: In this case, however, x_3 and x_4 also fulfill the second condition for preparing an initial solution. In other words, in this problem x_3 and x_4 perform two functions. On the one hand, they act as *slack* variables in order to convert the set of inequalities into a set of equations, and, on the other hand, as *artificial* variables in order to introduce an initial solution. Such a solution is easily obtained by setting x_3 and x_4 equal to 100 and 80, respectively. In any optimal solution, however, the value of x_3 and x_4 must be zero. This is assured by assigning to these variables zero coefficients in the objective function. Thus, the terms (1.1) and (1.2) of the problem are converted to

$$(1.3) \qquad f_{\max} = 0.2x_1 + 0.3x_2 + 0x_3 + 0x_4,$$

subject to

$$(1.4) \qquad \begin{aligned} x_1 + 2x_2 + x_3 + 0x_4 &= 100, \\ x_1 + x_2 + 0x_3 + x_4 &= 80. \end{aligned}$$

From (1.4) we can obtain the tableau of detached coefficients

(1.5) $$(A|I|B) = \begin{pmatrix} 1 & 2 & 1 & 0 & 100 \\ 1 & 1 & 0 & 1 & 80 \end{pmatrix}.$$

We are now ready to set up the first simplex tableau for our problem.
Initial Solution.
Such a tableau containing an initial solution is shown in Table 1.1.

TABLE 1.1.

$P_r(Profit)$	c_j Solution Vectors	0.20 P_1	0.30 P_2	0 P_3	0 P_4	P_0
0 ←	P_3	1	2	1	0	100
0 →	P_4	1	1	0	1	80
	z_j	0	0	0	0	0
	$c_j - z_j$	0.20	0.30 ↑	0	0	

The first row of the table designated c_j contains the coefficients of the
function (1.3) of our problem. The first column in the body of the table
designated P_r contains the coefficients of the initial zero solution. The
second column indicates the vectors of the initial zero solution, and the
remaining columns in the body of the table contain tableau (1.5).

Note that the initial zero solution, the profit column P_r times column
P_0, is shown in z_j row under column P_0. It corresponds to the initial
solution

$$f'_{max} = 0.2(0) + 0.3(0) + 0(100) + 0(80) = 0 \text{ dollars}$$

found earlier with vector analysis (cf. Example 1.22, Chapter 9). In fact,
all the remaining z_j's values are obtained by multiplying column P_r times
the corresponding column P_1 through P_4 and adding the products for each
column.

The last row of this table is obtained by subtracting the z_j value from
the corresponding c_j value for each column.

The last row in Table 1.1 designated $c_j - z_j$ contains the so-called
indicators of a solution. In general, if for some column the indicator is
positive and some component in that column is positive, additional
iterations are needed. If *all* the indicators are zero or negative, an optimal solution has been found. With the above general points in mind, let
us continue our maximizing problem.

Example 1.1—*Continued.* Since the indicators under P_1 and P_2
columns in Table 1.1 are positive, additional iterations are necessary. In
other words, replacing either P_3 or P_4 row by P_1 or P_2 column will lead
us to another basic solution which will yield profits larger than zero.

First Iteration:

Finding this improved solution requires the following:

Step 1: Determine the replacing or *pivotal* column.

Since we want to maximize profits, column P_2 with the largest positive indicator $(c_j - z_j = \$0.30)$ should be the pivotal column (see arrow in Table 1.1).

Step 2: Determine the row to be replaced.

Dividing each component of P_0 column by the corresponding component of the replacing P_2 column, we have for rows

$$P_3 : \frac{100}{2} = 50 \quad \text{and} \quad P_4 : \frac{80}{1} = 80.$$

Since 50 is the smallest positive amount, P_3 row should be replaced (see arrow in Table 1.1). Any negative quotients are ignored.

Step 3: Find new or *pivotal* P_2 row to replace P_3 row.

The pivotal P_2 row is obtained by dividing each component of P_3 row by the component of the intersection of P_2 column and P_3 row, i.e., by 2 called the *pivot* component, as follows:

$$P_2 \rightarrow P_3 = \frac{1}{2}, \frac{2}{2}, \frac{1}{2}, \frac{0}{2}, \frac{100}{2}.$$

This P_2 pivotal row—$(\frac{1}{2}, 1, \frac{1}{2}, 0, 50)$—is shown with an arrow in Table 1.2 and with profit $\$0.30$ under P_r column.

TABLE 1.2.

P_r	c_j Solution Vectors	0.20 P_1	0.30 P_2	0 P_3	0 P_4	P_0
0.30	→ P_2	$\frac{1}{2}$	1	$\frac{1}{2}$	0	50
0	← P_4	$\frac{1}{2}$	0	$-\frac{1}{2}$	1	30
	z_j	0.15	0.30	0.15	0	15
	$c_j - z_j$	0.05	0	−0.15	0	
		↑				

Step 4: Use P_2 pivotal row to find new P_4 row.

The new P_4 row is obtained by the following procedure:

$$\begin{pmatrix} Old\ P_4 \\ Row \end{pmatrix} - \left(\begin{bmatrix} Component\ of\ Old \\ P_2\ Column\ and\ P_4 \\ Row \end{bmatrix} \cdot \begin{pmatrix} New\ P_2 \\ Row \end{pmatrix} \right) = \begin{pmatrix} New\ P_4 \\ Row \end{pmatrix}$$

1	−	(1)	·	$(\frac{1}{2})$	=	$\frac{1}{2}$
1	−	(1)	·	(1)	=	0
0	−	(1)	·	$(\frac{1}{2})$	=	$-\frac{1}{2}$
1	−	(1)	·	(0)	=	1
80	−	(1)	·	(50)	=	30

It is shown in Table 1.2.

Step 5: Determine new z_j and $c_j - z_j$ rows.

Multiplying each component of column P_r in Table 1.2 by the corresponding component of columns P_1 through P_0 and summing the products for each column, we get the new z_j row:

$$z_1 = (.30)(\tfrac{1}{2}) + (0)(\tfrac{1}{2}) = 0.15,$$

$$z_2 = (0.30)(1) + (0)(0) = 0.30,$$

$$z_3 = (0.30)(\tfrac{1}{2}) + (0)(-\tfrac{1}{2}) = 0.15,$$

$$z_4 = (0.30)(0) + (0)(1) = 0,$$

$$z_0 = (0.30)(50) + (0)(30) = 15.$$

Subtracting the new z_j row from c_j in Table 1.2 we obtain the new row of indicators.

Observe that the new feasible solution $z_0 = 15$ above corresponds to

$$f''_{\max} = 0.2(0) + 0.3(50) + 0(0) + 0(30) = 15 \text{ dollars}$$

found in Example 1.22 of the previous chapter. Since in the above example we have described a complete cycle or iteration of the simplex algorithm, we shall summarize the steps of the procedure before continuing our maximizing problem. The simplex tableau of the initial solution in Table 1.1 can be generalized as a tableau of detached coefficients $(A|I|B)$ shown in Table 1.3 for a system of m equations in

TABLE 1.3.

P_r	Solution Vectors	c_1 P_1	c_2 P_2	$\cdots$	c_n P_n	0 P_{n+1}	$\cdots$	0 P_{n+m}	P_0
0	P_{n+1}	a_{11}	a_{12}	$\cdots$	a_{1n}	1	$\cdots$ 0		b_1
0	P_{n+2}	a_{21}	a_{22}	$\cdots$	a_{2n}	0	$\cdots$ 0		b_2
$\cdot$	$\cdot$	$\cdot$	$\cdot$		$\cdot$	$\cdot$			$\cdot$
$\cdot$	$\cdot$	$\cdot$	$\cdot$		$\cdot$	$\cdot$			$\cdot$
$\cdot$	$\cdot$	$\cdot$	$\cdot$		$\cdot$	$\cdot$			$\cdot$
0	P_{n+m}	a_{m1}	a_{m2}	$\cdots$	a_{mn}	0	$\cdots$ 1		b_m
z_j		0	0	$\cdots$	0	0	$\cdots$ 0		0
$c_j - z_j$		c_1	c_2	$\cdots$	c_n	0	$\cdots$ 0		

n unknowns. Let P_j ($j = 0, 1, 2, \ldots n + m$) be any column vector and P_i ($i = n + 1, n + 2, \ldots, n + m$) be any row vector of that tableau. Let P_k be the *pivotal column vector*, a_{ik} the *pivot component*, and P_w the *pivotal row vector*. The steps required for repeated iterations are conveniently summarized in a flow chart form as follows:

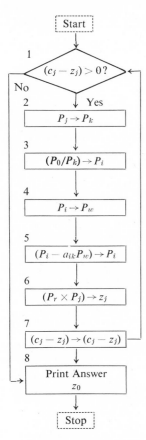

Set up the initial simplex tableau.

1. Are there one or more positive indicators?

2. Select P_j with the largest positive indicator. Call it pivotal column P_k.

3. Divide each component of P_0 by the corresponding component of P_k. The P_i with the smallest positive b_i/a_{ik} is to be replaced.

4. Divide old P_i to be replaced by pivot a_{ik} to find new P_i. Call new P_i the pivotal row P_w. Enter P_w and its c_j value in new tableau.

5. Find new P_i's, other than the replaced one, by subtracting from each component of old P_i's the corresponding product $a_{ik}P_w$. Enter new P_i's in new tableau.

6. Multiply P_r by each P_j in the new tableau to find new z_j's. Enter new z_j's in new tableau.

7. Find new indicators by subtracting from each c_j corresponding new z_j. Enter new indicators $c_j - z_j$ in new tableau.

8. Computation is ended. Optimal solution is the value of z_j under P_0.

The above flow chart has been designed to show the major steps involved in each iteration and not for computer programming. Let us now go back to our maximizing problem.

Example 1.1—*Continued.* Since the indicator P_1 in Table 1.2 is positive, additional iterations are necessary.

Second Iteration:

We shall follow the same steps as previously without explanations.

Step 1: Since z_1 is the only positive indicator, P_1 is the pivotal P_k (see arrow in Table 1.2).

Step 2: The row vector to be replaced is P_4, since for

$$P_2 : \frac{50}{\frac{1}{2}} = 100 \quad \text{and} \quad P_4 : \frac{30}{\frac{1}{2}} = 60.$$

Step 3: The pivotal P_w row vector is found to be

$$P_1 \to P_4 = \frac{1}{2} \Big/ \frac{1}{2}, \ 0 \Big/ \frac{1}{2}, \ -\frac{1}{2} \Big/ \frac{1}{2}, \ 1 \Big/ \frac{1}{2}, \ 30 \Big/ \frac{1}{2} = 1, \ 0, \ -1, \ 2, \ 60.$$

It is shown in new tableau of Table 1.4 with profit 0.20 entered under P_r column.

TABLE 1.4.

P_r	c_j Solution Vectors	0.20 P_1	0.30 P_2	0 P_3	0 P_4	 P_0
0.30	P_2	0	1	1	-1	20
0.20	$\rightarrow$ P_1	1	0	-1	2	60
	z_j	0.20	0.30	0.10	0.10	18
	$c_j - z_j$	0	0	-0.10	-0.10	

Step 4: Using P_1 pivotal row, we obtain a new P_2 as follows:

$$\begin{pmatrix} Old\ P_2 \\ Row \end{pmatrix} - \left[(a_{21} = \tfrac{1}{2}) \cdot \begin{pmatrix} P_w = New\ P_1 \\ Row \end{pmatrix} \right] = \begin{pmatrix} New\ P_2 \\ Row \end{pmatrix}$$

$\tfrac{1}{2}$	$-$	$(\tfrac{1}{2})$	$\cdot$	(1)	$=$ 0
1	$-$	$(\tfrac{1}{2})$	$\cdot$	(0)	$=$ 1
$\tfrac{1}{2}$	$-$	$(\tfrac{1}{2})$	$\cdot$	(-1)	$=$ 1
0	$-$	$(\tfrac{1}{2})$	$\cdot$	(2)	$=$ -1
50	$-$	$(\tfrac{1}{2})$	$\cdot$	(60)	$=$ 20

The new P_2 row is entered in Table 1.4.
Step 5: The new z_j values are

$$z_1 = (0.30)(0) + (0.20)(1) = 0.20,$$
$$z_2 = (0.30)(1) + (0.20)(0) = 0.30,$$
$$z_3 = (0.30)(1) + (0.20)(-1) = 0.10,$$
$$z_4 = (0.30)(-1) + (0.20)(2) = 0.10,$$
$$z_0 = (0.30)(20) + (0.20)(60) = 18.$$

These values, together with the new indicators obtained by subtracting the new z_j's from c_j's, are shown in Table 1.4.

Since all indicators are zero or negative, $z_0 = 18$ is an optimal feasible solution.

Observe that the solution of the above problem corresponds to the optimal solution

$$f'''_{max} = 0.2(60) + 0.3(20) + 0(0) + 0(0) = 18 \text{ dollars}$$

found in Example 1.22 of the preceding chapter. Also, the problem is solved in a four-dimensional space as already explained in vector analysis, and if P_1 and P_2 rows in Table 1.4 are interchanged, the content of this table represents tableau $(I|A^{-1}|X)$ found in Example 2.17 of the previous chapter.

1.2. A Minimizing Problem. In solving a maximizing problem by the simplex method we have seen how an initial solution is prepared when the restraints of the problem are less-than-equal-to inequalities. Solving a minimizing problem will give us the opportunity to show how an initial solution is prepared when the restraints of a problem are equations or greater-than-equal-to inequalities.

Example 1.2. In Example 2.3 of Chapter 8 the minimizing problem of BB Iron Works Company was expressed as follows:

(1.6) $$f_{min} = 3x_1 + 8x_2,$$

subject to

(1.7) $$4x_1 + 6x_2 = 120,$$
$$x_1 \leqslant 12,$$
$$x_2 \geqslant 16.$$

Converting (1.7) to a set of linear equations requires the addition of a positive slack variable to the second restraint and a negative slack variable to the third restraint. Thus, we obtain the set of equations

(1.8) $$4x_1 + 6x_2 = 120,$$
$$x_1 + x_4 = 12,$$
$$x_2 - x_6 = 16,$$

where x_4 and x_6 are the required slack variables for fulfilling the first condition in the preparation of an initial solution. Given (1.8), an initial solution is ordinarily generated by the addition of unit positive artificial variables. Thus, the artificial variables x_3 and x_5 are added to the first and third restraints of (1.8), respectively. With x_3 and x_5 and the slack variable x_4 previously added to the second restraint (1.8) the second condition for the preparation of an initial solution is met. From (1.8) we obtain

(1.9) $$4x_1 + 6x_2 + x_3 = 120,$$
$$x_1 + x_4 = 12,$$
$$x_2 + x_5 - x_6 = 16.$$

An initial solution is easily obtained from (1.9) by setting x_3, x_4, and x_5 equal to 120, 12, and 16, respectively. However, the artificial variables x_3 and x_5 must be driven out of any optimal solution. Thus, while the slacks x_4 and x_6 are given a zero coefficient in the objective function, the artificials x_3 and x_5 are driven out of an optimal solution by assigning to each one a positive large coefficient in the objective function.

On the basis of the above explanations the objective function (1.6) and the set of restraints (1.9) of our minimizing problem may be expressed in proper notation as follows:

(1.10) $$f_{min} = 3x_1 + 8x_2 + Mx_3 + 0x_4 + Mx_5 + 0x_6,$$

subject to

$$(1.11) \quad \begin{aligned} 4x_1 + 6x_2 + \ x_3 + 0x_4 + 0x_5 + 0x_6 &= 120, \\ x_1 + 0x_2 + 0x_3 + \ x_4 + 0x_5 + 0x_6 &= 12, \\ 0x_1 + \ x_2 + 0x_3 + 0x_4 + \ x_5 - \ x_6 &= 16, \end{aligned}$$

where an M coefficient representing a very large number is given to x_3 and x_5 in the objective function.

After the proper variables have been introduced, a minimizing problem is solved with the simplex algorithm used in solving a maximizing problem. The only basic difference is with the interpretation of the signs of the indicators. Now, if for some column the indicator is *negative* and some component in that column is positive, additional iterations are needed; and if all the indicators are zero or *positive*, an optimal solution has been found. With the above preliminary remarks in mind let us solve our minimizing problem.

Example 1.2—*Continued.* An initial solution to our minimizing problem can now be easily obtained from (1.10) and (1.11). The tableau of this solution is shown in Table 1.5. The reader may become familiar with this

TABLE 1.5.

$P_c(Cost)$	c_j Solution Vectors	3 P_1	8 P_2	M P_3	0 P_4	M P_5	0 P_6	P_0
M	P_3	4	6	1	0	0	0	120
0	P_4	1	0	0	1	0	0	12
M ←	P_5	0	1	0	0	1	−1	16
	z_j	$4M$	$7M$	M	0	M	$-M$	$136M$
	$c_j - z_j$	$3-4M$	$8-7M$ ↑	0	0	0	M	

tableau by preparing one of his own. The initial solution is

$$f'_{min} = 3(0) + 8(0) + M(120) + 0(12) + M(16) + 0(0) = 136M,$$

representing a very large cost. Obviously, additional iterations can reduce this cost inasmuch as some indicators in Table 1.5 are negative.

We shall carry out the steps for the first iteration without explanations.
First Iteration:
Following the previously described steps, we have the following:

Step 1: Since we want to make costs as small as possible, P_2 column in Table 1.5 with the most negative indicator $8 - 7M$ (remember M is a very large number) is the pivotal P_k.

Step 2: Observing that for

$$P_3 : \frac{120}{6} = 20; P_4 : \frac{12}{0} \text{ not defined}; P_5 : \frac{16}{1} = 16.$$

P_5 is the row vector which should be replaced.

Step 3: The pivotal P_w row vector is

$$P_2 \to P_5 = \frac{0}{1} \; \frac{1}{1} \; \frac{0}{1} \; \frac{0}{1} \; \frac{1}{1} \; -\frac{1}{1} \; \frac{16}{1} = 0, \, 1, \, 0, \, 0, \, 1, \, -1, \, 16,$$

as shown in Table 1.6 with the cost 8 written under P_c column.

TABLE 1.6.

P_c		c_j Solution Vectors	3 P_1	8 P_2	M P_3	0 P_4	M P_5	0 P_6	P_0
M	$\leftarrow$	P_3	4	0	1	0	-6	6	24
0		P_4	1	0	0	1	0	0	12
8	$\to$	P_2	0	1	0	0	1	-1	16
		z_j	$4M$	8	M	0	$8-6M$	$6M-8$	$128+24M$
		$c_j - z_j$	$3-4M$	0	0	0	$7M-8$	$8-6M$ $\uparrow$	

Step 4: The new P_3 and P_4 row vectors shown in Table 1.6 are obtained as follows:

New P_3 Row		New P_4 Row	
$4 - (6)(0) = 4$		$1 - (0)(0) = 1$	
$6 - (6)(1) = 0$		$0 - (0)(1) = 0$	
$1 - (6)(0) = 1$		$0 - (0)(0) = 0$	
$0 - (6)(0) = 0$		$1 - (0)(0) = 1$	
$0 - (6)(1) = -6$		$0 - (0)(1) = 0$	
$0 - (6)(-1) = 6$		$0 - (0)(-1) = 0$	
$120 - (6)(16) = 24$		$12 - (0)(16) = 12$	

Step 5: The z_j's and the new indicators are also shown in Table 1.6. The new feasible solution is

$$f''_{min} = 3(0) + 8(16) + M(24) + 0(12) + M(0) + 0(0) = 128 + 24M.$$

Since additional iterations are necessary, in order to economize space, only the simplex tableaus of the required second and third iterations are shown in Tables 1.7 and 1.8, respectively. The reader may carry out the computational steps to verify the entries to these tableaus.

Since all the indicators in Table 1.8 are zero or positive, an optimal minimal solution has been found.

You may notice that the second iteration in the above example yields

$$f'''_{min} = 3(0) + 8(20) + M(0) + 0(12) + M(0) + 0(4) = 160 \text{ dollars}$$

and the third iteration

$$f^{IV}_{min} = 3(6) + 8(16) + M(0) + 0(6) + M(0) + 0(0) = 146 \text{ dollars}$$

the optimal minimum solution found in Example 2.3 of Chapter 8. Also, tableau $(I|A^{-1}|X)$ in Table 1.8 can be formed by the components of P_1 and P_2 row vectors and P_1, P_2, P_3, and P_5 column vectors. Finally, note the fact that the second iteration could have been omitted by selecting P_1 instead of P_6 column as the pivotal P_k in Table 1.6. It is an indication that the simplex method leads with certainty to the optimal solution, but not always through the shortest computational route.

TABLE 1.7.

P_c		Solution Vectors	3 P_1	8 P_2	M P_3	0 P_4	M P_5	0 P_6	P_0
0	⇄	P_6	2/3	0	1/6	0	-1	1	4
0		P_4	1	0	0	1	0	0	12
8		P_2	2/3	1	1/6	0	0	0	20
		z_j	16/3	8	4/3	0	0	0	160
		$c_j - z_j$	$-7/3$ ↑	0	$M - 4/3$	0	M	0	

TABLE 1.8.

P_c		Solution Vectors	3 P_1	8 P_2	M P_3	0 P_4	M P_5	0 P_6	P_0
3	→	P_1	1	0	1/4	0	$-3/2$	3/2	6
0		P_4	0	0	$-1/4$	1	3/2	$-3/2$	6
8		P_2	0	1	0	0	1	-1	16
		z_j	3	8	3/4	0	7/2	$-7/2$	146
		$c_j - z_j$	0	0	$M - 3/4$	0	$M - 7/2$	7/2	

1.3. The Case of Degeneracy.

We have already mentioned that redundant restraints may lead to degeneracy. However, redundant restraints do not always lead to degeneracy; nor is predicting degeneracy an easy matter. Fortunately, the simplex method can usually cope effectively with degenerate linear programming problems. How to recognize degeneracy and how a degenerate problem may be solved are illustrated below.

Example 1.3. Consider the original Quality Baking Company maximizing problem with the added restraint that cookie mix is limited to 18 pounds and that $0.2x_1 + 0.3x_2 \leqslant 18$.
Initial Solution:
The simplex tableau of the initial solution to this problem in Table 1.9

differs from the tableau in Table 1.1 only with the addition of the new restraint $2x_1 + 3x_2 \leqslant 180$.

TABLE 1.9.

P_r		c_j Solution Vectors	0.20 P_1	0.30 P_2	0 P_3	0 P_4	0 P_5	P_0
0	←	P_3	1	2	1	0	0	100
0		P_4	1	1	0	1	0	80
0		P_5	2	3	0	0	1	180
		z_j	0	0	0	0	0	0
	$c_j - z_j$		0.20	0.30	0	0	0	
				↑				

First Iteration:
Following the established rules and doing the necessary computations, we obtain the simplex tableau of the first iteration in Table 1.10, where we have substituted P_2 column for P_3 row.

TABLE 1.10.

P_r		c_j Solution Vectors	0.20 P_1	0.30 P_2	0 P_3	0 P_4	0 P_5	P_0
0.30	→	P_2	1/2	1	1/2	0	0	50
0?	←	P_4	1/2	0	−1/2	1	0	30
0?	←	P_5	1/2	0	−3/2	0	1	30
		z_j	0.15	0.30	0.15	0	0	15
	$c_j - z_j$		0.05	0	−0.15	0	0	
			↑					

Second Iteration:
We start with P_1 column as the pivotal P_k. In determining, however, which row vector should be replaced, we run into difficulty since

$$P_2 : \frac{50}{\frac{1}{2}} = 100; \quad P_4 : \frac{30}{\frac{1}{2}} = 60; \quad P_5 : \frac{30}{\frac{1}{2}} = 60,$$

where both P_4 and P_5 row vectors are equally acceptable for replacement. This condition indicates that degeneracy exists. One of the methods of overcoming this difficulty is to replace one of the tie row vectors at random and carry out the computations. If the first row vector leads to no solution, one of the other vectors is randomly selected. In the present case, either P_4 or P_5 row vectors lead to the optimal solution, the former shown in Table 1.11 and the latter in Table 1.12. It is the same solution found in Table 1.4.

TABLE 1.11.

P_r	c_j Solution Vectors	0.20 P_1	0.30 P_2	0 P_3	0 P_4	0 P_5	P_0
0.30	P_2	0	1	2	0	-1	20
0	P_4	0	0	1	1	-1	0
0.20 →	P_1	1	0	-3	0	2	60
	z_j	0.20	0.30	0	0	0.10	18
	$c_j - z_j$	0	0	0	0	-0.10	

TABLE 1.12.

P_r	c_j Solution Vectors	0.20 P_1	0.30 P_2	0 P_3	0 P_4	0 P_5	P_0
0.30	P_2	0	1	1	-1	0	20
0.20 →	P_1	1	0	-1	2	0	60
0	P_5	0	0	-1	-1	1	0
	z_j	0.20	0.30	0.10	0.10	0	18
	$c_j - z_j$	0	0	-0.10	-0.10	0	

The reader can obtain a geometric representation of the solution set of this problem by drawing the half space of inequality $2x_1 + 3x_2 \leqslant 180$ in a diagram, such as the one shown in Figure 1.2 of Chapter 8.

1.4. A Few Additional Points. We shall wind up our discussion of the simplex method with a few points of importance.

In addition to the optimal solution to the primal problem, the simplex tableau contains the corresponding optimal solution to the dual. For instance, the optimal solution to the dual of the primal problem in Table 1.4 can be found in the z_j row under columns P_3 and P_4 of this table. It is $z_3 = 0.10$ and $z_4 = 0.10$, exactly the solution found for the same dual problem in Example 2.9 of the previous chapter. This information may be valuable, for the number of iterations required for solving a problem may range from equal to as many as twice the number of the restraints of the problem. Hence, substantial economies in computational work may be realized in solving real-size problems where the number of restraints is greater than the number of unknowns if an optimal solution is found to the primal problem by solving the dual.

Another point of importance concerns the rules for setting up a problem to be solved by the simplex method. Such rules for handling the restraints and the objective function of an ordinary linear programming problem are conveniently summarized in Table 1.13. Problems other than ordinary may require modification of these rules. For instance, in Example 1.2 a zero coefficient was given to the objective function for the positive slack x_4 because of the peculiarities of this problem. For an

TABLE 1.13.

When the restraint is—	For the objective function of a—	
	1. *Max. problem*	2. *Min. problem*
I. *A "≤" inequality,* add a positive slack variable.	*assign,* a zero coefficient.	*assign,* M coefficient.
II. *A "≥" inequality,* add one negative slack and one positive artificial variable.	A zero coefficient to the negative and $-M$ to the artificial.	A zero coefficient to the negative and M to the artificial.
III. *An equality,* add a positive artificial variable.	$-M$ coefficient.	M coefficient.

ordinary minimizing problem, however, an M coefficient is assigned as shown in Table 1.13.

Finally, a maximizing or minimizing linear programming problem has no solution if the components of the pivotal column are zero or negative. In business operations, however, problems with no optimal solution are likely to occur because of misstated restraints and computational errors rather than for other reasons.

With these remarks in mind let us proceed to another special, yet important, linear programming method.

PROBLEMS

1.1. Carry out the computations and verify the entries to the simplex tableaus in Tables 1.7 and 1.8 in Example 1.2.

1.2. For the second iteration in Example 1.2 use P_1 instead of P_6 column vector as the pivotal P_k and verify the fact that the simplex method may not always lead to the optimal solution through the shortest computational route.

1.3. Carry out the computations and verify the entries to the simplex tableaus in Tables 1.10, 1.11, and 1.12 in Example 1.3. Obtain a geometric representation of the solution set of the problem by drawing the half space of $2x_1 + 3x_2 \leq 180$ in a diagram such as the diagram in Figure 1.2 of Chapter 8.

1.4. From each table below form tableau $(I|A^{-1}|X)$ and show that the solution vector $X = A^{-1}B$.
a) Table 1.4.
b) Table 1.8.
c) Table 1.12.

1.5. Solve by the simplex method the problems in the following examples of Chapter 8.
a) Example 1.7.
b) Example 2.7.

1.6. Use the simplex algorithm to solve the following dual problems of the previous chapter.
a) In Example 2.9.
b) In Example 2.11.

1.7. To the maximizing problem in Example 1.1 add the restraint indicated in each case below and solve the new problem by the simplex method. Verify each solution graphically.
a) $0.2x_1 + 0.2x_2 \leqslant 16$ (cookie mix).
b) $x_1 \geqslant 60$.
c) $x_2 \geqslant 20$.
d) $x_1 + x_2 \leqslant 160$ (cookie mix).
e) $x_2 = 20$.
f) $x_2 \geqslant 25$.

1.8. To the minimizing problem of AAA Department Stores Inc., in Example 1.7 of Chapter 8 add the restraint indicated in each case below and solve the new problem by the simplex method. Verify each solution graphically.
a) $x_1 \leqslant 22$.
b) $x_2 = 6$.
c) $2x_1 + 4x_2 \leqslant 90$.

1.9. Find the solution of the following linear programming problems of Chapter 8 by the simplex method.
a) Problem 1.13.
b) Problem 1.14.
c) Problem 1.15.
d) Problem 2.15.

1.10. Using the same restraints and the objective function indicated below, solve each problem of Chapter 8 by the simplex method.
a) The problem in Example 1.3 when—
  (1) $f_{max} = \$0.30x_1 + \$0.20x_2$,
  (2) $f_{max} = \$0.10x_1 + \$0.30x_2$.
b) The problem in Example 1.7 when —
  (1) $f_{min} = \$20x_1 + \$60x_2$,
  (2) $f_{min} = \$60x_1 + \$30x_2$.

1.11. Find the dual of the following linear programming problems of Chapter 8, interpret it, and solve it by the simplex method.
a) Problem 1.13.
b) Problem 1.14.
c) Problem 1.15.
d) Problem 2.15.

1.12. For Problem 1.14 of Chapter 8—
a) Find the solution by the simplex method.
b) Find the dual of the above problem and solve it by the simplex method. Verify the fact that finding the solution to the primal by solving the dual requires fewer iterations.

1.13. The managers of Popular Fund Inc., an investment company, consider the following types of securities:

Type:	A_1	A_2	B_1	B_2	C_1	C_2
Yield:	3.5%	3%	3%	5%	4.5%	4%

The policy of the fund is that at least 45 percent of the available cash should be invested in securities of type *A*, but no more than 30 percent and 35 percent in *B* and *C* securities, respectively. How should available funds be invested so that the maximum yield be obtained? What is this maximum yield? For what type of securities will investment fall short of the requirements?
a) Solve this problem with simple arithmetic.
b) Solve it by the simplex method. (Cf. reference 11 pp. 48 ff.)

*2. THE TRANSPORTATION METHOD

Showing how the simplex and transportation methods are related is our first objective in this section. After establishing this connection we shall illustrate the computational procedure of the transportation method with appropriate motivating examples, one for minimizing cost and one for maximizing profit. In the remaining part of this section we shall show how to handle degeneracy and discuss other complications.

2.1. Transportation Problems and the Simplex Method.

We have already pointed out that in addition to *linearity*, certain problems require a *one-to-one rate of substitution between variables*. Such problems are called transportation problems, and the iterative method which can be used advantageously to solve them is called *transportation method*. This term has been used since the computational procedure was first demonstrated by F. L. Hitchcock in 1941, although the method is used to solve problems which have nothing to do with transportation. In fact, the term is a misnomer inasmuch as the method is applicable to any source-to-destination-type problem which meets the following conditions:

1. As in the general case, the objective function and the equations of the corresponding restraints are *linear*.
2. The rate of substitution between the varying unknown quantities is one-to-one, i.e., the units of the variables are *homogeneous*.
3. The restraints of the problem require that the sum of *source capacities* must *equal* the sum of *destination requirements*.

Example 2.1. Continental Lines Company, a trucking firm engaged in interstate transportation, receives weekly orders from an electronics manufacturer to transport electronics parts from the three factories of the company to three assembly locations. The current order required transporting the following tonnage:

Capacities		Requirements	
Factories	Tonnage	Assembly Locations	Tonnage
F_1	75	A_1	40
F_2	50	A_2	55
F_3	30	A_3	60
Total	155	Total	155

Since the parts to be transported are identical, it does not matter which factory supplies a particular assembly location. Neither does transportation cost per ton vary for a particular route as long as tonnage is in multiples of five tons which represents a full truckload. Variations, however, in distance, road conditions, and other factors contribute to substantial differences in the cost of transporting a ton of electronic parts over each of the nine possible routes as shown below:

	A_1	A_2	A_3
F_1	\$10	\$30	\$40
F_2	\$30	\$30	\$30
F_3	\$30	\$20	\$20

The management of Continental Lines wishes to find the route combination with the minimum cost.

In mathematical terms this problem may be expressed as follows:

$$(2.1) \quad f_{\min} = 10x_{11} + 30x_{12} + 40x_{13} + 30x_{21} + 30x_{22} \\ + 30x_{23} + 30x_{31} + 20x_{32} + 20x_{33},$$

subject to

$$(2.2) \quad \begin{aligned} x_{11} + x_{12} + x_{13} &\leqslant 75, \\ x_{21} + x_{22} + x_{23} &\leqslant 50, \\ x_{31} + x_{32} + x_{33} &\leqslant 30, \\ x_{11} + x_{21} + x_{31} &\leqslant 40, \\ x_{12} + x_{22} + x_{32} &\leqslant 55, \\ x_{13} + x_{23} + x_{33} &\leqslant 60. \end{aligned}$$

The above example involves a typical transportation-type problem. In addition to linearity the units of the variables are homogeneous and source capacities equal destination requirements as required. A problem such as this may be solved by the simplex method.

Example 2.1—*Continued.* Observe that the objective function (2.1) and the restraints (2.2) of our problem contain nine unknowns, the number of factories times the number of assembly locations; and that there are six restraints, the number of factories plus the number of assembly locations.

In fact, one of the restraints is redundant. Let any set of x_{ij} shipments satisfy the capacity restrictions of the factories and meet the requirements of two of the assembly locations. Since the total factory capacity should equal the total requirements of the locations, the shipment to the third location is a residual defined by the previous restrictions and just sufficient to satisfy the requirements of this last location. Thus, in solving this problem by the simplex method, any one of the six restraints should be left out to avoid degeneracy.

Let x_{ij} be the tonnage to be transported from the ith factory to the jth assembly location. Then leaving out the last of the restraints (2.2) and introducing the required positive slack variables, we have

$$(2.3) \quad f_{\min} = 10x_{11} + 30x_{12} + 40x_{13} + 30x_{21} + 30x_{22} + \\ + 30x_{23} + 30x_{31} + 20x_{32} + 20x_{33} + Mx_{14} + \\ + Mx_{24} + Mx_{34} + Mx_{44} + Mx_{54},$$

subject to

$$x_{11} + \ x_{12} + \ x_{13} + 0x_{21} + 0x_{22} + 0x_{23} + 0x_{31} + 0x_{32} + \\ + 0x_{33} + \ x_{14} + 0x_{24} + 0x_{34} + 0x_{44} + 0x_{54} = 75.$$

$$0x_{11} + 0x_{12} + 0x_{13} + \ x_{21} + \ x_{22} + \ x_{23} + 0x_{31} + 0x_{32} + \\ + 0x_{33} + 0x_{14} + \ x_{24} + 0x_{34} + 0x_{44} + 0x_{54} = 50.$$

$$(2.4) \quad 0x_{11} + 0x_{12} + 0x_{13} + 0x_{21} + 0x_{22} + 0x_{23} + \ x_{31} + \ x_{32} + \\ + \ x_{33} + 0x_{14} + 0x_{24} + \ x_{34} + 0x_{44} + 0x_{54} = 30.$$

$$x_{11} + 0x_{12} + 0x_{13} + \ x_{21} + 0x_{22} + 0x_{23} + \ x_{31} + 0x_{32} + \\ + 0x_{33} + 0x_{14} + 0x_{24} + 0x_{34} + \ x_{44} + 0x_{54} = 40.$$

$$0x_{11} + \ x_{12} + 0x_{13} + 0x_{21} + \ x_{22} + 0x_{23} + 0x_{31} + \ x_{32} + \\ + 0x_{33} + 0x_{14} + 0x_{24} + 0x_{34} + 0x_{44} + \ x_{54} = 55.$$

From (2.3) and (2.4) the simplex tableau for the initial solution to the above problem can be easily prepared. It is left for the reader to prepare such a tableau and solve the problem by the simplex method.

Thus, the simplex algorithm can solve any transportation-type problem such as the above, which can be solved by the special transportation method. However, the latter technique deserves particular attention. In the first place, the method has numerous applications in business operations as well as in economics. In the second place, unlike the simplex algorithm which frequently requires high-speed computers, the computational simplicity of the transportation method requires no more than pencil and paper for solving most real-world transportation-type problems.

2.2. A Minimizing Problem. Although the reader will find a variety of source-to-destination-type problems at the end of this section, in illustrating the transportation method we shall follow the established tradition. We shall demonstrate the method with the problem in Example 2.1, which requires minimizing transportation cost.

We have already explained why one of the six restraints in Example 2.1 is redundant. In general, let S be the number of sources and D the number of destinations of a transportation-type problem, where $S > 1$ and $D > 1$. Then, the number of unknowns is $S \times D$ and the number of the required restraints for solving the problem by the simplex method is $S + D - 1$. In other words, in the system of $S + D$ corresponding linear equations $S + D - 1$ are linearly independent. The number of required restraints is also important for solving a problem by the transportation method, as we shall shortly realize.

Example 2.1—*Continued.* Consider the problem of Continental Lines Company. In setting it up, the given data may be conveniently arranged in tabular form, as shown in Table 2.1. The marginal figures in the right-hand side column and bottom row, called *rim requirements*, represent the

TABLE 2.1.

Assemblies \ Factories	A_1	A_2	A_3	Available Tonnage
F_1	10 ⓐ40	30 ㉕	40 ⑩	75
F_2	30 0	30 0	30 ㊿	50
F_3	30 0	20 ㉚	20 0	30
Required tonnage	40	55	60	155

available and required tonnage of electronic parts, respectively. Each of the nine boxes in the body of the table, representing one of the nine possible routes of the problem, is divided by a broken line into an upper and lower triangle. The figure in each upper triangle represents the cost of transporting one ton of electronic parts via the designated $F_i A_j$ route. For instance, the cost per ton via route $F_1 A_1$, i.e., from factory F_1 to assembly location A_1 is \$10. The circled number or the zero in the lower triangle of each route box will be explained shortly. In the meantime, the reader may observe that the problem has all three formal characteristics of a source-to-destination-type problem; namely, linearity, homogeneity of units, and equality between available output and required input.

As in the case of the simplex method the transportation method consists of starting with an initial solution and moving from one basic solution to another in a finite number of iterations. In the transportation method, however, the initial solution is not the zero feasible solution, but one of chosen routes. Basically, there are two ways of choosing the routes for the initial solution: by inspection which may also represent existing practice and by the northwest corner rule. In either case the *number of chosen routes must be equal to $S + D - 1$*, i.e., one less than the sum of sources and destinations of the problem. What happens if more or less than $S + D - 1$ routes are chosen will be explained after we develop the initial solution to our problem.

Example 2.1—*Continued*. For the initial solution of Continental Lines Company we shall choose the routes by inspection. The northwest corner method is illustrated in one of the problems at the end of this section.

Initial Solution:

Since transporting electronic parts from factory F_1 to location A_1 is less costly than to any other location, we supply all 40 tons that A_1 needs from factory F_1. The assigned tonnage is shown in the lower triangle of the box in Table 2.1, which represents route F_1A_1. All available 30 tons from factory F_3 are assigned to location A_2, and the remaining required 25 tons for that location are supplied from factory F_1. Finally, all available 50 tons from factory F_2 are assigned to location A_3, and the remaining required 10 tons for that location are supplied from factory F_1. Thus, the largest tonnage is assigned to the least costly routes. Unused routes are assigned zero tonnage. Also, observe that exactly 5 or $3 + 3 - 1$ routes are used and that the obtained solution is feasible since it meets exactly the rim requirements or restraints of the problem. Substituting in the objective function (2.1), the cost of this initial solution is

$$f'_{min} = 10(40) + 30(25) + 40(10) + 30(0) + 30(0)$$
$$+ 30(50) + 30(0) + 20(30) + 20(0) = 3650 \text{ dollars.}$$

Assigning the available tonnage of electronic parts to assembly locations by inspection may be thought of as representing a rule of thumb which the management of Continental Lines has applied in the past. We have made a limited use of the available information in the sense that we have selected the least costly route(s) for *each* location. In real-world problems with more than nine routes, however, it would be a mere coincidence if such an initial solution is an optimal feasible solution, i.e., the least costly route combination (mix) for *all* locations. In order to test the initial solution, we must find the indirect cost differential of each unused route. If this cost differential which, for lack of a better term, we may call *indicator*, is negative or zero for all unused routes, the initial solution is an optimal solution; otherwise, additional iterations are necessary.

Let I_{ij} stand for the indicator of the ijth route and let us consider the unused route $F_2 A_1$. The indicator I_{21} consists of making a shipment to $F_2 A_1$ via routes *already used in the initial solution*. From Table 2.1 we can see that the cost differential is

$$I_{21} = F_2 A_3 - F_1 A_3 + F_1 A_1 - F_2 A_1 = 30 - 40 + 10 - 30 = -30.$$

This expression may be interpreted as follows: If we ship a ton from F_2 to A_1 at a cost of \$30, some compensating adjustments must be made in other routes in order to avoid violating the restraints of the problem. Thus, we must ship one ton less from F_2 to A_3 at a saving of \$30 (factory F_2 capacity), one ton more from F_1 to A_3 at a cost of \$40, and one ton less from F_1 to A_1 at a saving of \$10 (locations A_3 and A_1 requirements). In a similar manner, the indicators for the other three unused routes are computed as follows:

$$I_{22} = F_2 A_3 - F_1 A_3 + F_1 A_2 - F_2 A_2 = 30 - 40 + 30 - 30 = -10,$$
$$I_{31} = F_3 A_2 - F_1 A_2 + F_1 A_1 - F_3 A_1 = 20 - 30 + 10 - 30 = -30,$$
$$I_{33} = F_3 A_2 - F_1 A_2 + F_1 A_3 - F_3 A_3 = 20 - 30 + 40 - 20 = 10.$$

Since indicator I_{33} is positive, additional iterations are necessary.

Now we are in a position to appreciate the rule that the initial solution should involve $S + D - 1$ chosen routes. If less than that number were chosen, then we would have been unable to evaluate all unused routes. This is the case of degeneracy, which we shall discuss later. If more than that number were chosen, then for one or more unused routes there would have been more than one evaluation. Thus, if $S + D - 1$ routes are used, there is one and only one way of evaluating each unused route. With these general remarks in mind, let us continue our illustrative case.

Example 2.1—*Continued.* The positive indicator I_{33} implies that for every ton diverted to route $F_3 A_3$ we can save \$10 in transportation cost. Thus, if more than one indicator is positive, tonnage should be diverted to the route with the largest positive indicator. For routes with equal positive indicators either route can be chosen.
First Iteration:
Searching for an improved solution is done as follows:
Step 1: Find tonnage to be diverted to $F_3 A_3$.
The answer can be obtained from Table 2.2 where only the lower triangles of the routes from Table 2.1 are reproduced which are required to evaluate the unused route $F_3 A_3$. Let X be the number of tons to be

TABLE 2.2.

	A_2	A_3
F_1 }	$25 + X$	$10 - X$
F_3 }	$30 - X$	$0 + X$

diverted to route F_3A_3. In order to meet the restraints of the problem we must reduce the tonnage to routes F_3A_2 and F_1A_3 and increase the tonnage to route F_1A_2 by X tons. And since the transferable tonnage cannot be larger than the smallest available in routes F_1A_3 and F_3A_2, $X = 10$ tons.

Step 2: Find the cost of the new feasible solution.

The new feasible solution is shown in Table 2.3, where the required

TABLE 2.3.

Assemblies / Factories	A_1	A_2	A_3	Available Tonnage
F_1	$10 (40)	$30 (35)	$40 0	75
F_2	$30 0	$30 0	$30 (50)	50
F_3	$30 0	$20 (20)	$20 (10)	30
Required tonnage	40	55	60	155

transfer of 10 tons to F_3A_3 and the necessary compensating adjustments have been made. Substituting in the objective function (2.1), the cost of the new solution is

$$f''_{min} = 10(40) + 30(35) + 40(0) + 30(0) + 30(0)$$
$$+ 30(50) + 30(0) + 20(20) + 20(10) = 3550 \text{ dollars.}$$

Step 3: Find out if the new solution is an optimal.

The indicators of the unused routes are

$$I_{21} = F_2A_3 - F_3A_3 + F_3A_2 - F_1A_2 + F_1A_1 - F_2A_1 =$$
$$= 30 - 20 + 20 - 30 + 10 - 30 = -20,$$
$$I_{22} = F_2A_3 - F_3A_3 + F_3A_2 - F_2A_2 \quad = 30 - 20 + 20 - 30 = \quad 0,$$
$$I_{13} = F_1A_2 - F_3A_2 + F_3A_3 - F_1A_3 \quad = 30 - 20 + 20 - 40 = -10,$$
$$I_{31} = F_3A_2 - F_1A_2 + F_1A_1 - F_3A_1 \quad = 20 - 30 + 10 - 30 = -30,$$

since all the indicators are negative or zero, the new solution is optimal.

It is important to know that a zero indicator means that there is an alternative optimal solution. In the above case indicator I_{22} was found to be zero. Therefore, a solution with route F_2A_2 instead of route F_3A_2 is an alternative optimal solution to the problem of Continental Lines.

The reader may prepare a route table for this alternative optimal solution and verify that its total cost is $3550 as previously. In real-world problems the existence of alternative optimal solutions may introduce a desirable flexibility into the suboptimization process of managerial decisions.

2.3. A Maximizing Problem.

The only important difference between the procedure of solving a minimizing problem from that of a maximizing problem lies in the interpretation of the indicators. For a maximizing problem a solution is an optimal solution if all routes have a *positive* or zero indicator; otherwise, further iterations are necessary. In the latter case the unused route with the most *negative* indicator is the replacing route.

Example 2.2. Let us consider the case of Continental Lines again. This time, however, let us assume that the electronics manufacturer is paying a flat rate of $40 per ton to be transported via any of the nine possible routes. Since this rate is equal to the cost of transporting a ton of electronic parts via the costliest route F_1A_3, we may assume that the profit to Continental Lines for a particular route is the difference between the cost of that route and the cost of route F_1A_3. The profit per ton for each route is shown below:

	A_1	A_2	A_3
F_1	$30	$10	$0
F_2	$10	$10	$10
F_3	$10	$20	$20

The management of Continental Lines is now interested in finding the optimal solution for maximizing profits, i.e.,

$$(2.5) \quad f_{max} = 30x_{11} + 10x_{12} + 0x_{13} + 10x_{21} + 10x_{22} + 10x_{23} + \\ + 10x_{31} + 20x_{32} + 20x_{33},$$

subject to restraints (2.2).

Initial Solution:

Using the above profits, the rim requirements of the original problem, and the previously demonstrated inspection method of choosing routes, the initial solution is shown in Table 2.4. The circled numbers represent the assigned tonnage to be transported via the chosen routes. Substituting in the objective function (2.5), the profit of the initial solution is

$$f'_{max} = 30(40) + 10(25) + 0(10) + 10(0) + 10(0) + \\ + 10(50) + 10(0) + 20(30) + 20(0) = 2550 \text{ dollars.}$$

Is the initial an optimal solution? Computing the indicators, we have

$$I_{21} = F_2A_3 - F_1A_3 + F_1A_1 - F_2A_1 = 10 - 0 + 30 - 10 = 30,$$
$$I_{22} = F_2A_3 - F_1A_3 + F_1A_2 - F_2A_2 = 10 - 0 + 10 - 10 = 10,$$
$$I_{31} = F_3A_2 - F_1A_2 + F_1A_1 - F_3A_1 = 20 - 10 + 30 - 10 = 30,$$
$$I_{33} = F_3A_2 - F_1A_2 + F_1A_3 - F_3A_3 = 20 - 10 + 0 - 20 = -10.$$

TABLE 2.4.

Assemblies / Factories	A_1	A_2	A_3	Available Tonnage
F_1	$30 ⟨40⟩	$10 ⟨25⟩	$0 ⟨10⟩	75
F_2	$10 0	$10 0	$10 ⟨50⟩	50
F_3	$10 0	$20 ⟨30⟩	$20 0	30
Required tonnage	40	55	60	155

Since indicator I_{33} is negative, additional iterations are required.

First Iteration:

It is clear that for every ton diverted to route $F_3 A_3$, profits will increase by $10.

Step 1: Find the tonnage to be diverted to $F_3 A_3$.

Following the same procedure as in the minimizing problem (Table 2.2) we find that 10 tons can be diverted to this route.

Step 2: Find the profit of the new solution.

The new solution is shown in Table 2.5, where all the required changes have been made. Substituting in the objective function (2.5), the profit of

TABLE 2.5.

Assemblies / Factories	A_1	A_2	A_3	Available Tonnage
F_1	$30 ⟨40⟩	$10 ⟨35⟩	$0 0	75
F_2	$10 0	$10 0	$10 ⟨50⟩	50
F_3	$10 0	$20 ⟨20⟩	$20 ⟨10⟩	30
Required tonnage	40	55	60	155

the new solution is

$$f''_{max} = 30(40) + 10(35) + 0(0) + 10(0) + 10(0) +$$
$$+ 10(50) + 10(0) + 20(20) + 20(10) = 2650 \text{ dollars.}$$

Step 3: Find if the new solution is an optimal.
The positive indicators below show that the new solution is an optimal one;

$$I_{21} = F_2A_3 - F_3A_3 + F_3A_2 - F_1A_2 + F_1A_1 - F_2A_1$$
$$= 10 - 20 + 20 - 10 + 30 - 10 = 20,$$
$$I_{22} = F_2A_3 - F_3A_3 + F_3A_2 - F_2A_2 = 10 - 20 + 20 - 10 = 0,$$
$$I_{13} = F_1A_2 - F_3A_2 + F_3A_3 - F_1A_3 = 10 - 20 + 20 - 0 = 10,$$
$$I_{31} = F_3A_2 - F_1A_2 + F_1A_1 - F_3A_1 = 20 - 10 + 30 - 10 = 30.$$

It is interesting to note that route F_2A_2 with $I_{22} = 0$ is again an alternative optimal solution. Moreover, the optimal cost \$3550 of the minimizing problem, plus the optimal profit \$2650 of the maximizing problem, equals the total revenue \$6200 which Continental Lines would receive from the electronics firm at a flat rate of \$40 per transported ton.

2.4. The Case of Degeneracy. We have already pointed out that if the chosen routes in the initial solution (or any other solution at some stage of the solving process) are less than $S + D - 1$, degeneracy arises. This case occurs when a route table can be divided into two or more segments each of which satisfies the rim requirements of the sources and destinations it contains. We shall use an illustrative example to demonstrate a degeneracy case and how to handle it.

Example 2.3. Let us assume that the route table of the initial solution for the minimizing problem of Continental Lines is as shown in Table 2.6.

TABLE 2.6.

Factories \ Assemblies	A_1	A_2	A_3	Available Tonnage
F_1	\$10 40	\$30 0	\$40 30	70
F_2	\$30 0	\$30 0	\$30 30	30
F_3	\$30 0	\$20 55	\$20 0	55
Required tonnage	40	55	60	155

Observe that degeneracy arises—the chosen routes are four instead of the required five—because the table can be divided into two independent segments. The available tonnage of factories F_1 and F_2 satisfy exactly the requirements of assembly locations A_1 and A_3, while the available tonnage of factory F_3 satisfies exactly the requirements of location A_2.

If a situation such as the one above occurs, not all unused routes can be evaluated. In other words, we are unable to find the indicator of all unused routes since this step requires that only chosen routes should be used and there are not enough of them. In the above concrete case except for route F_2A_1 none of the other unused routes can be evaluated. This situation is generally called degeneracy. It can be handled as follows:

Example 2.3—*Continued.* We select one of the unused routes with low transportation cost, say F_3A_3, and assign to that route a fictitious tonnage T. This adjustment to Table 2.6 is shown in Table 2.7, where T

TABLE 2.7.

Assemblies Factories	A_1	A_2	A_3	Available Tonnage
F_1	\$10 ㊵	\$30 0	\$40 ㉚	70
F_2	\$30 0	\$30 0	\$30 ㉚	30
F_3	\$30 0	\$20 ㊻	\$20 ⓣ	$55 + T$
Required tonnage	40	55	$60 + T$	$155 + T$

tonnage is added to factory F_3 and assembly location A_3 in order to maintain the rim requirements. Substituting in the objective function (2.1), the cost of the initial solution is

$$f'_{min} = 10(40) + 30(0) + 40(30) + 30(0) + 30(0)$$
$$+ 30(30) + 30(0) + 20(55) + 20(T) = 3600 + 20T \text{ dollars.}$$

Since the chosen routes are exactly $3 + 3 - 1 = 5$, evaluation of the unused routes can proceed. If the above solution is optimal, the cost $20T$ of route F_3A_3 is ignored, otherwise the computations for the required iterations are carried out as explained. The reader will encounter no difficulty in solving this problem.

2.5. Additional Complications. At the beginning of this section we pointed out that the transportation method can be used to solve problems which meet the conditions of linearity, homogeneity of units, and equality of source capacities and destination requirements. More frequently than not, however, real-world problems present difficulties because they may not precisely meet these conditions. A number of devices have been invented which are designed to overcome such difficulties by converting a problem which is apparently difficult or impossible to handle into a proper form which is solvable by the transportation method. In concluding Part III of this textbook on linear programming we shall briefly discuss some of the most common cases.

Some problems may originally appear to lack the important requirements of linearity. It is possible that a source, say a factory, can supply a given quantity of a product at one cost and an additional quantity at a higher cost either because of overtime or higher costs in additional material. Similarly, a destination, say a local market area, may demand a given amount of factory products at one price and an additional quantity at a lower price. Such cases can be easily handled by treating the supplied quantities at each cost level and the demanded quantities at each price level as originating from separate sources and destinations.

In some other problems the original units may not be homogeneous. The yield of a raw material may depend on the type of product to be produced as well as the grade or quality of the raw material itself. Although such problems cannot usually be solved with linear programming, in some cases artificial units may be used to convert the problem into a solvable form.

And in still other problems the rim requirements may not be exactly met. One such common case is when source capacities may exceed destination requirements. In situations like these a dummy destination is introduced with slack requirements equal to the difference between total capacity and total actual requirements. The cost or profit of any unit diverted from any source to the dummy destination is set to zero, and the problem is solved as usual. In an optimal solution any source capacity assigned to the dummy destination is idle capacity. Similar arrangements are made in cases where destination requirements exceed source capacities.

The reader will have an opportunity to try these devices with some of the problems which follow.

PROBLEMS

2.1. Prepare a route table for the alternative optimal solution of the following problems and verify the fact that the result is the same as in the original optimal solution.

    a) The minimizing problem in Example 2.1, Table 2.3.
    b) The maximizing problem in Example 2.2, Table 2.5.

*2.2. Solve the degeneracy minimizing problem given in Table 2.7.

2.3. For each of the problems indicated below—
    i) Solve it by the simplex method.
    ii) Compare it with the solution of the same problem by the transportation method with respect to the initial solution and the iterations.
    iii) Discuss the reasons why the simplex method is more time consuming than the transportation method.
    *a) The minimizing problem in Example 2.1.
    b) The maximizing problem in Example 2.2.
    c) The degeneracy problem in Example 2.3.

2.4. Consider the minimizing problem in Example 2.1. Choosing the routes for the initial solution by the northwest corner method is shown below:

Assemblies / Factories	A_1	A_2	A_3	Available Tonnage
F_1	$10 (40)	$30 (35)	$40 0	~~75~~ ~~35~~ 0
F_2	$30 0	$30 (20)	$30 (30)	~~50~~ ~~30~~ 0
F_3	$30 0	$20 0	$20 (30)	~~30~~ 0
Required tonnage	~~40~~ 0	~~55~~ ~~20~~ 0	~~60~~ ~~30~~ 0	155

We start from the upper left-hand corner assigning 40 tons to route F_1A_1, i.e., whichever of the two figures in row F_1 and column A_1 is the smallest. After making the required subtractions on the margins of the route table we move to the next column A_2. We assign to route F_1A_2 whichever of the two figures in row F_1 and column A_2 is the smallest, in this case 35 tons. Since all available tonnage from factory F_1 has been allocated, we move to the next factory F_2 and repeat the above process of allocating the available tonnage from that factory. Finally, we do the same for factory F_3.

    For each problem below do the following:
    i) Set up the initial solution by the northwest corner method.
    ii) Find an optimal solution.

iii) Discuss the relative merits of the inspection and the northwest corner methods of setting up the initial solution.

*a) The minimizing problem in Example 2.1 whose initial solution is given as an illustration above.

b) The maximizing problem in Example 2.2.

c) The rim requirements of the maximizing problem in Example 2.2 but with profits as shown below:

	A_1	A_2	A_3
F_1	$15	$30	$20
F_2	$30	$25	$20
F_3	$20	$20	$25

d) The degeneracy minimizing problem in Example 2.3.

2.5. Let S_i be the ith source, D_j the jth destination, I_{ij} the ijth indicator, and X the number of units to be transferred in a transportation-type problem. Prepare a flow chart of the steps involved in solving:

a) A minimizing problem such as the problem in Example 2.1.

b) A maximizing problem as in Example 2.2.

*2.6. At peak traffic hours the traffic manager of Metropolitan Transportation Service is frequently faced with the problem of dispatching relief buses from the three garages of the company to three key locations of the traffic network. The data below show the number of relief bases available, the number of relief buses which are usually needed at each location, and the expected number of minutes required for a relief bus to reach a location via each possible route.

Locations / Garages	L_1	L_2	L_3	Available Buses
G_1	12	14	13	6
G_2	14	12	15	9
G_3	10	18	19	5
Required buses	8	4	8	20

The manager wants to allocate his available buses in such a way as to minimize the total time required for the buses to reach their designated location.

a) Find an optimal solution using the inspection method.

b) Find an optimal solution using the northwest corner method explained in Problem 2.4.

2.7. Let us assume that the available data for the traffic manager in Problem 2.6 are as follows:

Locations / Garages	L_1	L_2	L_3	Available Buses
G_1	10	14	16	8
G_2	14	11	12	7
G_3	9	10	10	5
Required buses	6	5	9	20

In the past the manager followed the practice of assigning 6 buses to route G_1L_1, 2 to G_1L_3, 7 to G_2L_3, and 5 to G_3L_2. He believed that he minimized time while serving the best interest of the public.

a) Compute the indicators for the manager's practice in order to find whether it represents an optimal solution; and, if it does not, find one using his assignment of buses as a starting point.

b) Discuss the possible conflict between optimizing time and the over-all objective of the Metropolitan Transportation Service to serve the public.

2.8. Because of competitive conditions Allied Department Stores are selling an item at $10 apiece. At this price the realizable profit margin is equal to the difference in the cost of purchasing the product from three suppliers and delivering it to the three stores of the company serving widely separated local markets. The acquisition cost per unit of product via each of the nine possible channels (routes) and the demanded and supplied number of units of the product are given below:

Markets / Suppliers	M_1	M_2	M_3	Supplied Units
S_1	$10	$8	$5	10
S_2	$8	$7	$10	30
S_3	$6	$3	$9	40
Demanded units	45	20	15	80

The purchasing manager argued that the product should be purchased via channels other than the ones with zero margins. However, the director of marketing research pointed out that exclusion of zero-margin channels does not secure optimal profit margin combinations. Can you resolve their argument?

2.9. Two plants of Prometheus Corporation are located near the source of primary raw materials because the company manufactures a weight-losing product. Since production is located away from consumer markets, freight is an important cost in marketing the company's product. From the viewpoint of transportation cost the continental United States is divided into three markets, East, West, and South. Freight rates per cwt from the plants to the distribution centers of each market are as follows:

	East	West	South
Plant 1 · · · · · · · · · ·	$0.50	$0.60	$0.30
Plant 2 · · · · · · · · ·	$0.70	$1.00	$0.40

Up until recently plant capacity, which amounted to a weekly output of 50,000 cwt from Plant 1 and 30,000 cwt from Plant 2, was sufficient to satisfy the requirements of the three markets. Growing demand, however, has increased the weekly weight requirements of the markets in spite of improved production processes, such as more efficient product design and miniaturization, as follows: East: 40,000 cwt; West: 35,000 cwt; South: 25,000 cwt. Before deciding how to satisfy the increased demand, management wanted to know the least overall expensive freight shipment of products to the markets. Solve.

2.10. In order to satisfy the increased demand for the product the management of Prometheus Corporation in Problem 2.9 considers two alternatives: using the existing plants and producing the additional output with overtime or building a new plant. Extensive marketing research revealed that this impressive increase in demand may be temporary. Hence, management decided temporarily in favor of the short-run alternative of increasing output with overtime rather than by expanding capacity.

The problem was how to allocate overtime output between the two plants so that the overall freight plus overtime cost would be at a minimum. One of the suggestions made by the director of research of the firm was to treat overtime cost as freight cost and solve the problem with linear programming. Overtime costs were expressed in terms of product weight at $0.20 per cwt. It was further assumed that overtime output will be allocated as follows: Plant 1 would supply East and South, while Plant 2 the West. Solve the problem.

2.11. A few years later demand for the product of Prometheus Corporation in Problem 2.10 increased steadily to 45,000 cwt, 55,000 cwt, and 40,000 cwt in East, West, and South, respectively. The management of the firm finally decided to build a new plant. Two sites are considered with freight rates per cwt as follows:

	East	West	South
Site 1 · · · · · · · · · ·	$0.60	$0.80	$0.50
Site 2 · · · · · · · · · ·	$0.70	$0.40	$0.80

Assuming that no other criteria but overall transportation costs are considered, which site should be selected for the new plant?

2.12. The personnel manager of a plant has the problem of assigning 50 newly recruited workers to three jobs. On the basis of experience, age, and seniority, the workers have been classified into three categories representing different hourly rates of pay. The pertinent data are conveniently summarized below:

Jobs / Categories	J_1	J_2	J_3	Available Workers
C_1	$2.00	$3.00	$2.50	20
C_2	$3.00	$2.50	$3.00	15
C_3	$2.50	$3.00	$2.00	15
Required workers	10	25	15	50

How should the manager assign the 50 workers so that the total hourly pay rate is at a minimum?

SUGGESTED REFERENCES

1. BIERMAN, HAROLD, *et al. Quantitative Analysis for Business Decisions*, pp. 198–217, 242–58. Homewood, Ill.: Richard D. Irwin, Inc., 1961. **(1, 2)**

2. BOULDING, K. E., AND SPIVEY, W. A. *Linear Programming and the Theory of the Firm*, pp. 89–93. New York: The Macmillan Co., 1960. **(1)**

3. BOWMAN, E. H., AND FETTER, R. B. *Analysis of Industrial Operations*, pp. 3–165. Homewood, Ill: Richard D. Irwin, Inc., 1959.

4. ———. *Analysis for Production Management*, pp. 77–125. Homewood, Ill: Richard D. Irwin, Inc., 1956. **(1, 2)**

5. CHURCHMAN, C. W., *et al. Introduction to Operations Research*, pp. 275–387. New York: John Wiley & Sons, Inc., 1957.

6. DORFMAN, ROBERT, *et al. Linear Programming and Economic Analysis*, pp. 80–93, 106–29. New York: McGraw-Hill Book Co., Inc., 1958. **(1, 2)**

7. FERGUSON, R. O., AND SARGENT, L. F. *Linear Programming: Fundamentals and Applications*. New York, McGraw-Hill Book Co., Inc., 1958.

8. HENDERSON, A., AND SCHLAIFER, R. "Mathematical Programming; Better Information for Better Decision Making," *Harvard Business Review*, May–June, 1954. **(2)**

9. KEMENY, JOHN G., *et al. Finite Mathematics with Business Applications*, pp. 384–400. Englewood Cliffs, N.J.: Prentice-Hall, Inc., 1962. **(1)**

10. STOCKTON, R. S. *Introduction to Linear Programming*, pp. 43–103. Boston: Allyn and Bacon, Inc., 1960. **(1, 2)**

11. VAJDA, S. *Readings in Linear Programming.* New York: John Wiley & Sons, Inc., 1958. **(1, 2)**

12. VAZSONYI, A. *Scientific Programming in Business and Industry*, pp. 99–170. New York: John Wiley & Sons, Inc., 1958. **(1, 2)**

PART IV

Elements of Calculus with Applications

Some ideas of calculus can be traced as far back as Greek antiquity. But credit for the development of the subject is given to the mathematician and philosopher Gottfried W. Leibniz (1646–1716) and to the mathematician and physicist Isaac Newton (1642–1727). They made the most significant contributions to the development of the mathematical system of calculus simultaneously and independently.

The calculus was originally developed in connection with the study of physical phenomena. Today, however, the powerful techniques of calculus are increasingly used by management to analyze and solve problems related to the economics of business and industrial operations. It is desirable, therefore, that we study the basic concepts of this special mathematical system of varying quantities and demonstrate how some of its techniques can be applied to concrete business situations.

In Part II we have shown how functions can be used to describe in mathematical terms relations between varying quantities in business operations. Among other matters, we were able to find the rate of change of one variable with respect to another and the minimum or maximum of a function. For handling efficiently and effectively matters such as the above, however, we need the powerful tools of differential and integral calculus. Basic ideas and applications of the former subject appear in Chapter 11 and of the latter in Chapter 12. In Chapter 13, we deal with selective applications of calculus in business operations and economic analysis.

Chapter 11

DIFFERENTIAL CALCULUS

THE FIRST section of this chapter deals with the fundamental concept of limit and the basic condition of continuity of functions. Thus, Section 1 is introductory since limits and continuity are required topics for both differential and integral calculus. In the remaining two sections of this chapter we are concerned with two important problems. One is that of finding the instantaneous rate of change. The question is: given a function, how can we find the marginal rate of change of the dependent variable y at *any* given value of the independent variable x? In Section 2 we shall develop some formulas which give definite answers to this question. The other problem is that of determining the maximum or the minimum of a function. In Section 3 we shall show how, with the new tools developed in the preceding section, we can handle optimization and other related problems.

1. THE LIMIT CONCEPT AND CONTINUITY OF A FUNCTION

The entire mathematical system of the differential and integral calculus is based on two concepts: *function* and *limit*. The function concept has been the subject matter of Section 1, Chapter 6. We peripherally touched upon the limit concept when we showed how the instantaneous or marginal rate of change can be estimated graphically in Section 3, Chapter 6.

Here, we shall first give a computational understanding of the limit concept. Second, we shall define and explain the limit of a function. Finally, we shall define continuity and discuss the conditions of continuity of a function.

1.1. A Computational Understanding of the Limit Concept.

In order to give a clear understanding of the limit concept we shall illustrate the *limiting process*. We shall use this process to find the marginal rate of change at a given value of the independent variable

x of a function by computing the average rate of change of the dependent variable y over successively smaller and smaller increments Δx.

Example 1.1. Let the function

$$f(x) = \frac{x^2}{100}, \qquad x \geqslant 0$$

considered earlier be given again, where x represents investment and $y = f(x)$ total wheat production in bushels. The empirically meaningful portion of the graph of this function is shown in Figure 1.1.

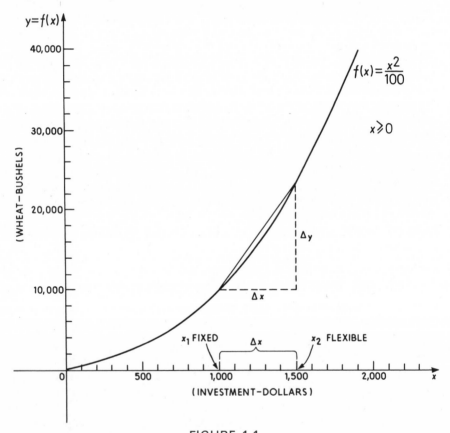

FIGURE 1.1.

We wish to find the marginal rate of wheat output at $x_1 = \$1000$. Of course, we cannot use $\Delta y/\Delta x$ over a given increment Δx to find the marginal rate at $x_1 = \$1000$ since the marginal rate is always changing for any Δx no matter how small. However, we can approximate this marginal rate by computing $\Delta y/\Delta x$ for smaller and smaller values of Δx.

Let $x_1 = 1000$ and let us consider the average rate of wheat output over a flexible investment increment from $x_1 = 1000$ to $x_2 = 1000 + \Delta x$. Note

that one end of this increment is fixed at x_1 as shown in Figure 1.1 while
the other at x_2 is changing depending on the value of Δx.

Substituting $x_1 = 1000$ and $x_2 = 1000 + \Delta x$ in $f(x) = x^2/100$, we have

$$f(1000) = \frac{(1000)^2}{100} = 10,000 ;$$

and

$$f(1000 + \Delta x) = \frac{(1000 + \Delta x)^2}{100} = 10,000 + 20\Delta x + \frac{(\Delta x)^2}{100} .$$

Then,

$$\Delta y = f(1000 + \Delta x) - f(1000)$$

$$= \underline{10,000} + 20\Delta x + \frac{(\Delta x)^2}{100} - \underline{10,000}$$

$$= 20\Delta x + \frac{(\Delta x)^2}{100} ;$$

and

$$\frac{\Delta y}{\Delta x} = 20 + \frac{\Delta x}{100}, \qquad \Delta x \neq 0$$

where $\Delta y/\Delta x$ is the average rate of wheat output over an incremental
investment Δx beginning at $x_1 = 1000$ and ending at $1000 + \Delta x$.

Now this increment is flexible in the sense that we can make its value
equal any quantity we wish by setting Δx equal to that quantity. Thus,
let $\Delta x = 500$.
Then

$$\frac{\Delta y}{\Delta x} = 20 + \frac{500}{100} = 25 .$$

Let $\Delta x = 100$. Then

$$\frac{\Delta y}{\Delta x} = 20 + \frac{100}{100} = 21 .$$

The values of $\Delta y/\Delta x$ for a few successively smaller values of Δx are shown
below:

Δx (dollars)	500	100	10	1	0.1
$\Delta y/\Delta x$ (bushels)	25	21	20.1	20.01	20.001

We can see that by taking the values of Δx near enough to zero we can
obtain values of the average rate of change as close to 20 bushels as we
wish. The smaller the increment Δx, i.e., the closer Δx is to zero, the
closer $\Delta y/\Delta x$ is to 20 bushels.

This fact may be stated in the following way: The difference between
$\Delta y/\Delta x$ and 20 can be made numerically as small as we please by choosing
a value of Δx which is near enough to zero. In other words, since

$$\frac{\Delta y}{\Delta x} = 20 + \frac{\Delta x}{100},$$

it follows that

$$20 - \frac{\Delta y}{\Delta x} = -\frac{\Delta x}{100}.$$

Since the smaller the value of Δx the smaller the difference $(20 - \Delta y/\Delta x)$ becomes, the marginal rate of wheat output must be 20 bushels at $x_1 = \$1000$. In such a case it is said that 20 bushels is the *limit* at $x_1 = \$1000$ as Δx gets closer and closer to zero.

The above illustration of the limiting process suggests a number of important points: First, the same approximation of the marginal rate can be obtained with negative increments Δx. In our example, we could approximate the marginal rate at $x_1 = 1000$ by considering an interval from $x_1 = 1000$ to $x_2 = 1000 - \Delta x$. But this task is left as an exercise. Second, although Δx can be as close to zero as we wish, it cannot be equal to zero since $\Delta y/\Delta x$ is not defined when $\Delta x = 0$. Third, unlike the approximate marginal rate of $19\frac{18}{101}$ bushels found graphically in Example 3.6 of Chapter 6, the limit of 20 bushels is the exact marginal rate at $x = \$1000$. It is not defined as the quotient $\Delta y/\Delta x$ no matter how small Δx is *but as the limit that $\Delta y/\Delta x$ approaches as $\Delta x \to 0$ read " as Δx gets closer and closer or approaches zero."*

In the above example we found the limit of $\Delta y/\Delta x$ as $\Delta x \to 0$ of a function at a given value of x. This limiting process is called *differentiation*. In the next section we shall introduce a mathematical expression called *derivative* with which we can obtain the limit of $\Delta y/\Delta x$ and hence the marginal rate of change of a function f at any value x in the domain of f. In the meantime, the limit concept just illustrated can also be used to define the limit of a function and to study the conditions of continuity of a function.

1.2. The Limit of a Function. *A function f is said to have a limit L as x approaches some fixed value c if, by choosing successive values of x close enough to c but different from c, the value of f may be made as close to L as we please.* The limit of a function is denoted by

(1.1)
$$\boxed{\underset{x \to c}{\text{limit}} f(x) = L,}$$

read " the limit of $f(x)$ as x approaches c is L."

Example 1.2. Consider again the function

$$f(x) = \frac{x^2}{100}, \qquad x \geqslant 0,$$

where x represents investment in dollars and $y = f(x)$ wheat production in bushels. Consider the function f in Figure 1.1 near the point $x = 1000$.

Write

$$f(1000 + \Delta x) = \frac{(1000 + \Delta x)^2}{100}.$$

At $\Delta x = 0$, $f(1000) = 10{,}000$. Now let Δx take on values

$$500, \ 100, \ 10, \ 1, \ 0.1, \ldots .$$

We find that f takes the corresponding values

$$22{,}500, \ 12{,}100, \ 10{,}201, \ 10{,}020.01, \ 10{,}002.001, \ldots ,$$

and approaches $L = 10{,}000$ as a limit as the value of Δx gets closer and closer to zero. The same result may be obtained if we let Δx take on negative values. Thus, an investment x approaches $c = \$1000$ from an increment less than or more than $\$1000$, i.e., as $x \to 1000$, the value of f approaches $L = 10{,}000$ bushels of wheat as a limit.

In regard to definition (1.1) of the limit of a function two important points must be emphasized:

First, the existence of the limit of a function f does not depend upon f being defined at $x = c$; in other words, the above definition is not concerned with the value of f at $x = c$ but with the values of f for all values of x near enough to c.

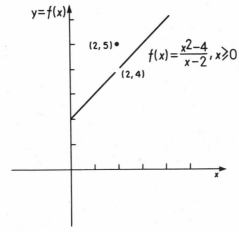

FIGURE 1.2.

Example 1.3. Let the function

$$f(x) = \frac{x^2 - 4}{x - 2}, \qquad x \geqslant 0$$

be given. The graph of the function is shown in Figure 1.2. At present, point $(2, 5)$ on the cc-plane should be ignored. In this case, the values of f exist for all values of x other than $x = 2$. For values $x \neq 2$ the value of f is the same as the value of function $g(x) = x + 2$, where $x \geqslant 0$, since

$$f(x) = \frac{x^2 - 4}{x - 2} = \frac{\cancel{(x - 2)}(x + 2)}{\cancel{(x - 2)}} = x + 2.$$

When $x = 2$, then function f is not defined since

$$f(2) = \frac{2^2 - 4}{2 - 2} = \frac{0}{0}.$$

Yet function f has a limit at $x = 2$. Consider the function f in Figure 1.2 near the point $x = 2$. Write

$$g(2 + \Delta x) = (2 + \Delta x) + 2.$$

Let Δx take on the values

$$1, \ 0.1, \ 0.01, \ 0.001, \ 0.0001, \ldots.$$

Then function g takes the corresponding values

$$5, \ 4.1, \ 4.01, \ 4.001, \ 4.0001, \ldots.$$

and approaches $L = 4$ as a limit as Δx approaches zero. The limit of g as $x \to 2$ is again 4 if we let Δx take on negative instead of positive values. Thus, by (1.1) we have

$$\lim_{x \to 2} (x + 2) = 4;$$

and it follows that

$$\lim_{x \to 2} \frac{x^2 - 4}{x - 2} = 4.$$

Second, for every open interval (a, b) containing c the difference $f(x) - L$ will be as close to zero as we please for all values of x other than c in this interval. One way to illustrate this point is with an example showing the opposite, namely, a case where we cannot make the difference $f(x) - L$ as close to zero as we wish.

Example 1.4. Let the function

$$f(x) = \begin{cases} 100 + 3x, & 0 \leqslant x \leqslant 1000 \\ 100 + 2x, & x > 1000, \end{cases}$$

where x represents units of an item and $y = f(x)$ the cost of production in dollars. The empirically meaningful portion of the graph of the function is shown in Figure 1.3. Observe that unit cost falls from \$3.00 to \$2.00 for production runs larger than 1000 units.

Consider the function f near the point $x = 1000$ and write

$$f(1000 + \Delta x) = 100 + 2(1000 + \Delta x), \quad x > 1000.$$

Let Δx take on the values

$$1, \quad 0.1, \quad 0.01, \quad 0.001, \quad 0.0001, \ldots$$

We find that f takes the corresponding values

$$2102, \quad 2100.2, \quad 2100.02, \quad 2100.002, \quad 2100.0002, \ldots,$$

and approaches $L_1 = 2100$ as a limit. Again, write

$$f(1000 + \Delta x) = 100 + 3(1000 + \Delta x), \qquad 0 \leqslant x \leqslant 1000.$$

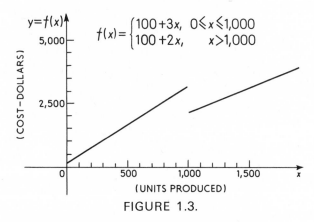

$$f(x) = \begin{cases} 100 + 3x, & 0 \leqslant x \leqslant 1,000 \\ 100 + 2x, & x > 1,000 \end{cases}$$

FIGURE 1.3.

Let Δx take on the values

$$-1, \quad -0.1, \quad -0.01, \quad -0.001, \quad -0.0001, \ldots.$$

We find that f takes the corresponding values

$$3097, \quad 3099.7, \quad 3099.97, \quad 3099.997, \quad 3099.9997, \ldots,$$

and approaches $L_2 = 3100$ as a limit. But $L_1 \neq L_2$ and for every open internal (a, b) containing $c = 1000$ we cannot make the difference $f(x) - L$ as close to zero as we please.

Note that in the above example the cost of production function f has no limit at $x = 1000$. For the limit L of a function f at a given value c of x exists if and only if the limit of successive values of f is L from *either* direction of the graph of f, i.e., if an only if $L_1 = L_2$.

1.3. Continuity of a Function. *A function f is continuous at some number c in the domain of f if*

(1.2)
$$\boxed{\lim_{x \to c} f(x) = f(c).}$$

Actually, condition (1.2) involves three conditions in one. Thus a function f is said to be continuous at some number c in the domain of f if—

I. $f(c)$ is defined,

II. The $\underset{x \to c}{\text{limit}} f(x)$ exists, and

III. The $\underset{x \to c}{\text{limit}} f(x) = f(c)$.

If any one of these three conditions is not satisfied, function f is said to be discontinuous at $x = c$. The following examples illustrate these three cases of discontinuity.

I. A function f may be discontinuous because the value of f at $x = c$ may not be defined although the limit of f at $x = c$ may exist.

Example 1.5. This case has already been discussed in Example 1.3. There, we have shown that the function

$$f(x) = \frac{x^2 - 4}{x - 2}$$

is not defined at $x = 2$, although the

$$\underset{x \to 2}{\text{limit}} \frac{x^2 - 4}{x - 2} = \underset{x \to 2}{\text{limit}} (x + 2) = 4.$$

Thus, function f is discontinuous at $x = 2$. In Figure 1.2 the discontinuity of f is shown as a break in the graph of f where point $(2, 4)$ has been removed. Point $(2, 5)$ should be ignored temporarily.

II. A function f may be discontinuous because the limit of f at $x = c$ does not exist.

Example 1.6. We have seen in Example 1.4 that the cost of production function

$$f(x) = \begin{cases} 100 + 3x, & 0 \leqslant x \leqslant 1000 \\ 100 + 2x, & x > 1000 \end{cases}$$

has no limit at $x = 1000$. Hence, function f is discontinuous at $x = 1000$. The discontinuity of f is shown in Figure 1.3 where its graph has a step at $x = 1000$.

III. A function f may be discontinuous because the limit is not the value of f at $x = c$, i.e.,

$$\underset{x \to c}{\text{limit}} f(x) \neq f(c).$$

Example 1.7. Consider the function in Example 1.5 but defined as follows.

$$f(x) = \begin{cases} \dfrac{x^2 - 4}{x - 2} & x \neq 2 \\ 5, & x = 2 \end{cases} \qquad x \geqslant 0.$$

The graph of the function is shown in Figure 1.2 with the only difference being that the previously missing point (2, 4) is now included, but raised one unit to become (2, 5). Function f is discontinuous because at $x = 2$ the limit of f is 4 while the value of f is 5, i.e.,

$$\lim_{x \to 2} f(x) = \frac{x^2 - 4}{x - 2} = \lim_{x \to 2} (x + 2) = 4 \neq f(2) = 5.$$

We can imagine that f is a cost of production function where x represents units of an item produced and $y = f(x)$ total production cost. In Example 1.5 the function is discontinuous because no production experience exists in the neighborhood of 2 units. In the present example the function is discontinuous because due to overtime, 2 units are produced at \$2.50 per unit instead of the regular \$2.00 per unit cost.

1.4. Recapitulation. From the mathematical standpoint algebraic functions involving polynomials, such as the function in Example 1.1, are continuous for all values of x. On the other hand, rational functions, such as functions in Examples 1.3 and 1.4, may not be continuous for all values of x. With the limit concept and continuity of a function we have laid out the foundations for what follows in this and the next two chapters.

PROBLEMS

1.1. Use the incremental method illustrated in Example 1.1 to find the instantaneous or marginal rate of wheat output at $x = 500$.

1.2. Verify the fact that the instantaneous rate of wheat output is 20 bushels at $x = \$1000$ as illustrated in Example 1.1 starting with an incremental Δx from $x_1 = \$1000$ to $x_2 = \$1000 - \Delta x$.

1.3. We have mentioned that the derivative of a function can give the instantaneous rate of change at *any* value of the independent variable x in the domain of a function. Consider the function $f(x) = x^2/100$ of Example 1.1 and do the following:

a) Find the values of the function for $500 \leqslant x \leqslant 1500$ at intervals of \$100, i.e., 500, 600, . . . , 1500 and sketch the graph of the function by plotting these points.

b) From the coordinates found in step (*a*) compute the average rate of change $\Delta y/\Delta x$.

c) Plot the points $(x + \Delta x/2, \Delta y/\Delta x)$ on the same cc-plane with the graph of the function.

d) Observing that the points in step (*c*) are the locus of a straight line, select the coordinates of two such points and derive the linear function whose graph is the straight line.

e) Verify the fact that this linear function is the derivative of the original function by finding the instantaneous rate of wheat output at $x = \$1000$.

1.4. Consider the function $S(x) = 1.5x - 45$ and do the following:

a) Show by selecting a few values of x that the average rate of change $\Delta y/\Delta x$ is the slope of the above function.

b) Explain why the slope of any linear function of form $f(x) = mx + b$ must be the derivative of such function.

1.5. For each function of Chapter 6 shown below find the marginal rate of change at the indicated values of the independent variable by the incremental method illustrated in Example 1.1 and explain its meaning.

*a) The average cost function per part

$$C(x) = \frac{x^2}{100} - 10x + 3000 \text{ in Example 3.8 at } x = 300 \text{ and } x = 700.$$

b) The total sales revenue function $S(p) = -1000p^2 + 10,000p$ in Example 3.9 at $p = 3$ and $p = 7$.

c) The total profit function $P(p) = -1000p^2 + 12,000p - 25,000$ in Example 3.9 at $p = 4$ and $p = 8$.

1.6. Let a portion of the graph of a function be as shown in the diagram below:

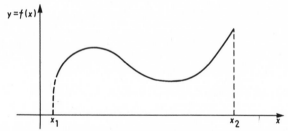

Describe how the instantaneous or marginal rate of y varies with respect to x as x increases from x_1 to x_2.

1.7. Frequently firms offer a discount on large order quantities in order to attract large orders and obtain economies from large production runs. Consider the function

$$C(x) = \begin{cases} 30x & 0 \leqslant x \leqslant 1000 \\ 28x & 1000 < x \leqslant 5000 \\ 24x & x > 5000, \end{cases}$$

where x is the number of units ordered and $y = C(x)$ the cost of purchasing x units of an item.

a) Sketch the graph of function C.

b) Find the limit of the function at $x = 500$, $x = 1000$, and $x = 5000$.

c) Explain why the function is discontinuous at $x = 1000$ and $x = 5000$.

1.8. If limit $f(x) = F$ and limit $g(x) = G$, then on the basis of the definition of the limit of a function the following theorems can be proved:

(1.8.1) $\lim_{x \to c} [f(x) \pm g(x)] = F \pm G,$

(1.8.2) $$\operatorname*{limit}_{x \to c} f(x) \cdot g(x) = F \cdot G,$$

(1.8.3) $$\operatorname*{limit}_{x \to c} \frac{f(x)}{g(x)} = \frac{F}{G}, \qquad G \neq 0.$$

Invoking the above theorems, which we assume proved, we can find the limit of a function. For instance, the limit of

$$f(x) = \frac{x^2 - 4}{x - 2}$$

in Example 1.3 as $x \to 2$ can be evaluated as follows:

$$\operatorname*{limit}_{x \to 2} \frac{x^2 - 4}{x - 2} = \operatorname*{limit}_{x \to 2} \frac{(x - 2)(x + 2)}{(x - 2)}$$

$$= \operatorname*{limit}_{x \to 2} \frac{x - 2}{x - 2} \cdot \operatorname*{limit}_{x \to 2} (x + 2) \qquad [\text{by } 1.8.2].$$

But

$$\operatorname*{limit}_{x \to 2} \frac{x - 2}{x - 2} = 1 \text{ since } \frac{x - 2}{x - 2} = 1 \text{ for } x \neq 2.$$

Hence,

$$\operatorname*{limit}_{x \to 2} \frac{x^2 - 4}{x - 2} = 1 \cdot \operatorname*{limit}_{x \to 2} (x + 2)$$

$$= \operatorname*{limit}_{x \to 2} x + \operatorname*{limit}_{x \to 2} 2 \qquad [\text{by } 1.8.1]$$

$$= 4.$$

On the basis of the above evaluate the following limits and explain why each function is continuous as the independent variable approaches the indicated value.

*a) $\operatorname*{limit}_{x \to 50} \dfrac{1000}{x}, \ x > 0.$

b) $\operatorname*{limit}_{x \to 1000} \dfrac{x^2}{100}, \ x \geqslant 0.$

*c) $\operatorname*{limit}_{x \to 50} (1.5x - 45), \ x \geqslant 40.$

d) $\operatorname*{limit}_{x \to 300} \left(\dfrac{x^2}{100} - 10x + 3000 \right), \ x \geqslant 0.$

e) $\operatorname*{limit}_{p \to 4} (-1000p^2 + 10{,}000), \ p \geqslant 0.$

f) $\operatorname*{limit}_{p \to 6} (-1000p^2 + 12{,}000p - 25{,}000), \ p \geqslant 0.$

1.9. Invoking the limit theorems given in Problem 1.8 find the limit of the following functions as x approaches the indicated value. Sketch the graph of each function and explain why each function is continuous or discontinuous at that value of x.

*a) $f(x) = \dfrac{3 - x}{6 - 2x}$, as $x \to 3$, $x \geqslant 0$.

*b) $f(x) = \dfrac{100}{x^2}$, as $x \to 0$, $x > 0$.

c) $f(x) = \dfrac{x - 1}{x^2 + x - 2}$, as $x \to 1$, $x \geqslant 0$.

d) $f(x) = \begin{cases} \dfrac{x - 4}{x^2 - 16}, & \text{for } x \neq 4 \\ 1, & \text{for } x = 4 \end{cases}$, as $x \to 4$, $x \geqslant 0$.

1.10. The manager of Electronics Supply Company, a firm engaged in the distribution of electronic parts, uses the following function

$$f(x) = \frac{1000}{x}, \quad x > 0,$$

where $y = f(x)$ represents the number of orders which can be filled for a varying size of orders x when the inventory of an item is kept at 1000 units.

a) Sketch the graph of the function.
b) Find the limit of f at $x = \infty$.
c) Is the function f continuous at $x = 0$. Why? Explain.

1.11. In Problem 2.10 of Chapter 6 the total transportation cost function for moving a carload over a 500-mile route may be expressed as follows:

$$f(x) = \begin{cases} \$0.50x, & \text{for } 0 \leqslant x \leqslant 100 \\ \$50, & \text{for } 100 < x \leqslant 200 \\ \$0.30x - \$10, & \text{for } 200 < x \leqslant 500 . \end{cases}$$

a) Sketch the graph of the above function.
b) Find the limit of the function as $x \to 150$ miles. Is the function continuous at $x = 150$? Why?
c) Find the limit of the function as $x \to 100$ miles. Is the function continuous at $x = 100$? Why?

1.12. Although Leibniz and Newton are considered the founders of the mathematical system of calculus, neither clarified the basic ideas of the subject. See reference 4 of this chapter's bibliography and read pp. 396–413 and 439–42. Then write a brief account of the gradual refinement of these basic ideas.

2. THE DERIVATIVE OF A FUNCTION; DIFFERENTIATION FORMULAS

In this section we shall first define the derivative of a function and introduce the necessary notation. Next, we shall show how this definition can be used to develop formulas for differentiating functions. In turn, we shall illustrate the application of such formulas for differentiating algebraic functions. Finally, we shall briefly discuss higher derivatives.

2.1 Definition of the Derivative. In the preceding section we have shown how we can find the instantaneous rate of change by taking the limit of the average rate of change $\Delta y/\Delta x$ as $\Delta x \to 0$ at a given value of x. This limit process called differentiation is the basis for defining the derivative of a function. The *derivative* of a function $y = f(x)$ at the number x is defined as

$$(2.1) \qquad \boxed{f'(x) = \lim_{\Delta x \to 0} \frac{f(x + \Delta x) - f(x)}{\Delta x},}$$

if this limit exists. Note that this definition is based on the limit concept and the condition of continuity. For if this limit does not exist, function f does not have a derivative at x.

The notation $f'(x)$ read "f prime of x" is used to denote the *value* which the derivative of f has at x. The *derivative* of function f defined by (2.1) is a function itself denoted by f'. A function which has a derivative is called a differentiable function.

It is important to realize that a derivative may be interpreted as the instantaneous rate of change of one variable with respect to another variable. Thus, if the function $y = f(x)$ has a derivative defined by (2.1), we may interpret $\Delta y/\Delta x$ as *average* rate of change and

$$(2.2) \qquad \boxed{f'(x) = \lim_{\Delta x \to 0} \frac{\Delta y}{\Delta x} = \lim_{\Delta x \to 0} \frac{f(x + \Delta x) - f(x)}{\Delta x}.}$$

as instantaneous rate of change of y with respect to x, where $\Delta y = f(x + \Delta x) - f(x)$. Therefore, finding the derivative of a function requires three steps: finding Δy, finding $\Delta y/\Delta x$, and taking the limit of $\Delta y/\Delta x$ as $\Delta x \to 0$.

Example 2.1. Find the derivative of

$$f(x) = \frac{x^2}{100},$$

where x represents investment in dollars and $y = f(x)$ wheat production in bushels.

Step 1: Find Δy.
For any x

$$f(x) = \frac{x^2}{100}.$$

Let Δx be any increment of x, positive or negative. Then

$$f(x + \Delta x) = \frac{(x + \Delta x)^2}{100}.$$

Since $\Delta y = f(x + \Delta x) - f(x)$, substituting we have

$$\Delta y = \frac{(x + \Delta x)^2}{100} - \frac{x^2}{100}$$

$$= \frac{\cancel{x^2} + 2x\Delta x + (\Delta x)^2 - \cancel{x^2}}{100}$$

$$= \frac{2x\Delta x + (\Delta x)^2}{100}.$$

Step 2: Find $\Delta y/\Delta x$.
Dividing Δy by Δx and simplifying, we get

$$\frac{\Delta y}{\Delta x} = \frac{2x}{100} + \frac{\Delta x}{100}.$$

Step 3: Take the limit of $\Delta y/\Delta x$ as $\Delta x \to 0$.

$$\lim_{\Delta x \to 0} \frac{\Delta y}{\Delta x} = \frac{2x}{100} = \frac{x}{50},$$

since the limit of $\Delta x/100$ is zero as $\Delta x \to 0$.

As previously explained, the derivative f' of a function f is a function itself. It can be used to find the instantaneous or marginal rate of change of f at any value of x.

Example 2.2. Consider the derivative

$$f'(x) = \frac{x}{50},$$

found in Example 2.1. Let $x = 1000$. Then

$$f'(1000) = \frac{1000}{50} = 20.$$

Note that the value of this derivative at $x = 1000$ is the marginal rate of change of wheat production found in Example 1.1 of the preceding section. Thus, the derivative f' is a function expressing the marginal rate of wheat output for any amount of investment of the differentiable function f.

For denoting the derivative of a function f at x we shall use the symbols

$$f'(x) \quad \text{and} \quad D_x f(x)$$

interchangeably. When the notation

$$y = f(x)$$

is used to denote a function f at x, then any of the following symbols

$$y', \quad D_x y, \quad \frac{dy}{dx}, \quad \text{and} \quad \frac{d}{dx} f(x)$$

may be used to denote the derivative of such function.

2.2 Differentiation Formulas.

The function and the limit concepts, the condition of continuity of a function, and the definition of the derivative represent the foundations of the mathematical system of differential calculus. With these tools at their disposal mathematicians were able to develop differentiation formulas or laws with which we are able to find the derivative of a given differentiable function. A few such formulas or laws are listed in Table 2.1 where $f(x)$ and $g(x)$ are values of functions f and g at x, respectively, and k and n are real constants. Additional formulas will be introduced as the need for them arises.

Before illustrating how these formulas can be used to find the derivative of a given function, we shall show how such formulas were developed by proving formulas 1, 2, and 3 in Table 2.1 only. The proof of some of the remaining formulas is left as an exercise for the interested reader.

TABLE 2.1.

A. *Constant and power functions:*
 1. If $f(x) = k$, then $f'(x) = 0$.
 2. If $f(x) = x$, then $f'(x) = 1$.
 3. $D_x[k \cdot f(x)] = k f'(x)$.
 4. If $f(x) = x^n$, then $f'(x) = nx^{n-1}$.

B. *Sum and difference of two functions:*
 5. $D_x[f(x) + g(x)] = f'(x) + g'(x)$.
 6. $D_x[f(x) - g(x)] = f'(x) - g'(x)$.

C. *Product and quotient of two functions:*
 7. $D_x[f(x) \cdot g(x)] = f(x) \cdot g'(x) + g(x) \cdot f'(x)$
 8. $D_x\left[\dfrac{f(x)}{g(x)}\right] = \dfrac{g(x) \cdot f'(x) - f(x) \cdot g'(x)}{g^2(x)}$.

D. *Powers of functions:*
 9. $D_x[f(x)]^n = n[f(x)]^{n-1} \cdot D_x f(x)$.

Example 2.3. Let $f(x) = k$ be given. We wish to prove that $f'(x) = 0$.
Proof:
If $f(x) = k$ (k is a real constant), then

$$\frac{\Delta y}{\Delta x} = \frac{k - k}{\Delta x} = 0,$$

for all $\Delta x \neq 0$; and

$$f'(x) = \underset{\Delta x \to 0}{\text{limit}} \frac{k-k}{\Delta x}; = \underset{\Delta x \to 0}{\text{limit}} 0 = 0 \qquad \text{[by 2.2].}$$

This ends the proof.

The result in the above example must be intuitively clear. *For the instantaneous rate of change of a constant function, say $f(x) = 3$, must be zero* since such a function depicts no change.

Example 2.4. Let $f(x) = x$ be given. We wish to prove that $f'(x) = 1$.
Proof:
If $f(x) = x$, then

$$\frac{\Delta y}{\Delta x} = \frac{(x + \Delta x) - x}{\Delta x} = \frac{\Delta x}{\Delta x},$$

and

$$f'(x) = \underset{\Delta x \to 0}{\text{limit}} \frac{\Delta y}{\Delta x} = \underset{\Delta x \to 0}{\text{limit}} \frac{\Delta x}{\Delta x} = \underset{\Delta x \to 0}{\text{limit}} 1 = 1 \qquad \text{[by 2.2].}$$

Thus, we have proved that $f'(x) = 1$.

Again the result of this example is intuitively clear *since for a linear function of the form $f(x) = mx + b$ where $m = 1$ the derivative must be one.*

Formula 3 states that *the derivative of a constant times a function is the constant times the derivative of the function.* For instance,

if $g(x) = 2x$, then
$$D_x(2x) = 2D_x x; \qquad \text{[by 3]};$$
and since
$$D_x x = 1 \qquad \text{[by 2]},$$
$$2D_x x = 2.$$

Example 2.5. Let $g(x) = kf(x)$. We wish to prove that $g'(x) = kf'(x)$.
Proof:
If $g(x) = kf(x)$, then

$$\frac{\Delta y}{\Delta x} = \frac{kf(x + \Delta x) - kf(x)}{\Delta x},$$

$$\frac{\Delta y}{\Delta x} = k\left[\frac{f(x + \Delta x) - f(x)}{\Delta x}\right], \qquad \text{by factoring } k;$$

$$\underset{\Delta x \to 0}{\text{limit}} \frac{\Delta y}{\Delta x} = \underset{\Delta x \to 0}{\text{limit}} k\left[\frac{f(x + \Delta x) - f(x)}{\Delta x}\right] \qquad \text{[by 2.2],}$$

$$\underset{\Delta x \to 0}{\text{limit}} \frac{\Delta y}{\Delta x} = k \underset{\Delta x \to 0}{\text{limit}}\left[\frac{f(x + \Delta x) - f(x)}{\Delta x}\right],$$

since the limit of a constant times a function is the constant times the limit of the function; therefore

$$g'(x) = kf'(x) \qquad \text{[by 2.2]}.$$

2.3. Application of Differentiation Formulas.

With the formulas in Table 2.1 we can find the derivative of the following algebraic functions. We shall explain each of them and illustrate their use with examples.

Formula 4 states that the *derivative of a power function* $f(x) = x^n$ is *n times the* $(n-1)st$ *power of x*.

Example 2.6. Find the derivative of the following functions:

$$a) \quad f(x) = x^3 ; \quad b) \quad g(x) = \frac{1}{x^4} ; \quad c) \quad y = \sqrt{x^3} .$$

Solutions:
From formula 4, we have
a) If $f(x) = x^3$, then

$$f'(x) = 3x^{3-1} = 3x^2 .$$

b) If $g(x) = 1/x^4$, then

$$g'(x) = D_x(x^{-4}) = -4x^{-4-1} = -4x^{-5} = -\frac{4}{x^5} .$$

c) If $y = \sqrt{x^3}$, then
$$y' = D_x(\sqrt{x^3}) = D_x(x^{3/2})$$
$$= \tfrac{3}{2}x^{3/2-1} = \tfrac{3}{2}x^{1/2} = \tfrac{3}{2}\sqrt{x} .$$

Observe that law 4 is a general case of formula 2 since the derivative of $f(x) = x^1$ is $f'(x) = 1x^{1-1} = 1x^0 = 1$.

Laws 5 and 6 state that the derivative of the sum (difference) of two functions is the sum (difference) of the derivatives of the functions.

Example 2.7. Differentiate the unit demand function

$$q = Q(p) = -1000p + 10{,}000,$$

where the independent variable p represents the price of the demanded number of mechanical toys q.

Solution:
If $q = -1000p + 10{,}000$, then

$$
\begin{aligned}
q' &= D_p(-1000p) + D_p 10{,}000 \qquad &\text{[by 6]},\\
&= D_p(-1000p) + 0 \qquad &\text{[by 1]},\\
&= -1000 D_p p \qquad &\text{[by 3]},\\
&= -1000 \qquad &\text{[by 2]}.
\end{aligned}
$$

Thus, the derivative $q' = -1000$ represents the reduction in the demand for the mechanical toy for each dollar increase in the price where $0 \leqslant p \leqslant 10$.

It is important to note that using p for x and q for y does not change the essential procedure of differentiating a function. Also, it should be noted that the derivative of a linear function, such as the one in the above example, is the slope of the graph of the function.

Example 2.8. Find the derivative of $P(x) = -2x^2 + 48x + 4320$.
Solution:
If $P(x) = -2x^2 + 48x + 4320$, then

$$
\begin{aligned}
P'(x) &= D_x(-2x^2) + D_x(48x) + D_x 4320 && \text{[by 5]}, \\
&= D_x(-2x^2) + D_x(48x) + 0 && \text{[by 1]}, \\
&= -2D_x(x^2) + 48 D_x(x) && \text{[by 3]}, \\
&= -4x + 48 && \text{[by 4]}.
\end{aligned}
$$

On the basis of the empirical situation described in the original example (Example 3.7, Chapter 6), $P'(x) = -4x + 48$ represents the marginal gross profit function for a given number of vacant apartment units.

Observe that the derivative of a quadratic function is a linear function.

In words, formula 7 states that *the derivative of the product of two functions is the first function times the derivative of the second function plus the second function times the derivative of the first function.*

Example 2.9. Differentiate $f(x) = (x^2 + 3)(x^3 - 5)$.
Solution:
If $f(x) = (x^2 + 3)(x^3 - 5)$, then

$$
\begin{aligned}
f'(x) &= (x^2 + 3) \cdot D_x(x^3 - 5) + (x^3 - 5) \cdot D_x(x^2 + 3) && \text{[by 7]}, \\
&= (x^2 + 3) \cdot [D_x(x^3) - D_x 5] + \\
& \qquad\qquad + (x^3 - 5) \cdot [D_x(x^2) + D_x 3] && \text{[by 5 and 6]}, \\
&= (x^2 + 3) \cdot 3x^2 + (x^3 - 5) \cdot 2x && \text{[by 1 and 4]}, \\
&= 3x^4 + 9x^2 + 2x^4 - 10x && \text{by multiplying}, \\
&= 5x^4 + 9x^2 - 10x, && \text{by collecting common factors.}
\end{aligned}
$$

Of course for differentiating the function in the above example we could simplify the function first and then differentiate.

Example 2.10. Simplifying the function in the previous example, we have

$$
f(x) = (x^2 + 3)(x^3 - 5) = x^5 + 3x^3 - 5x^2 - 15 .
$$

We differentiate the simplified function by invoking mentally the required laws of Table 2.1.
Solution:
If $f(x) = x^5 + 3x^3 - 5x^2 - 15$, then

$$
f'(x) = 5x^4 + 9x^2 - 10x ,
$$

as before.

Since rational functions are discontinuous for values of the independent variable x for which the denominator of the function is zero, formula 8 is of particular interest. It states that *the derivative of a quotient of two functions is the denominator (function) times the derivative of the numerator (function) minus the numerator times the derivative of the denominator all divided by the square of the denominator.*

Example 2.11. Differentiate

$$f(x) = \frac{x^2 - 4}{x - 2}.$$

Solution:

$$\text{If } f(x) = \frac{x^2 - 4}{x - 2}, \quad \text{for } x \neq 2,$$

then invoking the required laws of Table 2.1 we have

$$f'(x) = \frac{(x - 2)D_x(x^2 - 4) - (x^2 - 4) \cdot D_x(x - 2)}{(x - 2)^2}$$

$$= \frac{(x - 2) \cdot (2x) - (x^2 - 4)(1)}{(x - 2)^2}$$

$$= \frac{x^2 - 4x + 4}{(x - 2)^2}.$$

The reader may verify that for values $x \neq 2, f'(x)$ in the above example is identically one, i.e., $f'(x) = 1$.

Example 2.12. Find the derivative of $f(x) = 1000/x$.
Solution:
If $f(x) = 1000/x$, then

$$f'(x) = \frac{x \cdot D_x 1000 - 1000 \cdot D_x x}{x^2}$$

$$= -\frac{1000}{x^2} \qquad \text{[by 7, 1, and 2]}.$$

Finally, formula 9 can be used to differentiate powers of functions.

Example 2.13. Differentiate the functions (*a*) $f(x) = (x^2 + 5)^5$; and
(*b*) $g(x) = \dfrac{1}{(x^2 + 2x - 5)^2}.$

Solutions:
a) If $f(x) = (x^2 + 5)^5$, then

$$f'(x) = D_x(x^2 + 5)^5 = 5(x^2 + 5)^4 \cdot D_x(x^2 + 5)$$

$$= 5(x^2 + 5)^4 \cdot 2x$$

$$= 10x(x^2 + 5)^4.$$

b) If $f(x) = \dfrac{1}{(x^2 + 2x - 5)^2}$, then

$$f'(x) = D_x\left[\frac{1}{(x^2 + 2x - 5)^2}\right]$$

$$= D_x[(x^2 + 2x - 5)^{-2}]$$

$$= -2(x^2 + 2x - 5)^{-3} \cdot D_x(x^2 + 2x - 5)$$

$$= -2(x^2 + 2x - 5)^{-3} \cdot (2x + 2)$$

$$= -\frac{4x + 4}{(x^2 + 2x - 5)^3}.$$

2.4. Higher Derivatives. If f' is the derivative of the function f, then f' is called the *first derivative* of f; and the derivative of f' denoted by f'', is called the *second derivative* of f. Continuing this process we take the derivative f''', called the *third derivative* of f, and so on.

Example 2.14. Find the first four derivatives of

$$f(x) = x^4 - 4x^3 + 8.$$

Solution:
If $f(x) = x^4 - 4x^3 + 8$, then

$$f'(x) = 4x^3 - 12x^2,$$

$$f''(x) = 12x^2 - 24x,$$

$$f'''(x) = 24x - 24,$$

$$f^{\text{IV}}(x) = 24.$$

Of course the fifth and higher derivatives of the above function are all zero.

Although higher derivatives are important in many scientific applications, the first and the second derivatives are pertinent to our limited objectives. Since the second derivative is the derivative of the instantaneous rate of change, it simply tells us whether this marginal rate of change is changing at an increasing, decreasing, or constant rate.

Example 2.15. Find and interpret the second derivative of

$$f(x) = \frac{x^2}{100},$$

where x represents dollar investment and $y = f(x)$ total wheat output as previously explained.
Solution:
If $f(x) = x^2/100$, then

$$f'(x) = \frac{x}{50},$$

$$f''(x) = \frac{1}{50}.$$

While the first derivative, as already explained, indicates the marginal efficiency of capital, the second shows that this efficiency rate is increasing at a constant rate of $1/50$. For instance, if investment increases from $1000 to $1100, then

$$f'(1000) = \frac{1000}{50} = 20, \text{ and}$$

$$f'(1100) = \frac{1100}{50} = 22.$$

Hence, $\Delta y = 22 - 20 = 2$, $\Delta x = 1100 - 1000 = 100$, and

$$\frac{\Delta y}{\Delta x} = \frac{2}{100} = \frac{1}{50}.$$

2.5. Recapitulation. In this section we have shown how the laws of differentiation were developed and how we can use them to find the first and higher derivatives of an algebraic function. We have found that the first derivative represents the instantaneous or marginal rate of change of the dependent variable y with respect to the independent variable x; while the second derivative indicates whether this marginal rate is changing at an increasing, decreasing, or constant rate. Furthermore, we have seen that the first and second derivatives can be empirically meaningful, depending on the real-world situation the differentiable function describes. But the importance of the first and second derivatives of a function will be more fully demonstrated in the next section.

PROBLEMS

2.1. For each function taken from examples of Chapter 6 indicated below do the following:
  i) Find the derivative of the function using the definition of the derivative formula (2.2).
  ii) Check your answers to (i) by invoking step by step the differentiation laws in Table 2.1.
  iii) Explain the meaning of each derivative in empirical terms.
  a) $f(x) = 50x + 3000$, Example 1.1.
  b) $f^{-1}(x) = \frac{1}{50}x - 60$, Example 1.3.
  c) $S(x) = 0.15x - 4,550,000$, Example 2.4.
  d) $S(q) = 10q$, Example 2.5.
  e) $C(q) = 6.7q + 15,000,000$, Example 2.5.
  f) $C(x) = x^2/100 - 10x + 3000$, Example 3.8.
  g) $S(p) = -1000p^2 + 10,000p$, Example 3.9.
  h) $C(p) = -2000p + 25,000$, Example 3.9.
  i) $P(p) = -1000p^2 + 12,000p - 25,000$, Example 3.9.

2.2. The functions given below correspond to the indicated problems of Chapter 6. For each function answer (i), (ii), and (iii) of Problem 2.1 above.

*a) $f(t) = -1.5t + 100$, Problem 2.3.
b) $f(x) = 10,000 - 75x$, Problem 2.4.
c) $g(d) = 0.00625d + 1.00$, Problem 2.8.
d) $h(x) = -10x^2 + 80x + 2000$, Problem 3.9.
*e) $f(x) = -x^2 + 20x$, Problem 3.15.
f) $f(x) = x^2 - 100x + 4000$, Problem 3.16.

2.3. Use the steps of the proof shown in Example 2.5 to find the derivative of the following functions:

a) Functions *(a), (b), (c), (d), (e), (f), *(g), (h), and (i) of Problem 2.1.
b) Functions (a), (b), (c), (d), (e), and (f) of Problem 2.2.

2.4. Differentiate:

*a) $f(x) = 5x^6$.
b) $g(y) = \frac{1}{5}y^5 + \frac{1}{4}y^4 - \frac{1}{2}y^2$.
c) $f(z) = 1/4z^5$, $z \neq 0$.
d) $g(x) = 1/3x^3$, $x \neq 0$.
*e) $f(x) = \sqrt{6x^3}$.
f) $g(x) = \sqrt[3]{6x^2}$.
g) $f(x) = x^0$.

2.5. Differentiate:

*a) $f(x) = (2x + 1)(2 - 3x)$.
b) $f(y) = (y^2 + 4)(y^3 - 5)$.
c) $g(x) = (x - 1)(x^2 - 3x + 1)$.
d) $g(y) = y^3(3y^2 - 5y + 3)$.

2.6. Differentiate:

*a) $f(x) = \dfrac{3 - x}{6 - 2x}$, $x \neq 3$.

b) $f(y) = \dfrac{y - 1}{y^2 + y - 2}$, $y \neq 1$.

c) $g(x) = \dfrac{x - 4}{x^2 - 16}$, $x \neq 4$.

d) $g(y) = \dfrac{y^2 - k^2}{y^2 + k^2}$, k a constant.

2.7. Differentiate:

*a) $f(x) = (x^2 + 3)^5$.
b) $f(y) = (y^2 + 3y - 5)^3$.
c) $g(x) = (1 - x^2)^{20}$.

d) $g(y) = \dfrac{1}{y^2 + y - 2}$, $y \neq 1$.

e) $h(z) = \left(\dfrac{z^2 - 1}{z^2 + 1}\right)^2$.

2.8. Find the first three derivatives of—
*a) $y = 10x^6$.
*b) $g(x) = \sqrt{6x^3}$.
c) $x = (y^2 + 5)(y^2 - 5)$.
d) $u(x) = \dfrac{x+4}{x-4}$, $x \neq 4$.
e) $v(y) = (y + 2)^4$.

2.9. Find the second derivative of the following functions in Problem 2.1 and interpret its empirical meaning: *(a), (b), (c), (d), (e), (f), *(g), (h), and (i).

2.10. If $g(x) = \dfrac{f(x)}{k}$, where $f'(x)$ exists and $k \neq 0$, then using the definition of the derivative prove that

$$D_x\left(\frac{f(x)}{k}\right) = \frac{f'(x)}{k}.$$

2.11. On the basis of the proof in Problem 2.10, find:
*a) $D_x\left(\dfrac{x^2 + 2x - 5}{5}\right)$.

b) $D_x\left(\dfrac{2}{3}(-3x^2 + 2x + 10)\right)$.

2.12. If $f(x) = \dfrac{k}{u(x)}$, where $u'(x)$ exists and $u(x) \neq 0$, then using laws 8 and 1 in Table 2.1 prove that

$$\frac{d}{dx}\left(\frac{k}{u(x)}\right) = -\frac{ku'(x)}{u^2(x)}.$$

2.13. On the basis of the above proof, find:

*a) $\dfrac{d}{dx}\left(\dfrac{1}{x^2 - 1}\right)$, $x \neq 1$.

b) $\dfrac{d}{dx}\left(\dfrac{7}{x + 3}\right)$, $x \neq -3$.

c) $\dfrac{d}{dy}\left(\dfrac{1}{y^2 + y - 2}\right)$, $y \neq 1$.

2.14. Using the definition of the derivative prove that $D_x(mx + b) = m$.

2.15. If $f(x) = \dfrac{4x^3 + 6x^2 + 12x}{12}$, find—

a) $f'(x)$.
b) $f'(3)$.
c) $f'(a)$.
d) $f'(a^2 + 1)$.
e) $f'(1 - x)$.

2.16. We have seen that the derivative of a nonlinear function is the slope or tangent line at any point of the graph of the function; in other words, $f'(x) = m$, where m is the slope of the tangent to the graph of $f(x)$ at x. For instance, in Example 1.1 we have found that $f'(1000) = 20$. We can find the equation of the tangent at $x = 1000$ by substituting in the point-slope form (4.5) of Chapter 5,

$$y - y_1 = m(x - x_1).$$

Since $x_1 = 1000$, $y_1 = 10,000$, and $f'(1000) = 20$, we have

$$y - 10,000 = 20(x - 1000);$$
$$y = 20x - 20,000 + 10,000$$
$$= 20x - 10,000.$$

On the basis of the above example find equations of the tangent lines to the graph of each function below and sketch the graph of the function showing these tangent lines.

*a) $S(p) = -1000p^2 + 10,000p$ at $p = 3$, $p = 5$, and $p = 8$.
b) $f(x) = x^3 - 5x$, at $x = 3$, $x = 0$, and $x = -3$.

2.17. Using the definition of the derivative and the limit theorems in Problem 1.8 prove the following differentiation formulas in Table 2.1.
a) Formula 5.
b) Formula 6.
c) Formula 7. (*Hint:* To the difference quotient

$$\frac{f(x + \Delta x)g(x + \Delta x) - f(x)g(x)}{\Delta x}$$

add and subtract

$$\frac{f(x + \Delta x)g(x)}{\Delta x}$$

in order to separate the two functions, then use the limit theorems.)
d) Formula 8. (*Hint:* To the difference quotient

$$\frac{\dfrac{f(x + \Delta x)}{g(x + \Delta x)} - \dfrac{f(x)}{g(x)}}{\Delta x}$$

add and subtract

$$\frac{f(x)g(x)}{\Delta x g(x + \Delta x)g(x)}$$

then use the limit theorems.)

3. MAXIMUM AND MINIMUM VALUES; APPLICATIONS

Finding and analyzing the maximum or the minimum of quadratic functions was the subject matter of Section 3, Chapter 6. There, such analysis was carried out with the tools of algebra. Now we shall show

how differentiation may be used to study the maximum and minimum values of functions in general.

In this section we shall first define the maximum and minimum values of a function. Next we shall show how such values can be found with differentiation. This discussion will allow us to show some applications of differential calculus related to the maximum or minimum values of a function.

3.1. Maximum and Minimum Values of a Function.

Let $f(x_1)$ be a value of a function f at $x = x_1$ over the *closed interval* $[a, b]$, where $a \leqslant x_1 \leqslant b$. Then $f(x_1)$ is said to be a *relative maximum value* of f, if

$$f(x_1) \geqslant f(x_1 + \Delta x),$$

and a *relative minimum value* of f, if

$$f(x_1) \leqslant f(x_1 + \Delta x),$$

where $a \leqslant x_1 + \Delta x \leqslant b$ for all positive and negative values of Δx sufficiently close to zero.

Example 3.1. A portion of the graph of function

$$f(x) = x^3 + 3x^2 - 1$$

is sketched in Figure 3.1.

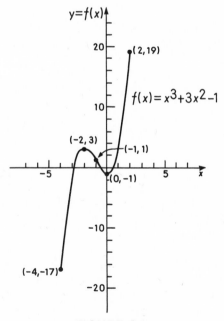

FIGURE 3.1.

It is clear that $f(-2)$ is a relative maximum value of the function in the closed interval $[-3, -1]$ since $f(-2) = 3$ is greater than any other value of the function in that interval. For instance, let $\Delta x = -1$. Since $x_1 = -2$, $x_1 + \Delta x = -3$ and $f(-3) = -1$. Let $\Delta x = 1$. Since $x_1 = -2$, $x_1 + \Delta x = -1$ and $f(-1) = 1$.

Similarly, $f(0)$ is a relative minimum value of the function in the closed interval $[-1, 1]$ since $f(0) = -1$ is smaller than any other value of the function in that interval. For instance, let $\Delta x = -1$. Since $x_1 = 0$, $x_1 + \Delta x = -1$ and $f(-1) = 1$ as previously. Let $\Delta x = 1$. Since $x_1 = 0$, $x_1 + \Delta x = 1$ and $f(1) = 3$.

It is important to note that in the above definition the term *relative* means that the value $f(x_1)$ of a function f is a maximum (minimum) when compared with the nearby values of the function over a closed interval. But $f(x_1)$ may not be a maximum (minimum) of a function f when compared with all possible values of f in a given interval containing x_1. Let $f(x_1)$ be a value of a function f at $x = x_1$ in the closed interval $[a, b]$, where $a \leqslant x_1 \leqslant b$. Then $f(x_1)$ is said to be an *absolute maximum value* of f, if

$$f(x_1) \geqslant f(x)$$

and an *absolute minimum value* of f, if

$$f(x_1) \leqslant f(x)$$

for all values of x in the given interval.

Example 3.2. Consider again the function

$$f(x) = x^3 + 3x^2 - 1$$

whose graph in the closed interval $[-4, 2]$ is sketched in Figure 3.1.

The values $f(-2)$ and $f(0)$ are relative maximum and minimum values of the function, respectively; while $f(2)$ and $f(-4)$ are absolute maximum and minimum values, respectively, in the given interval. Point $(-2, 3)$ on the graph is called the relative maximum point and $(0, -1)$ the relative minimum point.

From the above definitions it is obvious that whether a given value of a function is an absolute or a relative maximum (minimum) value depends on the given closed interval. In Example 3.2 we have found that the value $f(-2)$ of the function is a relative maximum value in the closed interval $[-4, 2]$. However, by the definition of absolute maximum (minimum) value the same value $f(-2)$ is an absolute maximum in the closed interval $[-3, -1]$. Thus, in order to find the absolute maximum (minimum) value of a function in a given closed interval we may first find, if possible, all the relative maximum (minimum) values of the function in that interval. The largest of such values algebraically is the absolute maximum and the smallest the absolute minimum value of the function in the given interval. A relative maximum (minimum) value of a function f is called an *extremum* of f; and from now on, when we speak of a maximum (minimum) without stating the interval we shall always mean extremum of a function.

3.2. Finding the Extrema of a Function.
Finding the relative maximum (minimum) of a function is based on a number of theorems. Here, we shall simply give the necessary definitions and explain a few theorems without formal proof.

Let a function f be continuous in the closed interval $[a, b]$ and let $x = x_1$ such that $a \leqslant x_1 \leqslant b$. If $f(x_1)$ is an extremum over the interval $[a, b]$, then x_1 is called a *critical* number of function f. For cases where the first derivative of f at $x = x_1$, i.e., $f'(x_1)$, exists, there is a theorem which states that an extremum cannot exist unless $f'(x_1) = 0$. This means that we can determine the critical numbers for which a function may have extrema by finding the first derivative of the function and solving it for zero.

Example 3.3. Consider again the function

$$f(x) = x^3 + 3x^2 - 1 .$$

Find the critical numbers of this function.
Solution:
The function is continuous and has a derivative

$$f'(x) = 3x^2 + 6x$$

for every x in the domain of the function. If $f'(x) = 0$, then

$$3x^2 + 6x = 0 , \text{ or}$$

$$3x(x + 2) = 0 .$$

Hence, $x_1 = -2$ and $x_2 = 0$, for which the above equation is satisfied, are the critical numbers of the function.

This example connects the above theorem with earlier discussions. We have seen that the derivative of a function represents the slope of the tangent at any given value of x in the domain of the function. Since the tangent at a maximum or a minimum point of the graph of the function is parallel to the x-axis with slope zero, the derivative must be equal to zero at that critical number of the function.

Note, however, that letting the first derivative of a function equal zero is a *necessary* condition for finding extrema, but *not a sufficient* condition for determining whether each critical number represents a maximum or a minimum. This is accomplished with the so-called first and second derivative tests for extrema.

The *first derivative test* is based on the following theorem: If a function

f is continuous and if x_1 is the only critical number of f in a closed interval $[a, b]$, then

(1) $f(x_1)$ is a maximum value of f if $f'(a) > 0$ and $f'(b) < 0$;
(2) $f(x_1)$ is a minimum value of f if $f'(a) < 0$ and $f'(b) > 0$.

Example 3.4. Find whether each of the critical numbers $x_1 = -2$ and $x_2 = 0$ of the function $f(x) = x^3 + 3x^2 - 1$ in Example 3.3 represents a maximum or a minimum value.

Solution:

Test critical number $x_1 = -2$:

Let the closed interval $[-3, -1]$, for which $x_1 = -2$ is the only critical number of the function be given. Since $a = -3$, substituting in $f'(x) = 3x^2 + 6x$ we have

$$f'(-3) = 3(-3)^2 + 6(-3) = 9 > 0;$$

and since $b = -1$,

$$f'(-1) = 3(-1)^2 + 6(-1) = -3 < 0.$$

Hence, $f(-2) = 3$ is a maximum value of the function.

Test critical number $x_2 = 0$:

Let the closed interval $[-1, 1]$, for which $x_2 = 0$ is the only critical number of the function, be given. Since $a = -1$,

$$f'(-1) = 3(-1)^2 + 6(-1) = -3 < 0;$$

and since $b = 1$,

$$f'(1) = 3(1)^2 + 6(1) = 9 > 0.$$

Hence, $f(0) = -1$ is a minimum value of the function. The above extrema $(-2, 3)$ and $(0, -1)$ are shown in Figure 3.1.

Finding the extrema of some functions by the first derivative test may be time consuming. In such cases it may be more convenient to employ the *second derivative test* for extrema. It is based on the following theorem: If $f'(x_1) = 0$ and $f''(x)$ exists for every value of x in an interval containing x_1 of a function f, then

(1) $f(x_1)$ is a maximum value of f if $f''(x_1) < 0$;
(2) $f(x_1)$ is a minimum value of f if $f''(x_1) > 0$.

Example 3.5. Apply the second derivative test to find whether each of the critical numbers $x_1 = -2$ and $x_2 = 0$ of the function $f(x) = x^3 + 3x^2 - 1$ in Example 3.3 represents a maximum or a minimum value.

Solution:

Differentiating the given function twice, we have

$$f'(x) = 3x^2 + 6x$$

and

$$f''(x) = 6x + 6.$$

Test critical number $x_1 = -2$:
Substituting $x_1 = -2$ in $f''(x)$, we get

$$f''(-2) = 6(-2) + 6 = -6 < 0.$$

Hence, $f(-2) = 3$ is a maximum value of the function as found previously.
Test critical number $x_2 = 0$:
Substituting $x_2 = 0$ in $f''(x)$, we have

$$f''(0) = 6(0) + 6 = 6 > 0.$$

Hence, $f(0) = -1$ is a minimum value of f as found previously.

All told, in order to find the extrema of a function, either of the two tests may be used, whichever is more convenient. Application of either test will locate all the extrema of a function in a given interval except end points, such as points $(-4, -17)$ and $(2, 19)$ in Figure 3.1. Such end points require a separate examination of the function. Furthermore, a function may have a maximum (minimum) value which cannot be identified because the first derivative of the function at a critical number does not exist. In still another case, a function may have an extremum which cannot be identified because the second derivative at a critical number is zero or does not exist. The reader will find exercises dealing with such cases among the problems of this section.

3.3. Inflection Points.

We have already seen that the concavity of the graph of a function is indicated by the sign of the second derivative. If the second derivative is negative, i.e., if $f''(x) < 0$, the graph of the function f at x is concave downward and if positive, i.e., if $f''(x) > 0$, the graph of f at x is concave upward. *A point $(x_1, f(x_1))$ is called a point of inflection if the graph of function f changes the direction of its concavity from downward to upward or vice versa.* A change in the concavity of the graph of f means that at $x = x_1, f''(x_1) = 0$. Thus, we can determine the critical numbers for which a continuous function f may have a point of inflection by finding the second derivative of f and solving it for zero.

Example 3.6. Find the point(s) of inflection of function f given in Example 3.1 and sketched in Figure 3.1 where

$$f(x) = x^3 + 3x^2 - 1.$$

Step 1. Find critical numbers.
Since

$$f''(x) = 6x + 6,$$

$f''(x) = 0$ when $x_1 = -1$. Hence, $x_1 = -1$ is the only critical number for an inflection point.
Step 2. Test critical number $x_1 = -1$.

Let $\Delta x = -1$. Since for $x = x_1 + \Delta x = -2$,

$$f''(-2) = 6(-2) + 6 = -6 < 0,$$

function f is concave downward at $x = -2$.
Let $\Delta x = 1$. Since for $x = x_1 + \Delta x = 0$,

$$f''(0) = 6(0) + 6 = 6 > 0,$$

function f is concave upward at $x = 0$. Therefore, point $(-1, 1)$ is an inflection point of the graph of f.

With the above example we illustrated the process of finding an inflection point of a decreasing function, where $f'(x_1) < 0$. Analogously, an increasing function f, where $f'(x_1) > 0$, has an inflection point if the graph of f changes the direction of its concavity at $x = x_1$. Furthermore, an inflection point may exist where a function is neither increasing nor decreasing at $x = x_1$, i.e., where $f'(x_1) = 0$. How to find an inflection point in the latter two cases will be illustrated presently.

3.4. Sketching the Graph of a Function. The above theory of extrema and points of inflection greatly facilitates the sketching of the graph of an algebraic function of third or higher order. The following example illustrates this point and at the same time summarizes our discussion on the tools of calculus which have been introduced in this section.

Example 3.7. Find extrema and inflection points of function f defined by

$$f(x) = x^4 - 8x^3 + 18x^2 - 27$$

and sketch its graph.
Solution:
Step 1. Find critical numbers.
Since

$$f'(x) = 4x^3 - 24x^2 + 36x$$
$$= 4x(x^2 - 6x + 9)$$
$$= 4x(x - 3)^2,$$

then $f'(x) = 0$ when $x = 0$ and $x = 3$.
Since

$$f''(x) = 12x^2 - 48x + 36,$$

then $f''(x) = 0$ when $x = 1$.

Hence, the critical numbers are

$$x_1 = 0, \quad x_2 = 1, \text{ and } x_3 = 3.$$

Step 2. Test critical number $x_1 = 0$.
Since

$$f''(0) = 12(0)^2 - 48(0) + 36 = 36 > 0,$$

$x_1 = 0$ is a critical value for a minimum point. Substituting $x_1 = 0$ in f we have

$$f(0) = (0)^4 - 8(0)^3 + 18(0)^2 - 27 = -27.$$

Point $(0, -27)$ in Figure 3.2 is a minimum with the graph of f concave upward in the neighborhood of $x_1 = 0$.

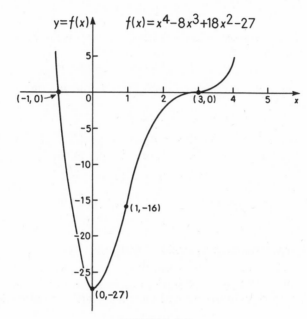

FIGURE 3.2.

Step 3. Test critical number $x_2 = 1$.
Since

$$f''(1) = 12(1)^2 - 48(1) + 36 = 0,$$

the second derivative test for extrema does not apply. However, $x_2 = 1$ is a critical value for an inflection point.

Let $\Delta x = -\frac{1}{2}$. Since for $x = x_2 + \Delta x = \frac{1}{2}$,

$$f''(\tfrac{1}{2}) = 12(\tfrac{1}{2})^2 - 48(\tfrac{1}{2}) + 36 = 15 > 0,$$

the graph of f is concave upward for $0 < x < 1$.
Let $\Delta x = 1$. Since for $x = x_2 + \Delta x = 2$,

$$f''(2) = 12(2)^2 - 48(2) + 36 = -12 < 0,$$

the graph of f is concave downward for $x > 1$.
Substituting $x_2 = 1$ in f, we have

$$f(1) = (1)^4 - 8(1)^3 + 18(1)^2 - 27 = -16.$$

Point $(1, -16)$ is an inflection point with the graph of f concave upward for $0 < x < 1$ and concave downward for $x > 1$ as shown in Figure 3.2.

Step 4. Test critical number $x_3 = 3$.
Since
$$f''(3) = 12(3)^2 - 48(3) + 36 = 0,$$
the second derivative test for extrema fails again. However, $x_3 = 3$ is a critical number for an inflection point since at $x = 2$,
$$f''(2) = -12 < 0$$
and the graph of f is concave downward for $1 < x < 3$ as shown previously; and at $x = 4$,
$$f''(4) = 12(4)^2 - 48(4) + 36 = 36 > 0$$
and the graph of f is concave upward for $x > 4$. Substituting $x_3 = 3$ in f, we have
$$f(3) = (3)^4 - 8(3)^3 + 18(3)^2 - 27 = 0.$$
Point $(3, 0)$ is an inflection point as shown in Figure 3.2.
Observe that $x = 3$ and $x = -1$ are the roots of equation
$$x^4 - 8x^3 + 18x^2 - 27 = 0.$$
Furthermore, the y-coordinate of the minimum point $(0, -27)$ is the y-intercept of f.

3.5. Optimization Analysis. In Chapter 6, Section 3, we had the opportunity to discuss the maximum or the minimum value of a function in connection with optimizing with quadratic functions. With the above theory of extrema we can have a second look at optimization analysis.

Example 3.8. Let the sales revenue function S and the cost function C be
$$S(x) = -2x^2 + 18x$$
and
$$C(x) = 6x,$$
where x represents units produced and sold, while revenue and cost are measured in dollars. Determine the maximum profit sales volume by finding and testing the total profit function for extrema.
Solution:
Step 1: Find the total profit function.
Since profits equal revenue minus cost, the total profit function P is
$$P(x) = S(x) - C(x)$$
$$= (-2x^2 + 18x) - (6x)$$
$$= -2x^2 + 12x.$$
Step 2: Find the critical value of P.
Differentiating we have,
$$P'(x) = -4x + 12.$$

Letting $P'(x) = 0$ and solving for x, we get

$$-4x + 12 = 0, \text{ and}$$

$$x = 3.$$

Hence, the critical value is $x = 3$.
 Step 3: Test critical number $x = 3$.
 The second derivative of P is

$$P''(x) = -4.$$

Substituting $x = 3$ in P, we obtain

$$P(3) = -2(3)^2 + 12(3)$$

$$= 18.$$

Since $P''(x) < 0$, point $(3,18)$ is a maximum.
 Therefore, the optimal output is 3 units and the realizable maximum profit $18.

For problems such as the one above there is another way of finding the optimal output with differential calculus. Since profit is the difference between total cost and total revenue, let us examine closer the cost and revenue functions. For every additional unit produced there is an incremental change in total production cost which represents the difference in total cost before and after such unit is produced. Similarly, for every additional unit sold there is an incremental change in total sales revenue which represents the difference in total sales revenue before and after such unit is sold. Profit is realized as long as the incremental increase in cost is less than the incremental increase in revenue. At what point will profits be largest? Maximum profit will be realized at the point where the incremental increase in revenue from the sale of one additional unit is sufficient to just cover the incremental increase in cost for producing that unit. In other words, profits will be at a maximum where marginal cost equals marginal revenue. This point can be proved very easily as follows:

Let S and C be the dollar sales revenue and cost functions defined by $S(x)$ and $C(x)$, respectively, where x represent units of an item. Then prove that for a sales volume where profit is at a maximum

$$S'(x) = C'(x).$$

Proof:
Since the profit function is

$$P(x) = S(x) - C(x),$$

differentiating we have

$$P'(x) = S'(x) - C'(x).$$

But at maximum profit $P'(x) = 0$.

Hence,

$$S'(x) - C'(x) = 0,$$

and

$$S'(x) = C'(x)$$

which ends the proof.

Example 3.9. This relationship is shown in Figure 3.3 for the functions $S(x) = -2x^2 + 18x$ and $C(x) = 6x$ given in the previous Example 3.8.

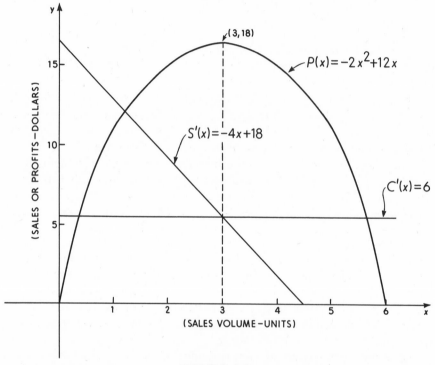

FIGURE 3.3.

Observe that at the optimal (largest profit) sales volume $x = 3$ and $S'(x) = C'(x) = 6$.

3.6. Additional Applications of Extrema.
Frequently a practical business problem asks for the largest area or volume, the least surface, or the lowest cost. Such a problem may be solved with application of the above theory of extrema by recognizing that the problem's solution is a maximum or a minimum value of some function. The following two examples illustrate such applications.

Example 3.10. A cattle rancher wishes to enclose a rectangular field with 400 yards of fencing. Find the dimensions of the field which encloses the largest area.

Solution:

Let x be the length, y the width, and A the area of the field. Then

(1) $$A = xy$$

and

(2) $$2x + 2y = 400.$$

Since A is the quantity to be maximized, we must express A as a function of one independent variable. Solving (2) for y, we have

$$y = 200 - x.$$

Substituting in (1), we obtain the function

$$A = f(x) = x(200 - x) = 200x - x^2, \qquad 0 < x < 200$$

which describes the area of the field. Clearly, the maximum area must occur for some value of x within the interval $0 \leqslant x \leqslant 200$ since $f(x) = 0$ at both end values of this interval. Thus, the solution of the problem requires finding and testing the critical number of the area function f.

Step 1: Find critical number.

Differentiating f, we find

$$f'(x) = 200 - 2x.$$

Now $f'(x) = 0$ when

$$200 - 2x = 0,$$

or $$x = 100.$$

Step 2: Test critical number $x = 100$.

Since

$$f'(99) = +2 \text{ and } f'(101) = -2,$$

$$f(100) = 200(100) - (100)^2 = 10,000$$

is a maximum value of f.

The required dimensions for the field with the largest area are $x = 100$ yards, and $y = 100$ yards, enclosing an area of 10,000 square yards.

Example 3.11. The manager of Industrial Designs Inc., a container and package designing firm, wishes to make a closed box with the following specifications: The box must have a square base and a volume of 27 cubic feet. Find the dimensions for a box with the smallest total surface. If the packaging material costs $0.01 per square foot, find the cost of the box.

Solution:

Let x be the side of the square base of the box. Then x^2 will be its surface and $2x^2$ will be the surface of the bottom and top of the box. Let y be the height of the box. Then $4xy$ will be the surface of the four sides of the box. Hence, the total surface of the box is described by the function where

$$f(x, y) = 2x^2 + 4xy, \qquad x > 0 \text{ and } y > 0.$$

Since the total volume of the box must be

$$x^2 y = 27,$$

solving for y we have

$$y = \frac{27}{x^2};$$

and substituting in f, we get

$$f(x) = 2x^2 + \frac{108}{x}.$$

Thus, the solution of the problem requires finding and testing for a minimum value of the surface function f.

Step 1: Find critical numbers.

Since

$$f'(x) = 4x - \frac{108}{x^2}$$

for every positive number x, the critical numbers of f are the positive solutions of the equation

$$4x - \frac{108}{x^2} = 0.$$

Solving for x, we have

$$4x^3 = 108,$$

or

$$x = 3$$

which is the only critical number of f.

Step 2: Test critical number $x = 3$.

Since

$$f''(x) = 4 + \frac{216}{x^3},$$

and

$$f''(3) = 12 > 0,$$

$$f(3) = 54$$

is a minimum value of f.

The required dimensions for a box with the smallest total surface are $3 \times 3 \times 3$. Its total surface is

$$f(3) = 2(3)^2 + 4(3)(3) = 54 \text{ square feet costing}$$

$$54 \times 0.01 = 0.54 \text{ dollars.}$$

3.7. Recapitulation. Our limited objective in this section has been to show a few elementary applications of the first and second derivatives of a continuous function. Although we dealt only with third order functions, the advantages of the new tools are apparent. We could find and test the extrema of a function quickly and accurately. In fact, the reader can very easily realize that the same analysis can be done on functions of higher than third order.

PROBLEMS

3.1. Find the extrema of each function by—
   i) The first derivative test.
   ii) The second derivative test.
   a) $f(x) = x^2 - x - 2$.
   b) $g(x) = -x^2 + 6x + 2$.
   c) $h(x) = -x^3 + 3x^2 + 1$.
   d) $s(x) = x^3 + 2x^2 + 5$.

3.2. Consider a portion of the graph of a function f shown below in the closed interval $[x_1, x_6]$. Indicate whether each of the values $f(x_1)$, $f(x_2), f(x_3), f(x_4), f(x_5)$, and $f(x_6)$ represents an absolute or a relative maximum (minimum) value of f.

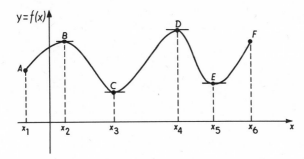

3.3. The functions given below were taken from Section 3 of Chapter 6. Test each function for extrema by
   i) the first derivative test and
   ii) the second derivative test.
   a) The gross profit function $P(x) = -2x^2 + 48x + 4320$ in Example 3.7.
   b) The production cost function $C(x) = x^2/100 - 10x + 3000$ in Example 3.8.
   c) The sales revenue function $S(p) = -1000p^2 + 10,000p$ in Example 3.9.

3.4. Find the extrema and inflection points and sketch the graph of the following functions:
   *a) The total wheat output function f where

$$f(x) = -\frac{8x^3}{10^6} + \frac{24x^2}{10^3} - 8x + 5000, \qquad 100 \leqslant x \leqslant 2000$$

and x represents capital outlay.

b) The total cost function f where

$$f(x) = \frac{x^3}{10^4} - \frac{9x^2}{10^2} + 18x + 3000 , \quad 100 \leqslant x \leqslant 550$$

and x represents number of parts produced per production run.

3.5. Consider Problem 1.14, Chapter 5.
  *a) Find the total profit function.
  b) Use differentiation to find the optimal waiting period for which the rancher will realize the maximum profit.
  *c) Find maximum profit.
  *d) Determine optimal quantity and profit per pound at optimal profit.
  e) Sketch the graphs of the total and marginal profit functions on the same cc-plane to verify the fact that at optimal waiting period total profit is largest and marginal profit is zero.

3.6. Let us assume that the manager of the railroad company in Problem 1.15, Chapter 5, would like to consider the additional costs amounting to one dollar for each extra passenger and decides to maximize net revenue instead of number of people served.
  *a) Find the net revenue function.
  b) Find the derivative of the revenue function and determine maximum net revenue.
  c) Determine number of passengers and optimal train fare per passenger at maximum net revenue.
  d) Sketch the graphs of the total net revenue and marginal revenue functions on the same cc-plane and verify the fact that marginal revenue is zero when total revenue is maximum.

3.7. For Problem 1.16, Chapter 5,
  a) Find total production cost function.
  b) Find maximum production cost and output by differentiating the total production cost function.
  c) Sketch the graphs of total and marginal cost functions on the same cc-plane, and verify the fact that marginal cost is zero when total production cost is at a maximum.

3.8. Let the unit demand function be $y = 20 - 2x$, where x represents units demanded and y price. Then the sales revenue function is $S(x) = yx = (20 - 2x)x = 20x - 2x^2$. Also, let the total cost function $C(x) = 4x$.
  *a) Since at maximum profit $S' = C'$, find optimal sales volume by differentiating the sales revenue and cost functions.
  *b) Find the profit function P and substitute for the optimal sales volume to find the maximum profit.
  c) Verify your answers to (*a*) and (*b*) by testing the profit function for extrema.
  d) Sketch the graphs of S and C functions on the same cc-plane and discuss the relationship among the variables involved with respect to the above optimal solution.

3.9. If the unit demand function is $y = 12 - 3x$, where x represents units demanded at price y, and the average cost function is $c = x + 4$,

a) Find the sales revenue S and total cost C functions.

b) Find optimal sales by differentiating S and C.

c) Find the profit function P and determine the maximum profit by substituting for optimal sales x.

d) Verify your answer to (b) by testing the profit function for extrema.

e) Sketch the graphs of S and C on the same cc-plane and the graphs of P, S', and C' on another cc-plane and discuss the relationship among the variables involved with respect to the above optimal solution.

3.10. Given the sales revenue function S and total cost function C where

$$S(x) = -\frac{6x^3}{10^6} + \frac{18x^2}{10^3} - 2x + 1000 \qquad\qquad x \geqslant 100,$$

$$C(x) = \frac{2x^2}{10^2} - 24x + 11,000,$$

and x represents units produced and sold while revenue and cost is measured in dollars,

a) Find the sales volume which represents the maximum profit.

b) Find the profit function P.

c) Verify your answer to (a) by testing the profit function P for extrema.

d) Find the maximum profit.

e) Sketch the graphs of P, S', and C' on the same cc-plane and discuss the relationship among the variables involved with respect to the above optimal solution.

3.11. Consider the sales revenue function $S(p) = -1000p^2 + 10,000p$ and the cost function $C(p) = -2000p + 25,000$, where p is the price of the mechanical toy of the pricing model for Toy Products, Inc., in Example 3.9 of Chapter 6.

a) Test the revenue function S for extrema as in Example 3.4.

b) Find the optimal price and maximum profit by marginal analysis including a graph as in Examples 3.8 and 3.9.

3.12. A cattle rancher wishes to enclose a rectangular field adjacent to a river. The side of the area on the river requires no fencing. For the other three sides of the area he has purchased 400 yards of fencing. Find the dimensions of the field which encloses the largest area.

3.13. The manager of Dependable Fences, Inc., received the following order from a rancher. The latter would like to use 24 miles of fence to enclose a rectangular pasture by first fencing the whole area and then dividing the area by running a fence across the middle.

a) What should the dimensions be so that the rancher can enclose the largest area?

b) What is the size of this area?

3.14. Suppose the same rancher would like to fence an area of 6 square miles in the same manner explained in Problem 3.13. What dimensions should the area have so that the amount of fence is minimized?

3.15. Let us assume that the manager in Example 3.11 plans to make an open box with a square base from 27 square feet of material. Find the dimensions so that the box will have a maximum volume.

*3.16. Suppose the manager in Example 3.11 would like to make another box with the following specifications: The box must have a square base made of material costing \$0.20 per square foot for the top and bottom and \$0.10 per square foot for the sides, and a volume of 16 cubic feet.

a) Find the dimensions of this box which minimize manufacturing costs.

b) Find minimum manufacturing costs.

3.17. Assume that the manager in Example 3.11 plans to make an open box from a square piece of cardboard 12×12 inches by cutting out the same size squares from the corners and folding up the sides.

a) Find how long the edge of the cutout squares should be for the box to have maximum volume.

b) Find this maximum volume.

3.18. The production manager of Fine Printing Company plans to include 80 square inches of actual printed matter in each page of a book under production. Each page should have a 2-inch-wide margin along the top and bottom and a 2.5-inch-wide margin along the sides. What are the most economical dimensions of each printed page?

3.19. Prove that of all rectangles with the same perimeter the square contains maximum area.

3.20. Find the first derivative of $f(x) = (x - 1)^{2/3} + 2$ and verify the fact that although $f(1)$ is a critical number, $f'(1)$ does not exist. Sketch the graph of the function.

3.21. Find the inflection points of the following functions:

a) $f(x) = x^3 - x^2 - 2$.

b) $g(x) = -x^3 + 6x^2 + 2$.

*c) $h(x) = -x^3 + 3x^2 + 1$.

d) $s(x) = x^3 + 2x^2 + 5$.

3.22. The tools of differential calculus greatly facilitate sketching the graph of a function. Sketch the graph of each function by finding its extrema and its points of inflection.

*a) $f(x) = x^3 - 3x^2$.

b) $f(x) = x^3 - 3x^2 + 4$.

c) $f(x) = x^4 - 8x^2$.

d) $f(x) = x^{1/3}$.

3.23. Sketch the graph of each function by finding the coordinates of its maxima (minima) and its inflection points. Verify the fact that at the point of inflection the first derivative of the function may be zero.

*a) $f(x) = x^4 - 4x^3 + 10$.

b) $f(x) = (x + 1)(x - 3)^3$.

c) $f(x) = (x + 1)^2(x - 2)^3$.

3.24. Given the signs of f' and f'' of a function f, indicate in the space provided whether each case may represent a maximum, minimum, or a point of inflection.

$f'(x)$	$f''(x)$	Type of Point
$-$	0	_____
0	$-$	_____
0	$+$	_____
$+$	0	_____
0	0	_____

3.25. The elasticity of a demand function f is defined as follows:

$$e = \frac{q}{p} \cdot f'(q),$$

where p is price and q quantity.

a) Find the elasticity of the demand function $p = f(q) = -2q^2 + 18$ for points $(1, 16)$ and $(2, 10)$.

b) Show that the elasticity of the demand function $p = f(q) = 100/q$ is unity for every value of q.

SUGGESTED REFERENCES

1. ANDREE, R. V. *Introduction to Calculus with Analytic Geometry*, pp. 91–166. New York: McGraw-Hill Book Co., Inc., 1962. (**1–3**)

2. EAVES, E. D., AND WILSON, R. L. *Introductory Mathematical Analysis*, pp. 102–26. Boston: Allyn and Bacon, Inc., 1961. (**1–3**)

3. JOHNSON, R. E., AND KIOKEMEISTER, F. L. *Calculus with Analytic Geometry*, pp. 58–144. Boston: Allyn and Bacon, Inc., 1959. (**1–3**)

4. KLINE, MORRIS. *Mathematics: A Cultural Approach*, pp. 396–416. Reading, Mass.: Addison-Wesley Publishing Co., Inc., 1962. (**1, 2**)

5. RICHARDSON, M. *Fundamentals of Mathematics*, pp. 299–325. Rev. ed. New York: The Macmillan Co., 1958. (**1–3**)

6. THOMAS, G. B. *Calculus and Analytic Geometry*, pp. 29–134. 3rd ed. Reading, Mass.: Addison-Wesley Publishing Co., Inc., 1962. (**1–3**)

7. THOMPSON, S. P. *Calculus Made Easy*, pp. 1–120. New York: The Macmillan Co., 1960. (**1–3**)

8. WESTERN, D. W., AND HAAG, V. H. *An Introduction to Mathematics*, pp. 371–402. New York: Henry Holt & Co., Inc., 1959. (**1–3**)

Chapter 12

INTEGRAL CALCULUS

IN THE FIRST section of the preceding chapter we explained carefully the limit concept; we defined the condition of continuity of functions; and we pointed out that the entire mathematical system of calculus is based on the concepts of limit and function. Here we shall use these basic ideas to develop the tools of integral calculus. We may conveniently divide the basics of integral calculus into two sections: the first dealing with the indefinite, the second with the definite integral. In our attempt to explain ideas we shall have the opportunity to show that the tools of integral calculus have extensions and applications to business situations as well.

1. ANTIDERIVATIVES AND THE INDEFINITE INTEGRAL

With respect to the indefinite integral, integration is sometimes called the process of antidifferentiation. Thus, our primary concern in this section is to show integration as the reverse of the process of differentiation. For in mathematics, one interpretation of the term "to integrate" means "to find a function whose derivative is given." Explaining, therefore, the process of antidifferentiation will pave the way for a definition of the indefinite integral and the introduction of the required notation. The remainder of this section deals with the use of formulas for integrating algebraic functions.

1.1. Differentiation Reversed: Antiderivatives. We have

already seen that to each differentiable function f there corresponds a derivative function f'. Now, we shall consider the reverse proposition. Let function f be given. Does there exist a function F such that f is the derivative of F? It can be proved that the answer to this question is yes if f is a continuous function. But let us consider an example.

Example 1.1. Let the function f be defined by

$$f(x) = \frac{x}{50}, \qquad x \geqslant 0$$

where $f(x) = F'(x)$, x represents capital investment in dollars, and $y = f(x)$ the marginal rate of wheat output. Find a function F such that $F' = f$.

Solution:

If $f(x) = \dfrac{x}{50}$,

then by reversing the process of differentiation, we have

$$F(x) = \frac{x^{1+1}}{50} \cdot \frac{1}{2} = \frac{x^2}{100}, \qquad x \geqslant 0$$

which is the total wheat output function discussed earlier.

Observe how differentiation has been reversed. If we were to differentiate function F we would have *multiplied* the coefficient of x by its exponent 2 and then we would have *subtracted* 1 from this exponent. In finding function F from the given function f we first *added* one to the exponent of x and then *divided* the coefficient of x by the new exponent 2.

In general, *a function F is called an antiderivative of a function f if* $f = F'$. We say *an* and not the antiderivative of f because F is one of infinitely many antiderivatives which can be derived from f. For since the derivative of a constant is zero, in reversing the differentiation process we get a function whose constant is undetermined and may take any value. Thus, in finding an antiderivative of a function an arbitrary constant C must always be added.

Example 1.2. In finding

$$F(x) = \frac{x^2}{100},$$

in Example 1.1 we omitted the constant C by simply assuming that $C = 0$. Actually, in reversing differentiation we should have found

$$y = F(x) + C = \frac{x^2}{100} + C$$

where C can be any real number.

The presence of an arbitrary constant C in antidifferentiation is not a disadvantage. On the contrary, a great deal of flexibility is introduced since the undetermined constant can take any value that the particular empirical situation demands.

Example 1.3. Consider the function

$$F(x) + C = \frac{x^2}{100} + C, \qquad x \geqslant 0$$

where x represents investment in dollars and $y = F(x) + C$ total production of wheat output in bushels.

Case 1: Assuming that no wheat can be produced from the land without capital investment, then

$$y = F_1(x) = \frac{x^2}{100}, \qquad x \geqslant 0$$

since

$$F(0) + C = \frac{(0)^2}{100} + C = 0,$$

and

$$C = 0.$$

Case 2: Assuming that the land is so fertile that 5000 bushels of wheat can be produced with no capital investment, then

$$y = F_2(x) = \frac{x^2}{100} + 5000, \qquad x \geqslant 0$$

since

$$F(0) + C = \frac{(0)^2}{100} + C = 5000,$$

and

$$C = 5000.$$

Case 3: On the other hand, assuming that an initial investment of $700 is required to clear and prepare the land for farming, then

$$y = F_3(x) = \frac{x^2}{100} - 4900, \qquad x \geqslant 0$$

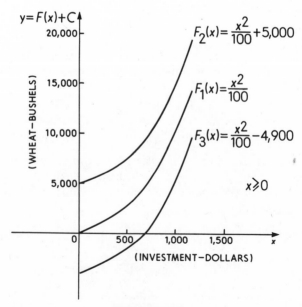

FIGURE 1.1.

since

$$F(700) + C = \frac{(700)^2}{100} + C = 0$$

and

$$100C = -490,000$$

$$C = -4900.$$

The empirically meaningful segments of the graphs of the above three functions are shown in Figure 1.1. Observe that all three graphs have the same marginal function

$$f(x) = \frac{x}{50},$$

but different y-intercepts because of the different values given to the constant C.

1.2. The Indefinite Integral. In reversing the process of differentiation we in fact performed the process of integration called *indefinite*. The function found with antidifferentiation is called the *indefinite integral*.

Let the function f be given. Then the indefinite integral of f is defined as

(1.1)
$$y = \int f(x)dx = F(x) + C,$$

where $f(x) = y' = F'(x)$ and the symbol $\int$, called *integral sign*, denotes the operation of integration. Equation (1.1) is read "the integral of $f(x)dx$ is $F(x) + C$." It is important to note that in equation (1.1) y represents the indefinite integral of $f(x)$ while $F(x)$ is *an* antiderivative of y where $C = 0$.

The notation of the indefinite integral may be interpreted in either of the following two ways:

Case 1: We may think of the symbol

$$\int \ldots dx$$

to mean "the integral of . . . with respect to x." Then the above symbol may be interpreted as the inverse of the symbol

$$\frac{d}{dx} \ldots,$$

which means "the derivative of . . . with respect to x."

Example 1.4. Let the function f be defined by

$$f(x) = \frac{x}{50},$$

where $f(x) = dy/dx$. Find the indefinite integral of f.
Solution:
If $f(x) = x/50$, then antidifferentiating we have

$$y = \int f(x)dx = \int \frac{x}{50} dx$$

$$= \frac{x^2}{100} + C,$$

as found previously.

Case 2: Or, we may think that before performing the operation indicated by the integral sign equation (1.1) is written as follows:

(1.2)
$$\boxed{dy = f(x)dx,}$$

where $f(x)$ is the derivative of y for every value of x in the closed interval $[a, b]$, dy is called the *differential of y*, and dx the *differential of x*. Then when the integral sign is introduced in equation (1.2), i.e., when we integrate both sides of this equation, we obtain

$$\int dy = \int f(x)dx$$

which by (1.1) becomes

(1.3)
$$\boxed{y = \int dy = F(x) + C.}$$

In this case we integrate the differential of function y to get the anti-derivative $F(x)$ plus some constant C. Thus we think of the integral sign $\int$ without considering dx as part of the symbol, to mean the operation which is the inverse of differentiation denoted by the symbol d.

Example 1.5. Find the indefinite integral of

$$\frac{dy}{dx} = \frac{x}{50}.$$

Solution:
From the definition of the differential of y in (1.2) we have

$$dy = \frac{x}{50} dx.$$

From past experience we know that

$$d\left(\frac{x^2}{100}\right) = \frac{x}{50}\,dx\ ;$$

and by antidifferentiation we obtain

$$y = \int d\left(\frac{x^2}{100}\right) = \int \frac{x}{50}\,dx = \frac{x^2}{100} + C.$$

All told, in either of the two interpretations of the notation in equation (1.1) the operation denoted by the integral sign denotes the inverse of the operation denoted by the symbol d for differentiation.

1.3. Integration Formulas; Integrating Algebraic Functions. So far we were able to show the intimate relationship that exists between the process of differentiation and that of indefinite integration. Now we are ready to introduce some integration formulas or laws which are part of the mathematical system of calculus and show how they can be applied. A number of integration laws are listed in Table 1.2, where $f(x)$ and $g(x)$ are values of functions f and g at x,

TABLE 1.2.

A. *Constant and power functions*:

1. If $f(x) = 0$, then $\int (0)dx = C$.

2. If $f(x) = 1$, then $\int (1)\,dx = x + C$.

3. $\int [k \cdot f(x)]dx = k \int f(x)dx = kF(x) + C$.

4. If $f(x) = x^n$, then $\int x^n dx = \frac{x^{n+1}}{n+1} + C, n \neq -1$.

B. *Sum and difference of two functions*:

5. $\int [f(x) + g(x)]dx = \int f(x)dx + \int g(x)dx = F(x) + G(x) + C$.

6. $\int [f(x) - g(x)]dx = \int f(x)dx - \int g(x)dx = F(x) - G(x) + C$.

C. *Powers of functions*:

7. $\int (ax + b)^n dx = \frac{(ax + b)^{n+1}}{a(n+1)} + C, n \neq -1, a \neq 0$.

respectively, and k, C, n, a, and b are real constants. Since integration, as defined earlier, requires the ability to guess the answer, formulas such as the ones listed in Table 1.2 may help to reduce the amount of guesswork which otherwise may be necessary. Additional formulas will be introduced when required.

We have seen that differentiation and indefinite integration are inverse operations of each other. Thus, for proving the laws of integration shown in Table 1.2 we need only to show that each of them rests on the fact that by differentiating the indefinite integral we find the function which was integrated called the *integrand*.

Example 1.6. The proof of formula 1, Table 1.2, rests on the fact that if

$$f(x) = 0$$

then

$$D_x\left[\int (0)dx\right] \quad D_xC = 0;$$

and of formula 2, Table 1.2, on the fact that if

$$f(x) = 1$$

then

$$D_x\left[\int (1)dx\right] = D_x(x + C) = 1.$$

Leaving the other formal proofs to the interested reader, we shall illustrate the use of each of the remaining formulas in Table 1.2 with concrete examples. The proof of each formula will be demonstrated by the "check" part of each solution.

Formula 3 states that *the indefinite integral of a constant times a function is the constant times the indefinite integral of the function plus C.*

Example 1.7. Integrate the function $f(x) = 2x$.
Solution:
Analysis:
If $f(x) = 2x$, then antidifferentiating we have

$$y = \int (2x)dx$$

$$= 2\int x\,dx \qquad \text{[by 3]}$$

$$= \frac{2x^{1+1}}{2} + C \qquad \text{[by 4]}$$

$$= x^2 + C.$$

Check:
If $y = x^2 + C$, then differentiating we get

$$D_xy = D_x(x^2 + C)$$

$$= 2x$$

the given integrand.

For illustrating the use of formula 4 which states that *the indefinite integral of a power function $f(x) = x^n$, $n \neq -1$, is $(1/(n + 1))$ times the* *unknown x raised to n + 1 plus C* we shall use the solutions in Example 2.6 of the preceding chapter.

Example 1.8. Integrate the following functions:

$$a)\ f(x) = 3x^2\ ;\quad b)\ g(x) = -\frac{4}{x^5}\ ;\quad \text{and}\quad c)\ y' = \frac{3}{2}\sqrt{x}\ .$$

Solutions:

a) If $f(x) = 3x^2$, then

$$y = \int (3x^2)dx = 3\int (x^2)dx \qquad \text{[by 3]}$$

$$= \frac{3x^{2+1}}{3} + C \qquad \text{[by 4]}$$

$$= x^3 + C\ .$$

b) If $g(x) = -4/x^5$, then

$$y = \int \left(-\frac{4}{x^5}\right)dx = \int (-4x^{-5})dx$$

$$= -4\int (x^{-5})dx \qquad \text{[by 3]}$$

$$= \frac{-4x^{-5+1}}{-4} + C$$

$$= x^{-4} + C$$

$$= \frac{1}{x^4} + C\ .$$

c) If $y' = \frac{3}{2}\sqrt{x}$, then

$$y = \int (\tfrac{3}{2}\sqrt{x})dx = \tfrac{3}{2}\int (\sqrt{x})dx \qquad \text{[by 3]}$$

$$= \tfrac{3}{2}\int x^{1/2}dx$$

$$= \frac{3}{2}\frac{x^{1/2+1}}{\frac{3}{2}} + C \qquad \text{[by 4]}$$

$$= x^{3/2} + C$$

$$= \sqrt{x^3} + C\ .$$

The "check" part of the solutions is given in the above-mentioned Example 2.6, of Chapter 11 where each of the given functions is an antiderivative of the corresponding indefinite integral found here.

Corresponding to similar differentiation formulas, laws 5 and 6 in Table 1.2 state that *the indefinite integral of the sum (difference) of two functions is the sum (difference) of the indefinite integrals of the functions plus C.*

Example 1.9. Find the indefinite integral of the following functions:

$$a)\ p(x) = -4x + 48 \quad \text{and} \quad b)\ f(x) = 5x^4 + 9x^2 - 10x.$$

Solutions:

a) If $p(x) = -4x + 48$, then

$$P(x) = \int (-4x + 48)dx = \int (-4x)dx + \int 48dx \qquad \text{[by 5]}$$

$$= -4 \int xdx + 48x + C \qquad \text{[by 2 and 3]}$$

$$= \frac{-4x^2}{2} + 48x + C \qquad \text{[by 4]}$$

$$= -2x^2 + 48x + C$$

b) if $f(x) = 5x^4 + 9x^2 - 10x$, then

$$y = \int (5x^4 + 9x^2 - 10x)dx$$

$$= \int (5x^4)dx + \int (9x^2)dx - \int (10x)dx \qquad \text{[by 5 and 6]}$$

$$= 5 \int x^4 dx + 9 \int x^2 dx - 10 \int xdx \qquad \text{[by 3]}$$

$$= \frac{5x^5}{5} + \frac{9x^3}{3} - \frac{10x^2}{2} + C \qquad \text{[by 4]}$$

$$= x^5 + 3x^3 - 5x^2 + C.$$

The "check" part of these solutions can be found in Examples 2.8 and 2.10 of the previous chapter where the given functions are antiderivatives of the above indefinite integrals, respectively.

Similarly, formula 7, being the reverse of rule 9 in Table 2.1 of Chapter 11 for differentiation, can be used to integrate some powers of functions.

Example 1.10. Integrate the following functions:

$$a)\ f(x) = (2x + 3)^4 \quad \text{and} \quad b)\ g(x) = \frac{1}{(3x + 2)^3}.$$

Solutions:

a) *Analysis:* If $f(x) = (2x + 3)^4$, then

$$y = \int (2x + 3)^4 dx = \frac{(2x + 3)^{4+1}}{2(4 + 1)} + C \qquad \text{[by 7]}$$

$$= \frac{(2x + 3)^5}{10} + C.$$

Check: If $y = \dfrac{(2x + 3)^5}{10} + C$, then

$$f(x) = D_x\left[\frac{(2x + 3)^5}{10} + C\right] = \frac{10D_x[(2x + 3)^5] - (2x + 3)^5 D_x 10}{100} + 0$$

$$= \frac{10 \cdot 5(2x + 3)^4 D_x(2x + 3) - 0}{100}$$

$$= \frac{\cancel{50}(2x + 3)^4 \cdot \cancel{2}}{\cancel{100}}$$

$$= (2x + 3)^4.$$

b) *Analysis:* If $g(x) = \dfrac{1}{(3x + 2)^3}$, then

$$y = \int \frac{1}{(3x + 2)^3}\, dx = \int (3x + 2)^{-3} dx$$

$$= \frac{(3x + 2)^{-3+1}}{3(-3 + 1)} + C \qquad\qquad \text{[by 7]}$$

$$= \frac{(3x + 2)^{-2}}{-6} + C$$

$$= \frac{1}{-6(3x + 2)^2} + C.$$

Check: If $y = \dfrac{1}{-6(3x + 2)^2} + C$, then

$$g(x) = D_x\left[\frac{1}{-6(3x + 2)^2} + C\right] = D_x\left[-\frac{(3x + 2)^{-2}}{6} + C\right]$$

$$= -\tfrac{1}{6}D_x(3x + 2)^{-2} + 0$$

$$= -\tfrac{1}{6}(-2)(3x + 2)^{-3} \cdot D_x(3x + 2)$$

$$= \cancel{\tfrac{2}{6}}(3x + 2)^{-3} \cdot \cancel{3}$$

$$= \frac{1}{(3x + 2)^3}.$$

1.4. Recapitulation. In this section we were able to accomplish the following. First, we explained the process of indefinite integration as the reverse of the differentiation process. Second, we introduced the indefinite integral and integral notation. Third, we introduced a few formulas or laws of integral calculus and discussed these laws as part of the mathematical system of calculus. Fourth, we showed how these laws can be used to integrate algebraic functions.

Needless to emphasize, from all this discussion the reader must be able to reach one important conclusion: The integral, like the differential calculus, is based on the limit and function concepts. This conclusion will be further substantiated in the next section.

PROBLEMS

1.1. For each function taken from examples of Chapter 6 indicated below do the following:
   i) Find the derivative of the function.
   ii) Integrate this derivative to find the indefinite integral.
   iii) On the basis of the empirical situation involved find the original function by determining the value of the constant C.
   a) $f(x) = 50x + 3000$, Example 1.2.
   b) $f^{-1}(x) = \dfrac{x}{50} - 60$, Example 1.3.
   c) $S(x) = 0.15x - 4{,}550{,}000$, Example 2.4.
   d) $S(q) = 10q$, Example 2.5.
   e) $C(q) = 6.7q + 15{,}000{,}000$, Example 2.5.
   f) $Q(p) = -1000p + 10{,}000$, Example 2.6.
   g) $P(x) = x^2/100 - 10x + 3000$, Example 3.8.
   h) $S(p) = -1000p^2 + 10{,}000p$, Example 3.9.
   i) $C(p) = -2000p + 25{,}000$, Example 3.9.
   j) $P(p) = -1000p^2 + 12{,}000p - 25{,}000$, Example 3.9.

1.2. The following functions correspond to the indicated problems of Chapter 6. For each function answer (i), (ii), and (iii) of the previous Problem 1.1.
   *a) $f(t) = -1.5t + 100$, Problem 2.3.
   b) $f(x) = 10{,}000 - 75x$, Problem 2.4.
   *c) $g(d) = 0.00625d + 1.00$, Problem 2.8.
   d) $h(x) = -10x^2 + 80x + 2000$, Problem 3.9.
   e) $f(x) = -x^2 + 20x$, Problem 3.15.
   f) $f(x) = x^2 - 100x + 4000$, Problem 3.16.

1.3. Find the antiderivative of each function below by determining the value of C for the indicated value of y and x.
   *a) $D_x y = 2x$, $y = 10$ when $x = 2$.
   b) $D_x y = 3x^2 + 2x + 5$, $y = 7$ when $x = 1$.
   c) $dy/dx = x^3 + x + 3$, $y = 10$ when $x = 2$.

1.4. Suppose the only data available about wheat production consists of six observations of capital outlay and the corresponding produced wheat shown below:

Investment x (Dollars)	Wheat Output y (Bushels)
500	12,500
800	17,000
1000	19,800
1300	22,200
1400	22,300
1800	21,500

a) Find the average rate of change of wheat output by dividing each incremental change Δy by the corresponding incremental change Δx.

b) Plot the point $\left(x + \dfrac{\Delta x}{2}, \dfrac{\Delta y}{\Delta x}\right)$ you have obtained from (a) on a cc-plane.

c) From a freehand straight line use points (1000, 10) and (1500, 0) to find a marginal wheat output function.

d) Find the total wheat output function from (c).

e) Sketch the graph of the total wheat output function and plot on the same cc-plane the points whose coordinates represent the six given observations.

f) Why may the total wheat output function be empirically meaningful for $500 \leqslant x \leqslant 1800$ only?

*1.5. The production manager of Precision Products, Inc., obtained the following cost data from producing seven runs of a small machine part for an arsenal of the U.S. Army:

Run	Number of Parts	Dollar Cost
1	200	1300
2	300	1000
3	400	800
4	500	650
5	600	600
6	700	950
7	800	1500

If fixed cost $C = 3000$, find a total cost function and answer (a), (b), (c) —points (500,0), (700,4)—, (d) and (e), as explained in Problem 1.4.

(f) Why may the total output function be empirically meaningful for $200 \leqslant x \leqslant 800$ only?

1.6. Feller Manufacturing Corporation hired an economist, Henry George, to aid management for making quantitative decisions. Immediately after being hired, the economist prepared a forecast of the demand for Feller's chief product, a set of spun aluminum dishware used extensively in private, public, and military hospitals, both in the United States and in foreign countries, for holding sterile instruments, sponges, hemostats, etc. According to his forecast the demand for this product, and Feller's other medical products, would increase sharply over the next quarter. Although daily production varied because of breakdowns on the production line and occasional high absenteeism, it averaged about 10,000 units of dishware per day.

After preparing his forecast the economist attempted to prepare a function relating the rate of change of production with respect to the number of workers. He eventually had to make several simplifying assumptions, and then on the basis of these assumptions he found that the rate of change of production with respect to the number of workers equals $200 - 3x^{1/2}$ where x stands not for the number of workers, but the *additional* number of workers. Mr. Feller felt somewhat uneasy when he saw the function, but after Mr. George explained how it was derived, Mr. Feller said, "Well, I understand it, but I want to test it before I use it. I'm going to have to hire an extra 25 men in a week or so. Will your function predict or forecast the total output of the plant?" Mr. George said, "Yes, it will." Mr. Feller replied, "Predict away."

a) What output should Mr. George predict?

b) If actual production rises to 15,000 what would Mr. Feller think of Mr. George's prediction? Please discuss.

1.7. Let function f be defined by

$$f(x) = 8000x^{-0.20}, \qquad x \geqslant 2$$

where x represents months and $y = f(x)$ the monthly rate of sales volume of an item one month after advertising is discontinued at $x = 0$.

a) What is the total sales volume of the item at $x = 10$?

b) Assuming that if advertising continues monthly sales would have remained at 10,000 items, what is the loss of sales volume at $x = 10$?

c) What is the rate of sales volume at $x = 10$?

d) Sketch the graph of the sales decay function f for $2 \leqslant x \leqslant 10$.

1.8. Find the equation of the curve with indicated slope and y-intercept or through indicated point.

*a) $m = 3x; y = 0$.

b) $m = 3x^2 - 4x; y = 3$.

*c) $m = 4; (1, 2)$.

d) $m = \frac{2}{3}; (-3, -2)$.

e) $m = \frac{3}{5}; y = -\frac{5}{3}$.

f) $m = 5x; (0, 3)$.

1.9. The second derivative and the slope of the tangent at a specified point of each curve are given below. Find the equation of each curve.

*a) $D_x^2 y = -6; m = -4; (1, 2)$.

b) $D_x^2 y = 10; m = 6; (2, 3)$.

1.10. Integrate each of the following and check by differentiating:

*a) $D_x y = 3x^2$.

*b) $dy/dx = 4x^3$.

c) $D_v u = 3v^2 + 2v - 3$.

d) $dx/dy = 30y^5$.

e) $D_y x = y^4 + y^3 - y$.

1.11. Evaluate each of the following by invoking the laws in Table 1.2.:

*a) $\int (4x^3 - 4x^2 + 4)dx$.

b) $\int (2x^5 - 6x^2 + 1)dx$.

c) $\int (3y^3 - 2y^2 + y + 2)dy$.

1.12. Evaluate each of the following and check by differentiating:

*a) $\int (2x + 5)^3 \, dx$.

b) $\int (5x + 5)^{10} \, dx$.

c) $\int \left(\frac{4}{(x + 2)^4} \right) dx$.

d) $\int \left(\frac{5}{(2x + 3)^5} \right) dx$.

1.13. Simplify each of the following functions by multiplying and then find the indefinite integral. Check result by differentiating.

*a) $f(x) = (2x + 3)(x - 2)$.

b) $g(x) = (3x - 5)(3x + 5)$.

c) $h(x) = (x + 2)^2(x - 2)^2$.

1.14. It can be shown that dy is an approximation of Δy when dx is small. This means that if x changes by a small amount, the corresponding change in the function $f(x)$ is approximately dy. We can use this relationship to find the effect errors of measurement may have in finding areas and volumes.

*a) If there is an error of ± 0.10 feet in measuring the side of a square 40 feet on a side, what is the possible error in the area?

b) If the length of an edge of a box in the form of a cube is 3 ± 0.10 inches, what is the approximate volume of the box?

1.15. Evaluate each of the following and check by differentiating.

*a) $\int \left(-\frac{5}{4z^6} \right) dz$.

b) $\int \left(-\frac{1000}{x^2} \right) dx$.

c) $\int \left(\frac{3\sqrt{6x}}{2} \right) dx$.

d) $\int \left(\frac{2\sqrt[3]{6}}{3\sqrt[3]{x}} \right) dx$.

e) $\int (x^0) \, dx$.

1.16. Prove each of the following indefinite integrals by differentiation.

*a) $\int [k \cdot f(x)]dx = kF(x) + C$.

b) $\int x^n \, dx = \frac{x^{n+1}}{n + 1} + C$.

c) $\int [f(x) \pm g(x)]dx = F(x) \pm G(x) + C$.

d) $\displaystyle\int (ax + b)^n\, dx = \frac{(ax + b)^{n+1}}{a(n + 1)} + C\,,\, n \neq -1$.

1.17. Since $D_x \ln |x| = 1/x$,

$$\int \frac{1}{x}\, dx = \int x^{-1}\, dx = \ln |x| + C\,;$$

and since $D_x \ln |ax + b| = a(ax + b)^{-1}$,

$$\int \frac{1}{ax + b}\, dx = \int (ax + b)^{-1}\, dx = \frac{1}{a} \ln |ax + b| + C\,.$$

On the basis of the above two formulas and laws 4 and 7 in Table 1.2 we can evaluate any integral of the form

$$\int \frac{p(x)}{x^n}\, dx \qquad \text{and} \qquad \int \frac{p(x)}{ax + b}\, dx\,,$$

where $p(x)$ is a polynomial.
Evaluate:

*a) $\displaystyle\int \frac{x^3 - x^2 + 5}{x}\, dx$.   (*Hint:* Divide before integrating.)

b) $\displaystyle\int \frac{x^2 + 3}{\sqrt{x^2}}\, dx$.

c) $\displaystyle\int \frac{2x^2 - x + 5}{x + 2}\, dx$.   (*Hint:* Divide before integrating.)

d) $\displaystyle\int \frac{1}{3x + 3}\, dx$.

2. THE DEFINITE INTEGRAL; APPLICATIONS

With respect to the definite integral, integration is sometimes called the process of summation. In this section, therefore, we shall first show how the process of summation can be used to calculate an area under a curve. For in addition to the previous meaning the term "to integrate" also means "to indicate or give the sum or total of" areas bounded by curves, volumes of various solids, and other applications. Thus, the process of summation will lead us to a definition of the definite integral. We shall arrive at such a definition by showing how a total of a quantity such as an area can be computed exactly with calculus. Finding areas bounded by curves will be our next task. We shall conclude with a few applications of integral calculus.

2.1. Area under a Curve.   In geometry we learn how to find areas bounded by straight-line segments and by circles. The area of a

rectangle, for instance, is found by multiplying its length by its width. But difficulties arise in calculating an area bounded by a curve representing the graph of a second or higher-order function.

Let $f(x)$ be the value of a continuous and nonnegative function f, i.e., $f(x) \geqslant 0$, in the closed interval $[a, b]$. Consider, for instance, the problem of calculating area A, shown in Figure 2.1, which is bounded

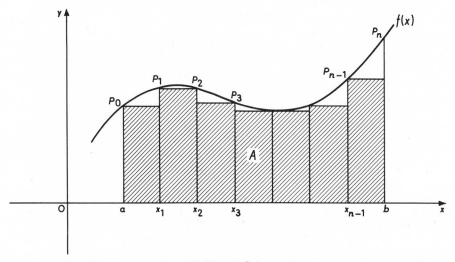

FIGURE 2.1.

above by the graph of the function, on the sides by vertical lines through $x = a$ and $x = b$, and below by the x-axis. Obviously, it is not clear how one goes about calculating area A.

Earlier, we have shown how we can use the limiting process to find the instantaneous rate of change of a function at a given value of the independent variable x. We can use a similar limiting process to find an area under a curve such as area A shown in Figure 2.1. We divide the area into n thin strips of uniform width $\Delta x = (b - a)/n$ by vertical lines through the end points $x = a$ and $x = b$ and many intermediate points $x_1, x_2, x_3, \ldots, x_{n-1}$. The area of each strip can be approximated by an inscribed rectangle. For instance, the area of strip $aP_0P_1x_1$ can be approximated by the shaded rectangle having altitude aP_0 and base ax_1. Since the length of the altitude aP_0 is the value of function f at $x = a$ and the length of the base is $\Delta x = x_1 - a$ the area of this rectangle is

$$f(a) \cdot \Delta x.$$

Similarly, the area of the second strip can be approximated by inscribing the shaded rectangle having area

$$f(x_1) \cdot \Delta x.$$

Thus, when the function increases with x, we always inscribe a rectangle in each strip whose area is the ordinate at the left-hand side of the strip times its base as already shown. When the function decreases with x, we use the ordinate of the right-hand side edge of each strip times its base to determine the area of the inscribed rectangle. For instance, the area of the third strip in Figure 2.1 can be approximated by inscribing a rectangle having area

$$f(x_3) \cdot \Delta x,$$

where $f(x_3)$ is the length of edge $x_3 P_3$.

In general, whether the function increases or decreases in the interval from a to b, there is some number c_1 between a and x_1 inclusive such that the area of the first inscribed rectangle is $f(c_1) \cdot \Delta x$; similarly, there is some number c_2 between x_1 and x_2 inclusive such that the area of the second inscribed rectangle is $f(c_2) \cdot \Delta x$; and there is some number c_i between x_i and x_{i+1} inclusive such that the area of the ith inscribed rectangle is $f(c_i) \cdot \Delta x$. Therefore, the sum of the areas of these n inscribed rectangles is

(2.1) $$S_n = f(c_1) \cdot \Delta x + f(c_2) \cdot \Delta x + \ldots + f(c_n) \cdot \Delta x.$$

Now, let n, the number of strips, increase to infinity. Then *area A is the limit of the sums of the areas of the inscribed rectangles as their number increases without bound.*
In symbols,

(2.2) $$A = \underset{n \to \infty}{\text{limit}}\, S_n = \underset{n \to \infty}{\text{limit}}\, [f(c_1) \cdot \Delta x + f(c_2) \cdot \Delta x + \ldots + f(c_n) \cdot \Delta x].$$

We shall use a simple example to illustrate this limiting process of finding areas under a curve.

Example 2.1. Let the marginal wheat output function $f(x) = x/50$ be given. We wish to find the total wheat output when capital outlay increases from $x = \$500$ to $x = \$1000$.

A geometric representation of the problem is shown in Figure 2.2 where total wheat output is represented by the area bounded by the graph of the function, the lines $x = 500$ and $x = 1000$, and the x-axis.

Let $n = 5$. Then, there are $n - 1 = 4$ intermediate points $x_1 = 600$, $x_2 = 700$, $x_3 = 800$, and $x_4 = 900$ which divide the interval $500 \leqslant x \leqslant 1000$ into 5 equal subintervals, each of length $\Delta x = 100$ since

$$\Delta x = \frac{b - a}{n} = \frac{1000 - 500}{5} = 100.$$

We can approximate the area by summing the areas of the inscribed shaded rectangles shown in Figure 2.2. Substituting in (2.1), we have

$$S_5 = f(500) \cdot \Delta x + f(600) \cdot \Delta x + f(700) \cdot \Delta x + f(800) \cdot \Delta x + f(900) \cdot \Delta x$$

$$= 10 \cdot 100 + 12 \cdot 100 + 14 \cdot 100 + 16 \cdot 100 + 18 \cdot 100$$

$$= 7000.$$

Since the area under the curve is larger than the sum S_5, the exact total wheat output is larger than 7000 bushels. However, we can improve this approximation by increasing n. Continuing this process, the reader

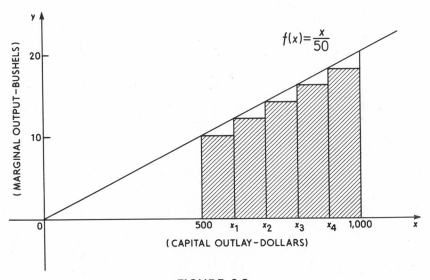

FIGURE 2.2.

can verify that as n increases, the value of S_n defined by (2.1) approaches the fixed number of 7500 bushels. Thus, by (2.2) the limit of S_n as n increases without bound is 7500. In symbols,

$$A = \lim_{n \to \infty} S_n = 7500.$$

It is important to know that we can obtain the same answer by using circumscribed instead of inscribed rectangles. Also, although simple, the above example amply illustrates the limiting process of finding an area under a curve in general. For, as we shall soon see, the definite integral is defined by expression (2.2).

2.2. Areas by Integration: The Definite Integral.
The limit of the sums of areas can be evaluated by integration. Essentially, this is what is known as the *fundamental theorem of integral calculus* which states that the definite integral is related to the indefinite integral. This theorem, proved by Newton and Leibnitz, represents a cornerstone in the development of the mathematical system of calculus. Instead of

proving this theorem, however, we shall follow the path broken by these two mathematicians to show how areas can be computed by calculus.

Let $f(x)$ be the value of a continuous and nonnegative function f in the closed interval $[a, b]$ and let x_1 be any value of x such that $a \leqslant x_1 \leqslant b$. We wish to find the area bounded by the graph of f, the lines $x = a$ and $x = b$, and the x-axis as shown in Figure 2.3. As x_1 increases, the cross-hatched area A also increases; in other words, area A is a function of the independent variable x_1.

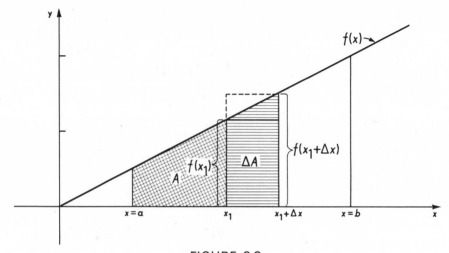

FIGURE 2.3.

Let ΔA, in Figure 2.3, be the incremental increase in area A as x_1 increases by Δx to $x_1 + \Delta x$. Apparently, ΔA is larger than the rectangle which is determined by the base Δx times the height $f(x_1)$ and smaller than the rectangle Δx times $f(x_1 + \Delta x)$, i.e.,

(2.3) $$f(x_1) \cdot \Delta x < \Delta A < f(x_1 + \Delta x) \cdot \Delta x .$$

Since Δx is a positive quantity, dividing (2.3) by Δx we have

(2.4) $$f(x_1) < \frac{\Delta A}{\Delta x} < f(x_1 + \Delta x).$$

Since function f is assumed to be continuous, we can observe from Figure 2.3 that $f(x_1 + \Delta x)$ approaches $f(x_1)$ as Δx approaches zero, i.e.,

(2.5) $$\lim_{\Delta x \to 0} f(x_1 + \Delta x) = f(x_1).$$

From (2.4) and (2.5) it follows that

(2.6) $$\lim_{\Delta x \to 0} \frac{\Delta A}{\Delta x} \geqslant f(x_1), \text{ and}$$

(2.7)
$$\lim_{\Delta x \to 0} \frac{\Delta A}{\Delta x} \leqslant f(x_1).$$

From inequalities (2.6) and (2.7) we must conclude that

(2.8)
$$\lim_{\Delta x \to 0} \frac{\Delta A}{\Delta x} = f(x_1).$$

However, as Δx approaches zero, $\Delta A / \Delta x$ approaches, as a limit, the instantaneous rate with which area A changes with respect to the variable x. Thus, by definition of the derivative of a function, (2.8) becomes

(2.9)
$$\lim_{\Delta x \to 0} \frac{\Delta A}{\Delta x} = \frac{dA}{dx} = f(x_1).$$

Inasmuch as x_1 can take any value of x in the interval $[a, b]$, we may substitute x for x_1 in (2.9) and we have

(2.10)
$$\frac{dA}{dx} = f(x).$$

This latter expression means that the rate with which area A is changing is always equal to the coordinate value $y = f(x)$ at any value x in the interval $[a, b]$. Also, it is important to know that with slight modifications the same argument would hold if the curve of f were falling instead of rising or if it represented the graph of a second or higher order function.

Now, we are ready to complete our discussion of finding areas by integration. From (2.10) we have

$$dA = f(x)dx.$$

Integrating, we find that area

$$A = \int dA = \int f(x)dx.$$

Let $F(x)$ be a function such that $F'(x) = f(x)$. Then

(2.11)
$$A = \int f(x)dx = F(x) + C.$$

From the diagram in Figure 2.3 we can see that A represents the area under the curve of f and between the lines $x = a$ and $x = x_1$. Also, we have pointed out that area A is a function of the independent variable x_1. Hence, when x_1 decreases, approaching $x = a$, area A also decreases; and when $x_1 = a$, area A equals zero. Thus, substituting $A = 0$ and $x = a$ in (2.11), we have

$$0 = F(a) + C, \text{ and}$$

$$C = -F(a).$$

Substituting $C = -F(a)$ in (2.11), we get

(2.12) $$A = F(x)F - (a)$$

which expresses the area between the fixed ordinate at $x = a$ and a variable ordinate at x. In order to find the area bounded by $x = a$ and $x = b$ we substitute $x = b$ in (2.12) and obtain

(2.13) $$A = F(b) - F(a).$$

In terms of the integral sign (2.13) becomes

(2.14) $$A = \int_a^b f(x)dx = F(b) - F(a).$$

Letter a at the bottom of the integral sign, called the *lower limit of integration*, represents the value of x at which the area begins. Letter b, called the *upper limit of integration*, represents the value of x at which the area ends. An integral such as the one in (2.14) is called a *definite integral*.

For applying the definite integral to specific problems it is convenient to use the form

(2.15) $$A = \int_a^b f(x)dx = F(x) \Big]_a^b = F(b) - F(a)$$

since this form includes the actual function $F(x)$ found by integration.

Example 2.2. Let the marginal wheat production function $f(x) = x/50$ be given. Find the increase in total wheat output when investment x increases from \$500 to \$1000.
Solution:
Substituting in (2.15) and integrating, we have

$$\int_{500}^{1000} \frac{x}{50} dx = \frac{x^2}{100} \Big]_{500}^{1000}$$

$$= \frac{(1000)^2}{100} - \frac{(500)^2}{100}$$

$$= 7500 \text{ bushels.}$$

It is important to note that the above answer is the same found in Example 2.1. The definite integral (2.15) may be also defined in terms of (2.2) as the limit of the sums of the areas of inscribed (circumscribed) rectangles as their number becomes infinitely large.

2.3. Finding Areas under a Curve. The formulas of integration introduced in the preceding section are equally applicable to the definite integral. In using these formulas to evaluate definite integrals, however, the area under the curve must be carefully defined. For the phrase "the area under the curve over an interval" means in fact the area which lies between the graph of the function and the x-axis over such interval. Since such an area may lie above and/or below the x-axis, or it may be bounded by the graphs of two functions, four major cases may be considered.

First, when the graph of a function over an interval lies above the x-axis. Then the area under the curve is given by (2.15). Such an area is shown in Figure 2.2 with Example 2.2 illustrating the case.

Second, when the graph of a function over an interval lies below the x-axis. Then the area under the curve is given by

(2.16)
$$A = -\int_a^b f(x)dx = -[F(b) - F(a)].$$

Example 2.3. Find the area A_1 shown in Figure 2.4 bounded by the graph of the function

$$f(x) = -x^2 + 13x - 30$$

over the interval $0 \leqslant x \leqslant 3$.

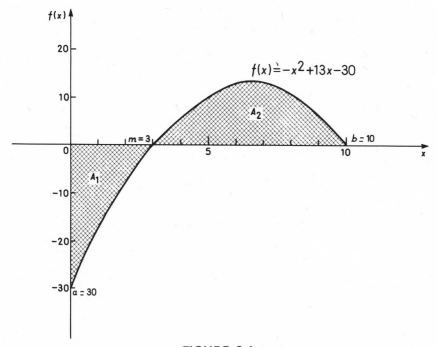

FIGURE 2.4.

Solution:
Substituting in (2.16), we obtain

$$A_1 = -\int_0^3 (-x^2 + 13x - 30)dx$$

$$= -\left(-\frac{x^3}{3} + \frac{13x^2}{2} - 30x\right)\Bigg]_0^3$$

$$= -\left[-\frac{(3)^3}{3} + \frac{13(3)^2}{2} - 30(3)\right] - 0$$

$$= -\left(-\frac{243}{6}\right)$$

$$= 40\tfrac{1}{2}.$$

Third, when the graph of a function over an interval lies partly above and partly below the x-axis. Then the area under the curve is given by

(2.17)
$$A = \int_a^b f(x)dx = -\int_a^m f(x)dx + \int_m^b f(x)dx ;$$

where the function is nonpositive for $x \leqslant m$ and nonnegative for $x \geqslant m$.

Example 2.4. Find the area bounded by

$$f(x) = -x^2 + 13x - 30$$

and the interval $0 \leqslant x \leqslant 10$ shown in Figure 2.4.

Solution:
Since the function is nonpositive for the interval $0 \leqslant x \leqslant 3$ bounding area A_1 and nonnegative for the interval $3 \leqslant x \leqslant 10$ bounding area A_2, substituting in (2.17) we obtain the value of the crosshatched area $A_1 + A_2$ as follows:

$$A = \int_0^{10} (-x^2 + 13x - 30)dx = A_1 + A_2$$

$$= -\int_0^3 (-x^2 + 13x - 30)dx + \int_3^{10} (-x^2 + 13x - 30)dx$$

$$= -\left(-\frac{x^3}{3} + \frac{13x^2}{2} - 30x\right)\Bigg]_0^3 + \left(-\frac{x^3}{3} + \frac{13x^2}{2} - 30x\right)\Bigg]_3^{10}$$

$$= \frac{243}{6} + \frac{343}{6} = 97\tfrac{2}{3},$$

where $A_1 = 40\tfrac{3}{6}$ and $A_2 = 57\tfrac{1}{6}$.

Observe that unless the two parts of the area in the above example are integrated separately, integration leads to a wrong answer.

Fourth, when an area over an interval is bounded by the graphs of two functions. Then such an area is given by

(2.18)
$$A = \int_a^b [g(x) - h(x)]dx,$$

where $g(x) \geqslant h(x)$ for all x in the interval $[a, b]$.

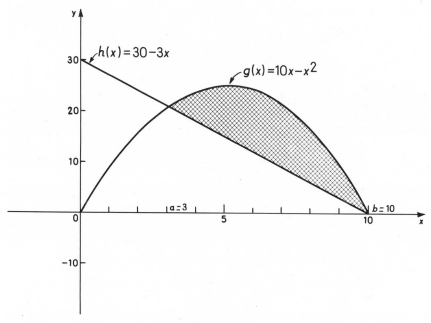

FIGURE 2.5.

Example 2.5. Find the crosshatched area in Figure 2.5 bounded by

$$g(x) = 10x - x^2$$

and

$$h(x) = 30 - 3x.$$

Solution:

At the points where the graphs of the two functions intersect, $g(x) = h(x)$ and $g(x) \geqslant h(x)$ for all values of x in $[a, b]$. Hence,

$$30 - 3x = 10x - x^2, \text{ or}$$

$$x^2 - 13x + 30 = 0,$$

$$(x - 3)(x - 10) = 0.$$

Since the last expression is satisfied for $x = 3$ and $x = 10$, the common points of the two graphs are $(3, 21)$ and $(10, 0)$; and the area in question bounded by the two graphs is in the interval $3 \leqslant x \leqslant 10$. Substituting in (2.18), we get

$$A = \int_3^{10} [(10x - x^2) - (30 - 3x)]dx$$

$$= \int_3^{10} (-x^2 + 13x - 30)dx$$

$$= \left(-\frac{x^3}{3} + \frac{13x^2}{2} - 30x\right)\Big]_3^{10}$$

$$= \frac{343}{6} = 57\tfrac{1}{6}.$$

2.4. Applications of Integral Calculus.

Integration in general, and the definite integral in particular, is used for solving a great number of physical problems involving areas, distances, volumes, lengths of curves, areas of surfaces of revolution, average value of a function, center of mass, centroid, work, hydrostatic force, and other more complicated problems. For illustrating the application of integral calculus to problems of business operations, we shall cite three cases.

Case 1:   In Section 3 of the preceding chapter we have shown how with differentiation we can find the maximum profit sales volume when the total sales volume and cost functions are given. Now we shall demonstrate how we can find total profits for a given sales volume when only the marginal sales revenue and cost functions are known.

Example 2.6. On the basis of experimental production runs of a new product the management of Metronics, Inc., a manufacturer of electrical and electronic products, obtained the following marginal cost of production function

$$c(x) = 1.6x - 4.5$$

where x represents units and $y = c(x)$ production cost in dollars. Since the price of the new product is fixed at \$3.5 per unit, the marginal sales revenue function is equal to that price, i.e.,

$$s(x) = 3.5.$$

Furthermore, it is known that fixed cost is \$7.00.
Question 1. What is the sales volume with the maximum profit?
Answer:
Since at maximum profit marginal revenue equals marginal cost, equating the above two functions and solving for x, we find that the sales volume with the maximum profit is

$$1.6x - 4.5 = 3.5,$$

$$x = 5 \text{ units.}$$

Question 2. What is the total profit at the optimal sales volume $x = 5$?

Answer:

First, integrating the marginal cost function c, we have

$$C(x) = \int c(x)dx = \int (1.6x - 4.5)dx = 0.8x^2 - 4.5x + C.$$

Since fixed cost is known to be $7.00, $C = 7$ and the total cost function is

$$C(x) = 0.8x^2 - 4.5x + 7.$$

Similarly, integrating the marginal sales revenue function s, we get

$$S(x) = \int s(x)dx = \int 3.5\, dx = 3.5x + C;$$

and since $C = 0$ when $x = 0$, we get the sales revenue function

$$S(x) = 3.5x.$$

Second, inasmuch as profits equal sales revenue minus cost, from $C(x)$ and $S(x)$ above we obtain the profit function

$$P(x) = S(x) - C(x)$$
$$= (3.5x) - (0.8x^2 - 4.5x + 7)$$
$$= -0.8x^2 + 8x - 7.$$

Third, substituting $x = 5$ in P, the maximum profit is

$$P(5) = -0.8(5)^2 + 8(5) - 7$$
$$= 13 \text{ dollars.}$$

Question 3. What is the increase in total profits if sales grow from 2 to 5 units?

Answer:

The answer can be obtained directly from the above derived profit function P by substituting the appropriate values for x. However, for the sake of demonstrating the definite integral, we shall use the given functions c and s. Their graphs are shown in Figure 2.6, where the crosshatched area represents the total profit in the interval $2 \leqslant x \leqslant 5$ of output units sold. Substituting the functions c and s in (2.18), we obtain

$$\int_2^5 [(3.5) - (1.6x - 4.5)]dx = \int_2^5 (-1.6x + 8)dx$$
$$= -0.8x^2 + 8x \Big]_2^5$$
$$= 7.2 \text{ dollars.}$$

Case 2 :   In certain production operations such as assembling of airframes, electronics, home appliances, and others, workers learn from experience so that direct labor input per unit of product steadily declines. The *rate* of reduction in direct labor requirements is described with the so-called *learning curve* which represents a power function of the general form

$$h(x) = kx^b,$$

where $y = h(x)$ is the hours of direct labor required to produce the xth unit, $-1 \leqslant b \leqslant 0$ and $k > 0$.

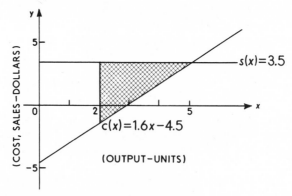

FIGURE 2.6.

The total man-hours of direct labor to produce an x number of units can be obtained by integrating function h. Thus,

$$H(x) = \int h(x)dx = \int kx^b \, dx$$

$$H(x) = \frac{kx^{b+1}}{b+1} + C.$$

Example 2.7. The production manager of Mathewson Electronics Corporation obtained the following function

$$h(x) = 1356.2x^{-0.3219},$$

where $y = h(x)$ represents the rate of labor hours required to assemble the xth unit of a complex new guidance system for missiles. The above function is based on the experience for assembling the first 50 units of the product (cf. discussion on learning curves in optional Section 2 of Chapter 7, especially Example 2.11).

The company was asked to bid on a new order of 100 additional units. For bidding successfully the management of the company wants to estimate, among other things, the total labor requirements for assembling the 100 units.

Solution:
This problem requires evaluating

$$\int_{50}^{150} h(x)dx = \int_{50}^{150} (1356.2x^{-0.3219})dx$$

$$= \frac{1356.2x^{-0.3219+1}}{0.6781} \Bigg]_{50}^{150}$$

$$= 2000x^{0.6781} \Bigg]_{50}^{150}$$

The value of the definite integral can be found with logarithms as follows:
Step 1: Find the value of upper limit.

$$\log 2000(150)^{0.6781} = \log 2000 + 0.6781 \log 150$$
$$= 3.3010 + 0.6781(2.1761)$$
$$= 3.3010 + 1.4756$$
$$= 4.7766; \text{ and}$$

$$2000(150)^{0.6781} = 59,800.$$

Step 2: Find the value of lower limit.

$$\log 2000(50)^{0.6781} = \log 2000 + 0.6781 \log 50$$
$$= 3.3010 + 0.6781(1.6990)$$
$$= 3.3010 + 1.1521$$
$$= 4.4531; \text{ and}$$

$$2000(50)^{0.6781} = 28,400.$$

Hence,

$$2000x^{0.6781} \Bigg]_{50}^{150} = 59,800 - 28,400 = 31,400,$$

which represents an estimate of the total number of labor hours required to assemble the additional 100 units.

Case 3:   Finally, we shall show how the definite integral can be used for expressing important economic concepts. Under certain assumptions consumers who would have been willing to pay more than the market price enjoy a gain, called *consumers' surplus.* Similarly, for a given supply curve producers who have been willing to sell at prices less than the market price enjoy a gain, called *producers' surplus.* One way of expressing these surplus concepts is in terms of areas.

Let D and S be the demand and supply functions of a commodity, respectively. Their graphs are shown in Figure 2.7. Also, let Q^* and P^*

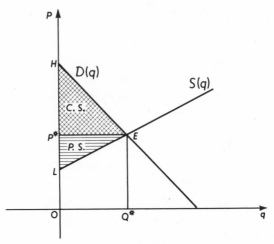

FIGURE 2.7.

be the market quantity and price, respectively, corresponding to the point E, where $D(q) = S(q)$.

The consumers' surplus (C.S.) is the cross hatched area defined by

$$\text{C.S.} = \int_0^{Q^*} D(q)dq - Q^*P^*$$

and producers' surplus (P.S.) is the area defined by

$$\text{P.S.} = Q^*P^* - \int_0^{Q^*} S(q)dq.$$

Example 2.8. Let the demand function

$$D(q) = 20 - 2q$$

and the supply function

$$S(q) = 2q + 4$$

be given, where $p = D(q) = S(q)$ represents price in dollars and q units of a commodity.

Solution:

Step 1: Find Q^* and P^*.

At the market or equilibrium quantity Q^*,

$$D(q) = S(q).$$

Hence, by substituting we have

$$20 - 2q = 2q + 4,$$

and

$$Q^* = 4.$$

Letting $Q^* = 4$ in D, we get

$$D(4) = 20 - 2(4)$$

and

$$P^* = 12.$$

Step 2: Find C.S. and P.S.
Substituting in the above formulas, we obtain

$$\text{C.S.} = \int_0^4 (20 - 2q)dq - (4)(12)$$

$$= 20q - q^2 \Big]_0^4 - 48$$

$$= 64 - 48$$

$$= 16 \text{ ; and}$$

$$\text{P.S.} = (4)(12) - \int_0^4 (2q + 4)dq$$

$$= 48 - (q^2 + 4q) \Big]_0^4$$

$$= 48 - 32$$

$$= 16.$$

Thus, consumers' surplus and producers' surplus each is equivalent to $16. The reader may sketch the appropriate diagram.

2.5. Recapitulation. In this and the preceding chapters we introduced the fundamental concepts of calculus; we explained a selective number of formulas for differentiating and integrating algebraic functions; and we illustrated, with numerous examples, the use of these basic tools in business situations. But analyzing and solving business problems, although sufficient to establish the connection between the mathematical and the empirical worlds, was a secondary task. Our primary purpose has been to lay down the foundations of the mathematical system of calculus. With this purpose accomplished, we shall proceed to more sophisticated, and more frequently than not, more realistic applications of this system.

PROBLEMS

2.1. Let the following marginal cost function be given

$$c(x) = \frac{x}{50} - 10, \qquad x \geqslant 0,$$

where x represents the number of parts produced and $y = c(x)$ the marginal cost rate in dollars.

 a) Sketch the graph of the function and use the limiting process explained in Example 2.1 to find the area under the curve over the closed interval [200, 500].
 b) Verify your answer to (*a*) by integration.
 c) Suppose interval [200, 500] represents the range of parts produced for most production runs in the past. Interpret your answer to (*a*) and (*b*) and suggest how this information may be useful to management.

2.2. Consider the function

$$h(x) = 50 - 2x, \qquad x \geqslant 0,$$

where x represents mail orders for an item and $y = h(x)$ the rate at which units of an item in stock are sold.
 a) Sketch the graph of the function and use the limiting process explained in Example 2.1 to find the area under the curve over the closed interval [5, 20].
 b) Verify your answer to (*a*) by integration.
 c) Suppose interval [5, 20] represents the range of mail orders per day for most working days in the past. Interpret your answer to (*a*) and (*b*) and suggest how this information may be useful to management.

2.3. Find the sum of the areas for $n = 10$ and $n = 20$ in Example 2.1 and thus verify that the value of S_n approaches 7500 as n increases.

2.4. Each function below is the first derivative of the function from the indicated example of Chapter 6.
 i) Sketch the graph of the function and find the area under the curve over the given interval.
 ii) Interpret your answer on the basis of the empirical situation involved in each case.
 a) $f'(x) = 50$, $100 \leqslant x \leqslant 200$, Example 1.2.
 b) $f'^{-1}(x) = \frac{1}{50}$, $5000 \leqslant x \leqslant 10{,}000$, Example 1.3.
 c) $S'(x) = 0.15$, 65 (million) $\leqslant x \leqslant 68$ (million), Example 2.4.
 d) $S'(q) = 10$, 4 (million) $\leqslant q \leqslant 5.7$ (million), Example 2.5.
 e) $C'(q) = 6.7$, 4 (million) $\leqslant q \leqslant 5.7$ (million), Example 2.5.
 f) $Q'(p) = -1000$, $3 \leqslant p \leqslant 9$, Example 2.6.
 g) $P'(x) = -4x + 48$, $5 \leqslant x \leqslant 15$, Example 3.7.
 h) $C'(x) = x/50 - 10$, $200 \leqslant x \leqslant 800$, Example 3.8.
 i) $S'(p) = -2000p + 10{,}000$, $3 \leqslant p \leqslant 9$, Example 3.9.
 j) $C'(p) = -2000$, $3 \leqslant p \leqslant 9$, Example 3.9.
 k) $P'(p) = -2000p + 12{,}000$, $3 \leqslant p \leqslant 9$, Example 3.9.

2.5. Each given derivative corresponds to the problem of Chapter 6 indicated below. For each case answer (i) and (ii) of Problem 2.4.
 *a) $f'(t) = -1.5$, $5 \leqslant t \leqslant 10$, Problem 2.3.
 b) $f'(x) = -75$, $0 \leqslant x \leqslant 135$, Problem 2.4.
 *c) $g'(d) = 0.00625$, $100 \leqslant d \leqslant 1000$, Problem 2.8.
 d) $h'(x) = -20x + 80$, $2 \leqslant x \leqslant 6$, Problem 3.9.

e) $f'(x) = -2x + 20$, $5 \leqslant x \leqslant 15$, Problem 3.15.
f) $f'(x) = 2x - 100$, $30 \leqslant x \leqslant 70$, Problem 3.16.

2.6. J. B. Hansen Company, a European outfit, developed a very efficient type of machinery for manufacturing new self-opening cans for beverages. This new machinery can be delivered f.o.b. in New York at a price of $45,375. The management of the company believes that the new machinery will meet the highly competitive market conditions in the United States. It can manufacture cans which do away with can openers. Furthermore, although the required adjustments immediately after installation may increase normal operating costs somewhat, cost savings will be considerable as workers learn how to operate the new machinery and sales volume increases rapidly. The rate of cost savings is given by the function

$$f(t) = 3000t, \qquad 0 \leqslant t \leqslant 6,$$

where t represents years and $y = f(t)$ the rate of dollar savings. This function was derived from test runs which simulated six years of normal operations.

*a) Would the new machinery pay for itself in six years?
*b) How many years of normal operations are required for the machinery to pay for itself?
*c) If transportation cost from New York to the factory, installation cost, and adjustment cost amount to $18,000, how long will it take for the new machinery to pay for itself?
d) Under the added cost in (c) and the implicitly stated assumptions in the problem, would you decide to purchase the new machinery or not? Defend your decision.

2.7. Consider Problem 2.6 but assume that purchase price and other costs for the new machinery amount to $43,200. Cost savings from the normal use of the machinery would permit a rate of depreciation depicted by the function

$$f(t) = \frac{43,200}{(t + 4)^3} + 36.$$

Assuming zero scrap value, how many years will it take for the new machinery to pay for itself? Sketch a diagram of the area under the curve.

2.8. Find the answer to question 3 in Example 2.6, using the profit function $P(x) = -0.8x^2 + 8x - 7$ and thus verify the answer found by integration. Sketch the graphs of P and P' on the same cc-plane and shade the area under graph of P' over the interval [2, 5]. Discuss the relationship between P and P' over [2, 5].

2.9. Let $S'(x) = -4x + 18$ and $C'(x) = 6$ be marginal dollar sales revenue and cost functions, of unit output x, respectively.
a) Indicate in a diagram the area which is bounded by the graphs of the two functions in the interval $0 \leqslant x \leqslant 3$.

*b) Find the increase in total profits when sales grow from 0 to 3 units using the formula (2.18) of the text.

*c) Find the total profit function by integrating the given marginal functions.

d) Verify your answer to (b) by using the total profit function you found in (c).

*2.10. Consider the marginal wheat output function

$$f'(x) = -\frac{24x^2}{10^6} + \frac{48x}{10^3} - 8$$

where x represents dollar investment.

a) Find the area under the curve in the interval

$$500 \leqslant x \leqslant 1000.$$

b) Intrepret your answer to (a).

c) Let $C = 5000$. Sketch the graphs of f and f' functions on the same cc-plane and shade the area under the graph of f' over the interval [500, 1000]. Discuss the relationship between f and f' over [500, 1000].

2.11. Consider the marginal cost of production function

$$f'(x) = \frac{3x^2}{10^4} - \frac{18x}{10^2} + 18,$$

where x represents number of parts produced.

a) Find the area over the curve in the interval $200 \leqslant x \leqslant 300$.

b) Interpret your answer to (a).

c) Let $C = 3000$. Sketch the graphs of f and f' functions on the same cc-plane and shade the area under the graph of f' over the interval [200, 300]. Discuss the relationship of f and f' over this interval.

2.12. Show with integral calculus, without doing the required arithmetic, that the area bounded by the functions $C(p) = -2000p + 25{,}000$ and $S(p) = -1000p^2 + 10{,}000p$ is equivalent to the area under the curve of the function

$$P(p) = -1000p^2 + 12{,}000p - 25{,}000$$

in the interval $p_1 \leqslant p \leqslant p_2$ where p_1 and p_2 represents the roots of the quadratic equation $-1000p^2 + 12{,}000p - 25{,}000 = 0$. Refer to Figure 3.7 of Chapter 6 for a visual understanding of the areas.

2.13. Kimballs and Karters Company, a large manufacturer of baby clothes, is considering the installation of a data processing system to handle their bookkeeping operations. Although selection of data processing equipment is a complex and difficult job, one of the criteria for selection is a function showing the total daily cost of operating a system for a given number of operational output units. Two system designs are considered with total costs

$$f(x) = \frac{x^2}{100} - 10x + 3000$$

for system A and

$$g(x) = \frac{2x^2}{100} - 16x + 3600$$

for system B.

a) Which of the two systems should the management of the company decide to install if daily requirements do not vary widely and the average number of operational output units are approximately 400? 500?

b) What would management's decision be if daily requirements vary widely from 100 to 700 operational units?

c) Sketch the area under the curve of each function in the interval $100 \leqslant x \leqslant 700$.

2.14. For each case below—
   i) Sketch the diagram of the area bounded by the graphs of the given functions.
   ii) Find the area.
   *a) $g(x) = 3x - x^2$ and $f(x) = x - 3$.
   b) $f(x) = x - 2$ and $g(x) = 2x - x^2$.
   c) $f(x) = x/5 + 2$ and $g(x) = 4$.
   d) $f(x) = 2(25 - x^2)$ and $h(x) = 4x + 2$, $x \geqslant 0$.

2.15. For each function below representing a learning curve and describing the rate of direct labor required to assemble or produce the xth unit of a product do the following:
   i) Find the total number of direct labor hours required to produce the indicated number of units.
   ii) Sketch the graph of the function and shade the area under the curve over the indicated interval.
   a) $f(x) = 485.4x^{-0.5146}$, $0 \leqslant x \leqslant 60$.
   b) $g(x) = 1695.6x^{-0.1522}$, $50 \leqslant x \leqslant 100$.
   c) $h(x) = 789.3x^{-0.7369}$, $0 \leqslant x \leqslant 50$.
   d) $g(x) = 3877x^{-0.2346}$, $60 \leqslant x \leqslant 120$.
   e) $g(x) = 3703.6x^{-0.0741}$, $200 \leqslant x \leqslant 300$.
   f) $f(x) = 3510x^{-0.4150}$, $0 \leqslant x \leqslant 100$.
   g) $h(x) = 567.6x^{-0.6216}$, $10 \leqslant x \leqslant 40$.

2.16. Sketch the appropriate diagram for the problem in Example 2.8 and shade the areas representing consumers' and producers' surpluses.

2.17. Consider the demand P and the supply S functions given in each case below:
   i) Sketch their graphs on the same cc-plane.
   ii) Find the consumers' and producers' surplus.
   iii) Shade the areas representing your answer in (ii).
   a) $D(q) = 22 - 2q$; $S(q) = 2q + 10$.
   b) $D(q) = 4$; $S(q) = (q/5) + 2$.
   c) $D(q) = 10 - (2/3)q$; $S(q) = 5$.
   *d) $D(q) = 2(25 - q^2)$; $S(q) = 4q + 2$.
   e) $D(q) = -q^2 - 4q + 60$; $S(q) = 5q + 8$.
   f) $D(q) = 10 - (9/4)q$; $S(q) = 2q^2 + \frac{1}{2}$.

SUGGESTED REFERENCES

1. ANDREE, R. V. *Introduction to Calculus with Analytic Geometry*, pp. 167–237. New York: McGraw-Hill Book Co., Inc., 1962. (**1, 2**)

2. COOLEY, H. R., *et al. Introduction to Mathematics*, pp. 497–519. Boston: Houghton Mifflin Co., 1949. (**1, 2**)

3. DAUS, P. H., AND WHYBURN, W. M. *Introduction to Mathematical Analysis*, pp. 118–23. Reading, Mass.: Addison-Wesley Publishing Co., Inc., 1958. (**2**)

4. EAVES, E. D., AND WILSON, R. L. *Introductory Mathematical Analysis*, pp. 127–51. Boston: Allyn and Bacon, Inc., 1961. (**1, 2**)

5. JOHNSON, R. E., AND KIOKEMEISTER, F. L. *Calculus with Analytic Geometry*, pp. 212–19, 222–29, and 301–4. Boston: Allyn and Bacon, Inc., 1959. (**1, 2**)

6. KLINE, MORRIS. *Mathematics: A Cultural Approach*, pp. 417–42. Reading, Mass.: Addison-Wesley Publishing Co., Inc., 1962. (**1, 2**)

7. THOMAS, G. B. *Calculus and Analytic Geometry*, pp. 155–64, 181–221. 3d ed. Reading, Mass.: Addison-Wesley Publishing Co., Inc., 1962. (**1–2**)

8. THOMPSON, S. P. *Calculus Made Easy*, pp. 182–225. New York: The Macmillan Co.. 1960. (**1, 2**)

9. WESTERN, D. W., AND HAAG, V. H. *An Introduction to Mathematics*, pp. 359–70 and 403–12. New York: Henry Holt & Co., Inc., 1959. (**1, 2**)

Chapter 13

SELECTED APPLICATIONS OF CALCULUS

IN THE PRECEDING two chapters our primary objective has been the introduction of basic concepts and tools of differential and integral calculus. Applications of this mathematical system, by necessity and design, occupied a subservient position. They were more or less limited and geared to serve the above primary purpose.

In this chapter we shall reverse our approach. Showing how calculus has been used to solve specific problems in business operations is the subject matter of Sections 1 and 2. Our attention will be focussed on a selective number of cases which do not require much more than what the reader has learned so far. Whatever additional tools are necessary will be introduced to the extent and at the time they are needed.

*1. CALCULUS IN BUSINESS OPERATIONS—1

The mathematics of three cases is explained in this section: an advertising budget problem, a minimum cost lot size formula for inventory control, and a model for determining optimal warehouse territories. All three cases require no more differential calculus than what the reader already knows.

1.1. An Advertising Budget Problem.

How much to spend on advertising is an important and difficult problem for the management of many companies. There is no universally applied method. Depending on the marketing and promotional objectives, as well as other considerations, several methods are employed. They range from setting up a sum arbitrarily to spending a sum representing a certain percentage of sales or matching the competitor's outlay. Here we shall demonstrate a case which takes into consideration the advertising budget of competitors.

Example 1.1. In Example 2.5 of Chapter 6 we have found that the forecast sales q of Continental Rubber and Tire Company were 5,650,000 tires. From the derived profit function $P(q) = 3.3q - 15,000,000$ we found that if actual sales were as forecast the company would make a profit of $3,645,-000 before taxes.

Mr. J. B., the president of the company, was confronted with another problem, namely, deciding how much the company should spend on advertising. Because the market for the type of tires the company was manufacturing was highly competitive, Mr. J. B. felt that the advertising budget of competitors should be considered. He wanted to know how a decision could be made which, unlike other conventional methods, does not ignore competitive advertising, and in such a case what his budget should be in order to maximize the company's profits.

Let x be the *unknown* advertising outlay of Mr. J. B.'s company. Let b represent the *known* budget of competitors which, for the sake of simplifying matters, we assume to represent one rival firm. We also assume that total industry sales are independent of the total amount spent on advertising and that the firm's share of sales is proportional to its share of the total industry advertising budget. Although the latter assumption may be unrealistic, it can be used for a first approximation to the analysis of the advertising budget of the firm. Let Q be the forecast potential sales volume in units for the entire industry. Then the company's expected sales volume of q will be equal to

$$Q\left(\frac{x}{x+b}\right).$$

Let f be the fixed and v the variable production costs for the industry; let p be the price per tire for both the company and its competitor. Then the total cost function will be

(1.1) $$C(x) = f + v\left(\frac{Qx}{x+b}\right) + x$$

and the dollar sales function

(1.2) $$S(x) = p\left(\frac{Qx}{x+b}\right).$$

Since the profit function $P(x) = S(x) - C(x)$, substituting for (1.1) and (1.2) we have

(1.3) $$P(x) = p\left(\frac{Qx}{x+b}\right) - \left[f + v\left(\frac{Qx}{x+b}\right) + x\right].$$

Taking the first derivative of $P(x)$ with respect to x, we get

$$P'(x) = \frac{pbQ}{(x+b)^2} - \left[\frac{vbQ}{(x+b)^2} + 1\right].$$

Letting $P'(x) = 0$ and solving for x, we get

(1.4) $$x = \sqrt{(p-v)bQ} - b,$$

the advertising outlay for the maximum profit (the reader may verify that $P(x)$ is a maximum at x by taking $P''(x)$.

Example 1.1—*Continued.* The marketing research department of Continental Rubber and Tire Company forecast an industry sales volume Q of 8,000,000 tires. Intelligence research has revealed that the competitors plan to spend on advertising an amount $b = \$500,000$.

Since $p = \$10$ and $v = \$6.7$ per tire,

$$x = \sqrt{(10 - 6.7)(0.5 \times 10^6)(8 \times 10^6)} - 5 \times 10^5$$

$$x \approx 3,134,000 \text{ dollars}$$

is the optimal advertising budget for the company.

Mr. J. B. felt that most of the simplifying assumptions of the above advertising "model" were not far from describing the competitive tire market of his company. He concluded that the answers which he could get from the "model" would be important for helping him to arrive at a final decision.

What is the expected profit of the Continental Rubber and Tire Company if management decides to spend the optimal advertising outlay? What will the sales volume of the company be then? How much should the company spend on advertising in order to maintain its original profit level of \$3,645,000? How does Mr. J. B.'s decision depend on the decisions which his competitors might make? It is left for the reader to answer and discuss the above questions. Also, for this and other advertising models, see reference 1, pp. 220–29, in this chapter's bibliography.

1.2. Finding the Minimum Cost Lot Size.

Inventory control is important for an efficiently functioning business firm. Although there is a growing variety of inventory control models, the central question in a typical inventory control problem is how to minimize the costs which are associated with obtaining and holding inventory.

Such inventory optimization involves two kinds of costs: *setup* and inventory *carrying* costs. Setup cost represents the expense for setting up the machinery to produce a *lot* of units of a certain commodity. Setup cost is called *reorder* cost if the case involves ordering a lot from a supplier rather than producing it. Carrying cost is incurred because the produced lot of goods must be carried in stock until sold. Inventory carrying cost includes charges such as insurance, storage, interest, depreciation, obsolescence, and property taxes.

The inventory optimization problem arises from the fact that when setup cost is low, carrying cost tends to be high and vice versa. For instance, suppose the monthly demand for a commodity is uniform and fixed at 300 units. Then all 300 units could be produced by setting up the equipment once. In such a case the 300 units will be stocked at the beginning of each month and sold during the month. Since demand is uniform, the average monthly inventory will be 150 units. This inventory could be reduced by producing smaller than 300-unit lots each setup. For instance, producing a 150-unit lot every 15 days will reduce the monthly inventory to 75 units, a 100-unit lot every 10 days to 50 units, and so on. As inventory goes down, carrying cost will tend to fall; however, since smaller inventory requires more frequent production setups, these costs will tend to rise. In other words, large inventories are associated with low setup and high carrying costs, while small inventories tend to have the opposite effect. Our problem is to find the minimum cost (setup plus carrying) lot size.

Minimum cost or *optimum lot size* formulae differ depending on the underlying assumptions of each inventory problem. We shall consider variations of the case where the demand for a product is uniform and fixed each period with price predetermined.

Example 1.2. After studying the situation, Mr. J. B., the president of the Continental Rubber and Tire Company, finally decides that sales for the year could very well be about 6,000,000 tires. In view of the previously made industry sales forecast and the planned advertising budget, he believes that a sales volume of this size is a rather conservative figure. His next problem is to find the optimum production lot size when carrying cost is $0.50 per tire per year and setup cost $15,000 per run.

It is assumed that the demand for tires is uniform throughout the year. Although this may not be true, the model could be later adjusted for actual monthly variations. Since price was predetermined, the optimum lot size can be found as follows:

Let x be the lot size. Then $x/2$ is the average inventory in stock throughout a period between production runs. Since the carrying cost is $0.50 per tire per year, the total cost for inventory carrying is

$$\frac{x}{2}(0.50) = \frac{x}{4}.$$

For an annual demand of 6,000,000 tires the number of production runs per year is $6,000,000/x$. Since the cost per each setup is $15,000, the total annual setup cost is

$$\frac{6,000,000}{x}(15,000) = \frac{9 \times 10^{10}}{x}.$$

The total annual inventory cost is the sum of carrying cost plus the setup cost, i.e.,

$$C(x) = \frac{x}{4} + \frac{9 \times 10^{10}}{x}.$$

Taking the first derivative of $C(x)$ with respect to x, we get

$$C'(x) = \frac{1}{4} - \frac{9 \times 10^{10}}{x^2}.$$

Letting $C'(x) = 0$ and solving for x as indicated below, we find the optimal lot size to be

$$\tfrac{1}{4} - \frac{9 \times 10^{10}}{x^2} = 0$$

$$x^2 = 36 \times 10^{10}$$

$$x = 600,000 \text{ tires.}$$

(The reader may take the second derivative to verify that $C(x)$ is indeed a maximum when $C'(x) = 0$. The above answer means that with each production run a tenth of a year's supply of tires should be made.

The cost of this optimum lot size will be

$$C(600,000) = \frac{6 \times 10^5}{4} + \frac{9 \times 10^{10}}{6 \times 10^5}$$

$$= 300,000 \text{ dollars per year.}$$

The general formula for the above optimum lot size problem can be very easily derived.

Let

$$x = \text{lot size,}$$

$$D = \text{uniform fixed demand per period,}$$

$$I = \text{carrying cost per item per period,}$$

$$S = \text{setup cost.}$$

Then

(1.5)
$$C(x) = \frac{x}{2} I + \frac{D}{x} S,$$

where $\frac{x}{2} I$ is the carrying cost and $\frac{D}{x} S$ is the setup cost per period.

Taking the first derivative of (1.5) with respect to x, we have

(1.6)
$$C'(x) = \frac{I}{2} - \frac{DS}{x^2}.$$

Letting (1.6) equal to zero and solving for x, we obtain the optimum lot size formula

$$\frac{I}{2} - \frac{DS}{x^2} = 0,$$

(1.7)
$$x = \sqrt{\frac{2DS}{I}}.$$

The above simple model may be modified to fit variations of the optimal lot size problem. In Example 1.2 inventory carrying cost is expressed in terms of $0.50 per tire per year. It varies directly with the number of units in stock. But not all carrying costs may be of this kind. Ware-housing cost, for instance, may vary with the maximum rather than average inventory size.

Let W be the warehousing carrying cost per unit of product. Then the total warehousing and variable carrying costs are Wx and $\frac{x}{2}I$, respectively. By (1.5) total cost per period would be

$$(1.8) \qquad C(x) = \frac{x}{2}I + Wx + \frac{D}{x}S.$$

Differentiating (1.8) with respect to x, we get

$$C'(x) = \frac{I}{2} + W - \frac{DS}{x^2};$$

and when

$$\frac{I}{2} + W - \frac{DS}{x^2} = 0,$$

$$(1.9) \qquad x = \sqrt{\frac{2DS}{I + 2W}}.$$

Further modifications of (1.7) may be made by introducing additional qualifications to the original problem. For instance, some setup costs may be fixed and others such as maintenance costs may vary with the maximum number of units processed per run. Let S be the fixed and V the variable setup costs. Then by (1.8) the total cost per period would be

$$(1.10) \qquad C(x) = \frac{x}{2}I + Wx + \frac{D}{x}S + Vx.$$

Differentiating (1.10) with respect to x, we have

$$C'(x) = \frac{I}{2} + W - \frac{DS}{x^2} + V;$$

and when

$$\frac{I}{2} + W - \frac{DS}{x^2} + V = 0,$$

$$(1.11) \qquad x = \sqrt{\frac{2DS}{I + 2W + 2V}}.$$

1.3. Determining Optimum Warehouse Territories.

This case, the last in this section, deals with a distribution or a scale of operations problem.

Example 1.3. L. B. Dailey, a wholesale distributor of frozen food, operates three warehouses for serving a metropolitan area of about 252 square miles. Although special studies were conducted in order to determine the best geographic location and the optimal refrigeration storage capacity for each warehouse, there was another problem which required special attention. Because of the special refrigeration requirements for handling frozen food, both storage and delivery (mainly transportation) costs are higher than usual. Furthermore, storage costs per pound of food are inversely related to the volume of business handled by each warehouse. They are falling when volume increases since fixed storage costs are spread over a larger volume But a larger volume for each warehouse means a larger area to be served which increases the costs associated with delivery since distances greater than previously must be covered. In other words, large volume of business is associated with falling storage costs per pound of food and rising delivery costs or vice versa. Mr Dailey wants to find out how large the territory of a warehouse should be so that its distribution cost can be a minimum. He feels that this information would be a valuable aid for determining whether additional warehouses may be needed to serve the entire metropolitan area with minimum distribution cost for the entire operation.

On the basis of the stated conditions of the above problem the average cost or cost per pound of distributed food may be considered as an appropriate unit for measuring the efficiency of warehousing operations. Let C represent the average cost. Then C will be equal to the sum of average storage costs S, delivery costs D, and residual costs R.

Since storage costs are inversely related to the volume of business V, such costs per pound of distributed food will be equal to S/V. Inasmuch as distance from the warehouse is the major factor for determining delivery costs, a way must be found for expressing this direct relationship between such costs and the territory served by a warehouse. Let x represent such a territory and imagine x as the area of a circle with a warehouse at its center. Then x is equal to πr^2, where r is the radius of x and π (pi) is an irrational number approximately equal to 3.14159 to five decimal places. Since territory x served by the warehouse increases in proportion to the square of the increase in distance, delivery costs will tend to vary directly with the square root of the increase in x, i.e., $D\sqrt{x}$. Finally, residual costs R are independent of volume or size of territory served by the warehouse. Thus, the dollar cost per pound of distributed food may be expressed by

(1.12) $$C(x) = R + \frac{S}{V} + D\sqrt{x},$$

where

$C =$ cost per pound of distributed food in dollars;
$x =$ area served by a warehouse in square miles;

V = volume of frozen food handled by a warehouse per month in pounds;

S = storage costs of a warehouse per month;

D = delivery costs such as gasoline, truck maintenance and repairs, driver's hourly pay, etc., varying with the square root of the territory;

R = residual costs such as taxes per pound of distributed food which cannot be classified as storage or delivery costs.

Since equation (1.12) contains two unknowns, volume V and territory x, it must be modified. It is reasonable to assume that sales are likely to be distributed uniformly over the entire metropolitan area. Thus sales density may be considered as a constant defined by

$$K = \frac{V}{x},$$

where K represents the monthly volume of business in pounds per square mile. Hence $V = Kx$; substituting $V = Kx$ in (1.12) we get

(1.13)
$$C(x) = R + \frac{S}{Kx} + D\sqrt{x}.$$

The minimum cost area can be found by the usual procedure of differentiating (1.13) with respect to x, letting the derivative equal to zero, and solving for x as follows:

Since

$$C(x) = R + \frac{S}{Kx} + Dx^{\frac{1}{2}},$$

then

$$C'(x) = -\frac{S}{Kx^2} + \tfrac{1}{2}Dx^{-\frac{1}{2}}$$

$$= -\frac{S}{Kx^2} + \frac{D}{2\sqrt{x}},$$

and when

$$-\frac{S}{Kx^2} + \frac{D}{2\sqrt{x}} = 0$$

$$\frac{S}{Kx^2} = \frac{D}{2\sqrt{x}}$$

$$2S\sqrt{x} = DKx^2$$

$$2S = DKx^{3/2}$$

(1.14)
$$x = \left(\frac{2S}{DK}\right)^{2/3}.$$

Expression (1.14) indicates that the optimal or minimum cost territory for a warehouse depends directly on storage costs S and inversely on delivery costs D and sales density K. The size of the territory is independent of the residual costs R. Now a quantitative decision rule has been established to aid Mr. Dailey's executive judgment.

Example 1.3—*Continued.* From the accounting records of the three warehouses, it was found that per warehouse $S = \$2000$ per month, $D = \$0.01$ per square root of territory, and $K = 1000$ pounds per square mile per month. Substituting in (1.14), we have

$$x = \left[\frac{2(2000)}{(0.01)1000} \right]^{2/3}$$

$$\log_{10} x = \tfrac{2}{3}\log_{10} 400$$

$$= \tfrac{2}{3}(2.60206)$$

$$= 1.73470 ; \quad \text{and}$$

$$x \approx 54.2 \text{ square miles.}$$

On the basis of the above optimum Mr. Dailey realized that his warehouses, as a group, are serving an area larger than the optimal. He felt that the model could help him determine optimal territories for each warehouse. Also, the above result indicated that another warehouse might be necessary. However, such a decision required further investigation of the sales-profit potential of the area as well as other aspects of his business.

From the viewpoint of costs relationships, the above model may be considered as a modification of the initial economic lot size model. However, the two differ with respect to the methods which may be required for obtaining the necessary data. In the lot size case, data are obtained from production cost records. In the present case, given a sufficient number of warehouses, statistical techniques may be used to determine the parameters S, D, and R of the model as well as to test the model itself. For a discussion on this point see reference 5 in this chapter's bibliography.

PROBLEMS

1.1. Suppose the management of Continental Rubber and Tire Company decides to spend the optimal $3,134,000 on advertising, find the company's volume and profit.

*1.2. Assume that the competitors of Continental Rubber and Tire Company in response to the latter's decision to spend $3,134,000 on advertising plan to raise their own advertising budget to $1,500,000.
  a) Find the optimal advertising budget, sales volume, and profit for the company.

b) On the basis of your findings in (a) what would you recommend to the company's management? Answer this question after you find—

(1) The company's advertising budget in order to maintain the original sales volume of 5,650,000 tires and the profit associated with that budget, if competitors plan to spend $500,000 on advertising; and

(2) The company's advertising budget and sales volume in order to just break even if competitors plan to spend $1,500,000 on advertising.

1.3. Use the second derivative test for extrema to verify that $P(x)$, (1.3) in the text, is indeed a maximum at $P'(x) = 0$.

1.4. Since the profit function (1.3) is a maximum at $P'(x) = 0$, marginal revenue must equal marginal cost at optimal x. Using the first derivative of (1.1) and (1.2) show that at optimal x,

$$p = v + \frac{(x + b)^2}{bQ}.$$

Verify this relationship by substituting for the values of p, v, b, Q, and x given in Example 1.1.

1.5. Use the second derivative test for extrema to verify that at

$$C'(x) = \tfrac{1}{4} - \frac{9 \times 10^6}{x^2} = 0,$$

$C(x)$ in Example 1.2 is indeed a minimum.

1.6. For each cost function given below verify that $C(x)$ is indeed a minimum by the second derivative test for extrema when $C'(x) = 0$.
*a) Function (1.5).
b) Function (1.8).
c) Function (1.10).

1.7. Use (1.5) and (1.7) to verify the optimum lot size and minimum total inventory cost found in Example 1.2.

1.8. Let the values of D, I, and S be as in Example 1.2. Then find the optimum lot size and its minimum total inventory cost when—
a) $W = \$0.05$.
b) $W = \$0.05$ and $V = \$0.15$.

1.9. For lot sizes of 4, 5, 6, 7, and 8 hundred thousand tires in Example 1.2—
*a) Find the total inventory cost, total and marginal carrying costs, and total and marginal setup costs.
b) Using proper scales on the y-axis, sketch the graphs of the functions from the values obtained in (a) on the same cc-plane. Explain the special relationship that exists between total and marginal functions.

1.10. A manufacturer needs 160 motors each of the 250 business days of the year for assembling an equivalent number of clothes dryers. He purchases these motors from another manufacturer at $20 apiece. In order to finance this expense, he borrows from a bank on short-term basis at a simple interest rate of 5 percent per annum. In addition, he has other inventory charges which amount to $1.00 per motor per year. The $20 price the manufacturer pays for each motor includes all shipping expenses except a fixed charge of $100 per shipment.

*a) How many motors should the manufacturer order each time in order to minimize his annual inventory cost? What is this cost? How many orders does he have to place each year?

b) Suppose that demand for the manufacturer's clothes dryer has increased to the point that he plans to expand production to 1600 clothes dryers a business day. Although other costs remain the same, he has to provide now for special storage space for the entire shipment. He figures warehousing cost will be $1.00 per motor. Under these new conditions, answer the questions in (a).

c) With the demand of 1600 motors a business day, the supplier informs him that because of rising labor costs he can no longer absorb shipping costs. Such costs amount to $2.00 per motor, but the fixed shipping charge per shipping has been reduced to $40 per order. Answer the questions in (a) if other conditions remain as in (b).

*1.11. Substitute for $x = \sqrt{2DS/I}$ in (1.5) to find the total inventory cost at the optimal lot size x. Use the data given in Example 1.2 to verify your formula.

1.12. Assume that a manufacturer for ordering the unprocessed units from his supplier for each setup pays a fixed cost F and a variable cost V per unit. Let I, D, and x be defined as in (1.5), then

$$C(x) = \frac{x}{2}I + \frac{D}{x}S + \frac{D}{x}(F + Vx).$$

*a) From the above total cost function derive the economic lot size formula.

b) How do costs F and V affect the economic lot size?

c) Let $D = 200,000$ units per month, $S = \$500$, and $F = \$500$ per setup, $I = \$1.00$ per unit per month, and $V = \$2.00$ per unit. Then find:

(1) The economic lot size x.
(2) The number of setups per month.
(3) The minimum total monthly cost.
(4) The minimum total cost per unit produced.

1.13. Let inventory I be a fraction of the total cost per unit of output defined by

$$I = K\left(\frac{S + F + Vx}{x}\right)$$

where K is a positive constant less than one and all other symbols are defined in Problem 1.12.

a) Find the total cost function.

b) From the total cost function derive the economic lot size formula.

c) How do costs F and V affect the economic lot size?

d) Let the values of D, S, F, and V be as given in Problem 1.12 (*c*) and $K = 0.50$, then find:

   (1) The economic lot size x.

   (2) The number of setups per month.

   (3) The minimum total monthly cost.

   (4) The minimum total cost per unit produced.

1.14. Show with a second derivative test for extrema that $C(x)$ is indeed a minimum at

(1.14) $$x = \left(\frac{2S}{DK}\right)^{2/3}.$$

1.15. Let residual costs $R = \$0.01$ per pound of distributed food and other data as given in Example 1.3. Find minimum cost $C(x)$ at optimal territory $x = 54.2$ square miles.

1.16. Consider the storage S/Kx, delivery $D\sqrt{x}$, and residual R costs in (1.13).

   **a*) Substitute for $x = 25$, 36, 49, 54.2, 64, 81, and 100 square miles and for $R = \$0.01$ per pound of distributed food in (1.13); use the values of K, S, and D given in Example 1.3; and find the S/Kx and $D\sqrt{x}$ costs for each value of x.

   b) Plot the coordinates obtained in (*a*) for each cost on the same cc-plane and connect the points to show graphically their inter-relationship.

1.17. In Example 1.3 the values of S, D, and K represent averages of the three warehouses. Let $R = \$0.01$ per pound for all three warehouses.

   a) Let us assume that $K_A = 1500$, $K_B = 1000$, and $K_C = 500$ for ware-houses A, B, and C, respectively, while the values of S, D, and R remain the same for all warehouses.

   (1) Find the optimal territory and the minimum cost for each ware-house.

   (2) In Example 1.3 the total optimal area is $3 \times 54.2 = 162.6$ square miles. What is the total optimal area now?

   b) Assuming that storage capacity is directly related to storage cost, $D = \$0.01$, and $K = 1000$ as in Example 1.3, how much should storage cost (capacity) increase per warehouse if the 252 square miles of the metropolitan area are to be served with the three ware-houses each having an optimal territory of $252/3 = 84$ square miles?

1.18. Rather than waiting until depletion, a retailer may reorder for an item before running out of stock. Let R be the reorder stock level, where $R > 0$, and let D, S, and I be defined as in (1.5),

$$C(x) = \frac{x}{2}I + \frac{D}{x}S,$$

   **a*) Find the total inventory cost function.

b) Derive the optimum lot size formula.

c) Let $D = 200$ items per month,

   $S = \$4.00$ cost of reordering,

   $I = \$0.01$ carrying cost per item per month,

   $R = 50$ items reorder level.

Find:

(1) Optimal lot size.

(2) Frequency of reordering.

(3) Minimum total inventory cost per month.

(4) Minimum inventory cost per item per month.

*2. CALCULUS IN BUSINESS OPERATIONS—2

Two cases are explained in this section. The first, dealing with a retailer's aggregate demand, may be considered as a continuation of previous material in two respects. It deals with the determination of demand which in inventory control models in the preceding section was assumed to be constant and given. Although more sophisticated than previous cases, it also requires only the techniques of calculus with which the reader is familiar. The second case deals with equipment investment analysis. It presupposes knowledge of Sections 2 and 3 of Chapter 7 on exponential functions and on the mathematics of investment and finance. The required calculus formulae for the exponential function e^x are supplied and explained here.

For the examples and the problems which require the use of a table of exponential functions, reference 10 in this chapter's bibliography was used. Needless to say, any other similar collection of tables will do.

2.1. Analysis of a Retailer's Aggregate Demand. In the preceding section we have discussed inventory models of *one* item when demand for that item is assumed to be predetermined and fixed. Here we shall make an analysis of the demand for all the items to be stocked by a retailer.

In analyzing a retailer's demand situation, first, we may develop a function expressing the demand of an individual consumer for a given retail store. Let D be the distance between a consumer's place of residence or work and the store. Then the costs of traveling to and from the store may be assumed to be directly related to D. They may be given by $c_d D$, where c_d is a positive constant. Let N be the number of items to be stocked by a retailer, what is the average distance which a shopper has to walk within the store for locating the spot where the item is kept? Let us assume that all items are kept on one story. Since more items for sale would require more space and since area increases as the square of the radius of a circle or the square of the length of the sides of a rectangle, that distance may be expected to increase as the square root of the

N items carried by the retailer. If the cost or difficulty associated with finding an item is directly related to that distance, then such a cost may be given by $c_n\sqrt{N}$ where c_n is a positive constant. Finally, other costs of shopping such as luncheons, baby sitting, etc., may be denoted by c_i. Then the total cost of shopping will be

$$(2.1) \qquad c_d D + c_n\sqrt{N} + c_i.$$

Let p be the probability that a consumer will find some item or items in the store which will make his trip successful, where $0 \leqslant p \leqslant 1$. In order to avoid making the model hopelessly complex, we must assume that p depends *only* on the number of items to be stocked, i.e., p is a function of N denoted by

$$(2.2) \qquad p(N).$$

The influence of price changes and informative advertising is assumed to remain unchanged. Unless a consumer is specifically informed about the variety and nature of the items carried by the store, $p(N)$ will be close to 1 only when N is very large or when a consumer is easily satisfied.

When does a consumer decide to shop at a specific store? Let w be the weight given by a consumer to $p(N)$ and v the weight given to the total cost of shopping, where w and v are positive constants determined subjectively. Then the decision to shop or not to shop will depend on the result from the weight which a consumer will give to the probability of successful shopping against the weight given to the cost of shopping. We can express this relationship with a function f such that

$$(2.3) \qquad f(N, D) = wp(N) - v(c_d D + c_n\sqrt{N} + c_i).$$

Thus a consumer will shop at that store if $f(N, D)$ is positive, i.e., if $wp(N)$, the weighted probability of successful shopping, is greater than $v(c_d D + c_n\sqrt{N} + c_i)$, the weighted cost of shopping. For lack of a better term, function f may be called the *propensity to shop* of an individual consumer. It measures the *net gain* which an individual consumer expects to get from entering a particular store. This net gain depends on N, the number of items on sale, and D, the consumer's distance from the store.

Second, we may determine the total physical sales volume for a particular retailer. We may assume, although later on we may modify our assumption, that at any distance from the store the volume of sales will vary directly with the proportion of individuals who have a positive propensity to shop. In other words, the number of items that a shopper decides to buy is independent of the items, N, available. Then the physical sales volume of a particular retailer will depend on the proportion of individuals with a positive propensity to shop at the store within the maximum shopping distance from the store.

For a given N, there will be a maximum distance D_m from the store where for a particular consumer it will be a matter of indifference whether to shop or not to shop if that consumer lives or works D_m distance from the store. In other words, for a given N an individual consumer is indifferent to shopping where (2.3) equals zero. Letting $f(N, D) = 0$ and solving for D, we get

(2.4)
$$D_m = \frac{wp(N) - v(c_n\sqrt{N} + c_i)}{vc_d}.$$

Moreover, we can take (2.3) to determine the proportion of the population which will decide to shop at a particular store, i.e., the proportion of the population with a positive propensity to shop. Letting capital letters correspond to the lower case letters in (2.3), the *aggregate* propensity to shop function may be denoted by

(2.5)
$$F(N, D) = WP(N) - V(C_d D + C_n\sqrt{N} + C_i).$$

Letting

$$A(N) = WP(N) - V(C_n\sqrt{N} + C_i),$$

function F in (2.5) may be written as

(2.6)
$$F(N, D) = A(N) - VC_d D,$$

where the term $A(N)$ depends on N and the term $VC_d D$ on D.

Next, we must determine the population within the area of a circle bounded by D_m, the maximum shopping distance from the store. Let K represent population density per square mile. Assuming that population is evenly distributed within the shopping area of radius D_m, this area is πD_m^2 and the population within this area is

(2.7)
$$P(D) = K\pi D_m^2,$$

where π is the irrational number 3.14 to the nearest two decimal digits.

From the aggregate propensity to shop (2.6) and the total population (2.7) of the area of a circle bounded by D_m, we can express the physical sales volume of the retailer as

(2.8)
$$S(N, D) = \int_0^{D_m} ([A(N) - VC_d D]2K\pi D) \, dD,$$

since, if continuous, $P'(D) = 2K\pi D$ for any D. Assuming that function (2.8) is continuous and integrating, we get

$$S(N, D) = 2\pi K \int_0^{D_m} [A(N)D - VC_d D^2] dD,$$

$$= 2\pi K \left[A(N)\frac{D^2}{2} - VC_d \frac{D^3}{3} \right]_0^{D_m}.$$

Evaluating at the limits and factoring out $D_m{}^2$, we have

(2.9) $$S(N, D) = 2\pi K D_m^2 \left[\frac{A(N)}{2} - VC_d \frac{D_m}{3} \right].$$

But from (2.4) and the definition of $A(N)$ for the aggregate case

$$D_m = \frac{A(N)}{VC_d}.$$

Substituting for D_m in (2.9) and doing the following simplifying operations, we obtain

$$S(N, D) = 2\pi K \frac{A(N)^2}{(VC_d)^2} \left[\frac{A(N)}{2} - VC_d \frac{A(N)}{3VC_d} \right]$$

$$= 2\pi K \frac{A(N)^3}{(VC_d)^2} \frac{VC_d}{VC_d} (\tfrac{1}{2} - \tfrac{1}{3})$$

$$= \tfrac{1}{3}\pi K \frac{A(N)^3}{(VC_d)^2} \frac{VC_d}{VC_d},$$

$$= \tfrac{1}{3}\pi K V C_d \frac{A(N)^3}{(VC_d)^3}$$

(2.10) $$S(N, D) = \tfrac{1}{3}\pi K V C_d D_m{}^3.$$

Thus, the physical volume of sales for a retailer is directly related to the cube of the maximum shopping distance.

What are the economic implications of the individual and aggregate propensities to shop? What are the major limitations of the retailer's model? At any rate, what is the value of this model from the theoretical as well as the empirical standpoints? For questions such as these, the reader is referred to the problems of this section. Also, for further details of this model and its relation to the retailer's optimum inventory, total costs, and profits, see reference 2 in this chapter's bibliography.

2.2. The Derivative and the Integral of e^x. In dealing with our second topic in this section—equipment investment analysis—we need some basic calculus formulas of the exponential function e^x.

In Section 2 of Chapter 7 we have shown how an exponential function with base a, where $a \neq e$, can be converted into an equivalent one with base e. Also, we pointed out then that this conversion may be desirable because exponential functions with base e are important in calculus. This is because e^x is its own derivative! We shall explain this important property without proof. The number e is defined by

$$e = \operatorname*{limit}_{t \to \infty} \left(1 + \frac{1}{t} \right)^t$$

where t is a positive integer. It can be shown that e is an irrational number approximately equal to 2.71828 to five decimal places. Also, it can be proved that

$$\underset{\Delta x \to 0}{\text{limit}} \frac{e^{\Delta x} - 1}{\Delta x} = 1$$

But by definition (2.11) of Chapter 11 the derivative of e^x is given by

$$D_x e^x = \underset{\Delta x \to 0}{\text{limit}} \frac{e^{x+\Delta x} - e^x}{\Delta x}$$

$$= e^x \underset{\Delta x \to 0}{\text{limit}} \frac{e^{\Delta x} - 1}{\Delta x}$$

from which we can infer that

$$D_x e^x = e^x.$$

A few differentiation and integration formulae of e^x are conveniently listed in Table 2.1 where $f(x)$ is the value of function f at x and a is a real constant. For illustrating the application of these formulae we shall have as examples some of the exponential functions from the forthcoming topic on investment analysis.

Differentiation formula 1 in Table 2.1 has already been explained.

TABLE 2.1.

A. *Differentiation formulae*:
    1. If $f(x) = e^x$, then $f'(x) = e^x$.
    2. If $f(x) = e^{-x}$, then $f'(x) = -e^{-x}$.
    3. If $f(x) = e^{ax}$, then $f'(x) = ae^{ax}$.
    4. If $f(x) = xe^{ax}$, then $f'(x) = e^{ax} + axe^{ax}$.

B. *Integration formulae*:
    5. If $f(x) = e^x$, then $\int e^x dx = e^x + C$.

    6. If $f(x) = e^{-x}$, then $\int e^{-x} dx = -e^{-x} + C$.

    7. If $f(x) = e^{ax}$, then $\int e^{ax} dx = \frac{e^{ax}}{a} + C$.

    8. If $f(x) = xe^{ax}$, then $\int xe^{ax} = \frac{xe^{ax}}{a} - \frac{e^{ax}}{a^2} + C$.

Formulae 2, 3, and 4 are based on rules already explained. For example, formula 4 is derived as follows:

$$D_x x e^{ax} = D_x x \cdot e^{ax} + x \cdot D_x e^{ax}$$
$$= e^{ax} + x e^{ax} \cdot D_x \, ax$$
$$= e^{ax} + a x e^{ax}.$$

Example 2.1. Differentiate the continuous function

$$f(t) = S(t)e^{-it}$$

with respect to t, where i is a real constant.

Solution:

$$D_t[S(t)e^{-it}] = D_t[S(t)]e^{-it} + S(t) \cdot D_t e^{-it}$$
$$= S'(t)e^{-it} + S(t)(-i)e^{-it}$$
$$= S'(t)e^{-it} - iS(t)e^{-it} \qquad \text{[by 2, 3, and 4]}.$$

Let $S(t) = 10{,}000e^{-0.02t}$ and $i = 0.10$. Then substituting in the above solution, differentiating, and simplifying we obtain

$$S'(t)e^{-it} - iS(t)e^{-it} = [D_t(10{,}000e^{-0.02t})]e^{-0.10t}$$
$$- (0.10)(10{,}000e^{-0.02t})e^{-0.10t}$$
$$= (-0.02)(10{,}000e^{-0.02t})e^{-0.10t} - 1000e^{-0.12t}$$
$$= -200e^{-0.12t} - 1000e^{-0.12t} \qquad \text{[by 2 and 3]}$$
$$= -1200e^{-0.12t}.$$

Similarly, since the integration formulae in Table 2.1 are based on laws already explained earlier, we shall have only two examples.

Example 2.2. Evaluate the integral

$$\int_0^{10} (105 + 10e^{0.05t})e^{-0.10t}dt.$$

Solution:

$$\int_0^{10} (105 + 10e^{0.05t})e^{-0.10t}dt = \int_0^{10} 105e^{-0.10t}dt + \int_0^{10} 10e^{-0.05t}dt$$

$$= \frac{105e^{-0.10t}}{-0.10}\bigg|_0^{10} + \frac{10e^{-0.05t}}{-0.05}\bigg|_0^{10} \qquad \text{[by 6 and 7]}$$

$$= -1050e^{-1} - (-1050e^0) - 200e^{-0.5} - (-2000e^0),$$

and from a table of exponential functions,

$$= -1050(0.367879) + 1050 - 200(0.606531) + 200$$
$$= -386.27 + 1050 - 121.31 + 200$$
$$= 742.42.$$

Example 2.3. Evaluate the integral

$$\int_0^{11} 170te^{-0.10t}dt$$

Solution:

$$\int_0^{11} 170te^{-0.10t}\,dt = 170 \int_0^{11} te^{-0.10t}dt$$

$$= 170 \left(\frac{te^{-0.10t}}{-0.10} - \frac{e^{-0.10t}}{(-0.10)^2}\right)\Bigg|_0^{11} \qquad\qquad\qquad \text{[by 8]}$$

$$= 170(-10t - 100)e^{-0.10t}\Bigg|_0^{11}$$

$$= 170[-10(11) - 100]e^{-10(11)} - 170[-10(0) - 100]e^0$$

$$= 170[-210(0.332871)] + 17{,}000$$

$$= 170(-69.91) + 17{,}000$$

$$= -11{,}884.70 + 17{,}000$$

$$= 5115.30.$$

2.3. Equipment Investment Analysis: Maximum Profit Model.

In a production process the life of most equipment may extend almost indefinitely with proper maintenance and by replacing worn out parts. However, as equipment gets older its productivity tends to fall while maintenance and repair costs tend to rise. In other words, such equipment is subject to diminishing efficiency. This situation raises the problem of finding the time in the life of the equipment which is associated with the maximum present value of the investment.

The present problem is analogous to the investment problems which we had in Section 3 of Chapter 7 with two important differences. At that time we dealt with the present value of a *discrete* stream of net earnings. Now we shall deal with the present value of a *continuous* stream of net earnings. This point requires careful explaining. In the discrete case the present value P of the expected stream of net earnings is expressed by

(2.11)
$$P = \sum_{j=1}^{n} \frac{A_j}{(1+i)^j},$$

which is explained in Chapter 7, formula (3.15). In the continuous case the present value of an investment which corresponds to (2.11) may be denoted by

(2.12)
$$P(t) = \int_0^T A(t)e^{-it}dt,$$

where

$P(t)$ = present value function on an investment in the interval $0 \leqslant t \leqslant T$,
$A(t)$ = net earnings function at t,
T = life of the equipment in years,
e^{-it} = present value factor when the annual rate of return i is discounted continuously over time t.

Observe that the present value of the return on an investment is the definite integral of the function $A(t)e^{-it}$ evaluated in the interval $0 \leqslant t \leqslant T$. In order to be able to understand and appreciate (2.12) we must explain the exponential function e^{-it}.

In the discrete case net earnings at the end of the nth year are multiplied by the present value factor $\dfrac{1}{(1 + i)^n}$, where i is the annual rate of return on investment discounted annually. When i is discounted t times a year, then the effective discounting rate will be $\dfrac{1}{\left(1 + \dfrac{i}{t}\right)^t}$ (see formula (3.5) in Chapter 7). Now it can be easily proved that

$$\lim_{t \to \infty}\left(1 + \frac{i}{t}\right)^t = e^{it}.$$

For continuous discounting we let t get larger and larger approaching infinity, then on the basis of the above theorem which is assumed to be proved we have

$$\lim_{t \to \infty}\frac{1}{\left(1 + \dfrac{i}{t}\right)^t} = \frac{1}{e^{it}} = e^{-it}.$$

Thus the integrand $A(t)e^{-it}$ in (2.12) expresses the present value of a continuous stream of expected net earnings at time t.

In addition to the above important difference there is another one. In the discrete case, we find the present value of a machine for a given period of years. This period may represent a machine's expected operational life or a period chosen arbitrarily. In the continuous case this period is unknown. Now our problem is to find the optimal economic life of a machine associated with the maximum present value of net earnings or profits. Thus this maximum profit model permits selection of equipment on the basis of the optimal economic life of the investment rather than on the present value of such investment for a given period of years.

Let T be the unknown optimal economic life of a piece of equipment, $R(t)$ the expected revenue and $M(t)$ the maintenance-repair cost functions at time t, $S(T)$ the salvage or resale value of the machine at time T, and C the initial purchase and installation cost. Then

$$(2.13) \qquad V(T) = \int_0^T R(t)e^{-it}dt - \int_0^T M(t)e^{-it}dt + S(T)e^{-it} - C,$$

where

$V(T) = $ present value of the equipment if salvaged or sold at time T,

$\int_0^T R(t)e^{-it} = $ present value of the continuous stream of revenues from time 0 to time T,

$\int_0^T M(t)e^{-it} = $ present value of the continuous stream of maintenance-repair cost from 0 to T,

$S(T)e^{-iT} = $ present value of the salvage or resale price at time T,

$i = $ minimum rate of return which management expects to earn on this type of investment, sometimes called the *internal rate of return*.

Since there is only one salvage value at time T, $S(T)$ is not integrated. At this point the reader may be able to appreciate the refinements and the convenience afforded by equation (2.13) over a corresponding equation in the discrete case.

The optimal economic life T of a piece of equipment may be determined with the following steps:

First, differentiating (2.13) with respect to T, we have

$$(2.14) \qquad V'(T) = R(T)e^{-iT} - M(T)e^{-iT} - iS(T)e^{-iT} + S'(T)e^{-iT} - 0.$$

Note that the derivative of each definite integral in (2.13) is the corresponding integrand evaluated at T since $R(0)$ and $M(0)$ are constants. Differentiation of $S(T)e^{-iT}$ has already been shown in Example 2.1.

Second, setting (2.14) equal to zero, dividing by e^{-iT}, and transposing terms, we get

$$R(T)e^{-iT} - M(T)e^{-iT} - iS(T)e^{-iT} + S'(T)e^{-iT} = \overset{\bullet}{0}$$

and finally

$$(2.15) \qquad R(T) - M(T) = iS(T) - S'(T).$$

It is important to note that the optimal economic life of a piece of equipment is reached when the difference between falling revenue and rising maintenance cost just equals the interest on the salvage value plus the rate with which salvage value is declining. [$S'(T)$ is negative so that with the minus sign it becomes positive.]

Third, given the three functions in (2.15) and i for a specific piece of equipment, we can find the optimal economic life of it by solving for T. Also, by solving (2.13) for the optimal T we can find the maximum present value of net earnings or profits on this investment. The following example illustrates this last step.

Example 2.4. On the basis of available data and in cooperation with the manager in charge of production, the comptroller's office of continental Rubber and Tire Company obtained the following functions and parameters about a new machine which will enable the company to automate production of tires:

$$C = \$10,000$$

$$R(t) = \$3000e^{-0.10t}$$

$$M(t) = \$105 + \$10e^{0.05t}$$

$$S(t) = \$10,000e^{-0.02t}$$

$$i = 10 \text{ percent per annum,}$$

where the symbols are defined in (2.13).

A. *Determine the optimal economic life of this machine.*

Step 1: Since $S'(t) = (-0.02)(10,000e^{-0.02t})$, substituting $R(t)$, $M(t)$, $S(t)$, $S'(T)$, and i in (2.15) and simplifying we get

$$3000e^{-0.10T} - (105 + 10e^{0.05T})$$
$$= (0.10)(10,000e^{-0.02T}) - (-0.02)(10,000e^{-0.02T})$$
$$= 3000e^{-0.10T} - 10e^{0.05T} - 1200e^{-0.02T} = 105.$$

Step 2: The above equation can be solved by trial and error for various values of T. From a table of exponential functions with base e we can find that the optimal T equals approximately 10 years since for $T = 10$ the solution is

$$3000(0.367879) - 10(1.6487) - 1200(0.81873) \approx 104.67.$$

B. *Find the maximum present value of the above machine.*

Step 1: Substituting the given functions and optimal $T = 10$ in (2.13) and simplifying, we have

$$V(10) = \int_0^{10} (3000e^{-0.10t})e^{-0.10t}dt - \int_0^{10} (105 + 10e^{0.05t})e^{-0.10t}dt$$

$$+ (10,000e^{-0.02T})e^{-0.10T} - 10,000,$$

$$V(10) = \int_0^{10} 3000e^{-0.20t}dt - \int_0^{10} 105e^{-0.10t}dt$$

$$- \int_0^{10} 10e^{-0.05t}dt + 10,000e^{-0.12T} - 10,000.$$

Step 2: Integrating and evaluating the limits (0, 10), we have

$$V(10) = \left(\frac{3000}{-0.20}e^{-0.20t}\right)\Big|_0^{10} - \left(\frac{105}{-0.10}e^{-0.10t}\right)\Big|_0^{10}$$

$$- \left(\frac{10}{-0.05}e^{-0.05t}\right)\Big|_0^{10} + 10,000e^{-0.12T} - 10,000,$$

$$V(10) = -15{,}000e^{-2} - (-15{,}000e^0) - (-1050e^{-1} + 1050e^0)$$
$$- (-200e^{-0.5} + 200e^0) + 10{,}000e^{-1.2} - 10{,}000.$$

Step 3: Using a table of exponential functions and doing the required computations, we finally obtain

$$V(10) = -15{,}000(0.135335) + 15{,}000 + 1050(0.367879)$$
$$- 1050 + 200(0.606531) - 200 + 10{,}000(0.301194) - 10{,}000$$

$$V(10) = 5239.49 \text{ dollars,}$$

which is the maximum present worth of the machine.

In sum, the optimal economic life T means that the end of the tenth year the machine will pay for itself, earn a 10 percent return on the investment, and have a maximum cash value of $5239.49.

In the above model we assume that a firm employs a single machine. It is implied that production will terminate at the end of the economic life of this single piece of equipment, or better, there is no "intention" of replacing the machine. Our model may be called, for lack of a better term, an *equipment selection model.* It may be used as a criterion for selecting the most profitable among alternative equipment investment opportunities. But also it can be modified for an investment analysis of different situations. We may consider the situation, for instance, where a firm continues production for an indefinite period of time employing a chain of machines. Our model can be modified to determine the optimal replacement cycle on this chain of machines, or become an *equipment replacement model.* In many situations it may be difficult or impossible to obtain reliable information about the earning capacity of equipment. This may be particularly true when more than one machine is employed in the production process. Our model can be modified to a *minimum cost model* for replacement of equipment.

PROBLEMS

2.1. Consider the individual propensity to shop function (2.3) and discuss how $f(N, D)$ will vary with the number of items on sale N—
   a) When $N = 0$.
   b) When N is very large.
   c) For intermediate values of N and a small value of D.

2.2. Let D be a constant. Then with the second derivative test for extrema show that function f of (2.3), if continuous, has at least one minimum.

2.3. Explain and discuss the following statements in terms of the variables of the individual propensity to shop function (2.3).
   a) Increased variety, i.e., large N, is an advantage to a consumer only up to a point.
   b) The minimum N necessary to induce a consumer to shop at a particular store will increase with his distance D from the store.
   c) For every value of N, there is a maximum D_m.

    d) The optimum N is independent of D. (*Hint:* Let D be a constant, then differentiate with respect to N.)

2.4. Explain and discuss the following statements in terms of the variables of (2.5) and (2.10).

    a) The model explains why large retailers tend to locate at metropolitan centers.

    b) The model is consistent with the rise of suburban shopping centers.

    c) The analysis is consistent with the rise of giant supermarkets in grocery retailing.

2.5. In developing the retailer's model the assumption, obviously false, was made that at any distance from the store the volume of sales will vary directly with the proportion of individuals who have a positive propensity to shop. On the basis of total sales volume (2.10) explain in terms of the effect of N on D_m why this assumption may be modified.

2.6. The retailer's model may be considered as a first approximation to a systematic analysis of real-world situations. In this connection discuss the following:

    a) The importance of the assumption that for a particular store N and D are the chief factors in attracting customers.

    b) The difficulties involved in estimating the parameters of the model empirically.

2.7. Differentiate each function below and, using a table of exponential functions find the value of each derivative at $x = 2$.

    *a) $f(x) = e^{2x}$.

    *b) $g(x) = e^{4x} - 4e^{3x} + e^{-2x}$.

    c) $h(x) = e^{x^2+3}$.

    d) $f(x) = 10xe^{-(x^3+1)}$.

2.8. Differentiate the following functions taken from Section 2, Chapter 7.

    *a) $f(x) = e^{0.69315x}$.

    b) $S(t) = 77{,}500e^{-0.25615t}$.

    c) $g(x) = a^x = e^{x \ln a}$.

2.9. Evaluate the integral using a table of exponential functions.

    *a) $\displaystyle\int_0^3 e^{0.5x}dx$.

    *b) $\displaystyle\int_2^5 e^{-0.3x}dx$.

    c) $\displaystyle\int_1^2 -e^{2x+3}dx$.

    d) $\displaystyle\int_1^2 3xe^{-3x}dx$.

2.10. Let $S(t) = -19{,}851.625e^{-0.25618t}$ be given.

    a) Evaluate

$$\int_0^5 (-19{,}851.625e^{-0.25618t})dt.$$

b) Refer to Example 2.6 in Chapter 7 and explain the empirical meaning of the answer you found in (a).

2.11. Show that

a) $\int (e^{ax} + axe^{ax})dx = xe^{ax} + C.$

b) $D_x \left[\dfrac{xe^{ax}}{a} - \dfrac{e^{ax}}{a^2} + C \right] = xe^{ax}.$

*2.12. Suppose, in addition to the machine in Example 2.4, the management of Continental Rubber and Tire Company considers another machine with the following information:

$$C = \$10,000$$
$$R(t) = 4000 - 260t,$$
$$M(t) = 200 + 40t,$$
$$S(t) = 10,000e^{-0.10t}$$
$$i = 10 \text{ percent per annum},$$

where the symbols are defined in (2.13). Which machine should management decide to install?

2.13. The optimal economic life of a machine can be found by (2.15) which can also be written as

$$R(T) + S'(T) = M(T) + iS(T).$$

Using the functions given in Example 2.4, find the values of $R(t) + S'(T)$ and the values of $M(T) + iS(T)$ when $t = 8, 9, 10, 11,$ and 12. On the basis of these values, sketch their graphs and verify that the curves intersect at $t = 10$.

2.14. The present value equation (1.14) in the continuous case corresponds to equation

$$V = \sum_{t=1}^{T} \dfrac{R_t - M_t}{(1 + i)^t} + \dfrac{S(T)}{(1 + i)^t} - C$$

in the discrete case.

a) Consider the data given in Example 2.4 and find the values of R_t and M_t from the corresponding functions $R(t)$ and $M(t)$ for $t = 1, 2, 3, 4, 5, 6, 7, 8, 9, 10$. Also, find $S(T)$ where $T = 10$. On the basis of this information and for $C = \$10,000$ and $i = 10$ percent, find the value of V which corresponds to the present value of the machine in the discrete case.

b) Explain the discrepancy which you find between V and $V(T)$. Would this discrepancy be smaller if the functions $R(t)$, $M(t)$, and $S(T)$ were linear instead of exponential? And/or the discrete values R_t and M_t were for every half year?

2.15. Substitute the data given in Example 2.4 in (2.14) and find that

$$V'(t) = 3000e^{-0.20t} - 105e^{-0.10t} - 10e^{-0.05t} - 1200e^{-0.12t}.$$

Letting $i = 0.10$, verify that $V(t)$ is a maximum at $t = 10$ by—

a) Finding that $V'(10) = 0$, $V'(9) > 0$, and $V'(11) < 0$.

b) Taking the second derivative of $V(t)$ and finding that $V''(10) < 0$.

2.16. In Example 2.4 we have found that at $T = 10$ the present value of the machine is a maximum amounting to \$5239.49, thereafter declining. Nonetheless, the investment should remain profitable until $V(T) = 0$. Substitute for the data in Example 2.4 in (2.13) and find the value of T for which $V(T)$ should equal to zero. Explain why this may not be true.

SUGGESTED REFERENCES

1. BASS, F. M., *et al.* (eds.). *Mathematical Models and Methods in Marketing*, pp. 220–29, 515–17, 524–25, 532–33. Homewood, Ill.: Richard D. Irwin, Inc., 1961. **(1)**

2. BAUMOL, W. J., AND IDE, E. A. "Variety in Retailing," *Management Science*, Vol. III, No. 1 (October, 1956), pp. 93–101. Reprinted in F. BASS *et al. Mathematical Models and Methods in Marketing*, pp. 121–44. Homewood, Ill.: Richard D. Irwin, Inc., 1961. **(2)**

3. BIERMAN, HAROLD, *et al. Quantitative Analysis for Business Decisions*, pp. 70–72, 317–28. Homewood, Ill.: Richard D. Irwin, Inc., 1961. **(1, 2)**

4. BOWMAN, E. H., AND FETTER, R. B. *Analysis for Production Management*, pp. 69–86, 65–75. Homewood, Ill.: Richard D. Irwin, Inc., 1961. **(1, 2)**

5. ———, AND STEWART, J. B. "A Model for Scale of Operations," *Journal of Marketing* (January, 1956), pp. 242–47. **(1)**

6. DEAN, B. V., *et al. Mathematics for Modern Management*, pp. 140–42, 160–67. New York: John Wiley & Sons, Inc., 1963. **(1)**

7. HOWELL, J. E., AND TEICHROEW, D. *Mathematical Analysis for Business Decisions*, pp. 72–78, 88–89, 222–26. Homewood, Ill.: Richard D. Irwin, Inc., 1963. **(1, 2)**

8. JOHNSON, R. E., AND KIOKEMEISTER, F. L. *Calculus with Analytic Geometry*, pp. 263–69, 315–16. Boston: Allyn and Bacon, Inc., 1959. **(2)**

9. NEMMERS, E. E. *Managerial Economics, Text and Cases*, pp. 179–82. New York: John Wiley & Sons, Inc., 1962. **(1)**

10. *Standard Mathematical Tables*, pp. 179–86. Cleveland, Ohio: Chemical Rubber Publishing Co., 1959. **(2)**

PART V

Probability with Statistical Applications

Up until this point, we have dealt with techniques of the mathematics of varying quantities under an important assumption, in most cases, that the relevant facts of a business situation are exactly known or certain. For instance, the demand function for an item discussed in connection with analytic geometry has been assumed to be a known quantity. Similarly, certainty has been one of our assumptions in linear programming and calculus. In sum, so far decision problems have been analyzed under conditions of certainty.

More frequently than not, however, managerial decisions must be made when the facts of the situation are uncertain. Since the consequences related to any managerial decision always lie in the future, prediction must be part of the analysis of any decision problem. But prediction inevitably carries with it uncertainty and probable error; events rarely turn out exactly as we plan them. With probability, the fifth and last subject in our course, we shall be given the opportunity to deal with decision problems under conditions of uncertainty.

Probability, like earlier subjects, is a mathematical system based on a few assumptions and definitions. With these as a base, a beautiful and extensive mathematical structure emerges which has a wide and rich variety of applications. With probability theory we build mathematical models and study the consequences of such models. A simple example will illustrate this point. A tossed coin has probability $\frac{1}{2}$ of coming up "heads." On the basis of this statement, we can develop a probability model for coin tosses which gives the probability that in n tosses, exactly k will be heads and $n - k$ tails. For instance, the probability that in all n tosses the coin turns up heads is $\left(\frac{1}{2}\right)^{n}$. Observe that the model is based on a number of assumptions: that the coin is "fair" and tossed a very large number of times; that the air of the atmosphere or other elements do not disturb outcomes; and that there are only two mutually exclusive and collectively exhaustive possibilities, namely, heads or tails, where all other possibilities such as the tossed coin being swallowed by a flying bird while in air or the coin falling on its edge are excluded. Although the model represents an idealized situation, we expect that it applies to real coins when they are tossed; moreover, it can be used as a reliable approximation for studying business situations with coin-tossing characteristics.

The term "statistics" is used to mean a variety of things. Nevertheless, many statisticians may agree with the general definition that "statistics is the art and science of gathering, analyzing, and making inferences from data" (p. 2, reference 4 in the bibliography of Chapter 14). From the decision-making point of view the following definition may sound more appropriate: "Statistics is a body of methods for making wise decisions in the face of uncertainty" (p. 3, reference 5 in the above-mentioned bibliography). Whatever the definition, the important matter is that statistics, especially the field of statistical inference, leans heavily on probability theory. Moreover, although there is hardly any disagreement about the theory of probability and its consequences from the mathematical standpoint, there are differences in the interpretation and use of probabilities. We shall elaborate on this point later. In the meantime, it suffices to say that such differences lead to two important schools of thought, each representing a separate branch in the field of statistics, the classical or orthodox statistics and the nonclassical or Bayesian statistics. After laying the essentials of probability theory in Chapters 14 and 15, we shall concentrate, for reasons which will become evident later, on a few applications of Bayesian statistics in Chapter 16.

Chapter 14

FROM SETS TO SAMPLE SPACES
AND EVENTS

WE SHALL devote this chapter to the development of two fundamental concepts of probability theory, the idea of a sample space and of an "event." Since, in introducing sample spaces in Section 1 and events in Section 2, sets and set operations are used extensively, the reader may find it helpful to review Chapter 1. With such a review he will be able to firmly establish for himself a logical and conceptual continuity with earlier discussions.

1. SETS AND SAMPLE SPACES

The theory of probability begins when we specify a sample space of a real or conceptual experiment. Therefore, our first task is to perform a number of simple experiments in order to introduce the important concept of a sample space for an experiment.

1.1. Sample Spaces: Definition. *A sample space of a real or conceptual experiment is a set of elements such that every possible outcome of the experiment corresponds to one and only one element in the set.* An element in a set serving as a sample space is called a *sample point*.

Example 1.1. Consider the experiment of tossing a coin once. Let the only outcomes of the experiment be heads, denoted by H, and tails, denoted by T. Then the set $\{H, T\}$ provides a list of the possible outcomes, where each outcome of the experiment corresponds to exactly one element of the set. This set is called a *sample space* for this experiment.

Similarly, we may consider the experiment of tossing two coins, say a nickel and a dime, once. On the assumption that heads, H, and tails, T, are the only possible outcomes, we can specify set

$$S = \{HH, HT, TH, TT\}$$

as a sample space for the experiment. Observe that each possible outcome of the experiment corresponds to exactly one element (pair of letters) or

509

sample point in the set S. For example, element or sample point HH denotes the outcome when both coins come up heads; element or sample point HT denotes the outcome when the nickel turns up heads and the dime tails, and so on.

In fact, instead of tossing two coins once we can consider the experiment of tossing one coin twice. We can specify the same set S above as a sample space for the new experiment. But this time the first letter of each element in the set denotes the outcome for the first toss and the second letter for the second toss.

Example 1.2. Consider the experiment of rolling a die once. Let the dots on each side represent the numbers 1 through 6. Can the set

$$D = \{1, 2, 3, 4, 5, 6\}$$

serve as a sample space for the experiment? Yes, since set D meets the requirements of the definition of a sample space. Do the sets

$$D_1 = \{4 \text{ or less, more than 3}\}$$

and

$$D_2 = \{\text{Less than 4, more than 4}\}$$

specify sample spaces for the experiment? No, because both violate the conditions of the definition of a sample space; outcome number 4 corresponds to both elements of D_1 and to neither element of D_2.

A sample space can be a finite or an infinite set; and the general theory of probability deals with both finite and infinite sample spaces. Here, we shall deal exclusively with finite sample spaces; in fact, our discussion is further restricted to the fundamentals of probability theory in the finite case.

It is important to realize that we have been speaking of *a* rather than *the* sample space for a particular experiment. This is so because there is more than one way of classifying the possible outcomes of a particular experiment and hence there is more than one sample space for each experiment.

Example 1.3. From the previous experiment of tossing two coins once, we may be interested instead in the *number* of heads in each outcome. Then the set

$$S_1 = \{2, 1, 0\},$$

where the numerals denote the number of heads, is another sample space for the same experiment. Again, suppose we are concerned only with whether the two coins come up alike, A, or different, D. Then the set

$$S_2 = \{A, D\}$$

is still another sample space for the same experiment.

Thus, we have specified three sets S, S_1, and S_2 which can serve as a sample space, for the same experiment, since all meet the requirements of the definition of a sample space. But set S is a more fundamental sample space for the experiment than sets S_1 and S_2. Neither S_1 nor S_2 contain a sufficiently detailed classification of the outcomes of the experiment to verify, for instance, the statement "the nickel falls heads and the dime tails." In other words, knowing which element of S occurs, we can readily specify which outcome in S_1 or S_2 occurs; but the reverse is not always true.

The fact that many sets may serve as a sample space for the same experiment raises an important question. Which one of the sample spaces is most suitable for describing the experiment? There is not any cut-and-dry rule on this point. Classification of possible outcomes of an experiment may range from a highly detailed to a very rough one. As a general guide the chosen sample space should include a classification of the possible outcomes of the experiment detailed enough so that all statements related to the problem at hand can be verified.

1.2. More on Sample Spaces. The idea of a sample space is so important for initiating the reader into the subject of probability that it is desirable to illustrate this concept further with Cartesian product sets and tree diagrams.

Earlier in our course, Section 3 of Chapter 5, we showed that the coordinates of a Cartesian coordinate plane represent an infinite Cartesian product set of ordered two-tuples. Also, a sample space of an experiment may be a Cartesian product set.

Example 1.4. Let $C_n = \{H, T\}$ be a sample space for tossing a nickel once and $C_d = \{H, T\}$ a sample space for tossing a dime once. Then we can obtain the Cartesian product set

$$C_n \times C_d = \{(H, H), (H, T), (T, H), (T, T)\},$$

where each ordered pair of letters is formed by combining each element of C_n with every element of C_d. Simplifying the notation by writing HH instead of (H, H), HT instead of (H, T), and so on, set $C_n \times C_d$ can be recognized as the set S which represents a sample space for the previously considered experiment of tossing two coins.

A useful way of listing all possible outcomes of the above experiment is with a *tree diagram* such as the one shown in Figure 1.1. Starting from a common point, we draw two lines for the two possible outcomes of tossing a nickel. Then from each line, we draw two lines for the two possible outcomes of tossing a dime. The total number of ways of completing both tosses (tasks) equals the total number of branches in the tree diagram. Thus, each branch represents a sample point in the sample space S for the experiment.

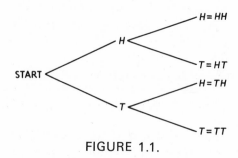

FIGURE 1.1.

We may observe that the process of determining the number of outcomes in the above experiment is similar to the process of determining the number of rows in a membership table. It can be generalized to include cases where there are *more than two* different ways of completing a task.

Example 1.5. Consider the experiment of rolling a white die and then a black die. We wish to specify a sample space for this experiment. The job of recording each outcome of the two rolls can be done by first writing down the number on the white die (task 1) and then the number on the black die (task 2). Since task 1 can be completed in 6 ways and then task 2 in 6 ways, the total number of outcomes is $6 \times 6 = 36$. These outcomes are shown in the body of Table 1.1. Each row of the table corresponds to

TABLE 1.1.

D_w \ D_b	1	2	3	4	5	6
1	(1, 1)	(1, 2)	(1, 3)	(1, 4)	(1, 5)	(1, 6)
2	(2, 1)	(2, 2)	(2, 3)	(2, 4)	(2, 5)	(2, 6)
3	(3, 1)	(3, 2)	(3, 3)	(3, 4)	(3, 5)	(3, 6)
4	(4, 1)	(4, 2)	(4, 3)	(4, 4)	(4, 5)	(4, 6)
5	(5, 1)	(5, 2)	(5, 3)	(5, 4)	(5, 5)	(5, 6)
6	(6, 1)	(6, 2)	(6, 3)	(6, 4)	(6, 5)	(6, 6)

a fixed outcome for the white die D_w and each column to a fixed outcome for the black die D_b. The 36 ordered pairs of numbers in the body of the table represent a sample space D for the experiment. For instance, the ordered pair (3, 4) in the third row and the fourth column denotes the outcome "white die shows 3, black die shows 4."

The sample space D shown in Table 1.1 is more fundamental than other sample spaces for the experiment such as

$$D_1 = \{2, 3, 4, 5, 6, 7, 8, 9, 10, 11, 12\},$$

where each number denotes the sum of the numbers shown on the two dice.

It can be easily recognized that the above sample space represents a Cartesian product set $D_w \times D_b$, where $D_w = D_b = \{1, 2, 3, 4, 5, 6\}$ and where the notation for Cartesian product sets has been maintained to avoid confusion.

Also, the 36 sample points of the sample space in Table 1.1 can be easily shown with a tree diagram. But this job is left for the reader.

Since we shall refer to this sample space frequently, the reader may place a bookmark for Table 1.1.

But a sample space need not be a Cartesian product set, as the following example illustrates.

Example 1.6. A cashier has a penny, a nickel, and a dime in her cash register. She takes two coins from the register, one first and then the other. What is a suitable sample space for this experiment?

There are three possibilities for task 1 of taking the first coin out of the register, but only two possibilities for task 2 of taking a second coin. The whole job can be done in $3 \times 2 = 6$ ways. This selection of the 2 coins is illustrated with a tree diagram in Figure 1.2, where letters P, N, and D stand for a penny, a nickel, and a dime, respectively.

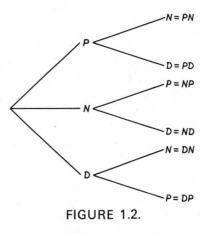

FIGURE 1.2.

Observe that the sample space $C = \{PN, PD, NP, ND, DN, DP\}$ for this experiment is not a Cartesian product set. After the first coin is taken out the original set $C_1 = \{P, N, D\}$ loses one of its elements.

In cases such as the above it is said that the experiment is performed *without replacement*. If the first coin were put back to the register before the second coin is taken out, then it is said that the experiment is performed *with replacement*. It is left for the reader to verify that performing the experiment in Example 1.6 with replacement results in a sample space with nine elements which is a Cartesian product set.

We shall see later, Section 3 of Chapter 15, that the above method of finding all possible outcomes of an experiment is an application of the *fundamental principle of counting*. In the meantime, we shall turn our attention in the next section to another important term used in probability theory.

PROBLEMS

1.1. For each experiment described below:

    i) Specify a detailed sample space.

    ii) Illustrate this sample space with a tree diagram (if feasible).

      iii) Specify another sample space less detailed than the first.

    *a) A coin is tossed three times.

    *b) Three coins are tossed once.

    c) Two coins are tossed twice.

    d) One card is selected from a standard deck of 52 playing cards.

    *e) A survey of families with two children is conducted. The sexes of the children ordered by age with the oldest child first are recorded.

    *f) The same as in (e), but the survey involves families with three children.

    g) The same as in (e), but the survey involves families with r children.

    h) A coin is tossed r times.

    i) r dice are rolled.

*1.2. Suppose the experiment in Example 1.6 is performed with replacement.

    a) Specify a suitable sample space.

    b) Illustrate with a tree diagram.

    c) Show that this sample space may be a Cartesian product set.

1.3. For each experiment described below do (i), (ii), and (iii) explained in Problem 1.1.

    a) A boy customer has a penny, a nickel, a dime, and a quarter in his pocket. Upon entering a candy store he takes two coins out of pocket, first one and then the other.

    b) The boy in (a) puts the first coin back in his pocket and then takes a second coin.

    c) Each letter of the word *MONEY* is written on a chip and the chips are placed in a hat. Two chips are selected, one after the other.

    d) The first chip in (c) is put back in the hat and then a second chip is selected.

1.4. In which of the experiments in Problem 1.3 (a), (b), (c), (d) may a sample space represent a Cartesian product set? If your answer is positive and the sample space is the Cartesian product set of a set A with itself, specify the set A. But whether your answer is positive or negative, explain why.

1.5. We have shown in the text that the sample spaces in Examples 1.4 and 1.5 are Cartesian product sets. Explain why the following sample spaces discussed in the text are not Cartesian product sets. Can they be illustrated with a tree diagram?

    a) $S_1 = \{2, 1, 0\}$.

    b) $S_2 = \{A, D\}$.

    c) $D_1 = \{2, 3, 4, 5, 6, 7, 8, 9, 10, 11, 12\}$.

1.6. Consider the sample space D of rolling two dice shown in Table 1.1. The number in each set below represents the sum of the numbers on the two rolled dice. Indicate which of the sets are suitable and which are not suitable sample spaces for the experiment. Explain why.

    *a) $S_1 = \{7; \text{not } 7\}$.

    *b) $S_2 = \{\text{odd number}; \text{less than } 4; \text{greater than } 4\}$.

    c) $S_3 = \{2, 3, 4, 5; \text{more than } 5\}$.

    d) $S_4 = \{3, 5, 7; \text{an even number}; 11\}$.

e) $S_5 = \{9, 12; 2, 4, 6, 11; 3, 5, 7, 8, 10\}$.

f) $S_6 = \{$at most 5; more than 5 and less than 9; 10, 12; 9, 11$\}$.

g) $S_7 = \{$more than 8; less than 4; 5, 7; 4, 6, 8$\}$.

1.7. An experiment consists of drawing one ball from an urn containing 5 white balls numbered 1 through 5 and 5 black balls numbered 6 through 10. Which of the following sets are suitable sample spaces for the experiment and which are not? Explain why.

*a) $S_1 = \{$black balls, white balls$\}$.

*b) $S_2 = \{1, 3, 5;$ even numbers$\}$.

c) $S_3 = \{$black balls; greater than 6$\}$.

d) $S_4 = \{1, 2, 3, 4, 5, 6, 7, 8, 9, 10, 11\}$.

e) $S_5 = \{1, 5, 6, 8, 10, 2, 3, 9, 4, 7\}$.

1.8. From the sample space D of rolling two dice shown in Table 1.1, specify three sample spaces of your own less fundamental than the one given.

1.9. Consider the sample space $S = \{HH, HT, TH, TT\}$, $S_1 = \{2, 1, 0\}$, and $S_2 = \{A, D\}$ of tossing two coins explained in text. Which of the sample spaces is the most suitable one for the following statements?

a) "The nickel falls tails and the dime heads."

b) "The outcome of the experiment is one heads and one tails."

c) "The outcome of the experiment is no heads."

1.10. Urn A contains 1 white and 2 red balls; and urn B contains 1 red and 2 white balls.

*a) Specify a suitable sample space for selecting an urn first and then drawing one ball from the chosen urn. Construct a tree diagram for this sample space.

b) Specify a suitable sample space for selecting an urn first and then drawing two balls from the chosen urn, one after another. Illustrate this with a tree diagram.

c) Specify a suitable sample space for selecting an urn first and then drawing two balls from the chosen urn, but putting the first ball back before drawing the second. Illustrate with a tree diagram.

1.11. Let G denote good parts and D defective parts turned out by a machine. Specify a sample space for selecting r parts from an endless stream of parts that the machine can produce. Discuss this sample space by comparing it with the sample space in Problems 1.1(h) in terms of a Cartesian product set.

1.12. The life insurance policies of adult policyholders of Continental Insurance Company are classified by sex—males (M) and females (F)—by marital status—unmarried (U), married (R), divorced or separated (D), and widowed (W)—by age—under 35 years (Y_1), between 35 and 50 years (Y_2), and over 50 years old (Y_3).

*a) Construct two tree diagrams: one with the three classification tasks in the order indicated above and another by reversing this order to age, marital status, and sex. What is the total number of classes? Does this number change by reversing the order with which the tasks are accomplished?

b) An experiment consists of selecting one policy from the files. Which of the sample spaces specified in (*a*) is a suitable sample space for the experiment? Discuss.

1.13. The manager of a restaurant plans a menu with a choice of fruit (*F*) or soup (*S*) for an appetizer, a choice of meat (*M*), fowl (*B*), or seafood (*W*) for the main course, and a choice of pie (*I*) or pudding (*D*) for dessert. One choice in each course makes a complete dinner.

a) Construct two tree diagrams: one with the three courses in the order specified above and another by reversing this order to dessert, main course, appetizer. What is the possible number of complete dinners? Is this number the same in both sample spaces?

b) An experiment consists of selecting one complete dinner. Which of the two sample spaces specified in (*a*) is suitable for this experiment?

2. EVENTS AND PARTITIONS

Closely related to the concept of a sample space is another technical term basic to the theory of probability, namely, an "event." After explaining the idea of an event, we shall discuss the following categories of events: simple and compound events, joint and mutually exclusive events, and partitions of events.

2.1. Definition. *An event is a statement which refers to a particular subset of a sample space for an experiment.*

Example 2.1. Consider the sample space *D* in Table 1.1 for rolling a white and a black die. The statement "the sum of the numbers on the dice is 3" is an event of the experiment. It refers to outcomes (1, 2) and (2, 1) which represent subset {(1, 2), (2, 1)} of the sample space *D*. The statement "a double six is thrown" is another event of the experiment. It refers to outcome (6, 6) which represents subset {(6, 6)} of the sample space *D*.

In general, let *E* be an event representing a subset of a given sample space *S* for an experiment. Then event *E* occurs when the outcome of the experiment corresponds to an element of the subset *E*. A sample space is the *mathematical counterpart* of an experiment. Since a sample space contains all possible outcomes, it serves as a *universal set* for all events related to the experiment. Conceptually, it may be convenient to think of a statement as the verbal counterpart (descriptive method of specifying a set) and its corresponding subset of *S* as the mathematical counterpart of an event (roster method of specifying a set).

Example 2.2. Let the sample space *S* = {*HH, HT, TH, TT*} of a previously considered experiment of tossing two coins once be given. The following is a list of the verbal and mathematical counterparts of a few events for this experiment.

	Statement	*Subset of S*
1.	Both coins fall alike.	$E = \{HH, TT\}$
2.	At least one coin falls heads.	$F = \{HH, HT, TH\}$
3.	Neither coin falls heads.	$F' = \{TT\}$
4.	Both coins fall alike *or* at least one coin heads.	$E \cup F = \{HH, HT, TH, TT\} = S$
5.	Both coins fall alike *and* at least one heads.	$E \cap F = \{HH\}$
6.	At least one coin falls heads *and* both tails.	$F \cap F' = \varnothing$

It may be recalled that the number of possible subsets which can be formed from a set having n elements is 2^n. Since the sample space S in the above example has four elements, there are 2^4 or 16 subsets and an equivalent number of events. Six of these events are listed above. It is left for the reader to prepare a list showing the verbal and mathematical counterparts of the remaining ten events.

Indeed, we have shown (Section 2 of Chapter 1) that for a sample space with as few as 30 elements the possible events are over one billion. In most cases, however, we shall be concerned with a very limited number of them only; and in this connection, we must explain certain categories of events which are important in subsequent discussions. Set terminology and operations can be advantageously used for introducing them.

2.2. Simple and Compound Events. A subset of a sample space S which contains only one element or sample point of S is called a *simple event*. Given a sample space, we have nonempty events and the empty or null event $\varnothing$. All nonempty events are either simple events or unions of two or more different simple events, which as a matter of convenience we may call *compound events*. Finally, the union of all simple events is the entire sample space. We shall use an example to illustrate this distinction between simple and compound events although, by analogy with sets, the reader may feel himself on familiar ground.

Example 2.3. Let us consider again the sample space D of rolling two dice shown in Table 1.1.

Subset $\{(1, 1)\}$ is a simple event; so are the 35 nonempty subsets corresponding to the remaining 35 elements of the sample space D. Certainly, the union of these 36 simple events is the entire sample space.

Consider the subsets

$$E = \{(1, 1), (2, 2), (3, 3), (4, 4), (5, 5), (6, 6)\},$$
$$F = \{(1, 5), (5, 1), (2, 4), (4, 2), (3, 3)\},$$
$$G = \{(5, 5), (5, 6), (6, 5), (6, 6)\},$$
$$E \cap F = \{(3, 3)\},$$
$$E \cap G = \{(5, 5), (6, 6)\},$$
$$F \cap G = \varnothing.$$

Subsets E, F, and G are all compound events since each of them is the union of more than one simple event. However, the intersection of subsets of D may be a simple event, such as $E \cap F$, a compound event, such as $E \cap G$, or the empty event, such as $F \cap G$. Similarly, the complement of a subset of D may be a simple, a compound, the empty event, or the sample space itself. For example, events E', F' G', $(E \cap F)'$, and $(E \cap G)'$ are all compound events while $(F \cap G)'$ is the sample space D; and event D' is the empty event. Finally, the complement of an event containing 35 of the 36 elements of D is a simple event.

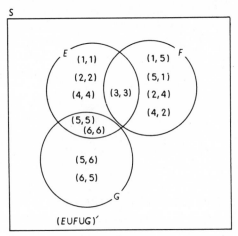

FIGURE 2.1.

2.3. Joint and Disjoint or Mutually Exclusive Events.

In Section 3 of Chapter 1 we have explained joint and disjoint or mutually exclusive sets. Analogously, we can speak of joint and mutually exclusive events.

Example 2.4. Let E, F, and G be events of D specified in Example 2.3 and shown in a Venn diagram in Figure 2.1. Subsets E and F are joint events since $E \cap F \neq \varnothing$. On the other hand, subsets F and G are disjoint or mutually exclusive events inasmuch as $F \cap G = \varnothing$.

In connection with probability, however, it is desirable to discuss further the number of elements or sample points in joint and mutually exclusive events. Let S be a sample space for an experiment; and let $n(S)$ denote the number of sample points in S. Suppose sets A and B are two disjoint events in S, then the number of sample points in the union of the two events, $A \cup B$, is the sum of the number of sample points in A and the number of sample points in B; in notation form

(2.1)
$$n(A \cup B) = n(A) + n(B) \quad \text{if } A \cap B = \varnothing.$$

Example 2.5. Formula (2.1) can be used to find the number of sample points in the union of events F and G specified in Example 2.4. Since $F \cap G = \varnothing$.

$$n(F \cup G) = n(F) + n(G) = 5 + 4 = 9 .$$

Suppose events A and B are not necessarily disjoint; events $A \cap B'$ and $A \cap B$ are disjoint and their union is the event A. This can be seen from Figure 2.2 where $A \cap B'$ is represented by region R_1, $A \cap B$ by region R_2,

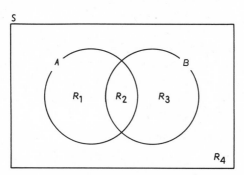

FIGURE 2.2.

and A by regions R_1 and R_2. Hence by formula (2.1)

$$n(A \cap B') + n(A \cap B) = n(A) .$$

Similarly, since $A \cap B$ and $A' \cap B$ are disjoint

$$n(A \cap B) + n(A' \cap B) = n(B) .$$

Adding the above two equations and subtracting $n(A \cap B)$ from both sides of the result, we have

$$n(A \cap B') + n(A \cap B) + n(A \cap B) + n(A' \cap B) = n(A) + n(B),$$

$$n(A \cap B') + \cancel{2}n(A \cap B) + n(A' \cap B) - n(\cancel{A \cap B}) = n(A) + n(B) - n(A \cap B),$$

$$n(A \cap B') + n(A \cap B) + n(A' \cap B) = n(A) + n(B) - n(A \cap B).$$

By referring to Figure 2.2 we can see that the number of sample points in the left-hand side of the last equation are represented by regions R_1, R_2, and R_3. Since these regions represent the union $A \cup B$,

$$n(A \cap B') + n(A \cap B) + n(A' \cap B) = n(A \cup B).$$

Substituting for this last expression in the above equation, we obtain the formula

(2.2)

$$\boxed{n(A \cup B) = n(A) + n(B) - n(A \cap B).}$$

Observe that formula (2.2) is valid for any events A and B. If $A \cap B = \varnothing$, then $n(A \cap B) = n(\varnothing) = 0$ and formula (2.2) reduces to (2.1).

Example 2.6. Consider the compound events E and F specified in Example 2.4. By formula (2.2) the number of the sample points in $E \cup F$ is

$$n(E \cup F) = n(E) + n(F) - n(E \cap F) = 6 + 5 - 1 = 10.$$

It is important to note that the one sample point in $E \cap F$, if not subtracted, would have been counted twice.

2.4. Partitions of Events. *A partition of a compound event E is a set of events which are (a) subsets of E, (b) mutually exclusive, and (c) collectively exhaustive.* In fact, since the simple events of a given sample space S are subsets of S, mutually exclusive, and collectively exhaustive, they are partitions of S.

Example 2.7. Consider the sample space

$$S = \{H, T\}$$

for tossing a coin once. Then events

$$E = \{H\} \text{ and } F = \{T\}$$

form a set such as

$$P_1 = \{E, F\}$$

which is a partition of sample space S. For E and F are subsets of S, i.e., $E \subseteq S$ and $F \subseteq S$; they are mutually exclusive, i.e., $E \cap F = \varnothing$; and they are collectively exhaustive, i.e., $E \cup F = S$, as required by the definition.

Observe that a partition of a compound event is a set of events. In the above example P_1 is a partition of sample space S representing a set with elements the subsets of S. But partitions need not represent the entire sample space for an experiment.

Example 2.8. Consider the compound event

$$E = \{(1, 1), (2, 2), (3, 3), (4, 4)\}$$

from the sample space D for rolling two dice. Events

$$E_1 = \{(1, 1), (2, 2)\} \text{ and } E_2 = \{(3, 3), (4, 4)\}$$

form a set such as

$$P_1 = \{E_1, E_2\}$$

which is a partition of E since
   a) $E_1 \subseteq E$ and $E_2 \subseteq E$,
   b) $E_1 \cap E_2 = \varnothing$, and
   c) $E_1 \cup E_2 = E$.

But events

$$E_3 = \{(5, 6), (2, 2), (3, 3)\} \text{ and } E_4 = \{(3, 3), (4, 4)\}$$

are not partitions of E since
 a) E_3 is not a subset of E,
 b) $E_3 \cap E_4 \neq \emptyset$, and
 c) $E_3 \cup E_4 \neq E$.

Partitioning as a process of classifying the elements of a set has wide applications. But, as we shall see later, it is of particular importance in probability. In the meantime, we wind up our discussion in this section with a motivating example making use of the basic ideas developed so far.

Example 2.9. The purchase of many consumer goods may involve various degrees of pre-planning. Items such as a pair of slacks or a suit may be the result of a few days or weeks of planning. Other more expensive purchases such as a car or a house may require planning ahead for a year or more before actual buying takes place.

Numerous intensive studies have been conducted of consumer planning for the purchase of durable goods such as television sets, refrigerators, washing machines, stoves, and automobiles. In one such study a randomly selected sample of 1000 individuals were asked whether they were planning to buy a new car in the next 12 months. A year later the same persons were interviewed again to find out whether they actually bought a new car. The response to both interviews (data hypothetical) is cross-tabulated in Table 2.1.

TABLE 2.1.

First Interview

		$P = $ (Planners)	$P' = $ (Nonplanners)	Row Totals
	$B = $ (Buyers)	$n(B \cap P) = 50$	$n(B \cap P') = 150$	$n(B) = 200$
Second Inter-view	$B' = $ (Nonbuyers)	$n(B' \cap P) = 200$	$n(B' \cap P') = 600$	$n(B') = 800$
	Column Totals	$n(P) = 250$	$n(P') = 750$	$n(\mathfrak{U}) = 1000$

We can perform the following experiment. We may imagine an urn with 1000 balls in it, each bearing the serial number of a respondent and the proper letters to denote the response of each individual to both interviews as shown in Table 2.1. There will be 50 balls numbered from 0001 to 0050 with letters P and B for the respondents who planned to buy and actually bought a new car; 200 balls numbered from 0051 to 0250 for the respondents who planned but did not buy a new car; and so on. The balls in the urn are thoroughly mixed, and one ball is drawn at random.

Question 1: What is a suitable sample space for the above experiment?

Answer:

If we are interested in individual respondents, a detailed sample space would be required containing a list of the serial number from 0001 through 1000. Then our sample space is

$$\mathfrak{U} = \{0001, 0002, 0003, \ldots, 1000\},$$

where the three dots stand for the serial numbers 0004 through 0999.

However, we may be only interested in the compound events P, B, P', and B' and the joint events $B \cap P$, $B \cap P'$, $B' \cap P$, and $B' \cap P'$ of $\mathfrak{U}$ defined in Table 2.1.

Question 2: What is the number of elements in a compound event such as $B \cup P$ of $\mathfrak{U}$?

Answer:

Since $B \cap P \neq \varnothing$, by formula (2.2) we have

$$n(B \cup P) = n(B) + n(P) - n(B \cap P) = 200 + 250 - 50 = 400.$$

Question 3: Let the events defined in Table 2.1 be given. Find a partition of the sample space $\mathfrak{U}$ shown in Table 2.1.

Answer:

One partition of $\mathfrak{U}$ is set

$$P_1 = \{B, B'\}.$$

The reader may list additional partitions of $\mathfrak{U}$, as well as partitions of compound events such as P, B, P', and B'.

Other categories of events will be discussed in connection with probabilities, our next subject.

PROBLEMS

2.1. Prepare a list of the verbal and mathematical counterparts of the remaining ten events in Example 2.2.

*2.2. One card is selected from a standard deck of 52 playing cards. Find the mathematical counterpart of the following events.
  a) The selected card is a diamond.
  b) The selected card is an ace.
  c) The selected card is an ace or a card of diamonds.

*2.3. Consider the experiment in Problem 1.1(f). Find the mathematical counterpart of the following events.
  a) The oldest of the three children is a boy.
  b) The youngest of the three children is a girl.
  c) The oldest is a boy and the youngest a girl.

2.4. Specify a suitable sample space for the experiment in Problem 1.3(*a*), and find the mathematical counterpart of the following events:
  a) The sum of the two coins is less than 15 cents.

b) The first coin is the dime and the sum of the two coins is 15 cents or more.

c) The sum of the two coins is 15 cents or more.

2.5. Specify a suitable sample space for the experiment in Problem 1.3(*d*) and find the mathematical counterpart of the following events.
   a) The first letter is a consonant.
   b) The second letter is a vowel.
   c) The first is a consonant and the second a vowel.

2.6. An experiment consists of rolling a white and a black die. A sample space for the experiment is shown in Table 1.1. Let E be the event that the sum on the two dice is odd, and F the event that the white die shows an even number.
   a) Find the mathematical counterparts of E and F.
   b) Write a verbal counterpart for $E \cap F$.
   c) Find the mathematical counterpart of $E \cup F$.

2.7. A sample space for rolling a white die and a black die is given in Table 1.1.
   a) Find the mathematical counterpart of the following events:
      *(1) White die shows 1 or 2.
      (2) Black die shows 4 or 5.
      (3) The sum on the two dice is greater than 7.
      (4) The sum on the two dice is greater than 12.
      (5) The sum on the two dice is 12 or less.
   b) Write a verbal counterpart for the following events:
      *(1) $E_1 = (1, 1), (2, 2), (3, 3), (4, 4), (5, 5), (6, 6)\}$.
      (2) $E_2 = \{(1, 5), (5, 1), (2, 4), (4, 2), (3, 3)\}$.
      (3) $E_3 = \{(5, 5), (6, 4), (4, 6), (5, 6), (6, 5), (6, 6)\}$.
      (4) $E_4 = D$.
      (5) $E_5 = \varnothing$.
      (6) $E_6 = \{(5, 1), (5, 2), (5, 3), (5, 4), 5, 5), (5, 6)\}$.
      (7) $E_7 = \{(1, 2), (2, 2), (3, 2), (4, 2), (5, 2), (6, 2)\}$.

2.8. Five salesmen of a company are considered as candidates for a three-member trade delegation to represent the company in an international trade conference. Let the letters A, B, C, D and E denote the salesmen.
   **a*) List the ten sample points of the appropriate sample space for selecting three salesmen for the trade delegation.
   b) Find the mathematical counterpart of the following events. How many sample points does each event contain?
      (1) Salesman A is selected.
      (2) Salesman D is selected.
      (3) Salesmen A *and* D are selected.
      (4) Salesman A *or* D is selected.
      (5) Salesman A is not selected.

2.9. An experiment is performed such as the one described in Problem 1.10(*a*). Let E be the event that urn A is selected and F the event that a white ball is drawn. Consider the events $E \cap F$, E', $E' \cap F$, F', $E \cup F$ and—

*a) Find the mathematical counterpart of each event.
b) Write a verbal counterpart of each event.

2.10. Let a sample space for tossing three coins be the set

$$S = \{HHH, HHT, HTH, THH, HTT, THT, TTH, TTT\}$$

Write an example illustrating each of the following events:
a) Simple events.
b) Compound events.
c) Complementary events.
d) Joint events.
e) Disjoint or mutually exclusive events.
f) Partitions (other than sample space S).

2.11. Find the number of sample points included in the following events using formula (2.1) or (2.2).
*a) $E \cup F$ in Example 2.2.
*b) $E \cup G$ in Example 2.3.
c) $E_1 \cup E_2$ in Example 2.8.
d) $E_3 \cup E_4$ in Example 2.8.
e) $B' \cup P'$ in Example 2.9.
f) $(B \cap P') \cup (B' \cap P)$ in Example 2.9.

2.12. Formula (2.2) may be generalized to determine the number of sample points in the union of three events. Let E_1, E_2, E_3 be such events. Then
$n(E_1 \cup E_2 \cup E_3) = n(E_1) + n(E_2) + n(E_3) - n(E_1 \cap E_2) - n(E_1 \cap E_3)$
$- n(E_2 \cap E_3) + n(E_1 \cap E_2 \cap E_3)$.
*a) Using the Venn diagram in Figure 2.1, verify the fact that the elements in $E \cup F \cup G$ are counted once and only once in the right-hand side of the above formula.
b) Using the laws of set operations in Table 4.1 of Chapter 1 and formula (2.2) prove the above formula.
c) Find the number of sample points in $E_1 \cup E_2 \cup E_3$ in Example 2.8.
d) Let E_3 and E_4 be as in Example 2.8 and let $E_5 = \{(5, 6), (5,5), (3, 3)\}$. Find the number of sample points in $E_3 \cup E_4 \cup E_5$.

2.13. Specify the additional partitions of $\mathcal{U}$ as well as the partitions of the compound events listed at the end of Example 2.9.

2.14. Let the sample space shown in Table 1.1 be given. Find whether in each case below the specified sets form partitions. If they do not, explain why.
a) $E_1 = \{(1, 1), (1, 2), (2, 1)\}$ and $E_2 = \{(1, 4), (4, 1)\}$ are partitions of $E = \{(1, 2), (1, 4), (1, 1), (2, 1), (4, 1)\}$.
b) $E_1 = \{(4, 2), (4, 3), (5, 2)\}$, $E_2 = \{(6, 3), (4, 6)\}$, and $E_3 = \{(3, 4), (2, 4)\}$ are partitions of $E = \{(3, 4), (6, 3), (5, 2), (2, 4), (4, 6), (4, 2)\}$.
c) $E_1 = \{(2, 3), (5, 6), (6, 6)\}$, $E_2 = \{(3, 2), (5, 6), (6, 5)\}$, and $E_3 = \{(4, 5), (5, 4)\}$ are partitions of $E = \{(4, 5), (2, 3), (5, 6), (5, 4), (6, 6), (3, 2), (6, 5)\}$.

d) $E_1 = \{(5, 4), (1, 2)\}$, $E_2 = \{(6, 1), (4, 4), (4, 6)\}$, and $E_3 = \{(2, 2), (1, 5)\}$ are partitions of $E = \{(5, 4), (2, 2), (1, 5), (1, 2), (6, 1), (4, 6), (4, 4), (5, 1)\}$.

2.15. A survey is conducted to find whether consumers who are "innovating" with their shopping habits differ from those who are reluctant to change their shopping list. Consumer behavior was observed in connection with the sale of a number of inexpensive new products of common use sold at grocery stores next to competing well-known brands. The 500 persons observed are classified as "innovators" if they switched, on sight, to the new product(s), or "noninnovators" if they did not, and by sex, as shown below.

	$M = Males$	$F = Females$	Row Totals
I = (Innovators)	$n(I \cap M) = 50$	$n(I \cap F) = 75$	$n(I) = 125$
N = (Noninnovators)	$n(N \cap M) = 100$	$n(N \cap F) = 275$	$n(N) = 375$
Column Totals	$n(M) = 150$	$n(F) = 350$	$n(S) = 500$

Suppose an experiment is conducted similar to the one explained in Example 2.9. Answer the following:
a) Specify a sample space S for the experiment.
b) Find the number of elements in the following compound events of S.
   (1) $I \cup M$.
   (2) $I \cup F$.
c) Specify three partitions of the sample space S.
d) Form partitions for the following compound events:
   (1) M; (2) F; (3) $I \cup M$; (4) $N \cup M$.

2.16. From Table 2.1 we can recognize two important partitions:

$$\mathcal{U}_2 = \{B, B'\} \text{ and } \mathcal{U}_3 = \{P, P'\},$$

where B stands for buyers, B' for nonbuyers, P for planners, and P' for nonplanners. From $\mathcal{U}_2$ and $\mathcal{U}_3$ we can form a new partition.

$$\mathcal{U}_1 = \{B \cap P, B' \cap P, B \cap P', B' \cap P'\},$$

where the respondents are classified according to both characteristics as shown in Table 2.1. Set $\mathcal{U}_1$ is called the *cross-partition* of $\mathcal{U}_2$ and $\mathcal{U}_3$.
In general, let

$$S_1 = \{E_1, E_2, \ldots, E_m\} \text{ and } S_2 = \{F_1, F_2, \ldots, F_n\}$$

be any partitions of a sample space S. Then the cross-partition of S_1 and S_2 is the set

$$S_3 = \{E_1 \cap F_1, \ldots, E_1 \cap F_n, \ldots, E_m \cap F_1, \ldots, E_m \cap F_n\}$$

consisting of all intersections $E_i \cap F_j$, where $i = 1, 2, 3, \ldots, m$ and $j = 1, 2, 3, \ldots, n$.

*a) Let the partitions of S be

$$S_1 = \{M, F\} \text{ and } S_2 = \{I, N\},$$

where the elements of S_1 and S_2 are defined in the table of Problem 2.15.

Find the cross-partition of S_1 and S_2.

b) Let the partitions of S be

$$S_1 = \{M, F\}, S_2 = \{U, R, D, W\}, \text{ and } S_3 = \{Y_1, Y_2, Y_3\}$$

where the elements of S_1, S_2, and S_3 are defined in Problem 1.12.
(1) Find the cross-partition of S_1 and S_2.
(2) Find the cross-partition of the cross-partition you found in (1) and S_3.

c) Let the partitions of S be

$$S_1 = \{F, S\}, S_2 = \{M, B, W\}, \text{ and } S_3 = \{I, D\},$$

where the elements of S_1, S_2, and S_3 are defined in Problem 1.13.
(1) Find the cross-partition of S_1 and S_2.
(2) Find the cross-partition of the cross-partition you found in (1) and S_3.

SUGGESTED REFERENCES

1. GOLDBERG, SAMUEL. *Probability: An Introduction*, pp. 45–54. Englewood Cliffs, N.J.: Prentice-Hall, Inc., 1960. **(1, 2)**

2. KEMENY, JOHN G., *et al. Finite Mathematics with Business Applications*, pp. 13–29, 84–97. Englewood Cliffs, N.J.: Prentice-Hall, Inc., 1962. **(1, 2)**

3. MATHEMATICAL ASSOCIATION OF AMERICA, COMMITTEE ON THE UNDER-GRADUATE PROGRAM. *Elementary Mathematics of Sets with Applications*, pp. 50–58. 1959. **(2)**

4. MOSTELLER, FREDERICK, *et al. Probability with Statistical Applications*, pp. 1–2, 55–81. Reading, Mass.: Addison-Wesley Publishing Co., Inc., 1961. **(1, 2)**

5. WALLIS, W. A., AND ROBERTS, H. V. *Statistics: A New Approach*, pp. 3–16. Glencoe, Ill.: The Free Press, 1956.

Chapter 15

PROBABILITIES AND COUNTING

WITH the ideas of a sample space and of an event now established, we are conceptually ready to study the essentials of the mathematical system of probability with finite sample spaces. The empirical problem associated with the probability of an event and the rules for assigning probabilities to events occupy Section 1. Conditional probability and Bayes' formula are illustrated with business applications in Section 2. Finally, Section 3 is devoted to the fundamental principle of counting, counting formulas, and binomial coefficients.

1. THE PROBABILITY OF AN EVENT; PROBABILITY RULES

The probability of an event, as a topic, is of great importance from the empirical as well as the mathematical standpoints. On the one hand, the probability of an event raises the empirical problem of assigning probabilities to events representing different real-world situations; on the other hand, assigning probabilities to events is based on axioms and theorems which constitute the mathematical system of probability.

We shall first have a brief discussion of the empirical problem of assigning probabilities to events. The remainder of this section is devoted to a bird's-eye view of probability theory as a mathematical system: we shall explain the basic rules for assigning probabilities to events, paying special attention to the addition rule and equiprobable events and to the multiplication rule and independent events.

1.1. The Empirical Problem of Assigning Probabilities to Events.

In speaking of the probability of an event, we generally mean a number from 0 to 1, inclusive, which indicates the relative frequency with which such an event is likely to occur if the experiment in question is repeated a large number of times. Thus, we say that the probability of a coin falling heads is $\frac{1}{2}$ because we believe that in a large number of tosses of a "fair" coin, half of them are likely to turn up heads. Although no one may quarrel with the above explanation of probability, there is an important empirical problem connected with the assignment of probabilities to events. This problem may be briefly stated in the form of two questions.

In the first place, if the probability of an event means the relative frequency with which that event occurs in a large number of trials, then *to which real-world events shall we assign probabilities*? In other words, to which problems shall we apply probability? Questions of this nature touch upon matters of definition, interpretation, and use of probability which have occupied the minds of many statisticians, mathematicians, and philosophers interested in probability theory. Perhaps the fact that probabilists talk about at least five kinds of probability may give one an idea of the different approaches to the subject. But all approaches to probability revolve around two pivotal viewpoints, the objective and the subjective.

Under the *objective* point of view, probability is applicable only to events which can be repeated a very large or infinite number of times under the same or nearly the same conditions. Thus, the objectivist talks about the probability of an event in connection with the tossing of a coin, the rolling of a die, or the manufacture of a mass-produced or processed item; he thinks of the probability of a good unit as a long-run ratio of the number of good units to the total large number of units produced by a machine. In sum, the objectivist assigns probabilities to events which can be repeated endlessly or nearly so, i.e., to events where there is a long-run ratio in sight; and, furthermore, he prefers to base his probabilities on no other kind of evidence than that which can be verified by repeated trials.

Example 1.1. Consider the sales record of an item sold by a retailer where the relative frequency indicates the ratio of the number of days a certain number of units were sold to the total 100 sales days:

Events: Units Sold	Days	Relative Frequency
1	5	0.05
2	8	0.08
3	25	0.25
4	27	0.27
5	20	0.20
6	8	0.08
7	7	0.07
Total	100	1.00

Would an objectivist assign each relative weight as the probability to the corresponding event? No, according to him the above relative frequency does not represent long-run ratios. Would experience based on more than 100 days change his position? No, for the fact remains that the events cannot, although they may, be repeated in the future under much the same conditions.

On the other hand, under the *subjective* viewpoint the probability of an event is a measure of personal belief about a particular situation; consequently, this school of thought is sometimes called *personalistic*. A case in point is Example 1.1. A subjectivist would assign the historical relative frequencies as probabilities to the corresponding events if he believes that past sales reflect the retailer's hunches and expectations about future sales of the item. Thus a personalist may assign probabilities to events connected with all the problems an objectivist would, and to many more. Since probability is a measure of subjective considerations, a personalist may assign probabilities to events even when historical data are extremely sparse or not available. In the absence of historical data, the retailer in Example 1.1 may assign a different relative weight to each sales volume and accept such weights as probabilities as long as he believes that they reflect his own personal experience from the sale of similar items and his hunches or expectations. Furthermore, on the same basis a subjectivist may apply probabilities to even unique events such as bidding on a contract, buying machinery, building a factory, or other similar events which by their nature may not be repeated frequently or at all.

As a consequence, the personalistic interpretation of probability raises the second question about assigning probabilities to events. Since probability is a subjective matter, different people may assign different probabilities to the same events; moreover, the same person may assign different probabilities to the same event at different times. Then, *how may we assess the probability of an event*? The subjectivists have developed techniques for assessing probabilities in decision problems of the kind mentioned above. We shall illustrate such techniques later in our course. In the meantime, one important observation cannot escape our attention. It must be obvious now that the subjective approach offers a wide range of opportunities for applying probability to managerial decision problems of general interest.

1.2. Basic Rules for Assigning Probabilities to Events.
Whether or not a probability should be assigned to an event and how this probability may be assessed are empirical, not mathematical, questions. As far as mathematics is concerned, the assignment of probabilities to the events of a sample space is arbitrary. It is based on certain rules called axioms or postulates. From the mathematical standpoint, the assignment of probabilities to events is axiomatic. These probability rules are conveniently listed in Table 1.1, where E and F are events of a

TABLE 1.1.

---

1. $P_r(E) \geqslant 0.$
2. $P_r(S) = 1.$
3. $P_r(E \cup F) = P_r(E) + P_r(F)$, if $E \cap F = \varnothing.$
4. $P_r(E) = \dfrac{n(E)}{n(S)}$, if each point of S is assigned the same probability.
5. $P_r(E \cap F) = P_r(E) \cdot P_r(F)$, if E and F are independent.

---

sample space S and $P_r(E)$ denotes the probability of event E. Together with the concepts of a sample space and of an event these rules form the basis of the mathematical system of probability. Since sets and set operations are used, probability may be considered as another "application" of Boolean algebra. While we shall devote the remainder of this section in explaining the above probability rules, a few of the theorems of this system appear as problems.

Rule 1: The probability of an event E in a sample space is a nonnegative number denoted by $P_r(E)$. Thus rule 1 is sometimes called the *positiveness* postulate inasmuch as the probability of an event is never negative; it is either positive or zero. Let $E = \{H\}$ be the event heads in tossing a coin, then $P_r (\{H\}) = P_r(E) = \frac{1}{2}$ is the probability of the coin falling heads.

Rule 2: The sum of the probabilities assigned to all simple events of a sample space S is 1, i.e., $P_r(S) = 1$. It is called the *certainty* postulate because the entire sample space is a certain event since it contains all possible simple events of the experiment.

An assignment of probabilities to the simple events of a sample space is said to be *acceptable* if it satisfies the conditions specified by the above two rules.

Example 1.2. Consider the sample space $S = \{H, T\}$ for tossing a coin once. The following are three acceptable assignments of probabilities to the two simple events heads $\{H\}$ and tails $\{T\}$ of the sample space S:

(1) $P_r(\{H\}) = \frac{1}{2}$ and $P_r(\{T\}) = \frac{1}{2}.$
(2) $P_r(\{H\}) = \frac{1}{3}$ and $P_r(\{T\}) = \frac{2}{3}.$
(3) $P_r(\{H\}) = 0$ and $P_r(\{T\}) = 1.$

From the mathematical standpoint, whether the probabilities in each of the three assignments are assessed objectively or subjectively or by any other in between approach, it does not matter; what matters is the fact that all assignments satisfy conditions specified by the positiveness and certainty postulates.

Example 1.3. Consider Example 1.1 and let

$$S = \{1, 2, 3, 4, 5, 6, 7\}$$

be a sample space representing the sales record of the retailer. The computed relative frequency is an acceptable assignment of probabilities to the simple events of S; but also any other relative frequency would be acceptable so long as it satisfies rules 1 and 2.

In fact, on the basis of these two rules we may conclude that the probability of each simple event E in a sample space S is at least 0, rule 1, and at most 1, rule 2, in symbols $0 \leqslant P_r(E) \leqslant 1$. Also, it can be easily proved that the probability of the empty event is zero, i.e., $P_r(\varnothing) = 0$. Thus, the empty event is also called an impossible event. Although nonempty events with zero probabilities are important in advanced work with infinite sample spaces, for our limited purposes this case can be eliminated; and nonempty events are assigned positive probabilities only.

1.3. The Addition Rule; Equiprobable Events. Let us now consider the addition of equiprobable and nonequiprobable events.

Rule 3: *The probability of the union of two mutually exclusive events E and F is the sum of their respective probabilities*, i.e., $P_r(E \cup F) = P_r(E) + P_r(F)$. This postulate is called the *addition* rule. Since all simple events of a sample space are mutually exclusive, we have already implied the addition rule in explaining rule 2. Furthermore, the addition rule is directly related to formula (2.1) of the preceding chapter for determining the number of elements or sample points in the union of two mutually exclusive events. In fact, this rule is particularly important for finding the probability of compound events; for, by assigning probabilities to simple events of a sample space, the probabilities of all other events are uniquely determined by addition.

Example 1.4. Let two coins be tossed. A sample space for the experiment is

$$S = \{HH, HT, TH, TT\}.$$

We wish to determine the probability of the event E that the two coins fall alike.

Solution:

With "fair" coins it is reasonable to insist that each of the four simple events in S be assigned probability $\frac{1}{4}$. Since the compound event E is

$$E = \{HH\} \cup \{TT\},$$

by the addition rule the probability of E is

$$P_r(E) = P_r(\{HH\}) + P_r(\{TT\})$$
$$= \tfrac{1}{4} + \tfrac{1}{4}$$
$$= \tfrac{1}{2}.$$

Needless to point out, in the above example had we assigned a probability other than $\frac{1}{4}$ to each simple event, $P_r(E)$ might be other than $\frac{1}{2}$. However, by assuming that the coins are "fair," we consider that each of the four simple events are *equiprobable or equally likely*. The term is used to denote an experiment where there is no reason to believe that every simple event has other than an equal chance of occurring. When we consider, for example, the experiment of throwing two "unbiased" dice, it is reasonable to insist that each of the 36 simple events of the now familiar sample space be equally likely with probability $\frac{1}{36}$. In general, when we say that an item is drawn "at random" or "randomly" from n different items, we usually mean that the n simple events of the appropriate sample space are equally likely, each being assigned probability $1/n$. For sample spaces with equiprobable sample points the following rule applies.

Rule 4: *Let* $n(S)$ *be the number of n equally likely sample points of a sample space S, and let* $n(E)$ *be the number of sample points in event E. Then the probability of E is the ratio* $n(E)/n(S)$.

Example 1.5. Let $\mathcal{U}$ be the sample space specified in Example 2.9 of the preceding chapter where $n(\mathcal{U})$ represents the 1000 individuals interviewed about their plans to buy a new car. We wish to determine the probability that if one of the 1000 balls is selected at random from the urn, that ball will represent a respondent who plans to buy a car. In symbols we wish to determine $P_r(P)$.

Solution 1:

Since the number of planners $n(P) = 250$ and the number of simple events $n(\mathcal{U}) = 1000$, by rule 4 we have

$$P_r(P) = \frac{n(P)}{n(\mathcal{U})} = \frac{250}{1000} = 0.25.$$

Solution 2:

The same answer may be obtained by using the addition rule. Inasmuch as selection is random, to each simple event we assign probability $1/1000$; and since we count 250 simple events in P, by the addition rule

$$P_r(P) = 250 \, \frac{1}{1000} = 0.25.$$

It is important to note that, if the simple events of a sample space are considered equally likely, in order to find the probability of a compound event E we need not know *which* but only count *how many* simple events are in E. It must be evident that for sample spaces with a large number of equiprobable events we need effective counting techniques in order to find the probability of a compound event. Such techniques are discussed in Section 3.

Of course, for sample spaces with simple events which are *not* equally likely in order to find the probability of a compound event E, we must know *which* simple events are in E and add their probabilities. One such case is encountered with sample spaces less fundamental than the ones discussed so far.

Example 1.6. Consider the sample space

$$D_1 = \{2, 3, 4, 5, 6, 7, 8, 9, 10, 11, 12\},$$

where each simple event represents a possible sum of the number shown on the two rolled dice. We wish to find the probability that the sum shown on the two dice is greater than ten.
Solution:
Let E be such a compound event, then

$$E = \{11\} \cup \{12\}.$$

By counting sample points in Table 1.1 of Chapter 14, we find that

$$P_r(\{11\}) = \frac{2}{36} \quad \text{and} \quad P_r(\{12\}) = \frac{1}{36};$$

and by the addition rule

$$P_r(E) = \frac{2}{36} + \frac{1}{36} = \frac{1}{12}.$$

Obviously, finding the probability of event E in the above example is facilitated by referring back to the more fundamental sample space D; and this example shows why it is desirable to specify a sample space as detailed as possible for the experiment. But referring to a more detailed sample space is not always possible. Here is one such case.

Example 1.7. Let us assume that the relative frequency in Example 1.1 does not represent the historical sales record for the item, but it represents arbitrary weights assigned by the retailer to the simple events of the sample space

$$S = \{1, 2, 3, 4, 5, 6, 7\}.$$

We wish to find the probability that sales will be four units or more.
Solution:
Let the event $E = \{4, 5, 6, 7\}$,
then

$$E = \{4\} \cup \{5\} \cup \{6\} \cup \{7\};$$

and

$$\begin{aligned} P_r(E) &= P_r(\{4\}) + P_r(\{5\}) + P_r(\{6\}) + P_r(\{7\}) \\ &= 0.27 + 0.20 + 0.08 + 0.07 \\ &= 0.62. \end{aligned}$$

It can be seen from the above example that the addition rule applies to more than two events as long as they are mutually exclusive. Thus, this rule is particularly useful for finding the probability of an event by adding the probabilities of events which form a partition of it.

How can we determine the probability of joint events? We have already proved formula (2.2) of Chapter 14 for determining the number of elements in the union of two joint events. On similar grounds, we can also prove the corresponding probability theorem for determining the probability of the union of two joint events E and F.

$$(1.1) \qquad P_r(E \cup F) = P_r(E) + P_r(F) - P_r(E \cap F) \quad \text{if} \quad E \cap F \neq \varnothing .$$

Example 1.8. Consider the sample space $\mathfrak{U}$ specified in Example 2.9. of the preceding Chapter, where $n(\mathfrak{U}) = 1000$ represents the individuals who were interviewed about the purchase of a new car. A ball is drawn from the urn at random and we wish to find the probability $P_r(P \cup B)$.
  Solution:
  Since $n(P) = 250$, $n(B) = 200$, and $n(P \cap B) = 50$, by rule 4,

$$P_r(P) = \frac{n(P)}{n(\mathfrak{U})} = \frac{250}{1000} = 0.25 ,$$

$$P_r(B) = \frac{n(B)}{n(\mathfrak{U})} = \frac{200}{1000} = 0.20 , \quad \text{and}$$

$$P_r(B \cap P) = \frac{n(B \cap P)}{n(\mathfrak{U})} = \frac{50}{1000} = 0.05 , \quad \text{respectively;}$$

and by the above formula (1.1) for addition

$$P_r(B \cup P) = P_r(B) + P_r(P) - P_r(B \cap P) = 0.20 + 0.25 - 0.05 = 0.40 .$$

1.4. The Product Rule; Independent Events.
The last rule in Table 1.1, rule 5, called the *product* rule is a condition for independent events. Since the study of independent events is important in probability, this product rule deserves careful treatment.
  Rule 5: Events E and F are independent if and only if the probability that both events occur equals the probability that E occurs times the probability that F occurs, i.e., $P_r(E \cap F) = P_r(E) \cdot P_r(F)$. In the present state of our knowledge the *only* way to find whether two events E and F are independent is by computing $P_r(E)$, $P_r(F)$, and $P_r(E \cap F)$, and then checking if the product rule is verified.

Example 1.9. An experiment consists of rolling a white die and then a black die.
  Let the following events be given:

$$E = \{x \,|\, x \text{ is white die shows } 1\}, \text{ and}$$
$$F = \{x \,|\, x \text{ is black die shows } 6\}.$$

Are events E and F independent?
  Solution:
  By specifying the sample space D shown in Table 1.1 of the preceding

chapter with 36 outcomes, we have

$$E = \{(1, 1), (1, 2), (1, 3), (1, 4), (1, 5), (1, 6)\},$$
$$F = \{(1, 6), (2, 6), (3, 6), (4, 6), (5, 6), (6, 6)\}, \text{ and}$$

Assigning probability $\frac{1}{36}$ to each simple event in D and counting, we have

$$P_r(E) = \frac{6}{36} = \frac{1}{6}, \qquad P_r(F) = \frac{6}{36} = \frac{1}{6}, \qquad \text{and} \qquad P_r(E \cap F) = \frac{1}{36}.$$

Therefore, the events E and F are independent since the product rule holds, i.e.,

$$P_r(E \cap F) = P_r(E)P_r(F)$$

$$\frac{1}{36} = \frac{1}{6} \times \frac{1}{6}.$$

In the above example the results agree with an intuitive approach to the problem. Let us concentrate on the white die. In a large number of throws of the two dice we shall expect that in about $\frac{1}{6}$ of them the white die will show 1. How many of these throws does the black die show 6? Since what the white die shows does not affect what the black die shows, we shall expect that $\frac{1}{6}$ of the throws where the white die shows 1 will have the black die showing 6; and the fraction of throws with white die showing 1 and the black die 6 shall be about $\frac{1}{6}$ of $\frac{1}{6}$, or $\frac{1}{36}$. However, intuition should not be trusted. It should be checked by applying the product rule.

Example 1.10. Consider the two-dice experiment in Example 1.9. Let the following events be given:
$E = \{x | x$ is the sum of the numbers shown on the two dice is 10$\}$, and
$F = \{x | x$ a double is thrown$\}$.
Are events E and F independent?
Solution:
By counting events in the familiar sample space D where each simple event is assigned probability $\frac{1}{36}$, we have

$$P_r(E) = \frac{3}{36} = \frac{1}{12}, \qquad P_r(F) = \frac{6}{36} = \frac{1}{6}, \qquad \text{and} \qquad P_r(E \cap F) = \frac{1}{36}.$$

Hence, events E and F are not independent since

$$P_r(E \cap F) \neq P_r(E) \cdot P_r(F),$$

$$\frac{1}{36} \neq \frac{1}{12} \times \frac{1}{6}.$$

Furthermore, independent events should not be confused with mutually exclusive events. In fact, we can prove the following theorem. *Let E and F be two independent events with nonzero probabilities. Then E and F must be joint events, i.e., nonmutually exclusive events having a common sample point.*

Proof: Events E and F can be either joint or disjoint, i.e., $E \cap F \neq \emptyset$ or $E \cap F = \emptyset$. Suppose $E \cap F = \emptyset$, then $P_r(E \cap F) = P_r(\emptyset) = 0$. Since E and F were assumed to be independent, by the product rule either $P_r(E) = 0$ or $P_r(F) = 0$. But this is contrary to the hypothesis that events E and F have nonzero probabilities. Therefore, events E and F must be joint, i.e., $E \cap F \neq \emptyset$, and the proof is completed.

On similar grounds it can be easily shown that if events E and F with nonzero probabilities are mutually exclusive, they are dependent.

We conclude this section with an example illustrating the application of independent events to business situations.

Example 1.11. Let the sample space $\mathfrak{U}$, specified in Example 2.9 of the preceding chapter, be given, where $n(\mathfrak{U}) = 1000$ represents the individuals who were interviewed about the purchase of a new car.

Question 1: Are the events P that the drawn ball represents a planner and B that it represents a buyer independent?

Answer:

In Example 1.8 we have found that $P_r(B) = 0.20$, $P_r(P) = 0.25$, and $P_r(B \cap P) = 0.05$. Since $0.05 = 0.25 \times 0.20$, the product rule holds and events B and P are independent.

Question 2: What conclusions can we draw from the above finding?

Answer:

Since events P and B were found to be independent, knowing that a respondent plans to buy a new car does not affect the probability $P_r(B) = 0.20$ that he will actually buy it. Therefore, the result of the first interview with respondents does not increase our chances to predict actual car buyers.

PROBLEMS

1.1.   Suppose you are an objectivist. To which of the following events would you apply and to which would you not apply probability? Defend your answer.

*a) A card is drawn from a well-shuffled deck of 52 playing cards.

*b) Of the 10,000 dealers representing a car manufacturer, 60 percent report monthly sales of 50,000 units and 40 percent 60,000 units.

c) An agreement is negotiated for the merger of two firms which is expected to be profitable.

d) A ball is drawn from the urn containing 1000 balls described in Example 2.9, Chapter 14.

e) Oil drilling is contemplated on a certain locality; previous oil drillings under similar prospects were 40 percent successful.

f) A light bulb is drawn from a large pile of light bulbs produced by a machine known to turn out 0.001 defective bulbs.

1.2. A sample space for tossing two coins is $S = \{HH, HT, TH, TT\}$ Let the simple events $E_1 = \{HH\}$, $E_2 = \{HT\}$, $E_3 = \{TH\}$, and $E_4 = \{TT\}$. Indicate whether each of the following assignments of probabilities to the simple events of S is acceptable. Explain why.

a) $P_r(E_1) = \frac{1}{3}$, $P_r(E_2 \cup E_3) = \frac{1}{3}$, $P_r(E_4) = \frac{1}{3}$.

b) $P_r(E_4) = \frac{1}{3}$, $P_r(E_2) = \frac{1}{2}$, $P_r(E_1) = \frac{1}{2}$, $P_r(E_3) = 0$.

c) $P_r(E_1) = P_r(E_2) = P_r(E_3) = P_r(E_4) = \frac{1}{4}$.

d) $P_r(E_2) = \frac{1}{2}$, $P_r(E_1) = P_r(E_3) = P_r(E_4) = \frac{1}{5}$.

1.3. For each experiment described below, specify a suitable sample space S, assign probabilities to its simple events, and find the probability of the indicated event.

a) Exactly two heads in three tosses of a coin.

b) Two heads and two tails in two tosses of two coins.

*c) A family with no girls among families with two children (cf. Problem 1.1(e), Chapter 14).

d) A family with no boys among families with three children (cf. Problem 1.1(f), Chapter 14).

e) A family with no boys among families with r children (cf. Problem 1.1(g), Chapter 14).

1.4. Let a sample space for rolling two dice be $D_1 = \{2, 3, 4, 5, 6, 7, 8, 9, 10, 11, 12\}$, where each simple event of D_1 represents the sum of the numbers shown on the two dice.

a) Explain why each assignment (A) through (D) of probabilities to the simple events of D_1 shown in the table below is acceptable.

b) Which of the four assignments is "natural," i.e., it would be reasonable to assign when a pair of "unbiased" dice is thrown?

c) Let x represent events on the x-axis and p probabilities on the y-axis of a cc-plane; plot the pairs of events-probabilities of the "natural" assignment and connect the point with a line. Discuss the characteristics of this curve.

Events	Probability Assignments			
	(A)	(B)	(C)	(D)
2	1/11	5/36	1/36	1/66
3	1/11	4/36	2/36	2/66
4	1/11	3/36	3/36	3/66
5	1/11	2/36	4/36	4/66
6	1/11	1/36	5/36	5/66
7	1/11	6/36	6/36	6/66
8	1/11	1/36	5/36	7/66
9	1/11	2/36	4/36	8/66
10	1/11	3/36	3/36	9/66
11	1/11	4/36	2/36	10/66
12	1/11	5/36	1/36	11/66

*1.5. Two "unbiased" dice are rolled. Find the probability that the sum of the numbers on the two dice is—
- *a*) Even.
- *b*) Odd and the first dice shows even.
- *c*) Less than five or a double is thrown.
- *d*) Two and twelve.
- *e*) Three or eleven.

1.6. One card is selected from a standard deck of 52 well-shuffled playing cards. Find the probability that the selected card is—
- *a*) A heart.
- *b*) A queen.
- *c*) The queen of hearts.
- *d*) A queen or a heart.
- *e*) A diamond and a heart.

*1.7. Consider Example 1.6 of Chapter 14, where a cashier has a penny, a nickel, and a dime in her cash register.
- *a*) Find the probability that the sum of the two coins she takes from the register at random and without replacement is less than 10 cents.
- *b*) Find the probability of the event described in (*a*) when experiment is with replacement.

1.8. Consider the experiments described in Problem 1.3 of Chapter 14. Specify a suitable sample space S for each one of them, assign probabilities to each simple event of S, and find the probability of the following events.
- *a) The sum of the two coins taken at random is more than 25 cents in the experiment of Problem 1.3(*a*).
- *b*) The sum of the two coins taken at random is more than 25 cents in the experiment of Problem 1.3(*b*).
- *c*) Both selected letters are vowels in the experiment of Problem 1.3(*c*).
- *d*) Both selected letters are vowels in the experiment of Problem 1.3(*d*).

1.9. Consider the experiment described in Problem 1.7 of Chapter 14. Find the probability that a randomly selected ball is—
- *a) Black.
- *b) Black and number 7.
- *c*) White and number 6.
- *d*) White or number 3.
- *e*) Black or number 5.

1.10. Find the probability of each event for the experiment described in the indicated problem.
- *a) A white ball is selected (Problem 1.10(*a*), Chapter 14).
- *b*) Two red balls are selected (Problem 1.10(*b*), Chapter 14).
- *c*) Two red balls are selected (Problem 1.10(*c*), Chapter 14).

*1.11. If the long-run ratio of a part being defective in Problem 1.11 of Chapter 14 is 0.01, what is the probability that two parts selected at random are both defective? three parts randomly selected are all defective? r parts randomly selected are all defective?

1.12. Find the probability of the event that—
 a) Classification $M \cap R \cap Y_1$ of policyholders of Continental Insurance Company is randomly selected (cf. Problem 1.12, Chapter 14).
 b) Complete dinner $S \cap M \cap I$ is randomly selected (cf. Problem 1.13, Chapter 14).

1.13. Specify a suitable sample space and assign probabilities to its simple events for forming a three-member trade delegation from five salesmen as described in Problem 2.8 of Chapter 14. Find the probability of the following events:
 a) $P_r(A)$.
 b) $P_r(D)$.
 c) $P_r(A \cap D)$.
 d) $P_r(A \cup D)$.
 e) $P_r(A')$.

1.14. Use rule 4 to determine the probability of the following events specified in Example 2.9 of Chapter 14 concerning the survey of car buyers:
 *a) $B' \cap P$.
 b) $B \cap P'$.
 c) $(B \cap P') \cup (B' \cap P')$.
 d) $(B \cap P) \cup (B' \cap P')$.
 e) $P_r(B \cup P)$.
 f) $P_r(B' \cup P)$.
 g) $P_r(B \cup P')$.
 h) $P_r(B' \cup P')$.

1.15. A sample of 1000 adults are asked whether they watch regularly a certain weekly variety show on television. The following is their response classified by age and education (data hypothetical):

Age	College	Watch Show	Response
Under 35	Yes	Yes	65
		No	85
	No	Yes	145
		No	105
35 or over	Yes	Yes	85
		No	115
	No	Yes	250
		No	150
		Total Respondents..........	1000

An experiment consists of selecting at random a ball from an urn containing 1000 balls, one for each respondent of the survey. Find the probability that the chosen respondent is—
 a) Under 35 years old.
 b) College educated.
 c) Thirty-five years or older and watches the show.

d) A regular viewer of the show.

e) Not college educated and watches the show.

f) College educated and watches the show.

1.16. Rather than talking in terms of probabilities, businessmen often talk about the odds for a business event. It may be desirable, therefore, to know how odds can be translated to probabilities and vice versa. Let *E* be any event, then the *odds in favor of or for E* are *a* to *b* if and only if

$$P_r(E) = \frac{a}{a+b}.$$

For example, let $P_r(E) = 0.8$. Then we write

$$P_r(E) = \frac{8}{10} = \frac{8}{8+2}.$$

Hence, the odds in favor of or for *E* are 8 to 2. Sometimes these odds are called the odds *against* the complement of *E*. Conversely, let the odds for *E* be 2 to 3, then

$$P_r(E) = \frac{2}{2+3} = 0.4.$$

a) Given the following odds for *E*, find $P_r(E)$.

   *(1) 1 to 1.   (4) 1 to 2.

   (2) 2 to 1.   (5) 20 to 1.

   (3) 3 to 1.   (6) 100 to 1.

b) Given $P_r(E)$, find the odds for *E*.

   *(1) $P_r(E) = 0.5$.   (4) $P_r(E) = 0.01$.

   (2) $P_r(E) = 0.1$.   (5) $P_r(E) = 0.99$.

   (3) $P_r(E) = \frac{1}{3}$.   (6) $P_r(E) = 0.25$.

*1.17. A survey of a large number of investors showed the following results: 10 percent of respondents were under 50 years of age and owned preferred stock; 60 percent were under 50 years old; and 75 percent did not own any preferred stock. What is the probability that an investor who is selected at random from among those interviewed

a) Will own preferred stock?

b) Will own preferred stock and be 50 years or older?

c) Will not own preferred stock and be 50 years or older?

1.18. Thirty red and seventy black balls are placed in an urn. After they are thoroughly mixed, a player is allowed to draw one ball. He wins a prize if he draws a red ball.

a) What is the probability of winning?

b) Suppose the player is allowed to toss a "fair" coin painted red on one side and black on the other before drawing the ball from the urn. He wins if the colors on the coin and the ball match. What is the probability of winning? Does it matter what the mixture of red and black balls in the urn is? Discuss.

c) Assume the player instead of tossing a coin, is allowed to call the color of the ball before drawing it. He wins the prize if the color he calls matches the color of the selected ball. What is the probability of winning then? Explain.

1.19. By analogy to formula (2.2) in text and on the basis of the formula explained in Problem 2.12 of Chapter 14, the probability of three joint events E_1, E_2, and E_3 is $P_r(E_1 \cup E_2 \cup E_3) = P_r(E_1) + P_r(E_2) + P_r(E_3) - P_r(E_1 \cap E_2) - P_r(E_1 \cap E_3) - P_r(E_2 \cap E_3) + P_r(E_1 \cap E_2 \cap E_3)$.

Use the above formula to find the probability of the following events from examples of Chapter 14.

*a) $P_r(E \cup F \cup G)$ in Example 2.3.

b) $P_r(E_1 \cup E_2 \cup E_3)$ in Example 2.8.

c) $P_r(B \cup P \cup B')$ in Example 2.9.

1.20. A subjectivist may point out that by assigning equal probabilities to heads and tails in tossing a fair coin "we *do not* and *cannot* 'prove' that the events are 'in fact' equally likely" (p. 446, reference 9 in bibliography at end of this chapter). Indeed, a subjectivist may argue that "although there are at least five kinds of probabilities, we can get along with just one kind, namely, subjective probability" (p. 13, reference 2 in bibliography at end of this chapter). What counter-argument would you advance if you were a staunch objectivist?

1.21. Consider the familiar sample space D of 36 outcomes for tossing one white die and one black die. Find whether the events given in each case are independent or dependent.

*a) "The white die shows less than 4" and "the black die shows more than 4."

*b) "The sum of the numbers on the 2 dice is 11" and the "white die shows other than 5."

c) "The white die shows odd" and "the black die shows even."

d) "The sum of the numbers on the 2 dice is less than 5" and "a double 6 is thrown."

1.22. Given the familiar sample space $S = \{HH, HT, TH, TT\}$ for tossing two coins, find whether the events in each case are independent or dependent.

a) "Not more than one head is shown" and "at least one of each face comes up."

b) "First coin shows heads "and "the two coins fall alike."

c) "Two coins fall alike" and "one shows heads and the other tails."

1.23. Consider the data about innovating buyers (cf. Problem 2.15, Chapter 14). Show that the events M and I are dependent. How does this dependence affect our ability to predict that a person is an innovating buyer if we know that he is a male?

1.24. Let E and F be two mutually exclusive events with nonzero probabilities. Then prove that events E and F cannot be independent.

1.25. Let E and F be independent events. Then it can be proved that the following pairs of events are also independent: (1) E and F', (2) E' and F, and (3) E' and F'.

a) Verify this theorem by using the data of Table 2.1 Example 2.9,

Chapter 14, where B and P are independent events as shown in Example 1.11 of this section.

b) Prove this theorem.

1.26. Let E and F be two events in a finite sample space S. Then on the basis of Boolean algebra and the rules in Table 1.1, prove the following theorems:

a) $P_r(\varnothing) = 0$. [*Hint:* Let $E = \varnothing$ and $F = S$. Then $P_r(\varnothing \cup S) = P_r(\varnothing) + P_r(S)$.]

b) $P_r(E) \leqslant P_r(F)$ if $E \subseteq F$. (*Hint:* Rules 1 and 3.)

c) $0 \leqslant P_r(E) \leqslant 1$. [*Hint:* Rule 2 and case (b) above.]

d) $P_r(E') = 1 - P_r(E)$. [*Hint:* $P_r(E \cup E') = P_r(E) + P_r(E')$ since $E \cap E' = \varnothing$.]

2. CONDITIONAL PROBABILITY; BAYES' FORMULA

In the preceding section we have talked about the product rule and independent events. We shall further study the product rule by now focusing our attention on the important case when it is not assumed that events are independent. In this connection we shall first introduce the notion of conditional probability. Then we shall study the use of conditional probability in assigning probabilities in a sample space and in revising the probability of an event in the light of additional information.

2.1. Conditional Probability.   Let E and F be two events in the sample space S, where $P_r(F) > 0$. Then the *conditional probability of E, given F, is denoted by $P_r(E|F)$ and is defined as*

(2.1)
$$P_r(E|F) = \frac{P_r(E \cap F)}{P_r(F)}.$$

The conditional probability $P_r(E|F)$ is not defined if $P_r(F) = 0$. Also, $E|F$ is *not* a symbol denoting a new set operation.

Example 2.1.   Let the sample space $\mathfrak{U}$, specified in Example 2.9 of the preceding chapter, be given, where $n(\mathfrak{U}) = 1000$ represents the individuals interviewed about plans for buying a new car. The original cross-tabulation of the 1000 responses to the two interviews is reproduced in Table 2.1, where the original frequencies are expressed as probabilities. The row and column probabilities such as $P_r(B)$ and $P_r(P)$ are called *marginal* while the probabilities of the intersection of two events such as $P_r(B \cap P)$ and $P_r(B' \cap P)$ and $P_r(B' \cap P')$ are called *joint*.

Now suppose a ball is selected at random from the urn described earlier for this experiment, and we are informed that it represents a respondent who plans to buy a new car. Knowing that the selected ball represents a

TABLE 2.1.

First Interview

	Planners	Nonplanners	
Buyers	$P_r(B \cap P) = 0.05$	$P_r(B \cap P') = 0.15$	$P_r(B) = 0.20$
Nonbuyers	$P_r(B' \cap P) = 0.20$	$P_r(B' \cap P') = 0.60$	$P_r(B') = 0.80$
	$P_r(P) = 0.25$	$P_r(P') = 0.75$	$P_r(\mathfrak{U}) = 1.00$

Second Inter-view (row labels for Buyers/Nonbuyers)

planner, what is the probability that it represents a buyer? In symbols, we wish to find $P_r(B|P)$.

Solution:

Since $P_r(B \cap P) = 0.05$ and $P_r(P) = 0.25$, by formula (2.1) we obtain

$$P_r(B|P) = \frac{0.05}{0.25} = 0.20 \,.$$

Observe that since $P_r(B|P) = P_r(B) = 0.20$, the probability of a person being a buyer is the same whether we know or not that the same person is a planner.

It is important to realize that we arrived at the same conclusion in demonstrating the application of independent events in Example 1.11. Then we concluded that because the events $P =$ "Planners" and $B =$ "Buyers" were found to be independent knowing a respondent is a planner does not affect the probability that he is a buyer of a new car. Thus for the independent events B and P the conditional probability of B, given P, equals the marginal probability of B, i.e., $P_r(B|P) = P_r(B)$. Indeed, it can be easily proved that the conditional probability of two independent events E and F with nonzero probabilities equals their respective marginal probability, i.e., $P_r(E|F) = P_r(E)$ and $P_r(F|E) = P_r(F)$. Even more than that, since all probabilities are referred to some sample space S, the probability of an event such as $P_r(E)$ is an abbreviation of

$$P_r(E|S) = \frac{P_r(E \cap S)}{P_r(S)} \,;$$

but the S is dropped since $P_r(E \cap S) = P_r(E)$ and $P_r(S) = 1$.

Example 2.1—*Continued.* In order to understand what a conditional probability means, we must have a close look at the sample space in Table 2.1. The knowledge that the drawn ball represents a planner eliminates that part of the sample space $\mathfrak{U}$ which represents nonplanners. They are no longer part of the sample space; the *reduced sample space is P, the given event*, consisting of only 250 sample points. It represents the shaded area in Table 2.1. Since these simple events are equiprobable and since only 50 of them represent buyers, by rule 4 the probability

$$P_r(B|P) = \frac{n(B \cap P)}{n(P)} = \frac{P_r(B \cap P)}{P_r(P)} = \frac{0.05}{0.25} = 0.20$$

as found by application of formula (2.1).

In sum, in the case where two events are independent, conditional probability is of no consequence; it becomes important, however, when two events are dependent.

Example 2.2. Instead of the probabilities shown in Table 2.1, let us assume that from the survey of consumer expectations for new cars the probabilities shown in Table 2.2 have been obtained. A ball is selected at

TABLE 2.2.

First Interview

		Planners	*Nonplanners*	
Second Interview	Buyers	$P_r(B \cap P) = 0.05$	$P_r(B \cap P') = 0.15$	$P_r(B) = 0.20$
	Nonbuyers	$P_r(B' \cap P) = 0.10$	$P_r(B' \cap P') = 0.70$	$P_r(B') = 0.80$
		$P_r(P) = 0.15$	$P_r(P') = 0.85$	$P_r(\mathfrak{U}) = 1.00$

random from the familiar urn of 1,000 balls. What is the probability that the ball represents an actual car buyer, given that it represents a planner?
Solution:
Since $P_r(B \cap P) = 0.05$ and $P_r(P) = 0.15$, by formula 2.1 we have

$$P_r(B|P) = \frac{0.05}{0.15} \approx 0.33.$$

Thus, knowing that the selected ball represents a planner has increased the probability that it represents an actual buyer from 0.20 to 0.33. Note that in this example events B and P are dependent since $P_r(B \cap P) \neq P_r(B)P_r(P)$.

It is important to realize that the response to the first interview in both surveys in Examples 2.1 and 2.2 can be used to estimate expected car sales statistically. In the latter case, however, the fact that events B and P are dependent may, for example, be advantageously used by management to discriminate between consumers who plan and those who do not plan to buy a new car for more effective sales promotion planning.

In other cases, however, the probability of an event E may *decrease* instead of increasing when the added information that event F has occurred is given.

Example 2.3. Let us assume that the randomly drawn ball in Example 2.2 represents again a planner. What is the probability that the ball represents a nonbuyer, given that it represents a planner?

Solution:

Applying formula (2.1), we have

$$P_r(B'|P) = \frac{P_r(B' \cap P)}{P_r(P)} = \frac{0.10}{0.15} \approx 0.67.$$

Therefore, the fact that the selected ball represents a planner has decreased the probability that it represents a nonbuyer from 0.80 before to about 0.67 after the additional information is given.

Let us now turn our attention to formula (2.1). The conditional probability of E, given F, may be, and more frequently than not is, entirely different from the marginal probability $P_r(E)$ and the joint probability $P_r(E \cap F)$. In other words, in real-world situation two events E and F are more frequently found to be dependent than independent. In this connection formula (2.1) leads to two important classes of applications of conditional probability which we study next: (*a*) assigning probabilities in a sample space, and (*b*) revising probabilities in the light of additional information.

2.2. The Product Rule; Dependent Events. Multiplying both sides of (2.1) by $P_r(F)$, we get

(2.2) $$P_r(E \cap F) = P_r(F) \cdot P_r(E|F).$$

Similarly, if $P_r(E) > 0$ by (2.1) we have

$$P_r(F|E) = \frac{P_r(F \cap E)}{P_r(E)};$$

and multiplying both sides by $P_r(E)$, we get

(2.3) $$P_r(F \cap E) = P_r(E) \cdot P_r(F|E).$$

Since from the commutative law for the intersection of two sets $E \cap F = F \cap E$, from (2.2) and (2.3) we obtain

(2.4) $$\boxed{P_r(E \cap F) = P_r(F) \cdot P_r(E|F) = P_r(E) \cdot P_r(F|E).}$$

This formula is the product rule for finding the joint probability of events E and F when they are assumed to be dependent; and we shall apply this rule frequently. At this point, however, it is important to note that formula (2.4) is a generalization of product rule 5 for independent events; for, if events E and F are assumed to be independent, this formula reduces to $P_r(E \cap F) = P_r(E) \cdot P_r(F)$ since in such a case $P_r(E|F) = P_r(E)$ and $P_r(F|E) = P_r(F)$. Thus the use of formula (2.4) will give us the opportunity to review the overall process of assigning probabilities to both independent and dependent events.

In this respect formula (2.4) is extensively used for computing probabilities of events specified in terms of a compound experiment. Most experiments we have considered may be described as a compounding of one or more trials. For example, tossing a coin twice may be described as a compound experiment involving two tasks or *trials*, each corresponding to a toss of the coin. The experiment with the survey data of consumer expectations in Examples 2.1 and 2.2 may be described in terms of a compound experiment where the first interview represents trial 1 and the second interview trial 2. In computing probabilities of events in sample spaces of these experiments we used the basic probability rules explained in the preceding section. But the same experiments may be most conveniently described as a compounding of two or more trials and the probabilities computed by applying formula (2.4). When the outcome on each trial of a compound experiment is independent of the outcome on a previous trial or trials, then such trials are called *independent*; and when the outcome on each trial of a compound experiment depends on the outcome of a previous trial or trials, then such trials are called *dependent*.

Let us first consider the case of a compound experiment with independent trials.

Example 2.4.   A fair coin is tossed once and once more. By the basic probability rules $P_r\{HT\} = \frac{1}{4}$.

But now we can compute the probability of the same event by formula (2.4). Let $E = \{H\}$ be the event on the first trial (toss). Then $P_r(E) = \frac{1}{2}$. Let $F|E = \{T\}$ be the event on the second trial, given that event E occurs on the first trial. Then $P_r(F|E) = \frac{1}{2}$. What is the probability that the coin falls heads on the first and tails on the second trial? In symbols, we wish to find $P_r(E \cap F)$.

Solution:

Since $P_r(E) = \frac{1}{2}$ and $P_r(F|E) = \frac{1}{2}$, by formula (2.4) we get

$$P_r(E \cap F) = \left(\frac{1}{2}\right)\left(\frac{1}{2}\right) = \frac{1}{4}$$

as previously.

Naturally, we can immediately recognize that formula of product rule 5 for independent events has actually been used since we have independent trial and $P_r(F|E) = P_r(F) = \frac{1}{2}$.

Let us now focus our attention on compound experiments with dependent trials, i.e., when the outcome on each trial depends on the outcome on a previous trial or trials.

Example 2.5.   Consider the experiment in Example 1.6 of Chapter 14 where the cashier takes two coins at random from the register containing a penny, a nickel, and a dime without replacement. Let the events P, N, and D denote a penny, a nickel, or a dime, respectively. What is the probability that the first coin is a penny and the second a nickel, i.e., $P_r(P \cap N)$?

Solution 1:

Since the first task (trial) can be done in three ways and the second task (trial) in two ways, there are $3 \times 2 = 6$ elements in the set representing a suitable sample space for the experiment (cf. tree diagram in Figure 1.2, Chapter 14). Since event $P \cap N$ is one of the six simple events of the specified sample space, $P_r(P \cap N) = \frac{1}{6}$.

Solution 2:

The same probability may be found by applying formula (2.4). Since there are three coins in the register, the probability of selecting at random the penny is $P_r(P) = \frac{1}{3}$. But the experiment is without replacement, so in the second trial there are only two coins, the nickel and the dime; the trials are dependent, and the probability of selecting randomly the nickel, given that the penny is selected in the first trial, is $P_r(N|P) = \frac{1}{2}$. Hence,

$$P_r(P \cap N) = P_r(P) \cdot P_r(N|P) = \left(\frac{1}{3}\right) \cdot \left(\frac{1}{2}\right) = \frac{1}{6},$$

as previously.

We can follow the same procedure in assigning probabilities to the other five events in the sample space as shown with a tree diagram in Figure 2.1. Observe that the sum of the probabilities on each branching

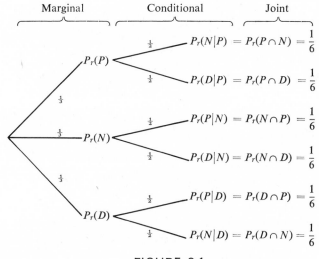

FIGURE 2.1.

of the tree diagram is 1 and the probability of each simple event is the product of a marginal and a conditional probability according to formula (2.4).

The above examples may suggest that assigning probabilities in a sample space by formula (2.4) may be an alternative method to finding probabilities by the basic rules of Section 1. This may not be usually true as the following example illustrates.

Example 2.6. An experiment consists of selecting at random three television tubes from a lot of five containing two defectives without replacement. We may specify a sample space for the experiment

$$S = \{GGG, GGD, GDG, GDD, DGG, DGD, DDG\},$$

where G denote a good and D a defective tube; and we are tempted to assign probability of $\frac{1}{7}$ to each simple event of S. Is this assignment of probabilities correct? Definitely not, under the conditions of the experiment.

The proper assignment of probabilities can only be done with the application of formula (2.4), the product rule for dependent events as shown in Figure 2.2. The order in which letters G and D appear indicates

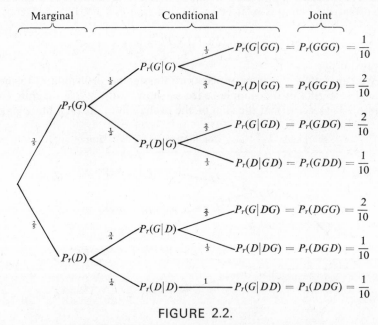

FIGURE 2.2.

the order in which a good or a defective tube has been selected. The symbol of intersection has been eliminated for convenience.

Observe that the simple events in the sample space are not equiprobable. The probability of each simple event is obtained by repeated applications of the product rule. For example, the joint probability for all three tubes being good is the marginal times the conditional of the second trial times the conditional of the third trial as follows:

$$P_r(G_1 \cap G_2 \cap G_3) = P_r(G_1) \cdot P(G_2|G_1) \cdot P_r(G_3|G_1 \cap G_2)$$

$$= \left(\frac{3}{5}\right)\left(\frac{1}{2}\right) \cdot \left(\frac{1}{3}\right) = \frac{1}{10},$$

where subscripts indicate first, second, and third trial and allow the introduction of the symbol for set intersection.

What is the probability of exactly two defectives? By the addition
rule, we have

$$P_r(G_1 \cap D_2 \cap D_3) + P_r(D_1 \cap G_2 \cap D_3) + P_r(D_1 \cap D_2 \cap G_3)$$
$$= \frac{1}{10} + \frac{1}{10} + \frac{1}{10} = \frac{3}{10}.$$

Unless two events E and F are independent there is no formula at
present for computing the joint probability $P_r(E \cap F)$ even if the mar-
ginals $P_r(E)$ and $P_r(F)$ are known. These three probabilities must be
computed individually from the sample space S. This may be a difficult
task when S contains a large number of sample points. But if the conditional probability is given, we can find $P_r(E \cap F)$ by applying formula
(2.4).

Example 2.7. On the basis of previous surveys and personal experience
the management of Tucker, Tucker, and Webster, Inc., an advertising
agency, estimates that 30 percent of the readers of a newspaper will read
a particular advertisement but of those who read the advertisement only
1 percent will purchase the advertised product. What is the probability
that a person reading the newspaper will read the advertisement and
purchase the advertised product?
Solution:
Let E be the event that a person reads the advertisement and F that he
purchases the product. Then $P_r(E) = 0.30$ and $P_r(F|E) = 0.01$ by formula
(2.4), the joint probability

$$P_r(E \cap F) = P_r(E) \cdot P_r(F|E) = (0.30) \cdot (0.01) = 0.003.$$

2.3. Bayes' Formula. Revision of probabilities, the second
important application of conditional probability, requires the famous
Bayes' formula, named after Thomas Bayes who first used it in a paper
published posthumously in 1763. We shall first show how this formula
is related to the conditional probability without giving a formal proof
of it. Then we shall illustrate its application to business problems.

Bayes' formula may be considered as a generalization of the conditional probability formula (2.1). For finding the conditional probability that the randomly selected ball in Example 2.2 represents a buyer,
given that it represents a planner, we used formula (2.1); in symbols

$$P_r(B|P) = \frac{P_r(B \cap P)}{P_r(P)}.$$

Since by (2.4) $P_r(B \cap P) = P_r(B) \cdot P_r(P|B)$ and $B \cap P$ and $B' \cap P$ are
partitions of P as shown in Table 2.2, the above conditional probability
is equivalent to

$$P_r(B|P) = \frac{P_r(B)P_r(P|B)}{P_r(B \cap P) + P_r(B' \cap P)};$$

and by applying formula (2.4) twice in the denominator, we get

$$(2.5) \qquad P_r(B|P) = \frac{P_r(B)P_r(P|B)}{P_r(B)P_r(P|B) + P_r(B')P_r(P|B')}.$$

Example 2.8. A newly hired car salesman is told by his manager that about 20 percent of the persons who inquire about new cars actually buy one while 80 percent do not. On the basis of sales experience during the first quarter of the year, the salesman finds that 25 percent of the persons who actually bought a new car did considerable pre-planning, while only 12.5 percent of those who did not buy a new car did such pre-planning. If a person is a planner, what is the probability that this person will buy a new car? What is the probability that such a person will not buy a car?
Solution:
It is given that $P_r(B) = 0.20, P_r(B') = 0.80, P_r(P|B) = 0.25,$ and $P_r(P|B') = 0.125$. Substituting these values in (2.5), we have

$$P_r(B|P) = \frac{(0.20) \cdot (0.25)}{(0.20)(0.25) + (0.80)(0.125)} = \frac{0.05}{0.15} \approx 0.33.$$

Analogously,

$$P_r(B'|P) = \frac{(0.80) \cdot (0.125)}{(0.20)(0.25) + (0.80)(0.125)} = \frac{0.10}{0.15} \approx 0.67.$$

Observe that application of formula (2.5) gives the same answer which we obtained by applying formula (2.1) in Examples 2.2 and 2.3. But (2.5) differs from the conditional probability formula in one significant respect: the joint probabilities $P_r(B \cap P)$ and $P_r(B' \cap P)$ are expressed as products of a marginal and a conditional probability by application of formula (2.4).

From (2.5) we can arrive at a general expression of Bayes' formula. Let events $E_1, E_2, \ldots, E_n$ be partitions of the sample space S with nonzero probabilities. Let E be any event of S such as $P(E) > 0$. Then for each $E_1, E_2, \ldots, E_n$, we have *Bayes' formula*:

$$(2.6) \qquad P_r(E_k|E) = \frac{P_r(E_k)P_r(E|E_k)}{P_r(E_1)P_r(E|E_1) + P_r(E_2)P_r(E|E_2) + \ldots + P_r(E_n)P_r(E|E_n)},$$

where $k = 1, 2, 3, \ldots, n$. Note that by (2.4) formula (2.6) can be written in the following equivalent form

$$(2.7) \qquad P_r(E_k|E) = \frac{P_r(E_k \cap E)}{P_r(E_1 \cap E) + P_r(E_2 \cap E) + \ldots + P_r(E_n \cap E)},$$

$k = 1, 2, 3, \ldots, n$. In order to appreciate the importance of this formula, let us have a close look at Example 2.8, which is its application.

TABLE 2.3.

Prior Probability (1)	Conditional Probability (2)	Joint Probability (3)	Posterior Probability (4)
$P_r(B) = 0.20$	$P_r(P\|B) = 0.250$	$P_r(B \cap P) = 0.05$	$P_r(B\|P) \approx 0.33$
$P_r(B') = 0.80$	$P_r(P\|B') = 0.125$	$P_r(B' \cap P) = 0.10$	$P_r(B'\|P) \approx 0.67$
		$P_r(B \cap P) + P_r(B' \cap P) = 0.15$	

Example 2.8—*Continued.* The computational steps for finding $P_r(B|P)$ and $P_r(B'|P)$ are conveniently summarized in Table 2.3. Each joint probability in column 3 is obtained by multiplying each marginal, called *prior*, probability by the corresponding conditional, columns 1 × 2. Then each revised probability, called *posterior*, is found by dividing each joint probability in column 3 by the sum of the joint probabilities.

In this case events B and B' are partitions of sample space $\mathfrak{U}$, called hypotheses. The new information is event P (the person is a planner). In the light of this additional information the prior probabilities $P_r(B)$ and $P_r(B')$ are revised to posterior probabilities $P_r(B|P)$ and $P_r(B'|P)$, respectively.

The above example illustrates in brief what can be accomplished with Bayes' formula. In general, we start with a set of hypotheses. They are expressed in terms of mutually exclusive and collectively exhaustive events $E_1, E_2, E_3, \ldots, E_n$, in other words, in terms of partitions of sample space S. The *a priori* probabilities to the hypotheses may be assigned on the basis of objective information or on the basis of personal experience reflecting the "intensity of belief" in each hypothesis. In Example 2.8, for instance, prior probabilities may represent past sales records, or reflect the manager's hunches, or a combination of both. With the new evidence becoming available, represented by event E, we revise our prior probabilities and obtain the *a posteriori* conditional probabilities. With this process, objective evidence revises our beliefs, strengthening the "intensity of our beliefs" in some hypotheses and weakening it in others. In Example 2.8, with the additional evidence that a person is a planner, the salesman's "intensity of belief," expressed in terms of probabilities, was strengthened for the event that such a person will purchase a new car and weakened for the event that he will not purchase a new car. The cycle may be repeated again and again, each time considering the posterior probabilities as priors and revising them into new posteriors in the light of additional information. For instance, the salesman in Example 2.8 may find that sales experience in the second quarter of the year justifies a probability $P_r(P|B) = 0.30$ and $P_r(P|B') = 0.10$. The reader may verify that the second class of posterior probabilities are $P_r(B|P) = 0.60$, and $P_r(B'|P) = 0.40$. Thus, the more information is accumulated, the less important the original prior probabilities become.

Bayes' formula is used in both classical and nonclassical statistics. The above discussion clearly shows, however, why this formula occupies a pivotal position in nonclassical statistics. Perhaps for this reason non-classical statistics is frequently called *Bayesian*.

There is another important matter which we should explain before concluding this section. In Example 2.8 we found the posterior probabilities given the event P (a person is a planner). We can very easily also find the posterior probabilities when P' (a person is not a planner) is given. This can be most advantageously illustrated with tree diagrams.

Example 2.8—*Continued.* Since 25 percent of the buyers of new cars were found to be planners, then 75 percent of them must be nonplanners, i.e., $P_r(P'|B) = 0.75$. Also, since $P_r(P|B') = 0.125$, then $P_r(P'|B') = 0.875$. The reader may compute $P_r(B|P')$ and $P_r(B'|P')$ by constructing a table similar to Table 2.3.

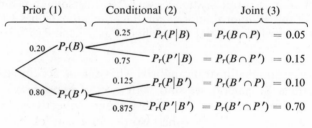

Prior (1)	Conditional (2)	Joint (3)
0.20 $P_r(B)$	0.25 $P_r(P|B)$	$= P_r(B \cap P)$ $= 0.05$
	0.75 $P_r(P'|B)$	$= P_r(B \cap P')$ $= 0.15$
0.80 $P_r(B')$	0.125 $P_r(P|B')$	$= P_r(B' \cap P)$ $= 0.10$
	0.875 $P_r(P'|B')$	$= P_r(B' \cap P')$ $= 0.70$

FIGURE 2.3.

As a recapitulation of the whole process of revising probabilities with Bayes' formula, we shall compute all four posterior probabilities as follows. The tree diagram in Figure 2.3 shows how we start with prior probabilities and find the set of joint probabilities, as columns 1 through 3 in Table 2.3. Then the joint probabilities are added to obtain the other

Marginal	Posterior (4)	Joint
0.15 $P_r(P)$	0.33 $P_r(B|P)$	$= P_r(B \cap P)$ $= 0.05$
	0.67 $P_r(B'|P)$	$= P_r(B' \cap P)$ $= 0.10$
0.85 $P_r(P')$	0.176 $P_r(B|P')$	$= P_r(B \cap P')$ $= 0.15$
	0.824 $P_r(B'|P')$	$= P_r(B' \cap P')$ $= 0.70$

FIGURE 2.4.

pair of marginal probabilities $P_r(P) = 0.15$ and $P_r(P') = 0.85$. These probabilities are shown in a tree diagram in Figure 2.4 together with the set of posterior probabilities. The latter are obtained by dividing the given joint probabilities by the appropriate marginal as shown in column 4 of Table 2.3.

Figures 2.3 and 2.4 should be compared with Table 2.2 as a review of the subject matter in this section. A sequence of a finite number of "experiments" where the outcome of each particular "experiment" depends on some element of chance, such as the one shown in Example 2.8, is sometimes called a *finite stochastic process*, after the Greek word "stochos" meaning "guess."

PROBLEMS

2.1. Two fair coins are tossed once. Find the conditional probability—
a) That the first falls heads, given that both fall alike.
   b) That both fall alike, given that the first falls heads.
   c) That the first falls heads and the second tails, given that they fall alike.

2.2. Three fair coins are tossed once. Find the following conditional probabilities. How does the given event affect the prior probability in each case? Are the events involved dependent or independent?
a) The third coin falls heads, given that the first coin falls tails.
   b) The second and third coins fall alike, given that the first coin falls heads.
   c) The second coin falls heads, given that the first coin falls heads.

2.3. A white die and a black die are rolled once. Find the following probabilities. How does the given event affect the prior probability in each case? Are the events involved dependent or independent?
a) The white die shows less than 3, given that the black die shows more than 3.
   b) Knowing that the white die shows other than 5, the sum of the numbers on the two dice is 11.
   c) If a double 6 is thrown, then the sum of the numbers on the two dice is less than 5.
   d) The black die shows even, knowing that the white die shows odd.

2.4. Two balls are drawn without replacement from an urn containing 1000 balls. If the composition of the balls in the urn is as indicated in each case below, what is the probability that—
a) Both balls represent planners and buyers in Table 2.1?
   b) The first ball represents a planner and nonbuyer and the second ball a buyer in Table 2.1?
   c) Both balls represent nonbuyers in Table 2.2?

2.5. Two cards are randomly selected from a standard deck of 52 well-shuffled playing cards without replacement. Find the probability that—
a) The two cards are diamonds.
   b) The first card represents the queen of hearts and the second a heart.
   c) *One* card represents number 2 and the *other* number 4.

2.6. Consider a cashier having a penny, a nickel, a dime, a quarter, and a half dollar in her cash register. She randomly selects two coins from her register.

   a) If selection is with replacement, what is the probability that the penny and the nickel are selected?

   b) If selection is without replacement, what is the probability of the event described in (*a*)?

2.7. Three salesmen are selected at random from a group of five salesmen, denoted by A, B, C, D, and E, to form a three-member trade delegation (cf. Problem 2.8, Chapter 14). What is the probability—

   *a) That C is selected, given that A is selected?

   b) Knowing that neither A nor B are selected, D is selected?

   c) E is selected if we know that A or B are selected?

2.8. The manager of Robert's Cleaning Company runs a weekly lottery as a promotional device. Each customer receives a ticket corresponding to a number in the lottery. During a particular week 100 tickets, numbered serially starting with number one, have been distributed. At the end of the week a number is selected at random and the winner receives the equivalent of ten dollars' worth of dry-cleaning service.

   a) What is the probability that the second digit of the winning number is greater than 4, given that the first digit is 5?

   b) What is the probability that, if the first digit of the winning number is 7, then the second digit is 5?

*2.9. Four partners decide independently whether to buy (B) or not to buy (N) new machinery for their factory. If it is known that two partners are in favor of buying a new machine, and if at least three are required for a decision, what is the probability that the new machine will be purchased?

*2.10. Consider the experiment of tossing a fair coin three times.

   a) Describe this experiment as a compounding of three trials by means of a tree diagram of the format shown in Figure 2.2.

   b) Discuss the sample space specified in (*a*) in terms of a Cartesian product set $S \times S \times S$, where $S = \{H, T\}$.

   c) Express with symbols the probability of a simple event on the above sample space as a product of a marginal and two successive conditional probabilities.

2.11. Urn A contains two white balls and one red ball and urn B contains one white and two red balls. For each experiment below, specify a suitable sample space S and assign probabilities to the simple events of S on the assumption that they are equally likely. Then describe the experiment as a compounding of two or three trials, using a tree diagram, and assign probabilities to each outcome of the experiment by the product rule formula, (2.4). Are the two sets of probabilities the same? Discuss.

   a) We randomly select an urn first and then a ball from the chosen urn.

b) From the randomly selected urn, two balls are drawn without replacement.

c) The same as in (b) but with replacement.

*2.12. A merchant of electrical appliances will accept a lot of 20 radios if a randomly selected sample of three contains no defectives. If the lot contains four defective radios, what is the probability that he will
*a) Accept the lot?
b) Reject the lot?

*2.13. Three advertising agencies A, B, and C compete for the account of a cigarette manufacturer. The manager of agency A thinks that the chances of winning this account are equal to B's and twice as good as C's. What is the probability for A to win this account? Suppose the manager of A is informed that agency B has withdrawn from the competition. What is the probability for A to win the account, given this new information?

2.14. A retailer has three television sets of make A, two of make B, and five of make C. If sales of different makes are random, what is the probability that in selling two television sets, both are of the same make?

2.15. We have mentioned in the text that Bayes' formula may be used repeatedly revising probabilities as new information becomes available.
a) Construct a table such as Table 2.3 and verify that the second class of posterior probabilities are $P_r(B|P) = 0.60$ and $P_r(B'|P) = 0.40$ when $P_r(P|B) = 0.30$ and $P_r(P|B') = 0.10$.
b) Suppose the salesman's experience during the third quarter of sales justifies $P_r(P|B) = 0.25$ and $P_r(P|B') = 0.15$. Consider the posteriors you verified in (a) as priors and revise them in the light of this additional information.

2.16. From Figures 2.3 and 2.4, present the required data in tabular form such as Table 2.3 to show that $P_r(B|P') = 0.176$ and $P_r(B'|P') = 0.824$ when $P_r(P'|B) = 0.75$ and $P_r(P'|B') = 0.875$.

2.17. A manufacturer receives 60 percent of special radio tubes for assembling radios from company A and 40 percent from company B. Experience has shown that 1 percent of the tubes produced by company A are defective, while the fraction defective for company B is 2 percent.
*a) Find the joint probabilities such as $P_r(A \cap G)$, $P_r(A \cap D)$, etc., where G stands for good and D for defective tubes by preparing a tree diagram such as the one shown in Figure 2.3.
b) Find the conditional probabilities such as $P_r(A|D)$ etc., by constructing a tree diagram similar to the one shown in Figure 2.4.
c) Prepare a table similar to Table 2.2. Does the event defective depend on the company?

2.18. A manufacturing operation is known to produce 20 percent defective parts. A test has been devised to detect defective parts which shows the following experience: A part known to be good will test good 70 percent of the time; a part which is known to be defective will test defective 80 percent of the time. Let a part be chosen at random and tested; if the test shows that the part is good, what is the probability that it is actually defective?

2.19. In blending whiskey, a panel of taste experts is often used to determine whether a given batch is distinguishable from previous batches. One method of testing the ability of an expert to distinguish is the following. He is presented with two pairs of samples, a pair of "matched" samples from the same batch and a pair of "odd" samples from two different batches. One of the two pairs is selected at random, and the expert is asked whether the pair is the matched or the odd. Past experience has shown that experts are right in picking a matched sample 70 percent of the time and in picking an odd sample 80 percent of the time. If an expert guesses right, what is the probability that the pair of samples is odd?

2.20. Let E and F be two events in a sample space. Given the definition of conditional probability, prove the following probability rules.
a) $P_r(E|F) = 0$, if $P_r(F) > 0$ and E and F are disjoint events.
b) $P_r(E|F) = P_r(E)$ and $P_r(F|E) = P_r(F)$, if E and F are independent events with nonzero probabilities.
c) $P_r(E|E) = 1$, where $P_r(E) > 0$.
d) $P_r(\varnothing|E) = 0$, where $P_r(E) > 0$.

3. COUNTING TECHNIQUES; BINOMIAL COEFFICIENTS

In explaining the fundamentals of probability theory, we have intentionally restricted our examples to experiments requiring sample spaces with a small number of sample points. Finding all possible outcomes of an experiment was a simple matter. It required no more than multiplying the small number of outcomes of one trial by the number of outcomes of another trial or constructing a tree diagram. But our brief treatment of probability would be incomplete without lifting this restriction. In many problems already studied, the probability of an event could be most efficiently determined with sophisticated counting techniques; still many other interesting and important problems cannot be easily solved without such techniques. This is particularly true in cases where finding the probability of a compound event requires no more than counting a large number of equiprobable sample points.

For accomplishing this task, we shall first fully explain the fundamental principle of counting. Then we shall develop a few basic permutation and combination formulas. Finally, we shall study binomial coefficients as an important application of counting techniques.

3.1. The Fundamental Principle of Counting.
We have already illustrated in Section 1 of Chapter 14 how this principle can be applied to determine the number of possible outcomes of an experiment. We pointed out then that the four outcomes for tossing two coins may

be considered as a product of the two outcomes for tossing the first coin (task 1) times the two outcomes for tossing the second coin. Similarly, we found that the total number of outcomes for rolling two dice is $6 \times 6 = 36$ and for selecting at random two coins without replacement from a register containing a penny, a nickel, and a dime is $3 \times 2 = 6$ (cf. Examples 1.5 and 1.6, Chapter 14). In general, in a job requiring two tasks (trials) for each of the N_1 ways of doing task one, we must have N_2 ways of doing task two. Hence, both tasks can be completed in $N_1 + N_1 + N_1 + \ldots + N_1$ ways, where there are N_2 terms in the sum. It follows from the definition of multiplication that the total number of ways of completing the whole job is the product $N_1 \cdot N_2$.

Would this principle be true for $n > 2$ tasks? Let us assume that the principle holds for any n tasks. In other words, if tasks $1, 2, 3, \ldots, n$ can be done in $N_1, N_2, N_3, \ldots, N_n$ ways, respectively, then there are $N_1 \cdot N_2 \cdot N_3 \ldots N_n$ ways of completing the whole job of n tasks. In turn, let us consider these n tasks as *one* task which can be completed in N different ways and assume that a new $(n + 1)$st task must be performed which can be done in N_{n+1} ways. But

$$N = N_1 \cdot N_2 \cdot N_3 \cdot \ldots \cdot N_n, \quad \text{and}$$

$$N \cdot N_{n+1} = N_1 \cdot N_2 \cdot N_3 \cdot \ldots \cdot N_n \cdot N_{n+1}.$$

Therefore, for any positive integer n, if the principle is true for n tasks, it must be true for $n + 1$ tasks. Since it has been proved to be true for $n = 2$ tasks, we conclude that it is true for n tasks, where n is any positive integer. Thus, we have proved by mathematical induction the *fundamental principle of counting* for determining the number of outcomes for any n tasks (trials) in a given experiment.

We shall illustrate the application of this principle with a probability problem involving a large number of possible outcomes.

Example 3.1. For advertising a new product the management of ACME, an advertising agency, plans a nationwide contest. To enter the contest, a person must submit a four-letter word naming the new product. Repetition of letters are allowed; but the first and the third letter of the word must consist of consonants, while the second and the fourth of vowels. Although a person can enter the contest more than once, no person can qualify if his word has already been submitted. A word will be selected *at random* from those submitted and the winner will receive a prize. The manufacturer of the new product felt that the contest would be an effective advertising device; he reserved the right, however, to decide whether his product would be named after the selected word.

What is the number of possible entries for the contest; and what is the probability of winning?

Solution:

According to the rules of the contest the number of possible entries cannot be larger than the number of four-letter words which can be possibly formed from the letters of the English alphabet. To complete the whole job of forming four-letter words, we must perform four tasks, i.e., $n = 4$. Selecting the first and third letters (tasks 1 and 3) can be done in 21 ways each, because repetition of consonants is allowed. For the same reason, selecting the second and the fourth letters (tasks 2 and 4) can be done in 5 ways. Thus, the whole job can be completed in $21 \cdot 5 \cdot 21 \cdot 5$ ways, and the total number of four-letter words is 11,025, which is also the number of possible entries for the contest; the probability of winning is $1/11{,}025$. (Cf. Rule 4, Section 1.)

Note that the above application of the fundamental principle of counting can be considered as a case involving an experiment with replacement. The same problem can be easily converted into a case of an experiment without replacement.

> **Example 3.1**—*Continued.* Suppose the rules of the contest planned by ACME's management provide that no consonant or vowel could be used more than once, what would our answer be then?
> *Solution:*
> The first and the second letter positions can be filled in 21 and 5 ways, respectively, as before. But the third and the fourth letter positions can now be filled in 20 and 4 ways, respectively, since the consonant and the vowel used to fill the first two-letter positions cannot be used again. Therefore, the number of possible four-letter words, and of course possible entries for the contest, is $21 \cdot 5 \cdot 20 \cdot 4 = 8400$; and the probability of winning is $1/8400$.

3.2. Permutations. It is important to note that in arranging a number of objects in a line by the fundamental principle of counting we take *order* into account. Such a line arrangement of a number of objects in a definite order is called a *permutation*. It follows, then, that the fundamental principle of counting is a general method for finding the number of permutations of sets of objects. Special formulas have been developed which shorten this general method of counting. We shall deal with them briefly.

At the outset we must get acquainted with factorials. For any positive integer n, the product of the integers from 1 to n is denoted by $n!$ and is called n *factorial*; in symbols

(3.1)
$$n! = n(n-1)(n-2) \cdot \ldots \cdot 3 \cdot 2 \cdot 1 = n(n-1)!$$

Example 3.2.

$$1! = 1,$$
$$2! = 2 \cdot 1 = 2 \cdot 1! = 2,$$
$$3! = 3 \cdot 2 \cdot 1 = 3 \cdot 2! = 6,$$
$$4! = 4 \cdot 3 \cdot 2 \cdot 1 = 4 \cdot 3! = 24,$$
$$6! = 6 \cdot 5 \cdot 4 \cdot 3 \cdot 2 \cdot 1 = 6 \cdot 5! = 720,$$
$$10! = 10 \cdot 9! = 3{,}628{,}800.$$

By special convention the zero factorial equals 1, i.e., $0! = 1$. Observe that factorials increase in size at a fantastic rate, making their computation laborious. For this reason special tables of factorials and their logorithms are available at great convenience (cf. p. 233, reference 10, at end of this chapter).

From (3.1) it is not difficult to deduce that factorials are permutations of n objects taken all together, without repetitions; for it can be easily proved by direct application of the fundamental principle of counting that if a set of different objects is taken all together without repetitions, the number of permutations is $n!$ and is denoted by $P(n, n)$. Thus,

(3.2)
$$P(n, n) = n(n - 1)(n - 2)\cdot\ldots\cdot3\cdot2\cdot1 = n!$$

Example 3.3. Consider a four-member board consisting of individuals A, B, C, and D. The positions of the chairman, treasurer, and secretary are determined in that order by drawing at random from a box containing the letters A, B, C, and D. If letter A is drawn first, individual A becomes the chairman; if letter C is drawn second, individual C becomes the treasurer, and so on. What is the probability that the board's composition will be $ACBD$?

Solution:

The chairman's position can be occupied by any of the 4 board members; after the chairman is chosen, the treasurer's position can be occupied by any of the three remaining board members, and so forth. Hence, by formula (3.2) we have

$$P(4, 4) = 4\cdot3\cdot2\cdot1 = 24$$

possible compositions of the board. Since $ACBD$ is one of them and since positions are filled randomly,

$$P_r(ACBD) = \frac{1}{24}.$$

In the above example we consider the permutations of n different objects from a set of n objects without repetitions, where $n = 4$. Frequently, we may wish to find the number of permutations of r different objects from a set of n objects without repetition, where $r < n$. On the basis of the fundamental principle of counting and by analogy to (3.2) the number of such permutations is

(3.3) $$P(n, r) = n(n - 1)(n - 2) \ldots (n - r + 1),$$

where $r < n$. Multiplying and dividing the right-hand side of (3.3) by $(n - r)!$, we have

$$P(n, r) = \frac{n(n - 1)(n - 2) \ldots (n - r + 1)(n - r)!}{(n - r)!};$$

and since the numerator is the product of all the positive integers from 1 to n, we obtain

(3.4)
$$P(n, r) = \frac{n!}{(n - r)!}.$$

Example 3.4. The manager of a department store has prepared six different displays for the season. The store has three display windows, each accommodating one display each day. The windows are situated in such a way that the order in which the displays are arranged is important. If the season lasts 40 days, does the manager have a sufficient number of display arrangements for the season?

Solution 1:

Since $n = 6$ and $r = 3$, by (3.3), we have

$$P(6, 3) = 6(6 - 1)(6 - 2) = 6 \cdot 5 \cdot 4 = 120,$$

more than enough for the season.

Solution 2:

The same answer can be obtained by substituting $n = 6$ and $r = 3$ in (3.4). Thus,

$$P(6, 3) = \frac{6!}{(6 - 3)!} = \frac{6 \cdot 5 \cdot 4 \cdot 3!}{3!} = 120,$$

as before.

In sum, we have studied three types of permutations: (*a*) *permutations where repetitions are allowed* by direct use of the fundamental principle of counting in Example 3.1; (*b*) *permutations of n things, all taken together without repetitions*, by direct use of the principle in Example 3.1 and by formula (3.2) in Example 3.3; and (*c*) *permutations of n things, taken r at a time without repetitions where* $r < n$, by formulas (3.3) or (3.4) in Example 3.4. The following example is given as a recapitulation of the application of permutations in probability.

Example 3.5. Encouraged by the success of the contest for naming the new product in Example 3.1, the management of ACME plans to advertise the product with the following half-hour television weekly show "Name That Product." Each week five persons, preferably selected from those who participated in the contest, will be interviewed by a well-known comedian on television. During the interview 100 words of the possible 11,025 will be selected and placed in an urn. Then each of the five television guests will draw at random a word from the urn with replacement. Any two or more players who draw the same word will win prizes. Among the things that ACME's mangement wanted to know in estimating the total cost of the show is the probability that at least two among the five guests will win.

Solution:

Since the five drawings will be with replacements, the sample space S of the "experiment" will consist of permutations of five words from a set of 100 words where repetitions are allowed. By the fundamental principle of counting the number of elements in S will be

$$n(S) = 100 \cdot 100 \cdot 100 \cdot 100 \cdot 100 = 100^5 \,.$$

(Observe that S is also specified by the Cartesian product set $S = A \times A \times A \times A \times A$, where $A = \{1, 2, 3, \ldots, 100\}$.)

Let E be the event that at least two of the five television guests have the same word(s). Then E', the complement of E, is the event that all five guests have drawn different words. In this problem it is easier to find $n(E)$ by finding $n(E')$ first. Now $n(E')$ consists of all permutations of five words from a set of 100 words without repetitions since this event occurs when no two guests draw the same word. Since $n = 100$ and $r = 5$, by formula (3.3)

$$n(E') = 100 \cdot 99 \cdot 98 \cdot 97 \cdot 96 = 9{,}034{,}502{,}400 \,,$$

or by formula (3.4),

$$n(E') = \frac{100!}{(100 - 5)!} = \frac{100 \cdot 99 \cdot 98 \cdot 97 \cdot 96 \cdot \cancel{95!}}{\cancel{95!}} = 9{,}034{,}502{,}400 \,.$$

Inasmuch as $E \cap E' = \varnothing$,

$$n(E) + n(E') = n(S)$$

[cf. formula (2.1), Chapter 14], and

$$n(E) = n(S) - n(E') \,.$$

Substituting for $n(S)$ and $n(E')$, we have

$$n(E) = 100^5 - 9{,}034{,}502{,}400$$
$$= 965{,}497{,}600 \,.$$

Hence, by rule 4 (Section 1) the probability that at least two of the five television guests will draw the same word(s) is

$$P_r(E) = \frac{n(E)}{n(S)} = \frac{965{,}497{,}600}{100^5} \approx 0.10 \,.$$

3.3. Combinations. A *selection* of different objects from a set of n objects *without* regard to their *order* is called a *combination*; the number of such combinations is denoted by

$$C(n, r), \quad \text{or} \quad \binom{n}{r},$$

read "number of combinations of n objects, taken r at a time," where $r \leq n$. The following example may help us study the difference between a permutation and a combination.

Example 3.6. Suppose the bylaws of the institution that the four-member board in Example 3.3 serves provide for the appointment of a three-member executive committee to carry out the everyday business of the institution.

Case 1: A box containing the letters A, B, C, and D, representing the four board members, is used to determine with random drawings the three committee members. The person whose name is drawn first has three votes; second, two votes; and third, one vote. What is the probability that the committee's composition is ABC?

Solution:

Since which name is drawn first, second, and third is important, *order counts*; we must specify a sample space S where elements are *permutations* of four persons taken three at a time. By formula (3.4) we have

$$P(4, 3) = \frac{4!}{(4-3)!} = \frac{4 \cdot 3 \cdot 2 \cdot 1}{1!} = 24.$$

The 24 permutations are listed in Table 3.1 in four groups.

TABLE 3.1.

	ABC, ACB	ABD, ADB	ACD, ADC	BCD, BDC
$P(4, 3)$	BAC, BCA	BAD, BDA	CAD, CDA	CBD, CDB
	CAB, CBA	DAB, DBA	DAC, DCA	DBC, DCB
$C(4, 3)$	$\{ABC\}$	$\{ABD\}$	$\{ACD\}$	$\{BCD\}$

Since each of the 24 elements in S is equally likely

$$P_r(ABC) = \frac{1}{24}.$$

Case 2: The same random process for appointing the three committeemen is used as in case 1; but each committee member has equal voting rights. What is the probability that the composition of the committee is again ABC?

Solution:

In this case the *order* in which the committee members are appointed *does not count*; we must specify a sample space S whose elements are *combinations* of four persons taken three at a time. How many combinations are there?

Since order does not count, all six permutations of A, B, and C will form one combination as shown in Table 3.1; all six permutations of A, B, and D will make up one combination, and so on; all told, there are four combinations and

$$P_r(\{A, B, C\}) = \frac{1}{4}.$$

The difference between permutations and combinations must be clear now; we speak of "arrangements" when concerned with permutations since order counts; but we speak of "selections" when interested in combinations since order does not count. Permutations are ordered r-tuples of r objects from a set of n objects; combinations are subsets containing r elements of a set containing n elements. In case 1 of Example 3.6, for instance, ABC and CBA are two ordered three-tuples representing two "different" committees because order of appointments counts, while in case 2 the same committee compositions make *one* set since {A, B, C} = {C, B, A} and *one* committee composition since order of appointments does not count. But how do we know whether permutations or combinations are involved in a particular problem? That depends on whether the nature of the problem indicates that order counts or not.

Observe that each combination in Table 3.1 can be arranged in 3! ways, i.e., in $3 \cdot 2 \cdot 1$ permutations. In order to find the total number of permutations we multiply the number of combinations by the number of permutations that can be arranged from the objects of each combination, in symbols

$$C(4, 3) \cdot 3! = P(4, 3) = 24.$$

In general, the number of permutations of n objects, taken r at a time, is

$$C(n, r) \cdot r! = P(n, r) = \frac{n!}{(n-r)!},$$

where $r \leq n$. Multiplying this equation by $1/r!$, we have

(3.5)
$$C(n, r) = \binom{n}{r} = \frac{n!}{r!(n-r)!}.$$

Example 3.7. Evaluate:

$$C(10, 4) = \binom{10}{4} = \frac{10!}{4!6!} = \frac{10 \cdot 9 \cdot 8 \cdot 7 \cdot \cancel{6!}}{4 \cdot 3 \cdot 2 \cdot 1 \cdot \cancel{6!}} = 210,$$

$$C(5, 1) = \binom{5}{1} = \frac{5!}{1!4!} = 5,$$

$$C(5, 5) = \binom{5}{5} = \frac{5!}{5!0!} = 1,$$

$$C(n, 1) = \binom{n}{1} = \frac{n!}{1!(n-1)!} = n,$$

$$C(n, n) = \binom{n}{n} = \frac{n!}{n!(n-n)!} = 1.$$

Example 3.8. For his forthcoming advertising campaign a manufacturer of toiletries considers two advertisers from each of the following media: newspapers, magazines, radio, and television. In planning his campaign he wants to know, among other things, in how many ways he can select three advertisers from the eight considered:

a) If each advertiser is equally eligible?
Solution:
Since it is clear that order does not count, by formula (3.5) we have

$$C(8, 3) = \frac{8!}{3!5!} = \frac{8 \cdot 7 \cdot 6 \cdot \cancel{5!}}{3 \cdot 2 \cdot 1 \cdot \cancel{5!}} = 56.$$

b) If two advertisers must be selected from the media which use the printed word and one from the media which use the air waves?
Solution:

The two advertisers using the printed word can be selected in $\binom{4}{2}$ ways; after they are selected, the one advertiser using the air waves can be selected in $\binom{4}{1}$ ways; and the number of possible combinations is

$$\binom{4}{2} \cdot \binom{4}{1} = \frac{4!}{2!2!} \cdot \frac{4!}{1!3!} = 6 \cdot 4 = 24.$$

c) If no two advertisers are selected from the same advertising medium?
Solution:
This means that the three advertisers must represent three media; they can be selected in $\binom{4}{3}$ ways. But after the three media are selected, two choices can be made from each medium. Hence, by fomula (3.5) and the fundamental principle of counting we have

$$\binom{4}{3} \cdot 2 \cdot 2 \cdot 2 = \frac{4!}{3!1!} \cdot 8 = 32.$$

3.4. Binomial Coefficients. One important application of formula (3.5) is that $\binom{n}{r}$ can be used to determine the coefficients of a binomial expansion. In illustrating this application we shall be able to further explain the connection of counting techniques with earlier discussions as well as prepare the reader for some optional material in Section 3 of the next chapter.

Consider the familiar sample space for tossing a fair coin twice:

$$S = \{HH, HT, TH, TT\}.$$

For convenience, let $P_r(\{H\}) = p$ and $P_r(\{T\}) = q$, where $q = 1 - p$ since $p + q = 1$. Inasmuch as each toss of the coin represents an independent trial, the probability of two heads in two tosses by the product rule is $P_r(\{HH\}) = p \cdot p = p^2$. In the same way we can obtain the probabilities of the other three simple events of S as shown in Figure 3.1.

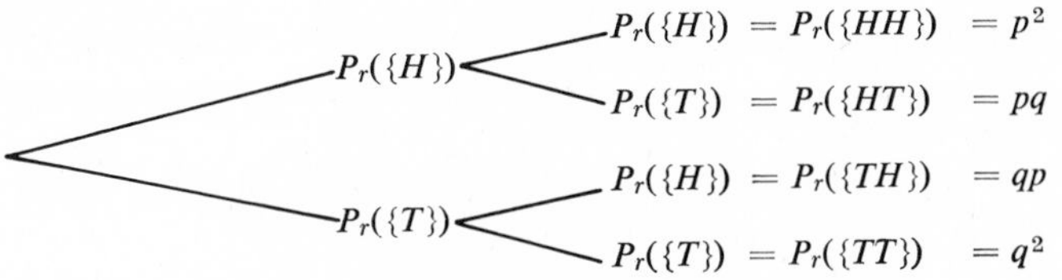

$$P_r(\{H\}) = P_r(\{HH\}) = p^2$$

$P_r(\{H\})$

$$P_r(\{T\}) = P_r(\{HT\}) = pq$$

$$P_r(\{H\}) = P_r(\{TH\}) = qp$$

$P_r(\{T\})$

$$P_r(\{T\}) = P_r(\{TT\}) = q^2$$

FIGURE 3.1.

Observe that the sum of these probabilities represents an expansion of the binomial $(p + q)$ to the second power; in symbols.

(3.6) $\qquad p^2 + pq + pq + q^2 = p^2 + 2pq + q^2 = (p + q)^2 .$

From the viewpoint of counting techniques, the above binomial expansion is important for the coefficient of each term in (3.6) can be determined by applying formula 3.5 as follows:

(3.7) $\qquad (p + q)^2 = \binom{2}{0}p^2 + \binom{2}{1}pq + \binom{2}{2}q^2 .$

Thus, for determining coefficient 1 of the first term p^2 in (3.7) we select none of the outcomes to be tails, i.e., $\binom{2}{0} = \dfrac{2!}{0!2!} = 1$; similarly, for the coefficient 2 of the middle term $2pq$ we select one of the outcomes to be heads and one tails, i.e., $\binom{2}{1} = \dfrac{2!}{1!1!} = 2$; and finally for the last term of (3.7) we select both outcomes to be tails, i.e., $\binom{2}{2} = \dfrac{2!}{2!0!} = 1$.

Observe that the sum of the coefficients $1 + 2 + 1$ equals 4, exactly the number of the simple events in S. The binomial expansion (3.7) can be also written as follows:

(3.8) $\qquad (p + q)^2 = \sum_{r=0}^{2} \binom{2}{r}p^{2-r}q^r .$

The Greek letter Σ (capital sigma) in (3.8) stands for the sum of the terms of (3.7) when $n = 2$ and r varies from 0 through 2. The symbol

$$\sum_{r=0}^{2}$$

means that we are to replace r by 0, 1, and 2, beginning at 0 and ending at 2, thus obtaining the three terms of (3.7) successively, and add the results.

In general, let n be any positive integer. Then

(3.9) $\qquad \boxed{(p + q)^n = \binom{n}{0}p^n + \binom{n}{1}p^{n-1}q + \binom{n}{2}p^{n-2}q^2 + \ldots + \binom{n}{n}q^n,}$

where p and q are any numbers. Instead of giving a formal proof of (3.9), called the *binomial theorem*, we shall explain it. In order to compute $(p + q)^n$ we start by letting $r = 0$ and raising p to the nth power; in fact, q is present since the first term of (3.9) can be written $\binom{n}{0}p^n q^0$ but because $q^0 = 1$, it is omitted. Number $\binom{n}{0}$ is obtained by formula (3.5). Letting $r = 1$ we obtain $\binom{n}{1}p^{n-1}q$, the second term of (3.9), where the power of p is reduced from n to $n - 1$ and the power of q increased from 0 to 1 with the sum of the powers of p and q being equal to n. Subsequent terms of (3.9) are obtained by successively letting $r = 2, 3, \ldots, n$ while the power of p is reduced and of q increased correspondingly, but with the sum of the powers of p and q being always equal to n. The last term of (3.9) is obtained when $r = n$ where $p^0 = 1$ is omitted and q is raised to the nth power. Expression (3.9) can be abbreviated to

(3.10)
$$(p + q)^n = \sum_{r=0}^{n} \binom{n}{r}p^{n-r}q^r,$$

where r varies from 0 through n.

In the binomial theorem p and q can be any numbers. Because we are interested in probabilities, however, we shall consider here the case where $p + q = 1$ and $0 \leqslant p \leqslant 1$. In particular, we are interested in the probability of an event occurring r times in n trials when p is given. Example 3.9 illustrates application of the binomial theorem when $p = q$.

Example 3.9. Find the probability of the following events.
a) All heads in five tosses of a fair coin.
Solution:
Since $p = \frac{1}{2}$, $n = 5$, and $r = 0$ by formula (3.9) we have

$$\binom{n}{r}p^n = \binom{5}{0}\left(\frac{1}{2}\right)^5 = \frac{5!}{0!5!}\left(\frac{1}{32}\right) = \frac{1}{32}.$$

b) At least three tails in five tosses of a fair coin.
Solution:
Let p and q be the probabilities for heads and tails, respectively. Since $p = q = \frac{1}{2}$, $n = 5$, and $r = 3, 4$, or 5 by formula (3.10) we get

$$\sum_{r=3}^{5} \binom{5}{r}p^{5-r}q^r = \binom{5}{3}p^2q^3 + \binom{5}{4}pq^4 + \binom{5}{5}q^5$$

$$= \frac{5!}{3!2!}\left(\frac{1}{2}\right)^2\left(\frac{1}{2}\right)^3 + \frac{5!}{4!1!}\left(\frac{1}{2}\right)\left(\frac{1}{2}\right)^4 + \frac{5!}{5!0!}\left(\frac{1}{2}\right)^5$$

$$= 10\left(\frac{1}{32}\right) + 5\left(\frac{1}{32}\right) + 1\left(\frac{1}{32}\right)$$

$$= \frac{1}{2}.$$

With the above example, where $p = q$, we simply illustrate the mechanistic aspects of applying the binomial theorem to find probabilities for the outcomes of an experiment. In real-world situations, however, cases with $p \neq q$ are likely to be by far more numerous and decidedly more important. Many business operations can or may be described in terms of independent trials where each trial is specified with a sample space containing two outcomes. For example, a machine turns out good or defective parts; an assembly line produces standard or substandard products; the clerks of a mail-order house ship out correctly or incorrectly filled orders; a ledger contains correctly or incorrectly recorded transactions; an inquiring customer purchases or does not purchase the merchandise on display; and so forth and so on. In such situations the binomial formula can be used to determine the probability of an outcome occurring r times in n trials given the probability of occurrence of the outcome.

Example 3.10. An electronic gadget is assembly-produced and then tested unit by unit on a special testing machine. Each unit is automatically classified by the machine as "good" or "defective." The probability p of a unit being classified by the machine as defective, called *average fraction defective*, is 0.10.

a) What is the probability that the testing machine will classify one defective out of five tested units?

Solution:

Since $p = 0.10$ and $q = 1 - p = 0.90$, by (3.8) we have

$$\binom{5}{4}(0.1)(0.9)^4 = \frac{5!}{4!1!}(0.06561) \approx 0.33$$

b) What is the probability that at least one out of five tested units is good?

Solution:

Let E be the above event. It turns out that it is easier to compute $P_r(E')$ and subtract from one as follows:

$$P_r(E') = \binom{5}{0}(0.10)^5 = \frac{5!}{0!5!}(0.10)^5 = 0.00001$$

and $P_r(E) = 1 - 0.00001 = 0.99999$.

The above example illustrates a stochastic process which will be further studied in Section 3 of the following chapter.

And one final item, the numbers $\binom{n}{r}$ in formula (3.5) are called *binomial coefficients* because they appear as coefficients in a binomial expansion. A convenient device for listing and calculating binomial coefficients is the so-called Pascal's triangle. Table 3.2 contains the first few rows of such a triangle. Observe that the first and last coefficients for each value of n are 1 since $\binom{n}{0} = \binom{n}{n} = 1$. Also, each row is symmetric, i.e., the second half of it is a mirror image of the first half, with the point of symmetry on the middle coefficient if n is even and between the two middle coefficients if n is odd. Furthermore, each coefficient in a row is the sum of two coefficients in the preceding row.

TABLE 3.2.

n \ r	0	1	2	3	4	5	6	7	8	9	10
0	1										
1	1	1									
2	1	2	1								
3	1	3	3	1							
4	1	4	6	4	1						
5	1	5	10	10	5	1					
6	1	6	15	20	15	6	1				
7	1	7	21	35	35	21	7	1			
8	1	8	28	56	70	56	28	8	1		
9	.	.	.	.	.	.	.	.	.	.	.
10	.	.	.	.	.	.	.	.	.	.	.

For example, starting with the row of coefficients for $n = 5$ and adding successive pairs, we have $1 + 5 = 6$, $5 + 10 = 15$, $10 + 10 = 20$, $10 + 5 = 15$, and $5 + 1 = 6$, which are the coefficients for $n = 6$. The reader may fill the rows for $n = 9$ and $n = 10$ himself.

PROBLEMS

*3.1. The manager of Quality Foods, a midwestern manufacturer, has decided to use three different sizes of boxes in marketing one of his new cold cereals. He has been advised to use a single bright color as background for each box size in order to maximize consumer's appeal for his product. Six different colors are considered. How many color arrangements can be formed for the three boxes—
    a) If each color can be used for any one of the three box sizes?
    b) If each color cannot be used more than once?

3.2. How many license plates can be made using two letters followed by a four-digit number—
    a) If repetitions are allowed?
    b) If repetitions are not allowed?

3.3. Sometimes one of the tasks for completing a job of permuting different objects from a set of n objects must be performed in a special way. In such a case, it may be advisable to do this special task first.
    a) Suppose the manager in Example 3.4 wants to reserve the third window for two particular displays of the six he has prepared. Does he have now a sufficient number of display arrangements for the season?

    b) Given the digits 1, 2, 3, 4, and 5, how many three-digit odd numbers can be formed from them if repetitions are not allowed?

3.4. Use formula (3.4) to evaluate the following:

    *a) $P(10, 3)$.   *c*) $P(15, 5)$.

    b) $P(50, 2)$.   *d*) $P(100, 5)$.

3.5. Evaluate $P(n, 0)$ and interpret it.

3.6. How many words can be formed from the *different* letters of the word *business*,

    a) All taken together without repetitions?

    b) Taken four at a time without repetitions?

    c) Taken five at a time with repetitions?

3.7. Given the digits 1, 2, and 3, list the two-digit numbers which can be formed—

    *a) When repetitions are allowed.

    b) When repetitions are not allowed.

    c) When repetitions are not allowed and order does not count.

    d) Repetitions are allowed but order does not count.

3.8. A bale of hay, a sheep, and a lion must be ferried by a small rowboat from one bank of a river to the other. However, the man in charge of the ferry service has a problem. The limited capacity of his boat permits the "safe" passage of not more than one of the above three items at a time, while for obvious reasons neither the sheep should be left alone with the bale of hay nor the lion alone with the sheep on either bank of the river. List the pair of items which can be possibly formed and devise a scheme which will allow the "safe" transport of the three items across the river.

*3.9. The manager of "Lakekatatina," an exclusive restaurant in a summer resort, plans four choices for an appetizer, ten choices for the main course, five choices for dessert, and six choices for beverages.

    a) How many different complete dinners are possible if one choice in each case makes a complete dinner?

    b) Suppose each customer represents an independent trial, what is the probability that three customers all will ask for the same complete dinner? for three different dinners? at least two will ask for the same dinner?

3.10. Mario Grandiozo's Pizza Corner offers the following toppings for the plain cheese base of his delicious pizzas: anchovies, mushrooms, onion, pepper, and sausage.

    a) How many different pizzas does he offer his customers?

    b) Suppose each customer represents an independent trial, what is the probability that four customers all will ask for the same pizza? for four different pizzas? at least two will ask for the same pizza?

3.11. An automobile dealer represents a manufacturer who produces five different models of cars; two of the models are produced in four body styles—sedan, hardtop, convertible, and station wagon; three of the models come as sedans and convertibles only; each model is available in six colors.

   a) How many distinguishable types of cars can the dealer have available?

   b) If each customer represents an independent trial, what is the probability that three customers all will buy identical cars; different cars? at least two will buy identical cars?

3.12. Consider the problem in Example 3.5.

   *a) Find the probability that at least two of r guests will win, where $r \leqslant 100$.

   b) By analogy to (a) find the probability that at least two of r people selected at random will have the same birthday, where $n = 365$ and $r \leqslant 365$.

3.13. Use formula (3.5) to evaluate the following:

   *a) $C(10, 3)$.   *c)* $C(15, 5)$.

   b) $C(50, 2)$.   *d)* $C(100, 5)$.

3.14. A building contractor considers hiring five carpenters; twelve apply for the jobs. In how many ways can he select five from the applicants?

*3.15. A personnel manager has five job openings for men only, four job openings for women only, and after filling these openings he has two jobs for men or women. Ten men and six women apply for the jobs. In how many ways can he fill these jobs?

3.16. A railway coach conductor finds that of the 18 passengers in a coach compartment, four refuse to ride facing backward and five refuse to ride facing forward. There are eight seats in the compartment facing backward and ten facing forward. He wishes to know in how many ways the 18 passengers can be seated—

   a) If arrangements are not considered.

   b) If arrangements are considered?

3.17. Apply the binomial theorem to expand—

   a) $(x + y)^7$.   **c)* $(1 - 0.01)^5$.

   b) $(1 - x)^5$.   *d)* $(1 - 2b)^4$.

3.18. Find the binomial coefficient of the following terms in a binomial expansion.

   *a) $p^4 q^5$.   *c)* $p^5 q^5$.

   b) p^9.   *d)* q^{10}.

3.19. The value of $(0.99)^5$ can be approximated by expanding the equivalent binomial $(1 - 0.01)^5$ and summing the terms. Use this method to approximate the value of the following to three decimal places.

   *a) $(1.01)^6$.   *c)* $(1.02)^5$.

   b) $(0.98)^5$.   *d)* $(0.97)^4$.

3.20. Evaluate each sum by expanding and computing individual terms.

   *a) $\sum_{r=0}^{3} 0.2)^{3-r}(0.8)^r$.

$b)$ $\displaystyle\sum_{r=0}^{5} (0.3)^{5-r}(0.7)^r.$

$c)$ $\displaystyle\sum_{r=5}^{7} (0.4)^{7-r}(0.6)^r.$

3.21. A fair coin is tossed six times.
   *$a)$ What is the probability that the number of times it will turn up heads is 0, 1, 2, 3, 4, 5, and 6?
   $b)$ Plot the results of (a) on a cc-plane (x-axis for events, y-axis for probabilities).
   $c)$ Draw a curve through these points and discuss its characteristics.

3.22. A balanced die is rolled five times.
   $a)$ What is the probability that the number of times the die shows 1 or 2 is 0, 1, 2, 3, 4, and 5?
   $b)$ Plot the results of (a) on a cc-plane (x-axis for events, y-axis for probabilities).
   $c)$ Draw a curve through these points and discuss its characteristics.

3.23. In a lot of 50 electronic components 10 are defective. A sample of four components is drawn at random. What is the probability that the sample contains 0, 1, 2, 3, 4 defectives—
   $a)$ If sampling is with replacement?
   $b)$ If sampling is without replacement?
   $c)$ Plot the results (a) and (b) on a cc-plane (x-axis for events, y-axis for probabilities).
   $d)$ Draw a curve through each set of points and compare these curves.

3.24. Find the binomial coefficients in Pascal's triangle. (Table 3.2) for
   $a)$ $n = 9$. $c)$ $n = 11$.
   $b)$ $n = 10$. $d)$ $n = 12$.

3.25. The average fraction defective of a machine *in control* is $p = 0.02$. The manager in charge of production employs the following decision rule. Each hour five parts are selected at random from those produced by the machine during the hour; if more than one of the parts is found defective, he stops and resets the machine; otherwise, the machine is considered to be in control and, hence, permitted to continue producing parts without being reset. What is the probability that the machine needs resetting?

SUGGESTED REFERENCES

1. GOLDBERG, SAMUEL. *Probability: An Introduction*, pp. 54–123, 132–57. Englewood Cliffs, N.J.: Prentice-Hall, Inc., 1960. (**1–3**)

2. GOOD, I. J. "Kinds of Probability," *Science*, Vol. CXXIX, No. 3347 (1959), pp. 443–47. (**1**)

3. KEMENY, JOHN G., *et al. Finite Mathematics with Business Applications*, pp. 99–186. Englewood Cliffs, N.J.: Prentice-Hall, Inc., 1962. (**1–3**)

4. KURNOW, ERNEST, *et al. Statistics for Business Decisions*, pp. 123–47. Homewood, Ill.: Richard D. Irwin, Inc., 1959. **(1–3)**

5. MATHEMATICAL ASSOCIATION OF AMERICA, COMMITTEE ON THE UNDER-GRADUATE PROGRAM. *Elementary Mathematics of Sets with Applications*, pp. 33–66. 1959. **(3)**

6. MODE, ELMER B. *Elements of Statistics*, pp. 87–97, 101–8. Englewood Cliffs, N.J.: Prentice-Hall, Inc., 1961. **(1–3)**

7. MOSTELLER, FREDERICK, *et al. Probability with Statistical Applications*, pp. 19–100. Reading, Mass.: Addison-Wesley Publishing Co., Inc., 1961. **(1–3)**

8. RICHARDSON, M. *College Algebra*, pp. 217–42. Al. ed. Englewood Cliffs, N.J.: Prentice-Hall, Inc., 1958. **(1–3)**

9. SCHLAIFER, ROBERT. *Introduction to Statistics for Business Decisions*, pp. 3–23, 121–35. New York: McGraw-Hill Book Co., Inc., 1961. **(1, 2)**

10. *Standard Mathematical Tables*, p. 233. Cleveland, Ohio: Chemical Rubber Publishing Co., 1959. **(3)**

Chapter 16

ELEMENTS OF BAYESIAN STATISTICS

IN THE two preceding chapters we studied the basic concepts and laws of the mathematical system of probability. This material may serve as a valuable background for both an introductory course in classical as well as in nonclassical or Bayesian statistics.

In this chapter, the last in our course, we shall give a brief account of Bayesian statistics. Bayes' formula is an important part of Bayesian statistics; yet the adjective "Bayesian" does not convey the true nature of this kind of statistics. The term *Bayesian statistics* is used in connection with *a body of quantitative techniques, including Bayes' formula, which are based on a personalistic interpretation of probability.* This is the main distinctive feature which separates Bayesian statistics from classical statistics.

The concepts of random variable, probability function, and expected value are explained in Section 1 of this chapter. This material can serve classical statistics as well; but the discussion here is designed to serve Bayesian statistics. Expected value as a tool for the analysis of decisions under uncertainty occupies Section 2. Finally, Section 3 is devoted to the binomial distribution and an application of this distribution involving the use of Bayes' formula.

*1. ASSESSMENT OF PROBABILITIES; EXPECTED VALUE

We have seen that the personalistic interpretation of probability raises the problem of assessing probabilities. Thus, for an orderly introduction of Bayesian statistics we first show how the probabilities of events may be assessed. Then the concepts of random variable, probability function, and expected value are defined and explained briefly.

1.1. Assessing Probabilities. In discussing the empirical problem of assigning probabilities to events, we pointed out that a subjectivist may assign probabilities to events which may represent a relative frequency of historical data or arbitrary weights reflecting the "intensity of his belief" in the occurrence of an event. But until this point we have refrained from showing how to assess subjective probabilities. Now we shall consider two representative cases: when the historical record includes a sufficient number of observations and when no historical record exists.

In connection with Example 1.1 of the preceding chapter, we said that a subjectivist may assign probabilities based on the retailer's sales record of 100 sales days if he believes that past sales reflect the retailer's hunches and expectations about sales of the item in future. In other words, unless we have reasons to believe that variations in sales can be attributed to specific and identifiable causes such as a storm, an earthquake, a buying rush, a long holiday, and the like, we may *assume* that the historical record is a randomly selected sample from a large number of possible future sales days. This statement requires further explaining.

Example 1.1. An urn contains 500 balls. Each ball has either the number 1, 2, 3, 4, 5, 6, or 7 on it representing the number of sold units of the item during a sales day; but we do not know how many balls of each kind the urn contains.

An experiment consists of drawing at random and with replacement 100 balls from the urn. Their distribution by number of units sold is shown in column 2 of Table 1.1. Suppose we repeat this experiment four additional times with the results shown in columns 3 through 6 of the same table. According to statistical theory the relative frequency shown in column 8 and obtained by combining the outcomes of the five samples can be taken as a close estimate of the actual ball composition in the urn. In fact, it can be shown that the relative frequency which can be obtained from the outcomes of all possible samples of 100 balls selected from 500 balls, will exactly represent the *actual* ball composition in the urn. But the above five samples sufficiently demonstrate our point. A sample of 100 balls drawn at random with replacement can be used to estimate the ball composition in the urn.

TABLE 1.1.

Units Sold (1)	100-day Samples					Total Days (7)	Relative Frequency (8)
	(2)	(3)	(4)	(5)	(6)		
1	5	0	6	3	6	20	0.04
2	8	15	5	10	17	55	0.11
3	25	21	22	18	24	110	0.22
4	27	23	32	29	19	130	0.26
5	20	23	20	25	22	110	0.22
6	8	13	15	9	10	55	0.11
7	7	5	0	6	2	20	0.04
Total	100	100	100	100	100	500	1.00

By analogy the historical sales record may be considered as a sample for estimating future demands for the product.

Observe that the outcome of the first sample in column 2 of Table 1.1 represents the historical sales record in the original example. Thus, the above experiment explains why the probabilities assigned to events at that time were the relative frequency of the historical data. Now we can introduce a refinement. Since variations in sales cannot be attributed to

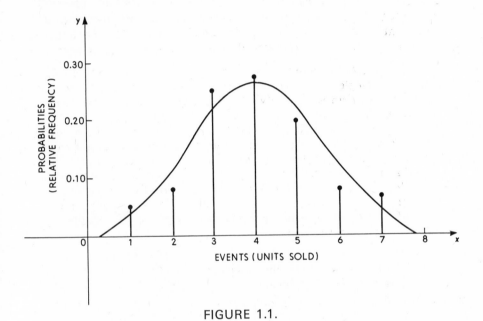

FIGURE 1.1.

assignable causes, we may assess probabilities by smoothing the original historical frequency. On a cc-plane we plot the points representing units sold and the corresponding frequency of each event as shown in Figure 1.1. Such a graph is called a *probability chart*. We draw a smooth freehand curve through these points. The curve is adjusted so that the sum of the smoothed relative weights representing the points on the curve add up to 1. (Why?) The smoothed relative frequency is shown in column 8 of Table 1.1. Thus, the effect of smoothing a frequency is similar to the effect obtained from taking repeated samples from the urn. In the latter case, we can improve our estimate of the ball composition in the urn; in the former case, we hope to obtain a better estimate of future demand.

Smoothing historical frequencies is particularly important if there are gaps in the data which cannot be attributed to assignable causes. In our illustration, however, either the original or the smoothed frequency may be used for further analysis without appreciably different results. Furthermore, whether probabilities are assigned on the basis of the original historical record or on the basis of a smoothed frequency they must reflect the judgment of the decision maker. From the personal-istic point of view, assignment of probabilities is judgmental; and the decision maker's judgment must be based more on an understanding of the real-world situation at hand, his expectations, and his attitude toward risk rather than on statistical theory.

The above observations lead to the other case of assessing probabili-ties, namely, when a decision maker is unwilling to base his probability assignment exclusively on historical data, or better, where a product is new without a previous sales record. Again we resort to an illustration.

Example 1.2. Suppose we are in the position of the retailer in the previous example. Since objective information is either useless or un-available, how can we quantify our "intensity of belief" in the future demand for our product?

Imagine an urn with 100 balls numbered serially from 001, 002, through 100. We can use this urn as a *reference lottery* to quantify our judgment about each sales event. Let E be the event "Tomorrow's demand is four units" and F the event "A ball is drawn from the urn marked 001 through 026." We may be asked to choose one or the other of the two events. If the event we choose occurs, we win a prize; otherwise, we get nothing.

With respect to this game the following three possibilities are open to us. We may believe that—

1. Event E is more likely than event F, i.e., $P_r(E) > P_r(F)$.
2. Event F is more likely than event E, i.e., $P_r(F) > P_r(E)$.
3. Events E and F are equally likely, i.e., $P_r(E) = P_r(F)$.

If we feel that the third possibility represents our best judgment, then $P_r(E) = 0.26$ since from the "reference lottery" $P_r(F) = 0.26$ and the two events are considered equiprobable. Suppose we feel that event E is more likely to occur than event F and choose event E to win. Then we increase the probability of F up to the point where we feel that it is a matter of indifference which event to choose in order to win, and assign the adjusted probability of F to event E since we again consider the events equiprob-able. We do the same thing if we feel that event F should be chosen with the only difference that $P_r(F)$ is adjusted downward until we consider the two events equiprobable.

We repeat the above process until all the simple events in the sample space are assigned probabilities. Then these probabilities are adjusted, if necessary, so that their sum is equal to one.

Of course, we could assign probabilities (judgmental weights) to events directly and without the help of any "yardstick." But the use of a reference lottery may be a valuable aid for quantifying our judgment in assessing probabilities.

For the sake of convenience and economy in our future illustrations we shall consider that the probabilities of the events in a sample space have been assessed.

1.2. Random Variables; Probability Functions.

The previous topic helped us to obtain a clear understanding of the personalistic interpretation of probability; and, at the same time, it prepared the ground for the introduction of the above-mentioned two basic probabilistic concepts.

A function X whose domain is a sample space S and whose range is some set of real numbers $x_1, x_2, x_3, \ldots, x_N$ is called a random variable.

Example 1.3. Consider the familiar sample space

$$S = \{HH, HT, TH, TT\}$$

for tossing a fair coin twice. Let X be the number of tails in an outcome of the experiment. Then

$$X(HH) = 0, \ X(HT) = X(TH) = 1, \ X(TT) = 2,$$

where X is the random variable with domain the sample space S and range the set of real numbers $\{0, 1, 2\}$. Observe that each element of the range of X represents one or more outcomes of the experiment.

It is important to realize that we can define more than one random variable on the same sample space.

Example 1.4. Consider again the sample space

$$S = \{HH, HT, TH, TT\}$$

for tossing a fair coin twice. Let Z be the random variable whose value for any element of S is the number 0 when the two tosses of the coin turn up alike and 1 when they turn up different. Then

$$Z(HH) = Z(TT) = 0 \text{ and } Z(HT) = Z(TH) = 1,$$

where the domain of the random variable Z is the sample space S and the range the set of real numbers $\{0, 1\}$.

Let X be a random variable whose possible values are the real numbers $x_1, x_2, x_3, \ldots, x_N$. Then the probability function f for each value x of X is given by

$$(1.1) \qquad \boxed{f(x) = P_r(X = x).}$$

Example 1.5. Let X be the random variable specified in Example 1.3. Then by (1.1) the probabilities of the possible values of the random variable X are

$$f(0) = P_r(X = 0) = (1)(\tfrac{1}{4}) = \frac{1}{4},$$

$$f(1) = P_r(X = 1) = (2)(\tfrac{1}{4}) = \frac{2}{4},$$

$$f(2) = P_r(X = 2) = (1)(\tfrac{1}{4}) = \frac{1}{4}.$$

Note that the coefficients 1, 2, 1 of the values of function f are the binomial coefficients $\begin{pmatrix} 2 \\ X \end{pmatrix}$ at $X = 0$, 1, and 2. The function f is a set of ordered pairs of numbers which may be conveniently summarized in the following table

$X = x$	0	1	2
$f(x)$	$\tfrac{1}{4}$	$\tfrac{2}{4}$	$\tfrac{1}{4}$

called a *probability table*. The first number in each pair of numbers in this table represents the value of the random variable X denoted by small letter x and the second the probability that X takes on at x.

Let Z be the random variable specified in Example 1.4. Then by (1.1) we obtain

$Z = z$	0	1
$f(z)$	$\tfrac{1}{2}$	$\tfrac{1}{2}$

where z is a given value of random variable Z and $f(z)$ the probability that Z takes on at z.

Example 1.6. Let D be the random variable denoting the demand for the retailer's item shown in column 1 of Table 1.1. Then by (1.1) we have

$D = d$	1	2	3	4	5	6	7
$f(d)$	0.04	0.11	0.22	0.26	0.22	0.11	0.04

where d represents the possible values of the random variable D and $f(d)$ is the probability that D takes on at d.

Let X be a random variable whose values are the real numbers x_1, x_2, $x_3, \ldots, x_N$. Then the cumulative distribution function F for each value x of X on less-than-or-equal-to basis is given by

(1.2)
$$\boxed{F(x) = P_r(X \leqslant x)}$$

and the cumulative distribution function G for each value x of X on more-than-or-equal-to basis is given by

(1.3)
$$\boxed{G(x) = P_r(X \geqslant x).}$$

Example 1.7. Consider the probability function in Example 1.6. From the given probability table and by (1.2), we have

$$F(1) = P_r(X \leqslant 1) = P_r(X = 1) = 0.04,$$

$$F(2) = P_r(X \leqslant 2) = P_r(X = 1) + P_r(X = 2)$$
$$= 0.04 + 0.11$$
$$= 0.15,$$
$$F(3) = P_r(X \leqslant 3) = P_r(X = 1) + P_r(X = 2) + P_r(X = 3)$$
$$= 0.04 + 0.11 + 0.22$$
$$= 0.37,$$

and so on. Continuing in this fashion, we obtain the following *cumulative probability table* for all values of X:

$X \leqslant x$	1	2	3	4	5	6	7
$F(x)$	0.04	0.15	0.37	0.63	0.85	0.96	1.00

Similarly, from the same probability table in Example 1.6 and by (1.3), we have

$$G(7) = P_r(X \geqslant 7) = P_r(X = 7) = 0.04,$$
$$G(6) = P_r(X \geqslant 6) = P_r(X = 6) + P_r(X = 7)$$
$$= 0.11 + 0.04$$
$$= 0.15,$$
$$G(5) = P_r(X \geqslant 5) = P_r(X = 5) + P_r(X = 6) + P_r(X = 7)$$
$$= 0.22 + 0.11 + 0.04$$
$$= 0.37,$$

and so on. Thus we obtain the following distribution table for all values of X:

$X \geqslant x$	1	2	3	4	5	6	7
$G(x)$	1.00	0.96	0.85	0.63	0.37	0.15	0.04

Statisticians often use the term *probability distribution* instead of probability function and *cumulative probability distribution* instead of cumulative distribution function. Also, since the random variable in Examples 1.6 and 1.7 is defined on the original simple events of the sample space, it is often called a *basic* random variable in order to be distinguished from other random variables which may be defined on the same sample space. We shall make use of this terminology in the next two sections of this chapter.

1.3. Expected Value. The *mean* of a random variable is one of the three frequently used measures of central tendency in a probability distribution. Because of our limited objective, the other two measures, namely the *median* and the *mode*, will not be discussed here. We shall concentrate on explaining the mean.

Example 1.8. Let the probability table of the probability function f in Example 1.5 be given:

$X = x$	0	1	2
$f(x)$	$\frac{1}{4}$	$\frac{2}{4}$	$\frac{1}{4}$

Find the mean of the random variable X.

Solution:

Multiplying each value of X by its corresponding probability and adding the products, we have

$$0\left(\frac{1}{4}\right) + 1\left(\frac{2}{4}\right) + 2\left(\frac{1}{4}\right) = 1,$$

which is the mean value of X.

It can be seen that computationally the mean of the above random variable X is not different from the *weighted average* of the possible values of X. For instance, if a student receives 76 points in three quizzes and 81 points in two quizzes in a course, his average grade from the five quizzes will be

$$76\left(\frac{3}{5}\right) + 81\left(\frac{2}{5}\right) = 78 \text{ points.}$$

In a probabilistic sense, however, the notion of the mean of a random variable differs from the notion of the average or arithmetic mean. When we speak of the mean of a random variable we mean that if an experiment is performed a great number of times, then the long-run average is likely or expected to be close to the mean of the random variable defined on the sample space of the experiment. If we repeat the experiment of tossing a coin twice many times, then on the average the number of heads per experiment is expected to be 1, the mean of the random variable X as computed in the above example. Perhaps for this reason the mean of a random variable X is called the *mathematical expectation* or the *expected value* of X.

In general, *let X be a random variable with probability function*

$X = x$	x_1	x_2	x_3	$\cdots$	x_N
$f(x)$	$f(x_1)$	$f(x_2)$	$f(x_3)$	$\cdots$	$f(x_N)$

Then the mathematical expectation of X denoted by $E(X)$, is the number

$$(1.4) \qquad E(X) = x_1 f(x_1) + x_2 f(x_2) + \ldots + x_N f(x_N) = \sum_{i=1}^{N} x_i f(x_i).$$

(The number $E(X)$ is also called by statisticians the *population mean*. It is denoted by the Greek letter μ, read "mew" and spelled "mu.")

Example 1.9. Consider the probability table of function f in Example 1.6:

$D = d$	1	2	3	4	5	6	7
$f(d)$	0.04	0.11	0.22	0.26	0.22	0.11	0.04

Find the expected value $E(D)$.

Solution:

From the above table and by (1.4) we have

$$E(D) = \sum_{i=1}^{7} d_i f(d_i)$$

$$= 1(0.04) + 2(0.11) + 3(0.22) + 4(0.26) + 5(0.22) + 6(0.11) + 7(0.04)$$

$$= 4.$$

Question 1: What does $E(D) = 4$ mean?

Answer:

It means that, although sales may vary from day to day, if a large number of sales days is considered, the average number of units sold per day is expected to be close to four units.

The reader may now be in a position to see how closely expected value is associated, on the one hand, with the empirical problem of assessing probabilities, and on the other hand, with the basic probability function.

Although the next section deals with applications of expected value to business situations, let us conclude this section with a motivating but simple example demonstrating such an application.

Example 1.10. The manager of a machine shop has a choice of competing for one of the two contracts shown in Table 1.2. After deducting all

TABLE 1.2.

Events	Contract A		Contract B	
	Probabilities	*Consequences*	*Probabilities*	*Consequences*
Contract awarded	0.50	+\$3000	0.40	+\$4000
Contract not awarded	0.50	−500	0.60	−700

costs, contract A nets \$3000 and contract B \$4000. The cost of preparing the proposal for contract A is \$500 and for B \$700, which will be a loss to the company if the contract is not awarded. If the probabilities shown in the table are assigned to the two events of each contract, which contract should be preferred?

Solution:

Let X_A be the random variable denoting the monetary consequences for contract A and X_B for contract B, then

$$E(X_A) = 3000(0.50) - 500(0.50) = +1250 \text{ dollars, and}$$

$$E(X_B) = 4000(0.40) - 700(0.60) = +1180 \text{ dollars.}$$

If expected monetary value is considered as an appropriate decision criterion, contract A should be preferred.

PROBLEMS

1.1. In cooperation with four other classmates perform the following experiment: On 100 paper slips write either the number 1, 2, 3, 4, 5, 6, or 7 in proportion to the relative frequency shown in column 8 of Table 1.1. Place the slips of paper in a hat and mix them thoroughly. Each participant should draw 20 paper slips at random and with replacement from the hat, recording the outcome of each drawing and mixing well the paper slips before the next drawing.
a) Prepare a table like Table 1.1 with the results of your experiment.
b) For each of the six relative frequencies (one from each participant and their sum) prepare a probability chart.
c) Draw a smooth freehand curve through the points of the probability chart representing the sum of the five original frequencies.
d) Combine the summary results of all the groups in your class and do (b) and (c).
e) Discuss your findings in (a) through (d).

1.2. In cooperation with four other classmates perform the following experiment: each person participating in the experiment should flip a coin ten times and record the number of heads the coin turns up in these ten trials; repeat this experiment nine more times. Thus, each participant will obtain a frequency distribution of the number of heads obtained from the ten repetitions of the experiment. Then answer (a), (b), (c), (d), and (e) described in Problem 1.1.

1.3. Secure the cooperation of a businessman and use the reference lottery device to obtain a probability function for one of his products. Whether you succeed or not in this attempt, write a short report of your findings and discuss your experience.

1.4. Construct a probability chart and draw a freehand smooth curve through the plotted points for the following probability functions:
a) The functions of X and Z in Example 1.5.
b) The function of D in Example 1.6.

1.5. If the points of a cumulative distribution function are plotted on a cc-plane and a smooth freehand line is drawn through the plotted points, the curve so obtained is called *ogive*. Obtain ogives for the following cumulative distribution functions in Example 1.7:
a) The function $F(x)$.
b) The function $G(x)$.

*1.6. Suppose the historical sales record of an item consists of extremely sparse data such as shown below:

Demand (Units Sold) (1)	Frequency (Days) (2)	Relative Frequency (3)	Cumulative Long-run Ratios (4)
8.........1		0.10	1/11
10.........1		0.10	2/11
13.........1		0.10	3/11
16.........1		0.10	4/11
17.........1		0.10	5/11
18.........1		0.10	6/11
20.........1		0.10	7/11
25.........1		0.10	8/11
29.........1		0.10	9/11
36.........1		0.10	10/11
Total	10	1.00	

Imagine an urn with 11,000 balls representing an equal number of sales days. The balls are arrayed in order of number of units sold and given a rank number so that the day with the smallest demand will have rank 1 and with the largest rank 11,000. Balls representing identical sales are ranked arbitrarily among themselves. It can be proved that if a sample of ten balls is drawn from the urn at random, the *expected* rank number of the ball with the lowest ranking in the sample will be 1000, the second-lowest 2000, and so on, and the ball with the highest ranking 10,000. This means that the smallest demand in a random sample of ten sales days is a reasonable estimate of the $\frac{1}{11}$, the second smallest of the $\frac{2}{11}$, and the highest of $\frac{10}{11}$ long-run ratio of the demand for the item as shown in column 4 above.

On the basis of the above experiment do the following:

a) Construct a less-than-or-equal-to cumulative probability table from columns 1 and 4.

b) Plot the values of that table on a cc-plane, where the *x*-axis denotes demand and the *y*-axis cumulative probabilities. Then fit a smooth freehand curve through the plotted points.

c) Prepare a cumulative and noncumulative probability table representing the smooth relative frequencies when demand is 10, 15, 20, 25, 30, and 35 units.

1.7. An experiment consists of rolling two dice. Let X be the random variable whose value for any outcome of the experiment is the sum of the numbers on the two dice.

a) Find and present the probability function of X in a probability table and in a probability chart.

b) Find $F(x)$ and $G(x)$, where functions F and G are defined by (1.2) and (1.3), respectively, and present each in a cumulative probability table.

c) Find $E(X)$ and explain its meaning.

*1.8. Let the random variable X in Problem 1.7 denote the gain or loss of a player who wins \$5.00 if the sum on the two dice is 2, 3, 11, or 12; wins \$4.00 if the sum is 4, 5, 9, or 10; and loses \$2.00 if the sum is 6, 7, or 8.

    a) Find the probability function of X and present it in a probability table and in a probability chart.

    b) What is the fair price for playing the game?

1.9. Three fair coins are tossed once. Let X be the random variable denoting the number of heads.

    *a) Find the probability function of X using the binomial formula (3.8) in Chapter 15.

    b) Construct a probability table and chart.

    c) Find $F(2)$ and $G(3)$, where function F and G are defined by (1.2) and (1.3), respectively.

    d) Find $E(X)$.

1.10. Three balls are drawn with replacement from an urn containing 1000 balls whose composition is shown in Table 2.1 of Chapter 15. Let the random variable X denote the number of respondents who are planners and buyers.

    a) Find and present the probability function of X in a probability table and in a probability chart.

    b) Find $F(X)$ and $G(X)$, where functions F and G are defined by (1.2) and (1.3), respectively, and present each in a cumulative probability table.

1.11. In a lot of ten items two are defective. A sample of four items is drawn at random. Let the random variable X denote the number of defective items in the sample. Answer the following when the sample is drawn (i) with replacement and (ii) without replacement.

    a) Find and present the probability function in a probability table and in a probability chart.

    b) Find $P_r(X \leqslant 1)$, $P_r(X \geqslant 1)$, $P_r(0 < X < 2)$.

    c) Find $E(X)$ and explain its meaning.

1.12. Consider the annual income of the following five individuals:

Persons	A	B	C	D	E
Income ($1000)	4	4	5	6	6

A committee of k individuals is selected from the five available, where $k = 1, 2, 3, 4, 5$. Let the random variable X denote the average income of the k individuals in the committee.

    a) Find and present the probability function of X for *each k* in a probability table and chart.

    b) Discuss the changes in the five probability functions in (*a*) as k increases. What is $E(X_k)$?

*1.13. Every year an organization conducts a lottery with a car costing \$3600 as a prize. If 2000 lottery tickets are expected to be sold, what is a fair price for a ticket?

1.14. A roulette player receives $36 for every dollar he bets on a winning number. If the wheel has 37 numbers 0, 1, 2, . . . , 36, is the game fair to the player? Why or why not?

1.15. The management of Puritan, a company operating a chain of dairy bars, plans to build a new unit in either of two locations. Management figures that the probability of the new unit being successful in location A is $\frac{3}{4}$ and that if it is successful it will bring an annual profit of $4000. If it is not successful, however, the management expects to lose $2000 a year. The probability of the unit succeeding in location B is only $\frac{1}{2}$ with $7000 annual expected profit. If the unit in location B turns out to be a failure, the annual loss is expected to amount to $2300.

a) Where should the company locate the unit?

b) Suppose the probability of success in location B is $\frac{5}{8}$, would this probability change management's decision in (*a*)?

*1.16. An automobile dealer believes that for the forthcoming new models he will sell three times as many compact as regular-size cars.

a) If the average selling price of a compact is $2200 and that of a regular $3200, what are his expected receipts per sale?

b) If he also believes that he will sell a car to 5 percent of the people who visit his showroom, what are his expected receipts per visitor?

1.17. A retail store manager plans to invest $1000 in order to obtain greater diversification of his inventory. If the workers of the only large manufacturing company in town do not go on strike, he expects to earn 2 percent a month from this investment; but if there is a strike, earnings are likely to fall to a loss of 1 percent monthly. For borrowing the $1000 he must pay an annual interest rate of 6 percent.

a) What probability should the retailer assign to the strike in order to break even with the cost of borrowing?

b) If the probability of a strike is 70 percent, what should the return from this investment be in order to break even?

1.18. In Example 2.4 of Chapter 6, we have shown how the management of Continental Rubber and Tire Company arrived at a sales forecast of $5.65 million. In order to double check this forecast, the marketing research department of the company compiled the following information. For each of the past 12 years realized dollar sales were expressed as percent of forecast sales, as shown below in a frequency distribution:

Actual as Percent of Forecast Sales	Frequency
95	1
96	2
101	4
105	3
109	2

a) What is the expected actual to forecast sales ratio?

b) In the light of your finding in (*a*), should original forecast sales be adjusted and by how much?

*2. EXPECTED VALUE AS A DECISION CRITERION

In the previous section we explained carefully expected value. This was necessary since, as we have seen in Example 1.10 of that section, this measure of central tendency can be used as a criterion for making decisions under uncertainty. In this section we shall show applications of expected value to business situations in a systematic way.

From the outset we must distinguish between *expected monetary value* and *expected utility*; and we must explain under what conditions each can be used as an appropriate guide for making decisions. After clarifying this crucial point, we shall show how expected profit, expected opportunity loss, and the critical ratio analysis can be used under either expected monetary value or expected utility to solve inventory problems which take into consideration the element of uncertainty.

2.1. Expected Monetary Value and Expected Utility.

The amount of risk that a person is willing to assume is a matter of personal preference. Suppose we are given the opportunity to win $1.00 if we correctly guess the outcome of tossing a fair coin; but we lose $0.50 if we guess wrong. A hungry person with only $0.50 in his pocket most likely may refuse to play the game; though the expected monetary value of this game is $1.00(0.50) − $0.50(0.50) = $0.25, the 0.50-0.50 chance that he may lose the only means of satisfying his pressing need may be overwhelming. But most people may be willing to bet since the loss of $0.50 is small compared with their resources and since they expect to win twice as much as they may lose. Suppose now that the stakes are raised to $1000 and $500, respectively. For most persons the 50 percent chance of losing $500 may be so important that they would rather do nothing than bet, although the expected monetary value for the game now is $250, or 1000 times greater than previously. In fact, if the stakes are raised sufficiently high, even a millionaire may refuse to bet.

The above illustration suggests that for a given person the importance attached to the use of money, called *utility*, is numerically equal to monetary value up to a given amount, even though such an amount may differ from one individual to another. In other words, in such a case utility is a linear function of monetary value. For sums greater than that given amount the utility of money is not a linear function of its monetary value. Then utility rather than monetary value becomes an appropriate measure of an individual's attitude towards risk; and it follows that expected value actually represents two criteria: *expected monetary value* and *expected utility*, hereafter abbreviated to "EMV" and "EXU," respectively, for convenience. This is an important distinction. It raises two crucial questions which we shall study immediately.

First, under what conditions is EMV an appropriate guide for making decisions? Of course, we can readily answer that as long as in the decision maker's opinion the utility of the amounts at stake is numerically equal to the monetary value of such amounts, then EMV is an appropriate criterion. But this answer is not satisfactory. It does not tell us how we can test that EMV is an appropriate guide. An example may illustrate how this can be done.

Example 2.1. The manager of the machine shop in Example 1.10 of the previous section chose EMV as a decision criterion. This choice may be explained by the fact that the probable loss of $500 is a relatively small amount compared with the amounts at stake in the normal course of his business. But how can we test that he has indeed chosen the correct criterion?

First, we must determine what the best and worst consequences are for the entire problem. If the manager decides to submit a proposal for contract A, the best and worst possible consequences are $+\$3000$ and $-\$500$, respectively; these consequences are also the best and worst for the entire problem inasmuch as the consequences of the alternative—not submitting the proposal—is certain to be zero dollars.

Second, we may ask the manager the following question: "Suppose you have a choice either to receive a specified amount of cash or be awarded contract A with $E(X) = \$1250$, would you (a) prefer the contract rather than the cash if the cash was less than $1250 and (b) prefer the cash rather than the contract if the cash was more than $1250?" If the manager answers yes to both questions, then it is almost certain that EMV is an appropriate criterion.

Although in principle the manager must be asked whether he would answer in the affirmative *any* questions of the above kind when *any* probability is assigned to the $3000 net earnings, usually another repetition of the above test will be sufficient to verify the manager's choice. For instance, we may ask the manager the following question: "Let us assume that you have already signed contract A, but with probabilities 0.10 and 0.90 assigned to $+\$3000$ and $-\$500$, respectively, so that EMV now for the contract is $-\$150$, would you (a) prefer to pay any amount of cash less than $150 for a contract release rather than carry out the contract and (b) prefer to carry out the contract rather than pay any amount greater than $150 for a contract release?" If he answers yes again to both questions we must be quite sure that the manager's utility function is linear and therefore using EMV as a decision criterion was the correct choice.

The above test can be applied to any decision problem involving more than two consequences. In general, for applying this test we must first determine the best and the worst consequences of the entire problem and then ask the decision maker questions of the kind described in the above example. His answers must be consistently in the affirmative. If his answer to any of these questions is negative, then there is indication that EMV is not an appropriate criterion; and such a case leads us to the second question.

If EXU rather than EMV is an appropriate decision criterion, how can we construct a utility curve in order to solve a decision problem? Though utility may not be directly measurable, we may be able to obtain a measure of it indirectly. If utility represents the importance an individual attaches to the use of money, utility must reflect his attitude toward risk under conditions of uncertainty. Thus, we may be able to construct an individual's utility schedule by observing his bets on a *reference lottery* as the following example illustrates:

Example 2.2. Let us assume that the manager of the machine shop in the previous example is confronted with the problem of deciding whether to bid for contract X or contract Y shown in Table 2.1. Let X_m and Y_m

TABLE 2.1.

	Contract X			Contract Y	
Events	Probabilities	Consequences (X_m)	Events	Probabilities	Consequences (Y_m)
A	0.25	+$30,000	D	0.20	+$35,000
B	0.45	+ 20,000	E	0.50	+ 10,000
C	0.30	− 25,000	F	0.30	− 15,000

be the random variables denoting the consequences of contracts X and Y, respectively. If EMV were an appropriate decision criterion, the manager should choose contract X since $E(X_m) = \$9000$, while $E(Y_m) = \$7500$. But because of limited working capital, the EMV test shows that the manager's utility function is nonlinear when such large amounts are at stake. Hence, for this problem EXU is rather an appropriate decision criterion. In order to apply this criterion we must assign utilities to the consequences of the decision problem; and, in order to do that, we must construct the manager's utility curve.

First, we set up a *reference lottery*. An urn contains a number of balls, some of them marked "win $35,000" and the remaining "lose $25,000," where the first amount represents the best and the second the worst consequences of the entire problem. A ticket entitles the holder of it to draw a ball from the urn at random. He wins or loses the amount indicated on the drawn ball.

Second, we establish a unit measuring utility. We may ask the manager the following question: "What would you consider as a fair price for a lottery ticket?" He may state an amount, say $11,000. Let p be the probability of winning $35,000. If $11,000 is a fair price for a ticket, then

$$35,000p + (1 - p)(-25,000) = 11,000 \text{ dollars}$$

and $p = 0.60$. Thus, the above question is equivalent to asking the manager: "What proportion of balls in the urn would you mark 'win $35,000' so that you would be just indifferent as to whether to buy a lottery ticket or not?" Since $p = 0.60$ reflects the manager's attitude toward risk, it may be taken as a measure to his utility of money. In order to avoid confusing utility with probability we may express it in terms of utility units, called *utiles*. Thus, multiplying 0.60 by 100, we have 60 utiles.

Third, we construct a utility curve for the manager. We have found that when $p=0.60$ the manager is indifferent as to whether to buy a lottery ticket, i.e., bid on *either* contract, or not buy a ticket, i.e., bid on *neither* contract. Hence, the two acts are equivalent and, in the manager's opinion, the consequence zero dollars for not bidding on either contract is worth 60 utiles. Point (0, 60) is plotted on a cc-plane shown in Figure 2.1, where

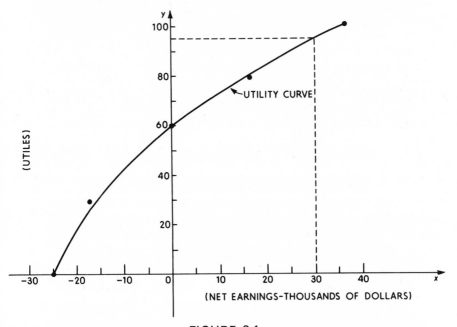

FIGURE 2.1.

the x-axis represents net earnings in thousands of dollars and the y-axis utility in utiles. Of course, the higher the proportion of winning balls in the urn, the higher the value of the lottery ticket; and if the urn contains only winning balls, $P_r(\$35,000)=1.00$ and $+\$35,000$ is worth 100 utiles. Similarly, the lower the proportion of winning balls in the urn, the lower the value of the lottery ticket; and if the urn contains no winning but only losing balls, $P_r(\$35,000)=0$ and $-\$25,000$ is worth 0 utiles. Points (35,000, 100) and (−25,000, 0) are plotted as shown in Figure 2.1. Then we may ask the manager "Suppose 50 percent of the balls in the urn are marked 'win \$35,000' and 50 percent 'lose \$0' what would you consider as a fair price for a lottery ticket?" He may answer that \$16,000 would be a fair price. Since we have found that the utility of \$35,000 is 100 utiles and of \$0 is 60 utiles, then the expected utility of \$16,000 is

$$(0.50)(60) + (0.50)(100) = 80 \text{ utiles.}$$

Similarly, we may ask, "Suppose 50 percent of the balls in the urn are marked 'lose $25,000' and 50 percent 'win $0,' what would you consider as a fair payment to you in order to play this game?" He may say that losing $25,000 may put him in such a tight financial position that he would be unwilling to bet unless he is paid $17,500. Since the utility of $-$25,000$ is 0 utiles and of $0 is 60 utiles, the expected utility of $-$17,500$ is

$$(0.50)(0) + (0.50)(60) = 30 \text{ utiles.}$$

Plotting the points $(16,000, 80)$ and $(-17,500, 30)$ as shown in Figure 2.1 and drawing a freehand smooth line through the five available points, we obtain the required utility curve. From this utility curve we can get the utilities that the manager would like to assign to all the consequences of his problem. For instance, for finding his utility for event A with $30,000 consequences we start upward following the broken line and to the left as shown in Figure 2.1. At the point where the broken line meets the y-axis we read 95 utiles, which is the manager's utility for $30,000. Table 2.2 shows the utilities which in this way can be assigned to all the consequences of the manager's problem. Let X_u and Y_u be the random variables denoting utilities for the consequences of contracts X and Y, respectively. Then

$$E(X_u) = 95(0.25) + 85(0.45) + 0(0.30) = 62 \text{ utiles}$$

and

$$E(Y_u) = 100(0.20) + 73(0.50) + 32(0.30) = 66.10 \text{ utiles.}$$

Since $E(Y_u) > E(X_u)$, the manager should submit a proposal for contract Y and not for contract X as we have found earlier by applying the EMV criterion.

TABLE 2.2.

	Contract X			Contract Y	
Events	Probabilities	Consequences (X_u, Utiles)	Events	Probabilities	Consequences (Y_u, Utiles)
A	0.25	95	D	0.20	100
B	0.45	85	E	0.50	73
C	0.30	0	F	0.30	32

A manager need not test the extreme consequences of every decision problem in order to find whether EMV or EXU is an appropriate criterion. Depending on the size of his working capital and the nature and condition of his operation, he may determine the maximum best and worst consequences for which he considers EMV to be an appropriate criterion; and he can delegate the solution of routine problems involving amounts below these maxima to his subordinates while he concentrates on problems whose amounts at stake require the application of the EXU criterion.

2.2. Expected Profit and Expected Opportunity Loss.

In the remaining part of this section we shall show how expected value can be used in solving inventory problems when the demand is not certain. In demonstrating this method we shall use the EMV criterion; but the same method is equally applicable when the maxima consequences at stake justify the application of the EXU criterion. Since our immediate concern is to introduce the method rather than to handle complex problems, we shall use a simple yet not entirely unrealistic situation.

Example 2.3. A retailer handles a perishable commodity which costs $1.00 and sells for $3.00 a unit. Since the commodity is worthless if not sold by the end of the day it is stocked, the retailer is forced to place an order for the item daily. This situation creates a problem, however. For if daily demand is greater than the ordered stock, his foregone gross profit is $2.00 per unit of unsatisfied demand let alone the possible loss of customer goodwill. If daily demand is less than the ordered stock, he loses $1.00 per overstocked unit. For the past 40 days demand for the commodity had been as follows:

Demand	0	1	2	3	4	5	(units)
Sales Days	4	6	12	10	6	2	(number)

The first step in analyzing a problem of this kind is to determine the net cash inflow, gross profit in our example, for each stock level. In short, if a given number of units is stocked, what is the net cash inflow for every number of units demanded? Let the random variable D denote the number of units demanded and Q a constant representing the number of units stocked. Then the net cash inflow of gross profit R can be determined by the function

$$(2.1) \qquad R(D) = \begin{cases} \$3D - \$1Q & \text{if} \quad D \leqslant Q \\ \$2Q & \text{if} \quad D > Q. \end{cases}$$

Example 2.3—*Continued.* The probability distribution obtained from the given data is shown in the first two columns of Table 2.3. The other entries in the body of this table represent the gross profit which the retailer will realize under each stock level and for each value of D. These entries are determined by substituting for D and Q in (2.1).

Let $Q = 0$. Then since no profit can be made without available stock, $R(D) = 0$ for all values of D. Let $Q = 1$. Then for $D = 0$ we get

$$R(0) = \$3(0) - \$1(1) = -\$1,$$

a loss representing the cost of stocking one unit; and for $D \geqslant 1$ we obtain

$$R(1) = \$3(1) - \$1(1) = +\$2,$$
$$R(2) = \$2(1) \qquad\qquad = +\$2,$$

and so forth as summarized in Table 2.3 under $Q = 1$. The reader may apply (2.1) to verify the gross profit entries for $Q = 2, 3, 4,$ and 5.

Observe that Table 2.3 contains the gross profit consequences of all possible outcomes of the problem. Such a table, without the relative frequencies, is called a *payoff table*. Since each profit entry in the payoff table is determined on the *condition* that a particular event will occur,

TABLE 2.3.

Events	*Probabilities*	*Stock Level*					
Demand D	$f(d) = P_r(D = d)$	$Q = 0$	1	2	3	4	5
0	0.10	$0*	−$1	−$2	−$3	−$4	−$5
1	0.15	0	+2*	+1	0	−1	−2
2	0.30	0	+2	+4*	+3	+2	+1
3	0.25	0	+2	+4	+6*	+5	+4
4	0.15	0	+2	+4	+6	+8*	+7
5	0.05	0	+2	+4	+6	+8	+10*
	1.00						

such a profit is called *conditional profit*. Also, it may be noted that only costs and revenues which are affected by changes of the stock level and of the demanded units are included in the analysis.

The second step consists of computing the *expected profit* for each stock level. The optimal stock level $Q*$ is the one with the largest expected profit.

Example 2.3—*Continued.* Let the random variable R_q denote the conditional profit when the stock level $Q = 0, 1, 2, 3, 4, 5$. Then from Table 2.3 we have

$$E(R_0) = 0(0.10) + 0(0.15) + 0(0.30) + 0(0.25) + 0(0.15) + 0(0.05) = 0,$$
$$\text{dollars.}$$
$$E(R_1) = -1(0.10) + 2(0.15) + 2(0.30) + 2(0.25) + 2(0.15) + 2(0.05) =$$
$$= 1.70 \text{ dollars.}$$

and so forth for $Q = 2, 3, 4,$ and 5 as summarized in Table 2.4. Since $E(R_q) = \$3.30$ is the largest expected profit, the optimal stock level is $Q* = 3$; and the retailer should order three units daily.

Note that in obtaining the above answer we used a *probability model* where, for a given stock level, the historical record of demand is conceived as a random process generating conditional profit outcomes. But randomness implies that the occurrence of future daily demand, like the outcome in rolling a die, is the result of an independent trial. Thus, in applying the model we assume that the demand of a particular day does not depend on the demand of the preceding or the following days. Furthermore, the demand for the commodity in question neither affects nor is it affected by the sale of other items in the store. In spite of these limitations, however, real-world situations may be found where the model can be advantageously applied as a first approximation; and the above qualifications may be introduced judgmentally in interpreting the results.

TABLE 2.4.

Stock Level Q	Expected Profit $E(R_q)$
0	$0
1	1.70
2	2.95
3*	3.30
4	2.90
5	2.05

A clearer understanding and appreciation of this model as an analytical tool for making decisions under uncertainty requires the introduction of the concept of *expected opportunity loss*; and in order to introduce this concept we must explain the meaning of conditional opportunity loss.

Example 2.4. Consider the payoff table in Table 2.3. If the retailer stocks three units and demand turns out to be three units then he has lost nothing; he has made the maximum profit he could have made when demand is for three units. If, however, demand turns out to be four units, the retailer loses the $2.00 profit he could have realized had he stocked four units. Since the retailer missed the *opportunity* of making $2.00, this foregone profit is called *conditional opportunity loss*.

From the above example we can see that foregone profit is zero when the retailer guesses correctly what the next day's demand will be, or equivalently when he has perfect information about future demand. It is a *positive* number, representing foregone profit in the above case, when the retailer has imperfect information. Thus, for a given number of units demanded the *conditional opportunity loss of a stock level may be defined as the difference between the conditional profit of that stock level and the conditional profit with perfect information.* This definition suggests a quick way of finding the conditional opportunity loss for all outcomes in a problem.

Example 2.4—*Continued.* In Table 2.3 the conditional profit with perfect information for each event is marked with an asterisk. We can obtain the conditional opportunity loss for each row if we subtract algebraically each conditional profit in that row from the starred number. For instance, when—

$D = 0$	$D = 1$	$D = 2$
$0^* - (0^*) \; = 0$	$2^* - (0) \quad = 2$	$4^* - (0) \; = 4$
$0^* - (-1) = 1$	$2^* - (2^*) \; = 0$	$4^* - (2) \; = 2$
$0^* - (-2) = 2$	$2^* - (1) \quad = 1$	$4^* - (4^*) = 0$
$0^* - (-3) = 3$	$2^* - (0) \quad = 2$	$4^* - (3) \; = 1$
$0^* - (-4) = 4$	$2^* - (-1) = 3$	$4^* - (2) \; = 2$
$0^* - (-5) = 5$	$2^* - (-2) = 4$	$4^* - (1) \; = 3$

and so forth for $D = 3, 4,$ and 5, as summarized in Table 2.5.

TABLE 2.5.

Demand D	Probabilities $f(d) = P_r(D = d)$	Stock Level					
		$Q = 0$	1	2	3	4	5
0	0.10	$0*	$1	$2	$3	$4	$5
1	0.15	2*	0	1	2	3	4
2	0.30	4*	2	0	1	2	3
3	0.25	6*	4	2	0	1	2
4	0.15	8*	6	4	2	0	1
5	0.05	10*	8	6	4	2	0
	1.00						

The expected opportunity loss can be very easily found from the conditional opportunity loss of all outcomes of a problem.

Example 2.4—*Continued.* Let the random variable L_q denote the conditional opportunity loss when the stock level $Q = 0, 1, 2, 3, 4,$ and 5. Then from Table 2.5 we have

$$E(L_0) = 0(0.10) + 2(0.15) + 4(0.30) + 6(0.25) + 8(0.15) + 10(0.05)$$
$$= 4.70 \text{ dollars},$$

$$E(L_1) = 1(0.10) + 0(0.15) + 2(0.30) + 4(0.25) + 6(0.15) + 8(0.05)$$
$$= 3.00 \text{ dollars},$$

and so forth for $Q = 2, 3, 4,$ and 5. The results are shown in Table 2.6.

TABLE 2.6.

Stock Level Q	Expected Opportunity Loss $E(L_q)$
0	$4.70
1	3.00
2	1.75
3*	1.40
4	1.80
5	2.65

It is important to note that expected opportunity loss in Table 2.6 is smallest when the optimal number of units are stocked, i.e., when

$Q^* = 3$. Furthermore, the results in this table can be advantageously used to decide whether an immediate decision should be made for optimal stocking or additional information should be obtained in order to improve our forecast. From the way the payoff table of conditional opportunity losses is obtained we can conclude that such losses for $Q = 0$, the numbers marked with an asterisk in Tables 2.3 and 2.5, represent the conditional profit with perfect information for each stock level. Thus, $E(L_0) = \$4.70$ is also the expected profit when the retailer has perfect knowledge of future demand. The difference between the expected profit of the optimal stock level under uncertainty, \$3.30 in our example, and the expected profit of the optimal stock level under certainty, \$4.70 in our case, is called the *cost of uncertainty* or *the expected value of perfect information (EVPI)*. Observe that EVPI equals \$1.40, the expected opportunity loss for $Q^* = 3$. Thus, by computing $E(L_q)$ rather than $E(R_q)$ we can determine simultaneously (*a*) the optimal stock level Q^* and (*b*) EVPI. The cost of uncertainty can be a useful guide to determining whether it is worthwhile to obtain additional information about the demand of a product before the final decision is reached about Q^*.

2.3. Critical Ratio Analysis.

The preceding presentation was designed to convey the concepts associated with using expected value as a criterion for making decisions under uncertainty. In many real-world inventory problems, however, the random variable "demand" will have values running into hundreds or even thousands with an equal number of stock level possibilities. Obviously, analysis of such a problem with the payoff table technique is unsuitable. We must find the *critical ratio* on the basis of which the optimal stock level Q^* can be quickly determined.

Let us consider again the retailer's demand in Example 2.3. We have seen that in the case of *underage*, i.e., when the retailer fails to stock one unit which could have been sold, the opportunity loss, heretofore called *loss* for convenience, is \$2.00. In the case of *overage*, i.e., when the retailer stocks one unit which cannot be sold, the loss is \$1.00. Let j denote the serial number of any incremental increase in demand for the commodity, where $j = 1, 2, 3, 4, 5$. The probability that the jth unit is demanded is equivalent to the probability that the total quantity demanded will be j or more units, i.e., equivalent to $P_r(D \geqslant j)$. Similarly, the probability that the jth unit will not be demanded is the same as the probability that the total quantity demanded will be less than j units, i.e., $P_r(D < j)$. Then for the jth unit the expected loss of underage will be $\$2P_r(D \geqslant j)$ and of overage $\$1P_r(D < j)$. This incremental analysis is conveniently summarized in Table 2.7. Observe that the total expected loss for the jth stock level is the sum of the incremental expected losses $\$1P_r(D < j)$ from column 5 and $\$2P_r(D \geqslant j)$ from column 3. For instance, let the stock level $j = 3$ units. Then the total expected loss is

$$[\$1(0.10) + \$1(0.25) + \$1(0.55)] + [\$2(0.20) + \$2(0.05)] = 1.40 \text{ dollars}.$$

exactly as found previously (Table 2.6).

TABLE 2.7.

Demand (D) of the jth Unit (1)	$P_r(D \geqslant j)$ (2)	Expected Loss of Underage $\$2P_r(D \geqslant j)$ (3)	$P_r(D < j)$ (4)	Expected Loss of Overage $\$1P_r(D < j)$ (5)
1	0.90	$1.80	0.10	$0.10 ⎤
2	0.75	1.50	0.25	0.25 ⎬
3	0.45	0.90	0.55	0.55 ⎦
4	0.20	0.40 ⎤	0.80	0.80
5	0.05	0.10 ⎦	0.95	0.95
6	0	0	1.00	1.00

Also, note that as demand increases the expected loss of underage decreases, while the expected loss of overage increases. This indicates that for every additional unit stocked total expected loss will keep decreasing until the point where the expected loss of overage for stocking one more unit exceeds the expected loss of underage for stocking that additional unit. For instance, the retailer in our example will keep increasing his stock to $Q = 3$; and he will stock no additional units since the expected loss of overage for stocking the fourth unit is $0.80, which is more than the expected loss of underage, $0.40. In general, let C_u be the loss of underage and C_o the loss of overage. Then the optimal stock level Q^* is where

$$(2.2) \qquad C_o P_r(D < j) < C_u P_r(D \geqslant j).$$

Since $P_r(D \geqslant j) = 1 - P_r(D < j)$, substituting in (2.2) and transposing terms we have

$$C_o P_r(D < j) < C_u [1 - P_r(D < j)],$$

$$P_r(D < j)[C_u + C_o] < C_u,$$

and the critical ratio for Q^* is

$$(2.3) \qquad \boxed{P_r(D < j) < \frac{C_u}{C_u + C_o}.}$$

Example 2.5. Since in our retailer's example $C_u = \$2.00$ and $C_o = \$1.00$, by (2.3) the critical ratio for Q^* is

$$P_r(D < j) < \frac{2}{2 + 1} \approx 0.67.$$

From column 4 of Table 2.7 we can see that the highest value of j for which $P_r(D < j) < 0.67$ is 3; hence $Q^* = 3$ as before.

PROBLEMS

2.1. Suppose the manager of another machine shop responds to the reference lottery in Example 2.2 as follows: (1) he is willing to play win $35,000 or lose $25,000 even if the expected value of the game is $-\$13,000$; (2) a fair price to play win, $35,000 or lose $0 is $25,000; and (3) he is willing to play win $0 or lose $25,000 if paid $10,000.
 *a) Construct a utility curve for this manager.
 b) Should he bid for contract X or Y shown in Table 2.1?
 c) Compare this manager's attitude toward risk with the attitude of the manager in Example 2.2.

*2.2. Consider contracts S and T and the utility curves X, Y, and Z shown below:

Contract S			Contract T		
Events	Probabilities	Consequences	Events	Probabilities	Consequences
A	0.30	$20,000	D	0.40	$15,000
B	0.40	5,000	E	0.20	10,000
C	0.30	−10,000	F	0.40	−5,000

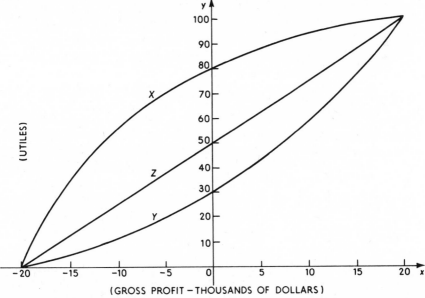

For each of the following businessmen select one of the utility curves which in your opinion reflects the businessman's attitude toward risk and find for which of the two contracts he should bid.

a) Mr. L. P. Gernes is supplied with sufficient working capital for his large operation. He believes that moderate risks should be self-insured.

b) Mr. Black is in such a tight financial position that a loss of $10,000 makes him feel very cautious and conservative.

c) Mr. White is a confirmed optimist.

2.3. Secure the cooperation of a businessman and use the EMV test to determine the approximate amounts beyond which his utility function may be nonlinear. Whether you succeed or not, write a short report on your experience.

2.4. Verify the entries in the payoff table of Table 2.3 for $Q = 2, 3, 4$, and 5 units.

2.5. Plot the points of expected profit and expected opportunity loss for each stock level shown in Table 2.4 and 2.6 on a cc-plane where the x-axis represents Q and the y-axis $E(R_q)$ and $E(L_q)$. Draw curves to connect the two sets of points. Discuss the relationship that may exist between these two curves.

*2.6. A certain product costs $4.00 to stock and sells for $5.00 a unit. Any unsold units at the end of the day are worthless. The decision to stock any number of units does not affect future sales or customer goodwill. The past daily record of sales is shown below:

Units Sold	4	5	6	7	8	9	10 or more
Sales Days	5	10	10	20	25	20	10

Assuming the retailer cannot stock more than ten units daily because of limited shelf space—

a) Construct a conditional profit table for $Q = 4, 5, 6, \ldots, 10$.
b) Find Q^* by computing $E(R_q)$.
c) Construct an opportunity loss payoff table for $Q = 4, 5, 6, \ldots, 10$.
d) Find Q^* by computing $E(L_q)$.
e) What is EVPI?

2.7. Suppose the product in Problem 2.6 sells for $5.00 but costs only $2.50 a unit. In addition, it can be salvaged and at the end of the day it is stocked at $1.00 a unit. Also, for every unit sold the merchant loses $0.50 profit for not selling a unit of another substitute product. Answer (a), (b), (c), (d), and (e) as described in Problem 2.6.

2.8. Use the critical ratio to find Q^* and EVPI in—
a) Problem 2.6.
b) Problem 2.7.

2.9. Flaky-Crust Pies, Inc., makes and distributes a large assortment of pies and other bakery products. For an ordinary pie the company charges its customers, largely restaurants and grocery stores, $0.50 a pie at a gross profit margin of 40 percent. The management of the company decides to market a new ready-to-serve frozen pie for $0.60 with a gross profit margin of 50 percent.

Since the new pie could be preserved in excellent condition under refrigeration for at least ten days, deliveries to customers were made once a week. Any unsold pies at the end of the week were sold to institutions under a different trade mark at one third the original price. Sales experience for the first 20 weeks, shown below, has convinced the management that for every two new pies sold the sale of one ordinary pie is lost.

Week	Sales in Thousand Units	Week	Sales in Thousand Units
1	8	11	10
2	6	12	9
3	9	13	7
4	5	14	10
5	10	15	10
6	7	16	9
7	10	17	12
8	11	18	11
9	7	19	14
10	12	20	13

a) Find Q^* using the critical ratio.

b) Find expected profit for Q^*.

c) The son of the president of Flaky Crust Pies, Inc., just out of college, argued that it would be worth the cost of telephoning the customers of the company every Monday morning in order to get an exact count of the number of pies which should be produced for the week. Is it worth obtaining this information if it costs $100?

*2.10. A florist, in order to satisfy the needs of a number of regular and sophisticated customers, stocks a highly perishable flower. A dozen flowers cost $3 and sell for $10. Any flowers not sold the day they are stocked are worthless. Demand in dozens of flowers has been as follows:

Demand	0	1	2	3	4	5
Rel. Frequency	0.1	0.2	0.3	0.2	0.1	0.1

a) Find Q^* using the critical ratio.

b) Find expected profit for Q^*.

c) Since EVPI or the cost of uncertainty represents a measure of the risk involved in a decision problem, what is the value of this risk in this case?

d) Assuming that failure to satisfy any one customer's request for this flower will result in future lost profits amounting to $5.10 (goodwill cost), in addition to the lost profit on the immediate sale, how many flowers should the florist stock?

e) What is the smallest goodwill cost of stocking five dozen flowers?

2.11. In Section 1 of Chapter 13 we considered a few inventory problems where the demand for the product was certain and given. Then carrying and reorder costs varied, and we wanted to find the size of the order which would minimize such costs. That analysis can be advantageously combined with the present analysis.

Consider Example 1.2 in Chapter 13 where demand was given at 6,000,000 tires. For the past ten years discrepancy of actual minus forecast demand in 100,000 of tires has been as follows:

Year	1	2	3	4	5	6	7	8	9	10
Discrepancy	+1	0	+6	+1	−5	+2	−2	+4	+8	−6

Let the current forecast be 6,000,000 tires as in the above mentioned example, $C_u = \$3.30$, and $C_o = \$6.70$.

a) Rank discrepancies in order from the most negative to the most positive and apply the method described in Problem 1.6 to assess probabilities.

b) From the smoothed curve obtained in (a) and making use of the fact that demand equals forecast plus discrepancy, assign probabilities to demand by relabelling the x-axis of the graph, i.e., letting demand 6,000,000 represent 0 discrepancy and so forth.

c) Find Q^* using the critical ratio.

d) Find $E(R_q)$ for Q^*.

e) How much may management spend on marketing research in order to obtain additional information about the demand for the product?

2.12. In a summer resort the manager of a small grocery store has supplied his summer customers with the Sunday issue of a daily newspaper. Each copy costs $0.35 and sells for $0.50. He has been informed that henceforth no unsold papers will be returnable. His past sales were:

Number	30	31	32	33	34	35	36	37	38	39	40
Rel. Frequency	0.02	0.04	0.06	0.08	0.15	0.18	0.15	0.11	0.10	0.08	0.03

a) Find Q^*.

b) Find the manager's expected profit for Q^*.

c) By how much is his expected profit reduced if the manager stocks one unit less than or one unit more than the optimum number of units?

d) Since the manager is afraid that he may lose regular summer customers if they find him an unreliable supply, he decides to order 40 copies each week. What is the cost of preserving his customer's goodwill? Since his customers are regular, what alternative solution do you recommend?

*3. BINOMIAL DISTRIBUTION; APPLICATION OF BAYES' FORMULA

In the preceding section we have shown how expected value based on a subjective interpretation of probability can be used as a decision criterion. In this section, the last in our course, we shall explain briefly the binomial distribution and demonstrate how Bayes' formula can be applied in statistical decision making; and, by doing so, we may be able to supply an explanation as to why the kind of statistics we have considered so far is called Bayesian.

The binomial distribution is important not only because it is a probability model for a great number of real-world situations, but also because it can be used as a basis for understanding other probability models. We shall begin by explaining Bernoulli trials and the binomial distribution. This will be done to the extent that will be necessary to demonstrate the application of Bayes' formula.

3.1. Bernoulli Trials. In discussing binomial coefficients in Section 3 of the preceding chapter we peripherally touched upon this and the next topic, namely, Bernoulli trials and the binomial distribution associated with such trials. Then we showed how the binomial theorem can be used to determine the probability of every event in a sample space specified by a process such as coin tossing, a machine turning out good or defective parts, an assembly line producing standard or substandard products, and so forth, where each trial contains two outcomes.

In standard statistical terminology one of the two possible outcomes on each trial of processes, such as the ones mentioned, is called a *success* and the other a *failure*. These terms are just convenient labels; and which of the two outcomes is called a success and which a failure is completely arbitrary. What is important, however, is that once we specify one outcome, for instance a defective part, a success and the other outcome, in this instance a good part, a failure, we must be consistent throughout the analysis of a problem. In general, let the two simple events in each trial of such a process be denoted by $\{S\}$ for success and $\{F\}$ for failure. For convenience, we let

$$(3.1) \qquad P_r(\{S\}) = p \quad \text{and} \quad P_r(\{F\}) = q,$$

where $p + q = 1$. Then such trials are called Bernoulli trials (after the mathematician James Bernoulli 1654–1705); and the process made up of such trials is a *Bernoulli process* if and only if the following conditions are met:

1. *Each trial specifies a sample space with two outcomes:* success S or failure F.
2. *The probability of a success*, denoted by p and defined in (3.1), *is the same on each trial.*
3. *The trials are independent.*

Of course, the above definition of a Bernoulli process describes an ideal situation, a probability model. In this connection, we can readily think of tossing a fair coin as a Bernoulli trial and the tossing of a coin 100 times as a Bernoulli process with 100 trials: the sample space of each trial consists of a success (say heads) or a failure (tails); $p = 0.50$; and the outcome in each trial (toss) is not affected by the outcome of preceding trials. But remember that we are still talking about an ideal experiment. Real-life mechanical processes may not meet the above conditions precisely, but they can be very close to the model so that they can be treated as Bernoulli processes.

Example 3.1. An automatic machine stamping out metal pieces for manufacturing purposes is frequently cited as an example of a physical process representing a Bernoulli process. For instance, consider a production run of 1000 metal pieces stamped by the automatic machine. Stamping of a metal piece may be considered to represent a trial of the process; and the 1000 pieces may contain a percentage of defective pieces found by inspection or other means. Under normal production conditions we believe that this percentage represents the probability, called in standard statistical terminology *average fraction defective* (also, cf. Example 3.10, Chapter 15), of a defective on each trial. Yet, the conditions of constancy of p and independence of trials may not be met exactly. During the production run, metal fatigue of the vital parts of the machine may set in, gradually increasing the number of defectives as production continues. Thus, p may not be quite the same for all 1000 trials. For all practical purposes, however, these deviations from the model do not make any appreciable difference; and the Bernoulli model can be used to study such a mechanical process.

Also, the Bernoulli model may be used advantageously to study real-world situations which by their nature may conform to the model less than automatic machines or assembly lines.

Example 3.2. The process of filling orders in a mail-order house may be one case in point. The task of filling a package with the requested merchandise ordered by a customer and addressing it correctly may be considered as a trial of the process, where success means that an order is improperly filled or addressed. Although p is likely to be less constant and the trials less independent in this case than in the case of the mechanical process in the previous example, the Bernoulli model may still be used to study the process.

In still other cases, the Bernoulli process may be used as a device to simulate business situations.

Example 3.3. The management of a newspaper with nationwide circulation considers a pocket-size book edition of last year's best articles which appeared in the magazine section of the Sunday issues of the newspaper. We can think of the demand for the book as a Bernoulli process. Each reader who notices the advertisement about the book may be considered as a trial, and success may be defined as the reader who decides to purchase the book. Under certain conditions simulation with the Bernoulli model may be used to determine the optimal survey sample size which should be taken in order to estimate the demand for the book.

It must be obvious with the above examples that the Bernoulli model can be used to describe or may be used to simulate an enormous variety of physical processes and situations. It is worthwhile, therefore, to study the probability function defined by the Bernoulli process.

3.2. The Binomial Distribution. In Section 3 of the preceding chapter we have shown how we can apply the binomial theorem (3.9) in order to determine the probability of events such as five heads (successes) in five tosses (trials) and at least three tails (failures) in five tosses (trials) in Example 3.9 of that section. We also illustrated the application of the binomial theorem when $p \neq q$. In Example 3.10 of the same section we found the probability that the testing machine will classify one or at least one as defective out of five electronic gadgets tested. In both samples we dealt with trials of a Bernoulli process. Let us now generalize the application of the binomial theorem.

Let the set $\{S, F\}$ represent a sample space for a Bernoulli trial with probability p for success defined by (3.1). Then the sample space for an experiment consisting of three Bernoulli trials is specified by the Cartesian product set $\{S, F\} \times \{S, F\} \times \{S, F\}$. By the fundamental principle of counting, the sample space for the experiment will contain $2^3 = 8$ ordered three-tuples as sample points. A listing of these sample

TABLE 3.1.

Sample Point (1)	Probability $P_r(R = r \mid n = 3, p)$ (2)	(3)
FFF	$qqq = q^3$	q^3
FFS	$qqp = pq^2$	
FSF	$qpq = pq^2$	$3pq^2$
SFF	$pqq = pq^2$	
FSS	$qpp = p^2q$	
SFS	$pqp = p^2q$	$3p^2q$
SSF	$ppq = p^2q$	
SSS	$ppp = p^3$	p^3

points is shown in column 1 of Table 3.1. Since the trials are independent, the probability of each simple event is obtained by applying the product rule, as shown in column 2 of this table. Let the random variable R denote the number of r successes where $r = 0, 1, 2, 3$ when $n = 3$ Bernoulli trials and p is the probability of success on each trial. The probability function or distribution of R is

$R = r$	0	1	2	3
$P_r(R = r \mid n = 3, p)$	q^3	$3pq^2$	$3p^2q$	p^3

.

Observe that $P_r(R = r|n = 3, p)$ read "the probability of $R = r$ given $n = 3$ and p" is also shown in column 3 of Table 3.1 for $r = 0, 1, 2, 3$; they are the terms of the binomial expansion $(q + p)^3$ where their sum equals 1 since $p + q = 1$. Since the coefficients 1, 3, 3, 1 in the above probability table are binomial coefficients, the above probability distribution is called a *binomial distribution*. It can be written as follows:

$$P_r(R = r|n = 3, p) = b(r|n = 3, p) = \binom{3}{r}p^r q^{3-r}, \qquad r = 0, 1, 2, 3,$$

where the expression $b(r|n = 3, p)$ is read "the binomial probability of r successes given $n = 3$ and probability of success p."

On the basis of the product rule for independent trials, the binomial theorem, and definition (3.1), the following theorem can be easily proved. Let the random variable R denote the number of r successes in n Bernoulli trials with probability p for a success on each trial. Then the binomial distribution of R is given by

$$(3.2) \qquad \boxed{P_r(R = r|n, p) = b(r|n, p) = \binom{n}{r}p^r q^{n-r},} \qquad (r = 0, 1, 2, \ldots, n).$$

The number of Bernoulli trials n and the probability of success p are called the *parameters* of the binomial distribution. Note that the binomial formula (3.2) defines not one, but a whole *family* of binomial distributions, one for every possible combination of the parameters n and p. However, once a choice is made of the values of n and p, the binomial distribution is uniquely determined.

Example 3.4. Suppose management believes that one out of five persons who will read the advertisement about the new pocket-size book edition of articles by the newspaper in Example 3.3 will purchase a copy of the book. If four persons who read the advertisement are selected at random, what is the probability that 0, 1, 2, 3, or all 4 persons will purchase the book?

Solution:

Since $p = \frac{1}{5} = 0.20$ and $n = 4$, by (3.2) we have

$$P_r(R = 0|n = 4, p = 0.20) = \binom{4}{0}(0.20)^0(0.80)^4 \approx 0.410$$

$$P_r(R = 1|n = 4, p = 0.20) = \binom{4}{1}(0.20)^1(0.80)^3 \approx 0.409$$

$$P_r(R = 2|n = 4, p = 0.20) = \binom{4}{2}(0.20)^2(0.80)^2 \approx 0.154$$

$$P_r(R = 3 | n = 4, p = 0.20) = \binom{4}{3}(0.20)^3(0.80)^1 \approx 0.025$$

$$P_r(R = 4 | n = 4, p = 0.20) = \binom{4}{4}(0.20)^4(0.80)^0 \approx 0.002$$

$$\sum_{R=0}^{n} P_r(R = r | n = 4, p = 0.20) = 1.00$$

Observe that the binomial distribution for a given combination of n and p is found by direct application of the binomial theorem.

For large values of n the computation of the probability of r successes for a given value of p becomes time consuming. This is especially true in many applications of the Bernoulli model when we would like to know the probability of at least or at most r successes. This requires the laborious task of finding the probabilities of $r, r + 1, r + 2, \ldots, n$ successes and adding these results. Fortunately, extensive tables have been constructed which contain the cumulative binomial distribution for a great number of n and p combinations. Such a small number of cumulative binomial distributions for $n = 3, 4, 5, 6, 7, 8, 9, 10,$ and 11 and for $p = 0.01, 0.10, 0.20, 0.30, 0.40,$ and 0.50 is given in Table 3.2. For each pair of these n and p values the uniquely specified cumulative binomial distribution for at least r successes is obtained by application of

(3.3) $\boxed{P_r(R \geqslant r | n, p) = b(r | n, p) + b(r + 1 | n, p) + \ldots + b(n | n, p).}$

Example 3.5. From the probabilities obtained in Example 3.4 and by (3.3) we have

$$P_r(R \geqslant 1 | n = 4, p = 0.20) = 0.409 + 0.154 + 0.025 + 0.002 = 0.590,$$

$$P_r(R \geqslant 2 | n = 4, p = 0.20) = 0.154 + 0.025 + 0.002 = 0.181,$$

$$P_r(R \geqslant 3 | n = 4, p = 0.20) = 0.025 + 0.002 = 0.027,$$

$$P_r(R \geqslant 4 | n = 4, p = 0.20) = 0.002,$$

as shown for $n = 4$, $p = 0.10$, and $r = 1, 2, 3, 4$, in Table 3.2.

Since we shall make frequent use of the cumulative binomial probabilities it may be worth our while to demonstrate how Table 3.2 can be used.

Example 3.6. Since Table 3.2 contains probabilities of the form $P_r(R \geqslant r | n, p)$, such probabilities can be read directly from the table; others can be obtained indirectly as shown below.

1. *Find $P_r(R \geqslant 1 | n = 5, p = 0.01)$:*
   This probability is 0.049; it is given opposite $r = 1$ in the table for $n = 5$ and $p = 0.01$.
2. *Find $P_r(R > 1 | n = 5, p = 0.01)$:*
   This probability is equivalent to $P_r(R \geqslant 2 | n = 5, p = 0.01)$ which is 0.001 opposite $r = 2$.

3. *Find $P_r(R < 1|n = 5, p = 0.01)$:*
   This is the $1 - P_r(R \geqslant 1|n = 5, p = 0.01) = 1 - 0.049 = 0.951$.
4. *Find $P_r(R \leqslant 1|n = 5, p = 0.01)$:*
   This is the probability of $1 - P_r(R \geqslant 2|n = 5, p = 0.01) = 1 - 0.001$
   $= 0.999$.
5. *Find $P_r(R = 1|n = 5, p = 0.01)$:*
   This probability is equal to $P_r(R \geqslant 1|n = 5, p = 0.01) - P_r(R \geqslant 2|$
   $n = 5, p = 0.01) = 0.049 - 0.001 = 0.048$.

TABLE 3.2.

$$P_r(R \geqslant r|n, p) = \sum_{R=r}^{n} b(r|n, p)$$

n	r	$p = 0.01$	$p = 0.10$	$p = 0.20$	$p = 0.30$	$p = 0.40$	$p = 0.50$
3	1	0.030	0.271	0.488	0.657	0.784	0.875
	2		0.028	0.104	0.216	0.352	0.500
	3		0.001	0.008	0.027	0.064	0.125
4	1	0.039	0.344	0.590	0.760	0.870	0.938
	2	0.001	0.052	0.181	0.348	0.525	0.688
	3		0.004	0.027	0.084	0.179	0.313
	4			0.002	0.008	0.026	0.063
5	1	0.049	0.410	0.672	0.832	0.922	0.969
	2	0.001	0.082	0.263	0.472	0.663	0.813
	3		0.009	0.058	0.163	0.317	0.500
	4		0.001	0.007	0.031	0.087	0.188
	5			0.002	0.010	0.031
6	1	0.059	0.469	0.738	0.882	0.953	0.984
	2	0.002	0.114	0.345	0.580	0.767	0.891
	3		0.016	0.099	0.256	0.456	0.656
	4		0.001	0.017	0.071	0.179	0.344
	5			0.002	0.011	0.041	0.109
	6				0.001	0.004	0.016
7	1	0.068	0.522	0.790	0.918	0.972	0.992
	2	0.002	0.150	0.423	0.671	0.841	0.938
	3		0.026	0.148	0.353	0.580	0.773
	4		0.003	0.033	0.126	0.290	0.500
	5			0.005	0.029	0.096	0.227
	6				0.004	0.019	0.063
	7					0.002	0.008
8	1	0.077	0.570	0.832	0.942	0.983	0.996
	2	0.003	0.187	0.497	0.745	0.894	0.965
	3		0.038	0.203	0.448	0.685	0.856
	4		0.005	0.056	0.194	0.406	0.637
	5			0.010	0.058	0.174	0.363
	6			0.001	0.011	0.050	0.145
	7				0.001	0.009	0.035
	8					0.001	0.004

TABLE 3.2. *(continued)**

$$P_r(R \geq r|n, p) = \sum_{R=r}^{n} b(r|n, p)$$

n	r	$p = 0.01$	$p = 0.10$	$p = 0.20$	$p = 0.30$	$p = 0.40$	$p = 0.50$
9	1	0.087	0.613	0.866	0.960	0.990	0.998
	2	0.003	0.225	0.564	0.804	0.930	0.981
	3		0.053	0.262	0.537	0.768	0.910
	4		0.008	0.086	0.270	0.517	0.746
	5		0.001	0.020	0.099	0.267	0.500
	6			0.003	0.025	0.099	0.254
	7				0.004	0.025	0.090
	8					0.004	0.020
	9						0.002
10	1	0.096	0.651	0.893	0.972	0.994	0.999
	2	0.004	0.264	0.624	0.851	0.954	0.989
	3		0.070	0.322	0.617	0.833	0.945
	4		0.013	0.121	0.350	0.618	0.828
	5		0.002	0.033	0.150	0.367	0.623
	6			0.006	0.047	0.166	0.377
	7			0.001	0.011	0.055	0.172
	8				0.002	0.012	0.055
	9					0.002	0.011
	10						0.001
11	1	0.105	0.686	0.914	0.980	0.996	0.999
	2	0.005	0.303	0.678	0.887	0.970	0.994
	3		0.090	0.383	0.687	0.881	0.967
	4		0.019	0.161	0.430	0.704	0.887
	5		0.003	0.050	0.210	0.467	0.726
	6			0.012	0.078	0.247	0.500
	7			0.002	0.022	0.099	0.274
	8				0.004	0.029	0.113
	9				0.001	0.006	0.033
	10					0.001	0.006
	11						0.001

* Values 0.0005 to 0.0009 inclusive rounded to 0.001.

The interested reader who would like to do additional work in this area is referred to extensive binomial tables in this chapter's bibliography (Refs. 12, 13, 14, 15).

3.3. Application of Bayes' Formula to a Decision Problem.

Although the binomial distribution has applications in a great variety of decision problems, we shall consider an application which gives rise to the opportunity of using Bayes' formula. It involves the problem of deciding between two alternative courses of action when the cost of either alternative depends on the unknown value of the parameter p of a Bernoulli process. As always, we shall use an example to illustrate this application.

Example 3.7. Metal Products Inc., uses an automatic machine to produce a certain part requiring a considerable amount of processing in order to meet assembly specifications. Each production run of 500 parts is taken to the assembly line and used in assembling one of the final products of the company. A part is considered defective if it fails to meet the required assembly specifications. Each defective part requires special hand fitting which costs $4.00 per piece.

In order to maintain high standards of performance before each production run begins, worn machine tools are replaced and the machine is set up by an operator. In setting up the machine the operator must make two delicate adjustments. If both adjustments are made properly the *process* average fraction defective of a production run $p = 0.01$. The machine is in state A which cannot be improved because of mechanical limitations. But the machine can have a poorer performance, as indicated in Table 3.3. If one of the delicate adjustments is not properly made by the opera-

TABLE 3.3.

State of Machine	Random Variable p	Prior Probability $P_r(p)$
A	0.01	0.70
B	0.10	0.20
C	0.20	0.10

tor, the machine is in state B with $p = 0.10$; and if both adjustments are improperly made, the machine is in state C with $p = 0.20$. On the other hand, a master mechanic can always make both adjustments properly so that the machine is certain to be in state A before a production run. But his fee for this job is $60 which would be a complete loss if the machine operator had made both adjustments properly.

From his experience with the machine the production manager believes that during a production run it would be safe to assume that the machine performs as a Bernoulli process. Furthermore, from past records of machine operators and long experience the production manager believes that the present machine operator is likely to set up the machine 70 percent of the time in state A, 20 percent in state B, and 10 percent in state C. In other words, the manager's prior probability distribution about the random variable p is as shown in Table 3.3.

The first question we may raise about our problem is the following: *If each production run contains 500 parts, should the manager* ACCEPT *the operator's setup and allow the machine to produce the parts or* REJECT *the operator's setup and invite the expert mechanic to check and readjust, if necessary, the machine before the production run begins?* In analyzing this decision problem, first we must prepare a payoff table, in this case a table of conditional costs, since we deal with a situation where costs instead of profits are given.

Example 3.7—*Continued.* If the manager *accepts* the operator's setup, then the expected number of defectives in the run will be $500p$. Since each defective costs $4.00 because it requires special hand fitting, the expected cost of these defectives will be $4 \times 500p = \$2000p$. Thus the conditional cost of acceptance will be $\$2000(0.01) = \$20$ if the machine happens to be in state A, $\$2000(0.10) = \$200$ if the machine is in state B, and $\$2000(0.20) = \$400$ if in state C as shown in column 3 of Table 3.4. If the manager

TABLE 3.4.

Random Variable p (1)	Prior Probability $P_r(p)$ (2)	Conditional Cost of—		Conditional Opportunity Loss of—	
		Acceptance (3)	Rejection (4)	Acceptance (5)	Rejection (6)
0.01	0.70	$ 20*	80	$ 0	$60
0.10	0.20	200	80*	120	0
0.20	0.10	400	80*	320	0

rejects the operator's setup, then the expected number of defectives will always be $500(0.01) = 5$ parts. This is so because no matter what the state of the machine happens to be when adjusted by the operator it is certain that the invited expert mechanic will readjust the machine in state A. Hence, the conditional cost will be $4 \times 5 = \$20$ plus the mechanic's fee of $60, or a total of $80 for each state, as shown in column 4 of Table 3.4.

Of course, we can compute the expected cost of acceptance or rejection of the operator's setup from Table 3.4 and select the course of action with the smallest expected cost. However, in this as well as in many other cases, it is better to determine the optimal course of action by computing the expected loss rather than the expected cost of each alternative. Since the expected loss of the optimal decision is the expected value of perfect information (EVPI, cf. Section 2 of this chapter), we shall see shortly that EVPI can be used for further analysis of our problem. The fact that the payoff table of the conditional opportunity loss, heretofore called *loss* for convenience, must be computed from a cost rather than from a profit payoff table makes little difference. In the preceding section we have seen that in order to compute a *loss* payoff table from a *profit* payoff table we subtract each entry in a given row from the *largest profit* entry in the same row. Computing a *loss* payoff table from a *cost* payoff table consists of subtracting the *smallest cost* entry in each row from all the entries in the same row. In either case the loss of the best possible decision is 0 and all other entries in each row of a loss payoff table are positive.

Example 3.7—*Continued.* The loss payoff table for our problem can be obtained from the cost payoff table, columns 3 and 4 of Table 3.4. The entry with the smallest cost is marked with an asterisk. Then this entry is subtracted from all entries in the same row. The loss payoff table obtained with this operation is shown in columns 5 and 6 of Table 3.4.

Let the random variables A and R denote the loss of acceptance and rejection, as shown in Table 3.4, respectively. Then the expected loss of each of the two courses of action in our problem is

$$E(A) = 0(0.70) + 120(0.20) + 320(0.10) = 56 \text{ dollars,}$$

$$E(R) = 60(0.70) + 0(0.20) + 0(0.10) = 42 \text{ dollars.}$$

These results mean that in a long number of production runs, each containing 500 parts, the loss, i.e., the cost which could have been eliminated with perfect information, will average $56 per run if the production manager *always accepts the* operator's setup but only $42 if he *always rejects* this setup and invites the master mechanic before each run. On the basis of this analysis, therefore, the production manager of Metal Products, Inc., should *always reject* the operator's setup thus reducing his expected loss by $14.

It is important to note that the above analysis of our problem is based on the prior probabilities that the production manager was willing to assign to the performance of the machine operator. The analysis was based entirely on prior information, i.e., prior to a given production run. Although the optimal decision with this analysis is for the manager to always reject the operator's setup, the expected loss of this decision or EVPI is $42. This means that the manager could afford to pay up to $42 in order to obtain additional information about the random variable p, i.e., the state of the machine after it has been adjusted by the operator and before each production run. Although we cannot obtain perfect information before a production run is completed, we can certainly obtain some additional information about p if we take a sample run; revise the manager's prior probabilities in the light of information obtained from the sample; and then determine the optimal course of action. Therefore, the second question we may raise about our problem is: *Does it pay to take a sample before a terminal decision about the optimal course of action?*

Example 3.7—*Continued.* Suppose it costs $2.00 to inspect a part and determine whether it is defective or not. We can arbitrarily choose the following decision rule: *Take a sample run of five parts and reject the operator's setup if at least one part is found defective; otherwise,* accept it.

The analysis of our problem under this rule, which in standard statistical terminology is called the *(5, 1) decision rule* or *(n, c) decision rule,* where in this case $n = 5$ and $c = 1$, is shown in Table 3.5. Columns 1 and 2 of this table copied from Table 3.4, are self-explanatory. The remaining entries in Table 3.5 involve the following steps:

Step 1: Find the conditional probabilities for the (5, 1) decision rule.

TABLE 3.5.

Random Variable p (1)	Prior Probability $P_r(p)$ (2)	Conditional (5, 1) $P_r(c \geqslant 1)$ Reject (3)	Conditional (5, 1) $P_r(c < 1)$ Accept (4)	Joint of Wrong Decision (5)	Loss of Wrong Decision Conditional (6)	Loss of Wrong Decision Expected (7)
0.01	0.70	0.049*	0.951	0.0343	$ 60	$ 2.06
0.10	0.20	0.410	0.590*	0.1180	120	14.16
0.20	0.10	0.672	0.328*	0.0328	320	10.50
						$26.72

These probabilities are obtained from the cumulative binomial probabilities of Table 3.2. The probability of finding at least one defective in a sample run of five parts is 0.049 when $p = 0.01$, 0.410 when $p = 0.10$, and 0.672 when $p = 0.20$. These are the probabilities of rejecting the operator's setup under the (5, 1) rule for each state of the machine, shown in column 1 of Table 3.5. Since $P_r(c < 1|n = 5, p) = 1 - P_r(c \geqslant 1|n = 5, p)$, the probabilities of accepting the operator's setup for each state of the machine can be easily obtained from column 3 by subtracting each probability of that column from 1. For instance, $P_r(c < 1|n = 5, p = 0.01) = 1 - 0.049 = 0.951$ and so forth. These probabilities are shown in column 4 of the table.

Step 2: Find the conditional probability of the wrong decision for each state of the machine.

Each such conditional probability in columns 3 and 4 of Table 3.5 is marked with an asterisk. When $p = 0.01$ the probability of the wrong decision is 0.049, since under the (5, 1) rule we reject the operator's setup, though the better decision is to accept it. Similarly, when $p = 0.10$ and $p = 0.20$ the probability of the wrong decision is 0.590 and 0.328, respectively, since we accept the operator's setup though the better decision is to reject it.

Step 3: Find the joint probability of each wrong decision.

Multiplying the prior times the conditional probability of the wrong decision for each state of the machine, column 2 times the starred figure in columns 3 or 4, we obtain the joint probabilities, shown in column 5.

Step 4: Find the expected loss of each wrong decision.

The entries in column 6 represent the conditional loss of the wrong decision for each state of the machine. They are obtained from the loss payoff table in Table 3.4. Multiplying each entry in this column by the corresponding joint probability, i.e., column 5 times column 6, we obtain the expected loss for each wrong decision in column 7. Total expected loss is $26.72.

Step 5: Find the total cost of sampling 5 parts.

Since it costs $2.00 to inspect each part in the sample, adding $2 × 5 = $10 to $26.72, the total cost of sampling is $36.72.

Thus it does pay to take a sample run before the production run begins since the cost of uncertainty (EVPI) has been reduced from $42 before sampling to $36.72 after sampling.

A decision rule involving an analysis such as the above is called *Bayes decision rule* since it is based on revising prior probabilities in the light of additional information obtained by means of a sample. In general, let n be the sample size and c be the critical number of defectives in the sample. Then there are as many (n, c) decision rules as the combinations of n and c; and the above result raises a third important question for our problem. *Which is the optimal (n, c) decision rule i.e., the rule which will reduce the cost of uncertainty to a minimum?*

Example 3.7—*Continued.* In order to find this optimal decision rule for our problem we must repeat the analysis of Table 3.5 for each different (n, c) rule. We start by first finding the best c given n; we repeat this step for a different n; and, finally, we find the optimal (n, c) by comparing the different values of n associated with the best c. Actual computations are left for the reader. We simply cite the results of this analysis.

Under rule $(5, 2)$ the total cost of sampling is \$55.68; it is higher for rule $(5, 3)$ because of the way this problem is structured. Hence, for $n = 5$ the best c is 1. For the same reason the best c for other values of n is also 1. The results for $c = 1$ and $n = 4, 5, 6, 7, 8, 9, 10, 11$ are shown in Table 3.6. It can be seen that the starred rule $(8, 1)$ is the optimal rule where EVPI is reduced from \$42 before sampling to \$34.94 after sampling.

TABLE 3.6.

Decision Rule (1)	Expected Loss (2)	Sampling Cost (3)	Cost of Uncertainty—EVPI (4)
(4, 1)	\$30.50	\$ 8.00	\$38.50
(5, 1)	26.72	10.00	36.72
(6, 1)	23.60	12.00	35.60
(7, 1)	21.05	14.00	35.05
(8, 1)*	18.94	16.00	34.94*
(9, 1)	17.19	18.00	35.19
(10, 1)	15.83	20.00	35.83
(11, 1)	14.70	22.00	36.70

The best course of action for a production run of 500 parts is to take a sample run of 8 parts and to accept the operator's setup if no defective parts are found in the sample; otherwise, to reject the operator's setup and invite the expert mechanic to check and readjust the machine before the production run begins. Sampling is better than no sampling since by the $(8, 1)$ decision rule the production manager of Metal Products, Inc., will be able to minimize the cost of uncertainty.

The above rule can be verified by computing the expected loss of acceptance and rejection of the operator's setup by straight application of Bayes' formula as follows:

Example 3.7—*Continued.* According to the optimal $(8, 1)$ rule the production manager should accept the operator's setup if he finds no defectives in a sample run of 8 parts, i.e., when $P_r(c = 0|n = 8, p)$. This means that when the sample contains no defectives, the expected loss of acceptance is less than the expected loss of rejection.

The complete analysis is shown in Table 3.7 where the posterior probabilities shown in column 5, are obtained by the application of Bayes'

TABLE 3.7.

Random Variable p	Prior Probability $P_r(p)$	Conditional Probability $P_r(c = 0 \mid n = 8, p)$	Joint Probability Cols. 2 × 3	Posterior Probability	Conditional Loss		Expected Loss	
					Accept	Reject	Accept	Reject
(1)	(2)	(3)	(4)	(5)	(6)	(7)	(8)	(9)
0.01	0.70	0.923	0.646	0.862	$0	$60	$0	$51.72
0.10	0.20	0.430	0.086	0.115	120	0	13.80	0
0.20	0.10	0.168	0.017	0.023	320	0	7.36	0
			0.749	1.000			*$21.16	$51.72

formula, as explained in Section 2 of Chapter 15. It can be seen that the expected loss of accepting the operator's setup is $21.16, which is much less than $51.72, the expected loss of rejecting it.

It is left for the reader to verify the fact that the expected loss of rejecting the operator's setup is less than the loss of accepting it when $c = 1$, i.e., when the conditional probability is $P_r(c = 1|n = 8, p)$.

It is important to realize that the optimal decision rule has been reached by considering all possible economic consequences of our problem under uncertainty; and we have obtained this result by applying the Bernoulli model in order to *simulate* all mutually exclusive and collectively exhaustive outcomes of our problem. Furthermore, the above analysis need not be confined to decision problems of production management only; it may as well be advantageously applied to other areas of business operations.

PROBLEMS

3.1. Using column 2 of Table 3.1, find the probability distribution of the number of failures when the probability of success is $p = 0.30$. Then verify your answer by obtaining the $P_r(R = r|n = 3, p = 0.30)$ from Table 3.2, where $r = 0, 1, 2, 3$ successes.

3.2. Let R be the random variable, where its value $r = 0, 1, 2, \ldots, 10$ represents the number of heads in tossing a fair coin ten times. Use Table 3.2 to find the probability function of R.

3.3. Suppose the process of filling mail orders in Example 3.2 has a process average fraction defective $p = 0.20$. If eight filled mail orders are selected at random, what is the probability that none of the orders is defective?

3.4. From Table 3.2 prepare a distribution table of the binomial distribution when the parameters are:
*a) $n = 6, p = 0.10$.
b) $n = 9, p = 0.20$.
c) $n = 11, p = 0.40$.

*3.5. Find the following probabilities from Table 3.2.
a) $P_r(R = 0 | n = 4, p = 0.01)$.
b) $P_r(R \geqslant 2 | n = 6, p = 0.10)$.
c) $P_r(R < 3 | n = 10, p = 0.20)$.
d) $P_r(R \leqslant 3 | n = 9, p = 0.30)$.
e) $P_r(R = 4 | n = 10, p = 0.40)$.
f) $P_r(R > 1 | n = 7, p = 0.50)$.

3.6. Consider Example 3.4. If ten persons who read the advertisement about the new pocket-size book edition of articles are selected at random, what is the probability that the following will purchase the book?
a) Exactly 4.   d) Less than 4.
b) More than 4.   e) Between 4 and 6 inclusive.
c) Four or more.   f) Four or less.

3.7. Consider Example 3.2. Suppose the manager of the mail-order house selects 11 filled mail orders. Although he believes that the process of filling orders performs as a Bernoulli process, the process average fraction defective varies from day to day and he does not know today's state of the process. What is the probability that the sample contains two or more incorrectly filled orders, given that the process average fraction defective is as follows:
a) $p = 0.01$?   d) $p = 0.30$?
b) $p = 0.10$?   e) $p = 0.40$?
c) $p = 0.20$?   f) $p = 0.50$?

*3.8. Suppose the automatic machines of a plant fail with probability q; machine failure is independent from machine to machine; and the plant stays in operation if at least half of the machines run. Consider a two-machine plant and a four-machine plant. What is the value of q for uninterrupted operations when—
a) The value of q is the same in both plants?
b) A two-machine plant is preferred?
c) A four-machine plant is preferred?
   (*Hint:* The probability that a machine does not fail is $p = 1 - q$.)

3.9. Suppose operations are not interrupted in three-machine and five-machine plants if more than half their machines run. If machines perform independently and q is the probability of failure for a single machine, for what values of q uninterrupted plant operation is—
a) The same in both plants?
b) A three-machine plant should be preferred?
c) A five-machine plant should be preferred?
   (*Hint:* The probability that a machine does not fail is $p = 1 - q$.)

3.10. On the basis of the binomial theorem, the product rule for independent trials, and definition (3.1) in the text prove the theorem that the binomial distribution of the random variable R is given by (3.2).

3.11. Compute the expected cost of accepting or rejecting the operator's setup from Table 3.4 and verify the fact that if no sample run is taken, the production manager of Metal Products, Inc., should always reject the operator's setup.

3.12. On the basis of the information given in Table 3.5 in the text do the following:
  a) Prepare a tree diagram showing the prior, conditional, and joint probabilities of all possible courses of action in the problem.
  b) Prepare a table showing the joint and marginal probabilities of the problem.

3.13. From the analysis of the decision rule (5, 1) in Table 3.5 find the conditional probabilities $P_r(c = 0 | n = 5, p)$ and $P_r(c = 1 | n = 5, p)$ and compute the posterior probabilities and expected loss of acceptance and rejection. Thus verify the fact that the production manager of Metal Products, Inc., should follow the (5, 1) decison rule of accepting the operator's setup if he finds no defectives in the sample and rejecting it if he does find one or more defectives rather than always rejecting this setup as he should have done without sampling.

3.14. Repeat the analysis shown in Table 3.5 of the text to verify the total sampling cost of each Bayes' decision rule below:
  a) (5, 2).   *e)* (8, 1).
  b) (4, 1).   *f)* (9, 1).
  c) (6, 1).   *g)* (10, 1).
  d) (7, 1).   *h)* (11, 1).

3.15. Let the x-axis represent different (n, c) decision rules and the y-axis the expected loss, cost of sampling, and EVPI in dollars. Sketch the graphs of the data given in Table 3.6 of the text. Discuss the relationship between expected loss, sampling cost, and EVPI.

3.16. Prepare a table such as Table 3.7 in the text to verify the fact that the expected loss of rejecting the operator's setup is less than the loss of accepting it when $c = 1$, i.e., when the conditional probability is $P_r(c = 1 | n = 8, p)$.

3.17. Like Table 3.2 extensive binomial tables may not include values for p greater than 0.50. Thus, when $p > 0.50$, the problem of finding probabilities from such tables must be rephrased in terms of $q = 1 - p$. For example, we wish to find

$$P_r(R \geqslant 2 | n = 5, p = 0.60).$$

Solution:

$$P_r(R \geqslant 2 | n = 5, p = 0.60) = P_r(R \leqslant 3 | n = 5, p = 0.40)$$
$$= 1 - P_r(R \geqslant 4 | n = 5, p = 0.40)$$
$$= 1 - 0.087$$
$$= 0.913.$$

On the basis of the above example, find—
a) $P_r(R \geqslant 5 | n = 10, p = 0.70)$.
b) $P_r(R \geqslant 2 | n = 11, p = 0.60)$.
c) $P_r(R \geqslant 2 | n = 9, p = 0.80)$.

SUGGESTED REFERENCES

1. BROSS, IRWIN D. J. *Design for Decision*, pp. 102–29. New York: The Macmillan Co., 1953. **(2, 3)**

2. EKEBLAD, FREDERICK A. *The Statistical Method in Business*, pp. 319–37. New York: John Wiley & Sons, Inc., 1962. **(3)**

3. GOLDBERG, SAMUEL. *Probability: An Introduction*, pp. 158–84, 252–61, 286–92. Englewood Cliffs, N.J.: Prentice-Hall, Inc., 1960. **(1–3)**

4. GREEN, PAUL E. "Bayesian Decision Theory in Pricing Strategy," *Journal of Marketing* (January, 1963). Reprinted in T. J. SIELAFF, *Statistics in Action*, pp. 169–85. San Jose, Calif.: The Lansford Press, 1963. **(3)**

5. ———. "Bayesian Decision Theory in Advertising," *Journal of Advertising* (December, 1962). Reprinted in T. J. SIELAFF, *Statistics in Action*, pp. 192–207. San Jose, Calif.: The Lansford Press, 1963. **(3)**

6. HANSEN, HARRY L. *Marketing: Text, Cases, and Readings*, pp. 404–18, 895–911. Homewood, Ill.: Richard D. Irwin, Inc, 1961. **(2)**

7. HARLAN, NEIL E., *et al. Managerial Economics: Text and Cases*. Homewood, Ill.: Richard D. Irwin, Inc., 1962. **(1, 2)**

8. KEMENY, JOHN G., *et al. Finite Mathematics with Business Applications*, pp. 186–93. Englewood Cliffs, N.J.: Prentice-Hall, Inc., 1962. **(1)**

9. KURNOW, ERNEST, *et al. Statistics for Business Decisions*, pp. 148–50. Homewood, Ill.: Richard D. Irwin, Inc., 1959. **(1)**

10. MOSTELLER, FREDERICK, *et al. Probability with Statistical Applications*, pp. 155–81, 224–30, 241–55, 258–62. Reading, Mass.: Addison-Wesley Publishing Co., Inc., 1961. **(1, 3)**

11. NETER, JOHN, AND WASSERMAN, WILLIAM. *Fundamental Statistics for Business and Economics*, pp. 301–12. 2nd ed. Boston, Mass.: Allyn and Bacon, Inc., 1961. **(3)**

12. SCHLAIFER, ROBERT. *Probability and Statistics for Business Decisions*, pp. 342–70, 508–18. New York: McGraw-Hill Book Co., Inc., 1959. **(3)**

13. ———. *Introduction to Statistics for Business Decisions*, pp. 24–63, 169–97. New York: McGraw-Hill Book Co., Inc., 1961. **(1–3)**

14. *Tables of the Cumulative Binomial Probability Distribution*, Annals of the Computation Laboratory of Harvard University, Vol. XXXV. Cambridge, Mass.: Harvard University Press, 1955. **(3)**

15. *Tables of the Binomial Probability Distribution*, Applied Mathematics Series, Vol. 6. Washington, D.C.: National Bureau of Standards, 1950.

ANSWERS TO PROBLEMS
MARKED WITH AN ASTERISK

CHAPTER 1

Section 1

1.1. *a)* $P = R$; $P \neq Q$; $Q \neq R$.

1.2. *a)* i) True.
ii) True.

1.3. *g)* $\{2, -4\}$; $P = \{x|x^2 + 2x - 8 = 0\}$; finite.

1.4. $M = \{x \in \mathcal{U}|x$ is a man$\}$,
$F = \{x \in \mathcal{U}|x$ is smoker of filter cigarettes$\}$,
$S_1 = \{x \in \mathcal{U}|x$ is a man who smokes filter cigarettes$\}$,

1.6. *a)* $B = \{$John Baker$\}$; $B = \{x \in P|x$ is owner of a store building$\}$
$A = \{\$50,000\}$; $A = \{x|x$ is an amount representing an asset$\}$.
$L = \{\$15,000\}$; $L = \{x|x$ is an amount representing a liability$\}$.
$W = \{\$35,000\}$; $W = \{x|x$ is an amount representing net worth$\}$.

1.7. *d)* $Q = \{x \in R|x^2 - 5x + 6 = 0\} = \{3, 2\}$; finite.

1.8. *b)* True.

Section 2

2.1. *b)* $P = Q$ is true by definition of set equality and $P \subseteq Q$ by definition of subsets.

617

2.5. *a)* W is not a subset of R since at least one wholesaler may not be a retailer.

b) P is a subset of B since all partnerships by definition represent business organizations.

2.9. *c)* i) False; $\{1, 2\} \subseteq \mathcal{U}.$ ·
ii) False; $\{1, 2\} \in 2^{\mathcal{U}}.$

2.10. *a)* Since $\varnothing$ is a subset of P.

Section 3

3.1.

	(a)	*(b)*
P'	$= \{b, c\}$	R_3 & R_4
Q'	$= \{a, d\}$	R_2 & R_4
$P \cup Q$	$= \{a, b, c, d\} = \mathcal{U}$	R_1 & R_2 & R_3
$P \cap Q$	$= \varnothing$	R_1
$P \cup Q'$	$= \{a, d\} = P$	R_1 & R_2 & R_4
$P' \cup Q$	$= \{b, c\} = Q$	R_1 & R_3 & R_4
$(P \cup Q)'$	$= \varnothing$	R_4
$(P \cap Q)'$	$= \{a, b, c, d\} = \mathcal{U}$	R_2 & R_3 & R_4

3.4. *a)*

$$P \cap Q = \{1, 2\},$$
$$P \cap S = \{1, 3\},$$
$$Q \cap S = \{1, 5\},$$
$$(P \cap Q)' = \{3, 4, 5, 6, 7, 8\},$$
$$(P \cap S)' = \{2, 4, 5, 6, 7, 8\},$$
$$(Q \cap S)' = \{2, 3, 4, 6, 7, 8\},$$
$$P \cup Q = \{1, 2, 3, 4, 5, 6\},$$
$$P \cup S = \{1, 2, 3, 4, 5, 7\},$$
$$Q \cup S = \{1, 2, 3, 5, 6, 7\},$$
$$(P \cup Q)' = \{7, 8\},$$
$$(P \cup S)' = \{6, 8\},$$
$$(Q \cup S)' = \{4, 8\},$$
$$(P \cap Q) \cap S = \{1\},$$
$$(P \cup Q) \cap S = \{1, 3, 5\},$$
$$S' = \{2, 4, 6, 8\},$$
$$S' \cap (P \cup Q) = \{2, 4, 6\},$$
$$[(P \cup Q) \cup S] \cap [(P \cap Q) \cap S]' = \{2, 3, 4, 5, 6, 7\}.$$

3.5. *b)* $[(A \cup B) \cup C]' = \varnothing.$

3.6. *a)*

Where $n(\mathcal{U})$, $n(A)$, etc. denotes the number of elements in $\mathcal{U}$.

3.8. *a*) $(P \cup Q)' = P' \cap Q' = R_7$ & R_8.

3.9. *a*)

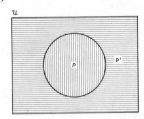

3.12. $\emptyset \subseteq P \cap (Q \cap R) \subseteq (P \cap Q) \cap R \subseteq P \cap Q \subseteq Q \cap P \subseteq Q \subseteq P \cup (Q \cup R) \subseteq (P \cup Q) \cup R \subseteq \mathcal{U} \subseteq \emptyset'$.

3.13. *a*) $\mathcal{U}$

$F \cap M$	$F \cap W$
30	40
$N \cap M$	$N \cap W$
20	10

$$M = (F \cap M) \cup (N \cap M)$$
$$W = (F \cap W) \cup (N \cap W)$$
$$F = (F \cap M) \cup (F \cap W)$$
$$N = (N \cap M) \cup (N \cap W)$$

3.14. *a*) Let $n(\mathcal{U})$ denote the number of respondents in $\mathcal{U}$. Then
$$n(P \cap 0) = 76,$$
$$n(T \cup R) = 248,$$
$$n[(T \cup 0)' \cap R] = 10,$$
$$n[(P \cup Q \cup R)' \cap (T \cup 0)'] = 25.$$

3.15. *a*) $S \cap C = \emptyset$.
   b) $W \cap R' \neq \emptyset$.

Section 4

4.4. *a*) $(A \cap B') \cup (A \cap C')$.
   b) $(A \cap C) \cup (B \cap C)$.
   c) $(A \cup B) \cap (B \cup C) \cap (A \cup C)$.

4.5. i) *a*) (1) $F \cup N = N$
             (2) $I \cup F = F$
             $\therefore I \cup N = N$
         b) $I \cup N = I \cup (F \cup N)$ [by hypothesis 1]
                 $= (I \cup F) \cup N$ [by law 3a]
                 $= F \cup N$ [by hypothesis 2]
                 $= N$ [by hypothesis 1]

                                                    QED

4.6. *c*) i) **T**
               T
               T
               T
   d) i) Statement $(p \cup q) \cup (p \cup q)'$ is logically true since the truth set assigned to this statement is the universal set.
   e) i) Symbolic logic.

4.7. i) *a*)

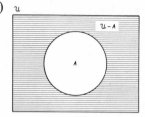 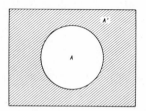

b) Since $\mathcal{U} - A = \mathcal{U} \cap A'$, $\mathcal{U} \cap A'$ A'

| $\in$ | $\notin$ | $\notin$ | $\notin$ |
| $\in$ | $\in$ | $\in$ | $\in$ |

c) $\mathcal{U} - A = \mathcal{U} \cap A'$ [by 11a]
          $= A'$ [by 1b]

QED

4.8. i) *a*)

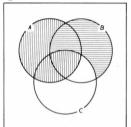

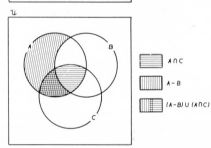

b) Since $A - (B - C) = A \cap (B \cap C')'$, we have

A	B	C		$B \cap C'$		$(B \cap C')'$		$A \cap (B \cap C')'$	
$\in$	$\in$	$\in$		$\in$	$\notin$ $\notin$		$\notin$	$\in$	$\in$ $\in$	$\in$
$\in$	$\in$	$\notin$		$\in$	$\in$ $\in$		$\in$	$\notin$	$\in$ $\notin$	$\notin$
$\in$	$\notin$	$\in$		$\notin$	$\notin$ $\notin$		$\notin$	$\in$	$\in$ $\in$	$\in$
$\in$	$\notin$	$\notin$		$\notin$	$\notin$ $\in$		$\notin$	$\in$	$\in$ $\in$	$\in$
$\notin$	$\in$	$\in$		$\in$	$\notin$ $\notin$		$\notin$	$\in$	$\notin$ $\notin$	$\in$
$\notin$	$\in$	$\notin$		$\in$	$\in$ $\in$		$\in$	$\notin$	$\notin$ $\notin$	$\notin$
$\notin$	$\notin$	$\in$		$\notin$	$\notin$ $\notin$		$\notin$	$\in$	$\notin$ $\notin$	$\in$
$\notin$	$\notin$	$\notin$		$\notin$	$\notin$ $\in$		$\notin$	$\in$	$\notin$ $\notin$	$\in$
*①	①	①		①	③ ②		③	④	① ⑤	④

* These numbers in this as well as in similar tables which
follow indicate the steps required in order to find the truth
value of each set.

Since $(A - B) \cup (A \cap C) = (A \cap B') \cup (A \cap C)$, we have

A	B	C		$A \cap B'$			$A \cap C$			$(A \cap B') \cup (A \cap C)$		
∈	∈	∈		∈	∉	∉		∈	∈	∈		∉	**∈**	∈
∈	∈	∉		∈	∉	∉		∈	∉	∉		∉	**∉**	∉
∈	∉	∈		∈	∈	∈		∈	∈	∈		∈	**∈**	∈
∈	∉	∉		∈	∈	∈		∈	∉	∉		∈	**∈**	∉
∉	∈	∈		∉	∉	∉		∉	∉	∉		∉	**∉**	∉
∉	∈	∉		∉	∉	∉		∉	∉	∉		∉	**∉**	∉
∉	∉	∈		∉	∉	∈		∉	∉	∈		∉	**∉**	∉
∉	∉	∉		∉	∉	∈		∉	∉	∉		∉	**∉**	∉
①	①	①		①	③	②		①	④	①		③	⑤	④

c) $A - (B - C)$
$$= A - (B \cap C') \qquad \text{[by 11a]}$$
$$= A \cap [(B \cap C')]' \qquad \text{[by 11a]}$$
$$= A \cap (B' \cup C) \qquad \text{[by 9b \& 8a]}$$
$$= (A \cap B') \cup (A \cap C) \qquad \text{[by 4b]}$$
$$= (A - B) \cup (A \cap C) \qquad \text{[by 11a]}$$
$$\text{QED}$$

4.9. i) a)

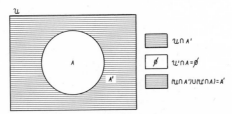

b) Since $\mathcal{U} \Delta A = (\mathcal{U} \cap A') \cup (\mathcal{U}' \cap A)$, we have

$\mathcal{U}$	A		$\mathcal{U} \cap A'$			$\mathcal{U}' \cap A$			$(\mathcal{U} \cap A') \cup (\mathcal{U}' \cap A)$			A'
∈	∈		∈	∉	∉		∉	∉	∈		∉	**∉**	∉	**∉**
∈	∉		∈	∈	∈		∉	∉	∉		∈	**∈**	∉	**∈**
①	①		①	③	②		④	⑤	①		③	⑥	⑤	②

c) $\mathcal{U} \Delta A$
$$= (\mathcal{U} \cap A') \cup (\mathcal{U}' \cap A) \qquad \text{[by 12a]}$$
$$= A' \cup (\varnothing \cap A) \qquad \text{[by 1b \& 10a]}$$
$$= A' \cup \varnothing \qquad \text{[by 5b]}$$
$$= A' \qquad \text{[by 1a]}$$
$$\text{QED}$$

4.10. i) a) See Figure 4.4 in text.
   b) Since $A \Delta B = (A \cap B') \cup (A' \cap B)$ and $B \Delta A = (B \cap A') \cup (B' \cap A)$, we have

A	B		$A \cap B'$			$A' \cap B$			$(A \cap B') \cup (A' \cap B)$			$(B \cap A') \cup (B' \cap A)$		
∈	∈		∈	∉	∉		∉	∉	∈		∉	**∉**	∉		∉	**∉**	∉
∈	∉		∈	∈	∈		∉	∉	∉		∈	**∈**	∉		∉	**∈**	∈
∉	∈		∉	∉	∉		∈	∈	∈		∉	**∈**	∈		∈	**∈**	∉
∉	∉		∉	∉	∈		∈	∉	∉		∉	**∉**	∉		∉	**∉**	∉
①	①		①	②	③		④	⑤	①		③	⑥	⑤		⑤	⑦	③

4.11. *a)*

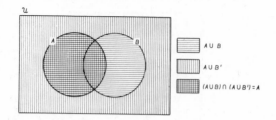

A	B		$A \cup B$			$A \cup B'$		$(A \cup B) \cap (A \cup B')$			A
$\in$	$\in$		$\in$ $\in$ $\in$			$\in$ $\in$ $\notin$		$\in$	$\in$	$\in$	$\in$
$\in$	$\notin$		$\in$ $\in$ $\notin$			$\in$ $\in$ $\in$		$\in$	$\in$	$\in$	$\in$
$\notin$	$\in$		$\notin$ $\in$ $\in$			$\notin$ $\notin$ $\notin$		$\in$	$\notin$	$\notin$	$\notin$
$\notin$	$\notin$		$\notin$ $\notin$ $\notin$			$\notin$ $\in$ $\in$		$\notin$	$\notin$	$\in$	$\notin$
①	①		①②①			①③②		②	④	③	①

4.12. *a)* $(A \cup B) \cap (A \cup B') = A \cup (B \cap B')$ [by 4a]

$\qquad\qquad\qquad\qquad\quad = A \cup \varnothing$ [by 7b]

$\qquad\qquad\qquad\qquad\quad = A$ [by 1a]

$\qquad\qquad\qquad\qquad\qquad\qquad\qquad\qquad$ QED

CHAPTER 2

Section 1

1.1. *a)* Set statement; it asserts a relation between the set of accounts receivables and the set of accounts representing assets.

b) Not a statement.

c) Propositional statement; it asserts a proposition not involving a set relation.

1.2. Let $T = \{x|x \text{ is a teen-ager}\}$ and $D = \{x|x \text{ is a car driver}\}$ be subsets of $\mathcal{U} = \{x|x \text{ is a person}\}$. Then

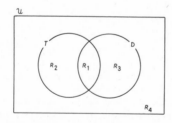

a) $T \cap D \neq \varnothing$; R_1 is not the null set.

b) $T \cap D = T$, or $T \cup D = D$, or $T \cap D' = \varnothing$; R_2 is the null set.

c) $T \cap D = \varnothing$; R_1 is the null set.

d) $T \cap D' \neq \varnothing$; R_2 is not the null set.

1.4. a) $p \cap q'$ b) $q \cap p'$ c) $p' \cup q'$
                F   F   F
                T   F   T
                F   T   T
                F   F   T

1.5. a) $p \cap q'$ b) $q \cap p'$ c) $p' \cap q'$
            T   F   T   F   F   F
              \/   \/   \/
              F   F   F

1.6. Let P and Q be the truth sets, shown below, assign to statements p and q, respectively.

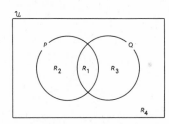

Then the truth set of each statement is represented by—
a) Region R_2.
b) Region R_3.
c) Region R_4.

1.8. a) $p \cap q$ = "Stock prices are rising *and* the stock market is bullish."
                T
                F
                F
                F

b) $p \cup q$ = "Stock prices are rising *or* the stock market is bullish."
                T
                T
                T
                F

c) $p \cap q'$ = "Stock prices are rising *and it is not true* that the stock
                F   market is bullish."
                T
                F
                F

1.9. i) $(p' \cap q')' = p \cup q$
                T   T
                T   T
                T   T
                F   F
        $p \cup q$ = "Stock prices are rising *or* the stock market is bullish."

1.10. *a)* $p = p \cup (p \cap q)$

T	T
T	T
F	F
F	F

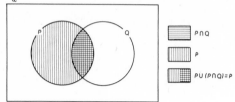

1.11. *a)* $p \cup (q' \cap r)$; TTTTFFTF.

1.12. *a)*

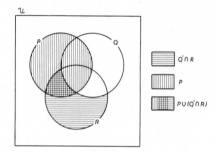

1.13. *a)* $p \ \cup \ (q' \cap r)$

$$
\begin{array}{ccc}
\text{T} & & \text{F F} \\
 & & \swarrow \\
 & & \text{F} \\
 & \searrow & \\
 & \text{T} &
\end{array}
$$

1.14. *a)* $(p \cap q) \cup r$ = "Costs are reduced *and* prices are reduced, *or* profits have increased."

$(p \cup r) \cap (q \cup r)$ = "Costs are reduced *or* profits have increased *and* prices are reduced *or* profits have increased."

$p\ q\ r$	$p \cap q$	$(p \cap q) \cup r$	$p \cup r$	$q \cup r$	$(p \cup r) \cap (q \cup r)$		
T T T	T T T	T *T* T	T T T	T T T	T	*T*	T
T T F	T T T	T *T* F	T T F	T T F	T	*T*	T
T F T	T F F	F *T* T	T T T	F T T	T	*T*	T
T F F	T F F	F *F* F	T T F	F F F	T	*F*	F
F T T	F F T	F *T* T	F T T	T T T	T	*T*	T
F T F	F F T	F *F* F	F F F	T T F	F	*F*	T
F F T	F F F	F *T* T	F T T	F T T	T	*T*	T
F F F	F F F	F *F* F	F F F	F F F	F	*F*	F
①①①	①②①	② ③①	①④①	①⑤①	④	⑥	⑤

1.14.

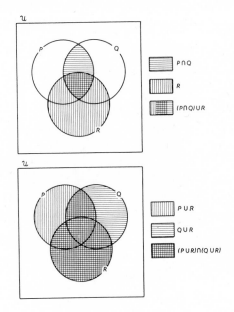

1.15. *a*) $P \cup P = P$ and $P \cap P = P$.

Section 2

2.3. *a*) Factual; TTTFTFTF.
  b) Factual; TFTTTTTT.
  c) Logically true; TTTTTTTT.
  d) Logically false or a self-contradiction; FFFFFFFF.

2.4. *a*)

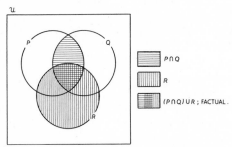

b)

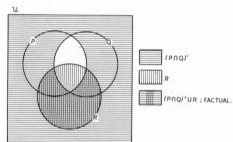

c)

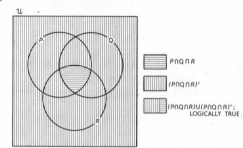

d)

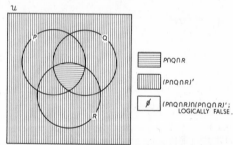

2.6. *a)* $(p \cap q) \cap (p \cap q)'$; logically false or a self-contradiction; FFFF.

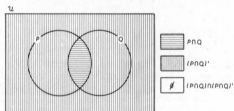

2.7. *a)* $(p \cap q) \cap (p \cap q)'$

CHAPTER 3

Section 1

1.2. Let P and Q be the sets assigned to statements $p =$ "There is full employment and $q =$ "There is prosperity," respectively. Then

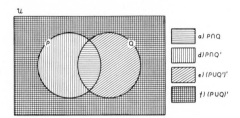

(boxed pattern)	a) $P \cap Q$
(dotted pattern)	d) $P \cap Q'$
(diagonal pattern)	e) $(P \cup Q')'$
(crosshatch pattern)	f) $(P \cup Q)'$

1.4. *a)* Not an implication if statements "There is full employment" and "There is prosperity" are assumed to be unrelated; the conditional becomes an implication if it is assumed that possibility T-F between the statements does not exist.

b) A relation of implication since if statement "Black is a customer" is a true statement, "His credit account represents receivables" must be true; in other words, possibility T-F does not exist.

1.6. *a)*

p'	q' ;	p' does not imply q' since possibility T-F exists;
F	F	statements are unrelated.
F	T	
T	F	
T	T	

f)

$p \cap q$	$p \cup q$;	$p \cap q$ implies $p \cup q$ since possibility T-F does not
T	T	exist.
F	T	
F	T	
F	F	

1.8. Let $p =$ "Interest rates determine bond prices."
$q =$ "Dividends determine stock prices."

a)

p	q ;	p does not imply q; possibility T-F exists; statements
T	T	are unrelated.
T	F	
F	T	
F	F	

f)

$p' \cap q'$	$p' \cup q'$;	$p' \cap q'$ implies $p' \cup q'$ since possibility
F	F	T-F does not exist.
F	T	
F	T	
T	T	

1.10. $(d) \to (b) \to (e) \to (a) \to (c)$

Consider statements (d) $[p \to (p' \to q)]'$ and (b) $p \cap q'$.

$$[p \to (p' \to q)]' \to [p \cap q']$$

F T	F
F T	T
F T	F
F T	F
①②	①

1.12. *a*) Argument is invalid.

p	q	$p \to q$	$(p \to q) \cap p'$	$[(p \to q) \cap p'] \to q'$
T	T	T T T	T F F	F T F
T	F	T F F	F F F	F T T
F	T	F T T	T T T	T F F
F	F	F T F	T T T	T T T
①	①	① ② ①	② ④ ③	④ ⑥ ⑤

1.14. Argument is valid.

p	q	$(p \to q)$	$(p \to q) \cap q'$	$[(p \to q) \cap q'] \to p'$
T	T	T T T	T F F	F T F
T	F	T F F	F F T	F T F
F	T	F T T	T F F	F T T
F	F	F T F	T T T	T T T
①	①	① ② ①	② ④ ③	④ ⑥ ⑤

Section 2

2.1. *a*) Let P and Q be the sets assigned to statements p and q, respectively. Then

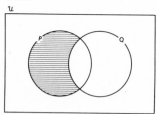

2.3. *a*) $p \to q$.

b) $q \to p$.

c) $p' \to q'$.

d) $q' \to p'$.

2.4. *a*) $p \to q$; conditional

b) $p \leftrightarrow q$; biconditional

c) $p \to q$; conditional

d) $p \to q$; conditional

e) $p \to q$; conditional

f) $p \to q$; conditional

g) $q \to p$; converse of conditional

2.6. $p \to q$ = "If White is a customer, then his account represents assets";
         it involves an implication since if p is true than q must be true.

2.7.   *a*) "If there is prosperity, then there is full employment and if there is
         full employment, then there is prosperity."

2.13. *a*) Logically true; law 9b.

p	q	$(p \cap q)$	$(p \cap q)'$	$p' \cup q'$	$(p \cap q)' \leftrightarrow (p' \cup q')$
T	T	T T T	T F	F F F	F T F
T	F	T F F	F T	F T T	T T T
F	T	F F T	F T	T T F	T T T
F	F	F F F	F T	T T T	T T T
①	①	①②①	② ③	④⑥⑤	③ ⑦ ⑥

Section 3

3.1.   *a*) (1)

p	q	$p \to q$	$(p \to q) \cap p$	$[(p \to q) \cap p] \to q$
T	T	T T T	T T T	T T T
T	F	T F F	F F T	F T F
F	T	F T T	T F F	F T T
F	F	F T F	T F F	F T F
①	①	①②①	② ④③	④ ⑤①

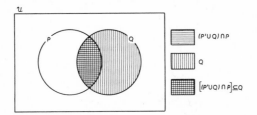

3.4. $(p \underset{\smile}{\cup})$ = "Our economy is in a state of recession *or* in a state of
         prosperity."
         p = "Our economy is in a state of recession."
         ∴ q' = ∴ "It is not true that our economy is in a state of prosperity."

p	q	$p \cup q$	$(p \cup q) \cap p$	$[(p \cup q) \cap p] \to q'$
T	T	T F T	F F T	F T F
T	F	T T F	T T T	T T T
F	T	F T T	T F F	F T F
F	F	F F F	F F F	F T T
①	①	①②①	② ③①	③ ⑤④

3.5. *a)*

p q r	p → r	r → q	p → q	(p → r) ∩ (r → q)	[(p → r) ∩ (r → q)] → (p → q)
T T T	T T T	T T T	T T T	T T T	T T T
T T F	T F F	F T T	T T T	F F T	F T T
T F T	T T T	T F F	T F F	T F F	F T F
T F F	T F F	F T F	T F F	F F T	F T F
F T T	F T T	T T T	F T T	T T T	T T T
F T F	F T F	F T T	F T T	T T T	T T T
F F T	F T T	T F F	F T F	T F F	F T T
F F F	F T F	F T F	F T F	T T T	T T T
①①①	①②①	①③①	①④①	② ⑤ ③	⑤⑥④

3.6. *a)*

p q	p ↔ q	(p ↔ q) ∩ p	[(p ↔ q) ∩ p] → q
T T	T T T	T T T	T T T
T F	T F F	F F T	F T F
F T	F F T	F F F	F T T
F F	F T F	T F F	F T F
① ①	①②①	② ③①	③ ④①

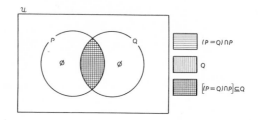

3.7. *a)* (p ∩ q)′ = "It is not true that there is an international crisis and a sharp drop in stock market prices."

p = "But there is an international crisis."

∴ q′ = ∴ "Stock market prices have not declined."

p q	p ∩ q	(p ∩ q)′	(p ∩ q)′ ∩ p	[(p ∩ q)′ ∩ p] → q′
T T	T T T	T F	F F T	F T F
T F	T F F	F T	T T T	T T T
F T	F F T	F T	T F F	F T F
F F	F F F	F T	T F F	F T T
① ①	①②①	② ③	③④①	④ ⑥⑤

3.9. *a)* A valid argument with an exclusive *or* premise such as [(p ⩡ q) ∩ p] → q′ (see Problem 3.4). Also, [(p ∪ q) ∩ p] → p. An invalid argument with an inclusive *or* premise such as [(p ∪ q) ∩ p] → q′ [see Problem 3.1 (c)].

3.10. *a*) i)

p	q	r		$p \to q$			$r' \to q'$			$(p \to q) \cap (r' \to q)'$		
T	T	T		T	T	T		F	T	F		T	T	T
T	T	F		T	T	T		T	F	F		T	F	F
T	F	T		T	F	F		F	T	T		F	F	T
T	F	F		T	F	F		T	T	T		F	F	T
F	T	T		F	T	T		F	T	F		T	T	T
F	T	F		F	T	T		T	F	F		T	F	F
F	F	T		F	T	F		F	T	T		T	T	T
F	F	F		F	T	F		T	T	T		T	T	T
①	①	①		①	②	①		③	⑤	④		②	⑥	⑤

ii) Since $(r' \to q') = (q \to r)$, conclusion $p \to r$ with a truth table TFTFTTTT is implied.

3.11. $[(a \to d) \cap (c \to p) \cap (s \to c) \cap (d \to s)] \to (a \to p)$,
where
    a = "Advertising is effective."
    d = "Demand for the new product will increase."
    c = "Production costs for the new product are reduced."
    p = "Prices will be reduced."
    s = "More units of the new product are sold."

3.12. $\{[f \to (w \cap n)] \cap [(w \cap n) \to b] \cap (b \to p) \cap (p \to f')\} \to (f \to f')$,
where
    f = "Farmers have more income,"
    w = "Farmers work hard,"
    n = "Nature cooperates,"
    b = "Farmers will have a bumper crop of wheat,"
    p = "Wheat prices will fall."

3.14. $\{[(w \cup p) \to i] \cap [i \to (c \cup l)] \cap (l \to u) \cap c' \cap u'\} \to (w \cup p)$,
where
    w = "Wages rise,"
    p = "Prices rise,"
    i = "There will be inflation,"
    c = "The government must impose controls,"
    l = "The cost of living will rise,"
    u = "The government will be unpopular."

3.15. $[(f \to p) \cap (p \to l) \cap l] \to f$,
where
    f = "The market of steel is perfectly free."
    p = "A single (steel) producer cannot affect prices."
    l = "There is a large number of (steel) producers."

Section 4

4.1. *a*) *O*   *e*) *A*
      b) *I*   *f*) *E*
      c) *O*   *g*) *I*
      d) *I*

4.3. *a*)

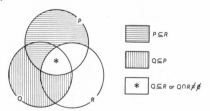

Figure 1: A hypothetical of mood *AAA*.
An existential of mood *AAI*.

4.5. *a*)   i) M = savings
            S = consumption
            P = investment
        ii) *AEE*
        iii) Figure 2: *PM* & *SM*, then *SP*.

4.8. *a*) Let $I = \{x|x \text{ is investment}\}$
            $S = \{x|x \text{ is savings}\}$
            $C = \{x|x \text{ is consumption}\}$.
        Then (1) $I \cap S = I$
             (2) $C \cap S = \varnothing$
             $\therefore C \cap I = \varnothing$
    Proof:

$$
\begin{aligned}
C \cap I &= C \cap (I \cap S) && \text{[by hypothesis 1]} \\
         &= (C \cap S) \cap I && \text{[by 2b \& 3b]} \\
         &= \varnothing \cap I && \text{[by hypothesis 2]} \\
         &= \varnothing && \text{[by 5b]}
\end{aligned}
$$

QED

(For invoked laws see Table 4.1 in Chapter 1.)

4.10. *a*) *AII*, hypothetical, figures 1 and 3.
        b) *AAA*, hypothetical, figure 1.
            AAI, existential, figures 1, 3, and 4.

4.11. *a*) A "All wages are personal income"
        I "Some managerial profits are wages"
        —————————————————————————
        $I \therefore$ "Some managerial profits are personal income"

4.12. *a*) Let P = Things which prevent inflation,
            S = Price and wage controls,
            M = Government policies against inflation.
        A "Only government policies against inflation can prevent inflation"
        A "Price and wage controls are the only government policies against inflation"
        —————————————————————————
        $A \therefore$ "Only price and wage controls can prevent inflation."

CHAPTER 4

Section 1

1.1. *a*) $\{\varnothing, \{1\}, \{2\}, \{3\}, \{4\}, \{5\}, \{1, 2\}, \{1, 3\}, \{1, 4\}, \{1, 5\}, \{2, 3\}, \{2, 4\},$
$\{2, 5\}, \{3, 4\}, \{3, 5\}, \{4, 5\}, \{1, 2, 3\}, \{1, 2, 4\}, \{1, 2, 5\}, \{1, 3, 4\},$
$\{1, 4, 5\}, \{1, 3, 5\}, \{2, 3, 4\}, \{2, 3, 5\}, \{2, 4, 5\}, \{3, 4, 5\}, \{1, 2, 3, 4\},$
$\{1, 2, 3, 5\}, \{1, 3, 4, 5\}, \{1, 2, 4, 5\}, \{2, 3, 4, 5\}, \{1, 2, 3, 4, 5\}\}$

1.2. *c*)

z$\underline{w}$xy	w$\underline{z}$xy	y$\underline{w}$xz	w$\underline{y}$xz	yzx$\underline{w}$	zyx$\underline{w}$
z$\underline{w}$yx	w$\underline{z}$yx	x$\underline{w}$yz	w$\underline{x}$yz	xzy$\underline{w}$	zxy$\underline{w}$
y$\underline{w}$zx	w$\underline{y}$zx	x$\underline{w}$zy	w$\underline{x}$zy	xyz$\underline{w}$	yxz$\underline{w}$
y$z$$\underline{w}$x	z$y$$\underline{w}$x	x$z$$\underline{w}$y	z$x$$\underline{w}$y	x$y$$\underline{w}$z	y$x$$\underline{w}$z

$$w : \frac{9}{12} \qquad x : \frac{1}{12}$$

$$z : \frac{1}{12} \qquad y : \frac{1}{12}$$

1.4. *a*) *Minimal winning:* All coalitions with $n/2 + 1$ members
Winning: All coalitions with $n/2 + 1$ or more members
Losing: All coalitions with $n/2 - 1$ or fewer members
Blocking: All coalitions with $n/2$ members.

1.5. *a*) No ties, chairman's power is zero.
b) $I = \frac{1}{5}$, the same as if chairman had one vote.

1.6. *a*) *Minimal winning:* Must include chairman and any other two members.
Winning: Must include chairman and any other two or more members.
Blocking: Any coalition which includes the chairman or any coalition of three or four members which does not include the chairman.
Losing: Any coalition of less than three members which does not include the chairman.

1.8. *a*) 500,000 to have a veto; 500,001 to be a dictator.

1.10. *a*) Phipps: $\frac{4}{6}$; Furth: $\frac{1}{6}$; Fuller: $\frac{1}{6}$.

1.12. *a*) $I = 1$.

Section 2

2.1. For *addition:*
$$\varnothing \cup \varnothing = \varnothing \qquad \text{[by 6a]}$$
$$\left.\begin{array}{l} \mathfrak{U} \cup \varnothing = \mathfrak{U} \\ \varnothing \cup \mathfrak{U} = \mathfrak{U} \end{array}\right\} \quad \text{[by 1a \& 2a]}$$
$$\mathfrak{U} \cup \mathfrak{U} = \mathfrak{U} \qquad \text{[by 5a]}$$
For *multiplication:*
$$\varnothing \cap \varnothing = \varnothing \qquad \text{[by 5b]}$$
$$\left.\begin{array}{l} \mathfrak{U} \cap \varnothing = \varnothing \\ \varnothing \cap \mathfrak{U} = \varnothing \end{array}\right\} \quad \text{[by 1b \& 2b]}$$
$$\mathfrak{U} \cap \mathfrak{U} = \mathfrak{U} \qquad \text{[by 6b]}$$

2.2.   Nine entries for modulus 3; 16 entries for modulus 4; and 100 entries for modulus 10.

<table>
<tr><td colspan="4">Addition</td><td colspan="4">Multiplication</td></tr>
<tr><td>+</td><td>0</td><td>1</td><td>2</td><td>·</td><td>0</td><td>1</td><td>2</td></tr>
<tr><td>0</td><td>0</td><td>1</td><td>2</td><td>0</td><td>0</td><td>0</td><td>0</td></tr>
<tr><td>1</td><td>1</td><td>2</td><td>0</td><td>1</td><td>0</td><td>1</td><td>2</td></tr>
<tr><td>2</td><td>2</td><td>0</td><td>1</td><td>2</td><td>0</td><td>2</td><td>1</td></tr>
</table>

2.3.   *a)*

(1) Decimal Number	(2) Binary Number	(3) Parity Bit	(4) Modulus 2 Even Parity
6	00110	0	0
7	00111	1	0
8	01000	1	0
9	01001	0	0
10	01010	0	0
11	01011	1	0
12	01100	0	0
13	01101	1	0
14	01110	1	0
15	01111	0	0
16	10000	1	0

2.4.   *a)* 11001.
       c) 10100.11.

2.5.   *a)* 118.
       c) 3.75.

2.6.   *a)* 1010; 10.
       b) 11111; 31.

2.7.   *a)* 1111.
       c) 10101.11.

2.8.   *a)* 10001.

2.9.   *a)* 1010.
       c) 10.10.

2.10. *a)*

$$\begin{array}{r} 101 \\ \times\ 111 \\ \hline 101 \\ 101 \\ 101 \\ \hline 100011 \end{array} \qquad \begin{array}{r} 101 \\ \times\ 111 \\ \hline 101 \\ 101 \\ \hline 1111 \\ 101 \\ \hline 100011 \end{array} \qquad \begin{array}{r} 5 \\ \times\ 7 \\ \hline 35 \end{array}$$

2.11. *a*) 1111.

  c) 0.001.

2.12. *a*)

```
      110                    6
 10/ 1101            2/  13
   −   10    001       −  2    1
     ──────             ────
     1011                 11
   −   10    010       −  2    2
     ──────             ────
     1001                  9
   −   10    011       −  2    3
     ──────             ────
      111                  7
   −   10    100       −  2    4
     ──────             ────
      101                  5
   −   10    101       −  2    5
     ──────             ────
       11                  3
   −   10    110       −  2    6
     ──────             ────
        1                  1
```

  c) Quotient 100; Remainder 0.0011 approximately.

2.13. *a*) Quotient 11; Remainder 0.

  c) Quotient 11; Remainder 0.

2.17. *a*)

Decimal	Octal	Decimal	Octal
1	1	16	20
2	2	17	21
3	3	18	22
4	4	19	23
5	5	20	24
6	6	21	25
7	7	22	26
8	10	23	27
9	11	24	30
10	12	25	31
11	13	26	32
12	14	27	33
13	15	28	34
14	16	29	35
15	17	30	36

2.19. *a*) 3, 4, 4.585, respectively.

Section 3

3.1.   *a)*

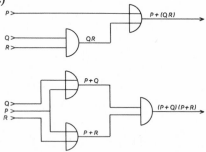

Left-hand side requires fewer switches.

b)

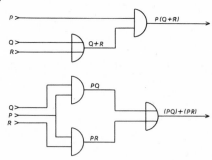

Left-hand side requires fewer switches.

3.2.   *a)*

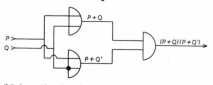

Using the basic symbols and invoking the laws of Boolean algebra, we have

$$(P \cup Q) \cap (P \cup Q') = P \cup (Q \cap Q')$$
$$= P \cup \varnothing$$
$$= P.$$

b)

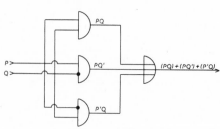

Using the basic symbols and invoking the laws of Boolean algebra, we have

$$
\begin{aligned}
(P \cap Q) \cup (P \cap Q') \cup (P' \cap Q) &= (P \cap Q) \cup (P' \cap Q) \cup \\
&\quad (P \cap Q') \cup (P \cap Q) \\
&= [(P \cap Q') \cup (P \cap Q)] \cup \\
&\quad [(P' \cap Q) \cup (P \cap Q)] \\
&= [P \cap (Q' \cup Q)] \cup [Q \cap \\
&\quad (P' \cup P')] \\
&= (P \cap \mathfrak{U}) \cup (Q \cap \mathfrak{U}) \\
&= P \cup Q.
\end{aligned}
$$

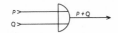

3.3. *a)*

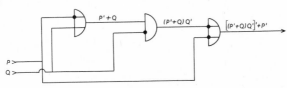

b)

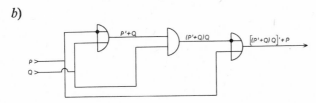

3.6. *a)* $PQ + P'Q'$ (biconditional or equality circuit).

3.7.

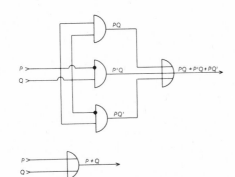

Circuit $PQ + P'Q + PQ'$ may be simplified to $P + Q$ as follows:

$$
\begin{aligned}
(P \cap Q) \cup (P' \cap Q) \cup (P \cap Q') &= \\
&= (P \cap Q) \cup (P' \cap Q) \cup (P \cap Q') \cup (P \cap Q) \\
&= [(P \cap Q') \cup (P \cap Q)] \cup [(P' \cap Q) \cup (P \cap Q)] \\
&= P \cup Q.
\end{aligned}
$$

(see omitted steps in 3.2b)

3.9. *a)*

P	Q	$P \cup Q$			$P' \cup Q'$			$(P \cup Q) \cap (P' \cup Q')$		
$\in$	$\in$	$\in$	$\in$	$\in$	$\notin$	$\notin$	$\notin$	$\in$	$\notin$	$\notin$
$\in$	$\notin$	$\in$	$\in$	$\notin$	$\notin$	$\in$	$\in$	$\in$	$\in$	$\in$
$\notin$	$\in$	$\notin$	$\in$	$\in$	$\in$	$\in$	$\notin$	$\in$	$\in$	$\in$
$\notin$	$\notin$	$\notin$	$\notin$	$\notin$	$\in$	$\in$	$\in$	$\notin$	$\notin$	$\in$
①	①	①②①			③⑤④			②	⑥	⑤

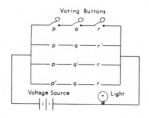

3.10. *a)*

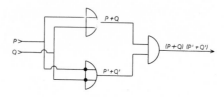

3.13. $2n - 1$.

Section 4

4.1. *a)*

Step	Description	
1	1011	U.R.
	0000	L.R.
2	0010	U.R.
	1011	L.R.
3	0001	U.R.
	1101	L.R.
4	0000	U.R.
	1110	L.R.

4.2. *a)*

Step	*Description*	
1	1000	U.R.
	1001	L.R.
2	0111	CT
	1001	L.R.
3	0000	U.R.

OF
| 0 | 0001 | L.R. |

4.3. *a)*

Step	*Description*	

| 1 | 1111 | U.R. |

L.R.   C

1	0000	1111
2	0111	1 | 111
3	1011	01 | 11
4	1101	001 | 1
5	1110	0001

4.4. *a)*

Step   *Description*

OF
| 1 | 0 | 1111 | L.R. |
| | | 101 | U.R. |

OF
| 2 | 0 | 1111 | L.R. |
| | + | 011 | CT |

OF ───────
| 1 | 0101 | L.R. |

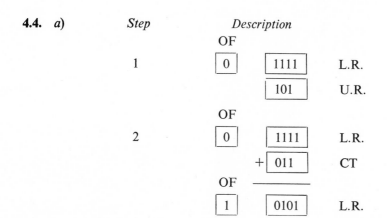
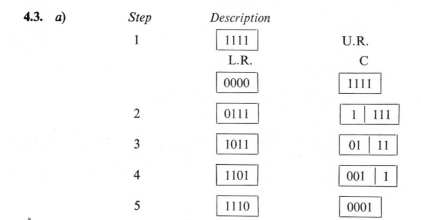

	C	OF		
3	0001	0	101	L.R.
			011	CT
		OF	———	
		1	000	L.R.
4	0011	0	000	L.R.
			+ 011	C.T.
			———	
		0	011	L.R.
5		0	011	L.R.
			+ 101	U.R.
			———	
	0011	1	000	L.R.

4.5. *a)*

	Step	Description	
	1	1010	U.R.
		0000	L.R.
	2	0101	U.R.
		1010	L.R.
	3	0111	U.R.
		1111	L.R.
	4	1000	CT
		1111	L.R.
	5	0000	U.R.
	OF		
	0	1000	L.R.

4.6. *a)*

Storage Address	*Instruction Routine*	*Address*
00	RDS = Read number 1011 in	09
01	RDS = Read number 0010 in	10
02	RDS = Read number 0001 in	11
03	CLA = Clear and add 1011 in	09
04	ADD = Add 0010 in	10
05	ADD = Add 0001 in	11
06	STA = Store accumulator in	09
07	PRT = Print result stored in	09
08	HLT = Stop	

————Encoded Instruction Routine————

Storage Address	*Instructions*
00000	1010 | 01001
00001	1010 | 01010
00010	1010 | 01011
00011	0001 | 01001
00100	0010 | 01010
00101	0010 | 01011
00110	0111 | 01001
00111	1000 | 01001
01000	0000 |

CHAPTER 5

Section 1

1.1. i) $x + 3x = 90$.
ii) $x = 22.5$.
iii) 23 and 67 freight cars.

1.2. i) $45x + (500 - x)60 = 25,000$.
ii) $x = 333.33$.
iii) \$333,000 at 4.5 percent and \$167,000 at 6 percent.

1.4. i) $S - 0.30S = 20 + 1$.
ii) $S = 30$.
iii) \$30.

1.5. *a)* i) $c + 0.40c = 0.70$.
ii) $c = 0.50$
iii) \$0.50

b)   i) $0.55x + (100 - x)0.35 = 50.$
   ii) $x = 75.$
   iii) A: 75 pounds; B: 25 pounds.

1.10. 1,078 toys.

1.11. 6 percent.

1.14. 10 weeks.

Section 2

2.1.   a) $x = 6.$
   d) $x = \pm 3.$

2.2.   a) $x = 4$; $3x - 12 = 0$, redundant.
   c) $x = 12$; $x - 3 - 9 = 0$, redundant.
   g) $x_1 = 7$, $x_2 = 4$; $x^2 - 11x + 28 = 0$, redundant.

2.3.   a) $x_1 = 10$, $x_2 = -3$; $x^2 - 7x - 30 = 0$, neither.
   d) $x_1 = 0$, $x_2 = 5$; $x^2 - 5x = 0$, redundant.

2.4.   a) $x_1 = -4$, $x_2 = 2$; $3x^2 + 6x - 24 = 0$, redundant.
   b) $x = 3 \pm \sqrt{11}$; $x^2 - 6x - 2 = 0$, neither.

2.6.   a) $x = \pm 5.$
   b) $x = \pm 5i.$
   d) $x = \pm 3i\sqrt{5}.$

2.7.   a) $(x + 2)(x - 3) = 0$; $x_1 = -2$, $x_2 = 3.$
   b) $(x - 3)(x - 2) = 0$; $x_1 = 3$, $x_2 = 2.$
   g) $(3x + 2)(3x + 2) = 0$; $x = -\frac{2}{3}.$

2.8.   a) $x^2 + 6x + 9 = 9$; $x_1 = 0$, $x_2 = -6.$
   b) $x^2 - 8x + 16 = 36$; $x_1 = 10$, $x_2 = -2.$

2.10.   a) $x(x^2 - 1) = 0$; $x_1 = 0$, $x_2 = 1$, $x_3 = -1.$

   b) $(x - 1)(x^2 + x + 1) = 0$; $x_1 = 1$, $x_2 = -\dfrac{1}{2} + \dfrac{i\sqrt{3}}{2}$,

   $x_3 = -\dfrac{1}{2} - \dfrac{i\sqrt{3}}{2}.$

   c) $u = \pm 1$ and $x^2 = \sqrt{\pm 1}$; $x_1 = 1$, $x_2 = -1$, $x_3 = 1i$, $x_4 = -1i.$

2.11.   a) $x^2 + x - 13 = 0$; second.

2.12.   b) i) $r_1 + r_2 = -2$ and $r_1 r_2 = 1$; $r_1 = -1$, $r_2 = -1.$
   c) i) $r_1 + r_2 = -2$; $r_2 = -5$, $k = -15.$

2.13.   b) i) $x^2 + x - 6 = 0.$
   v) $x^2 - 6x + 18 = 0.$

Section 3

3.1. *a*) i) $\overline{AB} = 6;\ \overline{BA} = -6.$
      ii) $|AB| = 6.$

    c) i) $\overline{AB} = -19;\ \overline{BA} = 19.$
      ii) $|AB| = 19.$

    h) i) $\overline{AB} = 0;\ \overline{BA} = 0.$
      ii) $|AB| = 0.$

3.3. *a*) $x' = 8.5.$

3.9. *a*) Let x_1 and x_2 be the coordinates of points A and B shown on a cc-line below.

$$
\begin{array}{ccc}
A & C & B \\
\hline
x_1 & \bar{x} & x_2
\end{array}
$$

We wish to prove that

$$\bar{x} = \frac{x_1 + 2x_2}{3},$$

where point C with coordinate $\bar{x}$ is $\frac{2}{3}$ of the distance $|AB|$.

Proof :

Since it is given that $\dfrac{\overline{AC}}{\overline{AB}} = \dfrac{\bar{x} - x_1}{x_2 - x_1} = \dfrac{2}{3}$, we have

$$2(x_2 - x_1) = 3(\bar{x} - x_1)$$

$$3\bar{x} = 3x_1 - 2x_1 + 2x_2$$

$$\bar{x} = \frac{x_1 + 2x_2}{3} \quad \text{QED}$$

The same holds true for $\dfrac{\overline{CA}}{\overline{BA}}$.

3.11. *a*) 5;
     b) ≈ 8.2
     e) ≈ 9.9
     g) ≈ 4.5

3.13. *a*) $Q_{\mathrm{I}},\ Q_{\mathrm{I}};$
     b) zero point, $Q_{\mathrm{I}};$
     e) $Q_{\mathrm{II}},\ Q_{\mathrm{IV}};$
     g) $Q_{\mathrm{III}},\ Q_{\mathrm{III}}.$

3.15. $(-5, 5),\ (-5, -5),\ (5, -5).$

3.18. $(-1.5, -1.5).$

Section 4

4.1. *a)*

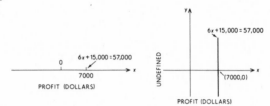

4.2. *a)*

4.5. *a)* i) $y = -2x + 2$, $m = -2$.

ii)

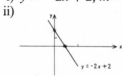

b) i) $y = -2x$.   ii)

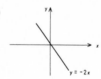

4.6. *a)*

b)

4.9. *a)* $2x + 5y = 50$.

b)

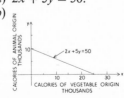

4.11. *a*), *b*), *c*)

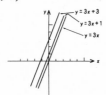

4.12. *a*)   i) $y = -\dfrac{3}{5}x - \dfrac{6}{5}$.

ii) $y = -\dfrac{3}{5}x + 3$.

iii)

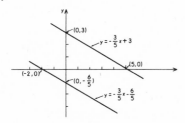

4.13. *a*)   i) $y + 5 = 3x - 18$.
ii) $y = 3x - 23$.
iii)

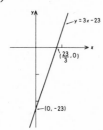

b)   i) $y - 7 = -\dfrac{1}{3}x - 1$.

ii) $y = -\dfrac{1}{3}x + 6$.

iii)

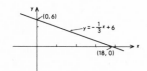

4.14. *a*) i) $y = 4x - 5$.
       ii)

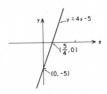

b) i) $y = 3x + 3$.
       ii)

4.15. *a*) i)

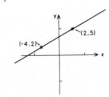

   ii) $y = \dfrac{1}{2} x + 4$.

b) i)

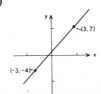

   ii) $y = \dfrac{11}{6} x + \dfrac{3}{2}$.

4.16. *a*) i) $y = -\dfrac{6}{5} x + 6$.

   ii) $m = -\dfrac{6}{5}$.

   iii)

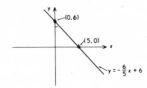

CHAPTER 6

Section 1

1.1. *a)* i) $f(x) = 2x$.

ii)

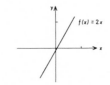

$$\frac{\Delta y}{\Delta x} = \frac{f(4) - f(1)}{4 - 1} = \frac{8 - 2}{3} = 2.$$

iii) $f^{-1}(y) = \tfrac{1}{2}y$.

iv)

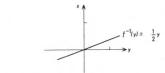

$$\frac{\Delta x}{\Delta y} = \frac{f^{-1}(4) - f^{-1}(1)}{4 - 1} = \frac{2 - \tfrac{1}{2}}{3} = \frac{1}{2}.$$

1.2. *a)* i) $f(x) = 2x$.

x	-4	-3	-2	-1	0	1	2	3	4
$y = f(x)$	-8	-6	-4	-2	0	2	4	6	8

ii)

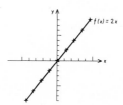

iii)

y	-8	-6	-4	-2	0	2	4	6	8
$x = f(y)$	-4	-3	-2	-1	0	1	2	3	4

iv) Yes, since above line is a portion of the graph of $f^{-1}(y) = \tfrac{1}{2}y$.

1.3. *a*) i) $p = -\frac{3}{2}q + 27$.

ii) Demand function: $m = -\frac{3}{2}$; when q increases by one unit price decreases by $\frac{3}{2}$ units.

iii)

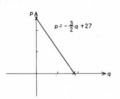

v) $q = -\frac{2}{3}p + 18$.

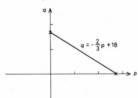

When p increases by one unit, q decreases by $\frac{2}{3}$ units.

1.5. *a*) $p = f(q)$.
  c) $P = f(F, V, R)$.

1.6. *a*) $f(x) = -50x + 2000$.
  b) x representing time in months is the independent, and y representing average undepreciated dollar value per truck the dependent variable.

1.7. *a*) *a*)

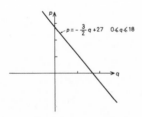

b) i) *Mathematical*:   *Empirical*:
        Domain: $-\infty < p < +\infty$.   Domain: $0 \leqslant p \leqslant 27$.
        Range: $-\infty < q < +\infty$.   Range: $0 \leqslant q \leqslant 18$.
    ii) *Mathematical*:   *Empirical*:
        Domain: $-\infty < q < +\infty$.   Domain: $0 \leqslant q \leqslant 18$.
        Range: $-\infty < p < +\infty$.   Range: $0 \leqslant p \leqslant 27$.

1.8. *a*)   i) (1, 1), (−1, 1), (2, 4), (−2, 4), (3, 9), (−3, 9), (0, 0), (4, 16), (−4, 16).

ii) Function.

iii)

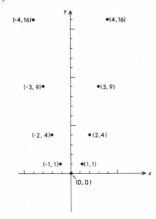

c)   i) (0, 0), (1, 1), (2, 2), (3, 3), (4, 4).

ii) Function.

iii)

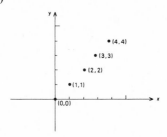

1.9. *a*)   i) Function.

ii) Domain: $x \geqslant 0$. Range: $y \geqslant 0$. Rule: When x is a certain value y is equal to that value.

iii)

b) i) Relation.
  ii) Domain: $x \geqslant 0$. Range: $-\infty < y < +\infty$.
  iii)

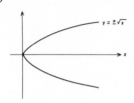

$$y = \pm\sqrt{x}$$

1.12. a) Domain: $x \neq 0$.
       Range: $y \neq 0$.
1.14. a) 6.
1.15. c) 4.
       d) $\sqrt{2}$.
       e) $\frac{1}{4}$.
1.16. a) -1.
       b) Not defined.
1.17. c) 3.
1.18. a) $S = P(1 + nr)$.
1.19. a) $x^2 + 2x$.
       b) $x^2 - 2x - 2$.

Section 2

2.5. a) $y + 100x - 2600 = 0$.
      b) $y = -100x + 2600$.
2.6. a) $f(h) = 3h$.
2.7. a) $f(t) = 450t + 20,000$.
2.8. a) $f(x) = 0.00625x + 1$.
2.9. a) $f(x) = 1.40x$.
2.10. a)

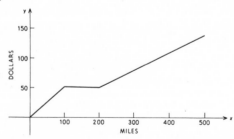

2.12. a) Sales: $S(x) = 0.20x$.
        Cost: $C(x) = 0.18x + 10,000,000$.
        Profit: $P(x) = 0.02x - 10,000,000$.

Section 3

3.1. *a)*

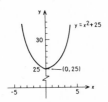

b)

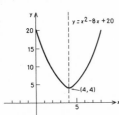

g)

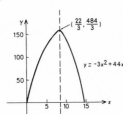

h)

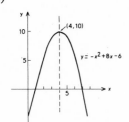

3.2. *a)* $b^2 - 4ac < 0$; graph does not touch the x-axis; roots of $x^2 + 25 = 0$ are conjugate complex numbers.

b) $b^2 - 4ac < 0$; graph does not touch the x-axis; roots of $x^2 - 8x + 20 = 0$ are conjugate complex numbers.

g) $b^2 - 4ac > 0$; graph crosses the x-axis at $x = 0$ and $x = \frac{44}{3}$ which represent the roots of $-3x^2 + 44x = 0$.

h) $b^2 - 4ac > 0$; graph crosses the x-axis at $x = 4 - \sqrt{10}$ and $x = 4 + \sqrt{10}$ which represent the roots of $-x^2 + 8x - 6 = 0$.

3.3. *a)* $a = 1 > 0$; graph concave upward.

   b) $a = 1 > 0$; graph concave upward.

   g) $a = -3 < 0$; graph concave downward.

   h) $a = -1 < 0$; graph concave downward.

3.6. *a)*

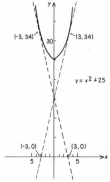

At $x = 3$; $m \approx 5\frac{2}{3}$. At $x = -3$; $m \approx -5\frac{2}{3}$.

g) At $x = 3$; $m \approx 26\frac{1}{5}$.

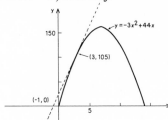

At $x = 7\frac{1}{3}$; $m = 0$.

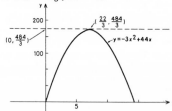

At $x = 9$; $m \approx -10\frac{1}{4}$.

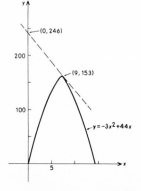

3.8. Five weeks.

   a) $9800.

   b) $0.035 per pound, 280,000 pounds.

   c)

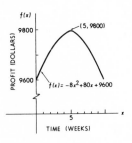

3.10. 1400 units.

   a) $3920.

   b) $2.80.

   c)

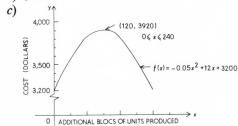

   d)

Run size	800	1050	1300	1400	1500	1750	2000
Unit cost	4.00	3.50	3.00	2.80	2.60	2.10	1.60

$$g(x) = -\frac{x}{500} + 5.6.$$

3.11. *a)* $P(x) = -2x^2 + 12x.$

   b) 3 units; price $12; profit, $18.

   c)

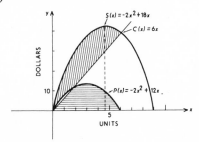

3.15. *b)* $f(x) = -x^2 + 20x.$

   d) $T(c) = -\dfrac{c^2}{400} + 11c - 12,000.$

3.16. *b*) $f(x) = x^2 - 100x + 4000.$

d)

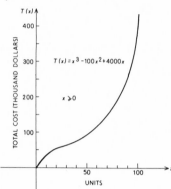

3.17. $f(x) = x^2 - 95x + 3750.$

3.18. *a*) $S(x) = -2x^2 + 152x.$
$P(x) = -3x^2 + 252x - 4000.$

3.19. *a*) $C(p) = vep + vb + f.$
b) $S(p) = ep^2 + bp.$
c) $P(p) = ep^2 + bp - vep - vb - f.$

CHAPTER 7

Section 1

1.3. Let $p^* = 7.536.$ Find $q^* \approx 5.97$ and check.

1.4. *a*) i) $q^* \approx 1.097; p^* \approx 6.194.$
c) i) $p^* \approx 4.03; q^* \approx 27.45.$
f) i) $p^* = \sqrt{18}; q^* = 36.$

1.5. *a*) i)

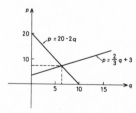

ii) $q^* = 6\frac{3}{8}; p^* = 7\frac{1}{4}.$

b) i)

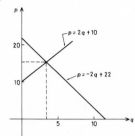

ii) $q^* = 3$; $p^* = 16$.

1.6. *a*) i)

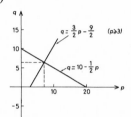

ii) $p^* = 7\frac{1}{4}$; $q^* = 6\frac{3}{8}$.

b) i)

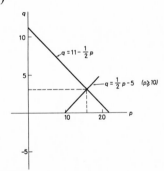

ii) $p^* = 16$; $q^* = 3$.

1.7. *a*) i)

ii) $q^* = 4$; $p^* = 18$.

d) i)

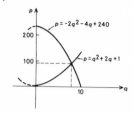

ii) $q^* = 7.98$; $p^* = 80.64$.

1.8. *a*) i)

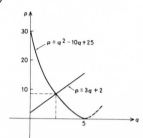

ii) $q^* \approx 2.1125$; $p^* \approx 8.34$.

1.9. *a*) i)

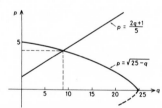

ii) $q^* \approx 9.375$; $p^* \approx 3.95$.

1.10. *a*) i)

ii) $q^* \approx 13.03$; $p^* \approx 4.60$.

1.11. *a*)   i)

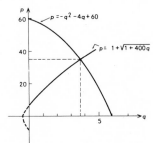

ii) $q^2 + 4q + \sqrt{1 + 400q} = 59$.
iii) Let $q = 4$. Find p and check.
    Let $q = 3.7$. Find p and check.

1.12. *a*) $p_1 = 3.5; p_2 = 4; q_1 = 9; q_2 = 20$.
Demand: $q_1 \leqslant 11\frac{1}{4}$ for $q_2 = 0$ and positive p_2 and $q_2 \leqslant 9\frac{3}{8}$ for $q_1 = 0$ and $p_1 > 0$. *Supply:* $q_1 > 0$ and $q_2 > 0$ as required. Results significant since equilibrium values satisfy above restrictions.

b) $p_1 = 5; p_2 = 6; q_1 = 6; q_2 = 4$.
Demand: $q_2 \leqslant 10$ for $q_2 = 0$ and $p_1 > 0$ and q_1 not restricted but $q_2 \leqslant 10$ for $p_1 > 0$. *Supply:* $q_1 > 0$ but $q_2 \leqslant \frac{7}{3}$ for $p_1 > 0$ and $q_1 \geqslant 2$; $q_2 \geqslant 2$ for $p_2 > 0$. Results not significant since equilibrium values do not satisfy all restrictions. $q_2 = 4$ while $q_2 \leqslant \frac{7}{3}$ for $p_2 > 0$.

c) $q_1 = 3; q_2 = 2; p_1 = 4; p_2 = 6$.
Demand: $p_1 \leqslant 12$ for $p_2 = 0$ and $q_2 > 0$ and $p_2 \leqslant 17$ for $p_1 = 0$ and $q_1 > 0$. *Supply:* $q_2 \leqslant 9$ for $p_1 = 0$. Results significant since equilibrium values satisfy above restrictions.

1.13. *a*)   i) $q^* = 11; p^* = 8$.
ii) $q_t = 10.2; p_t = 9.6$.
    $q_s = 11.4; p_s = 7.2$.
iii)

c)   i) $q^* \approx 1.33$; $p^* \approx 6.67$

    ii) $q_t \approx 1.06$; $p_t \approx 8.37$
       $q_s \approx 1.52$; $p_s = 5.04$.

    iii)

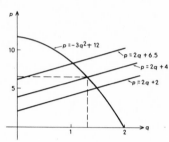

d)   i) $q^* = 10.4$; $p^* = 2.88$.

    ii) $q_t = 10$; $p_t = 3$.
       $q_s \approx 10.85$; $p_s \approx 2.77$.

    iii)

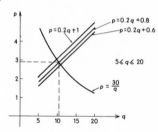

1.14. a)   i) For $p = 0.2q + 1$, $q^* = 10$ and $p^* = 3$.
           For $p = 0.1q + 2$, $q^* = 10$ and $p^* = 3$.

     ii) For $p = 0.2q + 1$, $q_t = 9.20$ and $p_t = 3.24$.
       For $p = 0.1q + 2$, $q_t = 9$ and $p_t = 3.30$.

    iii)

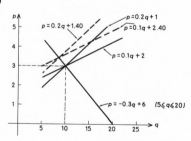

1.15. *a*) i) $q^* = 4$; $p^* = 10$.
      ii) For $p = 11$, $t = 3$; for $p = 8$, $s = 6$.
      iii)

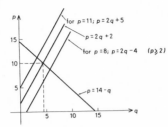

1.17. *a*)

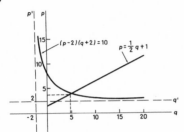

$q^* = 4.9$; $p^* = 3.45$.

Section 2

2.1. *a*) 8   [by 1].
      b) 9   [by 1].
      c) 81   [by 2].
      d) $\frac{1}{25}$ [by 5].
      e) 16   [by 6, 1].
      f) 4   [by 7, 1].
      g) 5^{10} [by 3].
      h) 1   [by 8].
      i) 1000   [by 4, 1].

      j) a^7 [by 2].
      k) $1/a$ [by 6].
      l) x^6/y^{10} [by 3].
      m) b^2/a^2 [by 6].
      n) a [by 7].
      o) 2   [by 5, 7].
      p) 2/3   [by 4, 7].
      q) 1   [by 8].
      r) 625   [by 2, 1].

2.2. *a*) $2 = \log_{10} 100$.
      b) $5 = \log_e 148.41$.
      c) $2 = \log_4 16$.

      d) $0 = \log_a 1$.
      e) $-3 = \log_5 1/125$.
      f) $\frac{1}{4} = \log_{16} 2$.

2.3. *a*) $10^0 \;\; = 1$.
      b) $2^6 \;\;\; = 64$.
      c) $10^{-2} = 0.01$.

      d) $e^1 \;\;\; = e$.
      e) $10^2 \;\; = 100$.
      f) $4^{3/2} = 8$.

2.4. *a*) 5.   *d*) 1.
      b) -4.   *e*) $\frac{1}{2}$.
      c) 10.   *f*) $-\frac{1}{4}$.

2.7. i) *a*) 1.8129.
        b) -0.8069 or $9.1931 - 10$.
       ii) *a*) 4.17439.
        b) -1.8579.

2.8. i) *a*) 14.
　　　　 b) 0.14.
　　 ii) *a*) 10.
　　　　 b) 105.
　　　　 c) 0.50.
2.10. *a*) i) $f(x) = e^{1.6094x}$.
　　　　　 ii) 25.
　　　 e) i) $f(x) = e^{2.3026x + 2.3026}$.
　　　　　 ii) 1000.
　　　 f) i) $f(x) = e^{-5.9914x}$.
　　　　　 ii) 0.00000625.
2.11. *a*) i) $f(x) = 10^{0.6990x}$.
　　　　　 ii) 25.
2.12. *a*) $x = 0$; $y = 77,500$.
　　　　　 $x = 1$; $y = 59,985$.
　　　　　 $x = 8$; $y = 9,998$.
　　　 b) $y = 77,500e^{-0.25618x}$.
　　　 c) $x = 0$; $y = 77,500$.
　　　　　 $x = 1$; $y = 59,985$.
　　　　　 $x = 8$; $y = 9,998$.
2.13. *b*) $E(t) = 100(0.951)^t$.
2.15. *b*) $S_1(x) = 0.9938(0.9943)^n (54,000,000 + 0.0016x)$.
　　　　　 $S_3(x) = 0.9993(0.9977)^n (40,000,000 + 0.0022x)$.
2.18. *b*) $f(x) = 1.63x^{0.9154}$.

Section 3

3.1. *a*) $A = \$12,750$.
3.2. *a*) $P = \$8000$.
3.3. *a*) $i = 5$ percent.
3.4. *a*) $n = 2$.
3.5. *a*) $A = \$162,900$.
3.6. *a*) $i \approx 4.5$ percent.
3.7. *a*) $r \approx 6.17$ percent.
3.8. *a*) $P = \$10,000$.
3.9. *a*) No, since $P = \$25,158 < \$26,000$.
　　　 b) Yes, since $P = \$26,628 > \$26,000$.
3.13. *a*) $i \approx 7.5$ percent.
3.19. *a*) $P = \$5$ million.

CHAPTER 8

Section 1

1.1. *a)* $x_1 < \frac{3}{2}$.

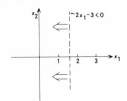

b) $x_1 \leqslant \frac{3}{2}$.

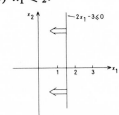

g) $x_1 \geqslant \frac{12}{7}$.

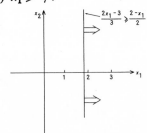

i) $-3 \leqslant x_1 \leqslant 3$ or $|x_1| \leqslant 3$.

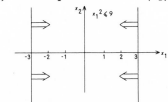

1.2.   *a)* (i)–(iii)

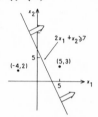

Closed half space.

c) (i)–(iii)

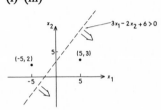

Open half space.

1.3.   *a)* 1.1.(*a*) and 1.1(*b*).
   b) 1.1(*b*) and 1.1(*c*).
   c) 1.2(*f*).
   d) 1.2(*a*).

1.4.   *a)* (i)

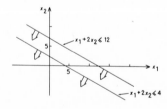

1.5.   *a)* (i)–(ii)

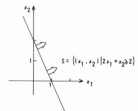

b) (i)–(ii)

$$S = \{(x_1, x_2) \mid 2x_1 + x_2 \geqslant 2 \text{ and } 2x_1 + x_2 \leqslant 2\}$$

1.6. *a*) (i)–(iii)

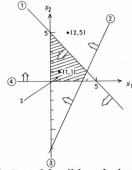

(1) $x_1 + x_2 \leqslant 5$
(2) $2x_1 - x_2 \leqslant 7$
(3) $x_1 \geqslant 0$
(4) $x_2 \geqslant 0$

iv) Set of feasible solutions is bounded and closed.
v) $S = \{(x_1, x_2) \mid x_1 + x_2 \leqslant 5 \text{ and } 2x_1 - x_2 \leqslant 7 \text{ and } x_1 \geqslant 0 \text{ and } x_2 \geqslant 0\}$.

g) (i)–(iii)

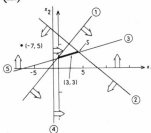

(1) $3x_1 - 2x_2 \geqslant -5$
(2) $x_1 + x_2 \leqslant 8$
(3) $x_1 - 3x_2 + 6 = 0$
(4) $x_1 \geqslant -13/7$
(5) $x_2 \geqslant 0$

iv) Set of feasible solutions is bounded and closed.
v) $S = \{(x_1, x_2) \mid 3x_1 - 2x_2 + 5 \geqslant 0 \text{ and } x_1 + x_2 \leqslant 8 \text{ and } x_1 - 3x_2 + 6 = 0 \text{ and } x_1 \geqslant -13/7 \text{ and } x_2 \geqslant 0\}$.

1.7.

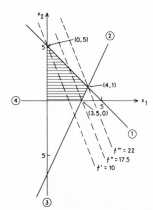

$f_{max} = 5x_1 + 2x_2$
subject to
(1) $x_1 + x_2 \leqslant 5$
(2) $2x_1 - x_2 \leqslant 7$
(3) $x_1 \geqslant 0$
(4) $x_2 \geqslant 0$

1.10.

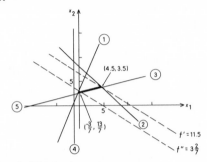

$$f_{min} = x_1 + 2x_2$$
subject to
(1) $3x_1 - 2x_2 \geqslant -5$
(2) $x_1 + x_2 \leqslant 8$
(3) $x_1 - 3x_2 + 6 = 0$
(4) $x_1 \geqslant -13/7$
(5) $x_2 \geqslant 0$

1.12. *a)* (1) $f_{max}(80, 0) = \$24.$
(2) $f_{max}(0, 50) = \$15.$

1.13.

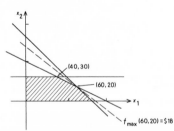

$x_1 = 2, \ x_2 = 3.$

1.14.

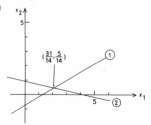

$x_1 = 60; \ x_2 = 20.$ Only 4 pounds of chocolate mix will be used.

Section 2

2.1. *a)* i) $x_1 = \frac{31}{14}; \ x_2 = \frac{5}{14}.$
ii) Independent.
iii)

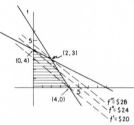

(1) $2x_1 - 4x_2 = 3$
(2) $x_1 + 5x_2 = 4$

c)   i) No common solution.
    ii) Inconsistent.
    iii)

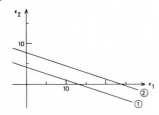

(1) $x_1 + 3x_2 = 12$
(2) $x_1 + 3x_2 = 24$

2.2. *a)* i) No common solution.
    ii) Inconsistent.
    iii)

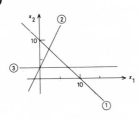

(1) $x_1 + x_2 = 10$
(2) $2x_1 - x_2 = -2$
(3) $x_2 = 3$

d)   i) $x_1 = 4;\ x_2 = 4.$
    ii) Consistent.
    iii)

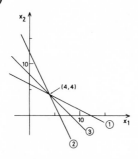

(1) $x_1 + 2x_2 = 12$
(2) $2x_1 + x_2 = 12$
(3) $x_1 + x_2 = 8$

2.3. *a)* i) $x_1 = 1;\ x_2 = 3;\ x_3 = 2.$
    ii) System consistent with a unique solution.

2.4. *c)* $x_1 = 2 - x_4;\ x_2 = 1 + 2x_4;\ x_3 = 3x_4 - 1;$
    system consistent with infinitely many solutions.

2.5. *a)* $f_{\min}(0, 20) = \$40.$

2.6.

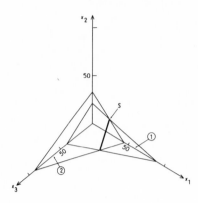

(1) $x_1 + 4x_2 + 2x_3 = 80$
(2) $2x_1 + 3x_2 + x_3 = 90$

2.7. *a)* $\left. \begin{matrix} x_1 + x_2 = 5 \\ 2x_1 - x_2 = 7 \end{matrix} \right\} \rightarrow \begin{matrix} x_1 + 0 = 4 \\ 0 + x_2 = 1 \end{matrix}$ $f_{max} = 5\,(4) + 2\,(1) = 22.$

2.11. *a)* $f_{min}(1, 3, 2) = \$22.$
b)

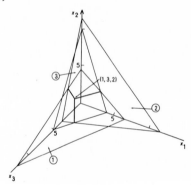

(1) $2x_1 + 3x_2 + x_3 \geqslant 13$
(2) $x_1 + x_2 + 4x_3 \geqslant 12$
(3) $3x_1 + x_2 + 2x_3 \geqslant 10$
   $x_i \geqslant 0 \;(i = 1, 2, 3)$

The set of feasible solution is unbounded.

2.12. *a)* $f_{max}(2, 3, 4) = \$52.$
b)

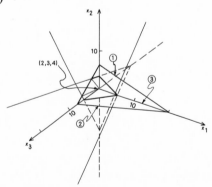

(1) $2x_1 + 3x_2 - x_3 \leqslant 9$
(2) $3x_1 - x_2 + 2x_3 \leqslant 11$
(3) $x_1 + 2x_2 + 3x_3 \leqslant 20$
   $x_i \geqslant 0 \;(i = 1, 2, 3)$

The set of feasible solutions is bounded and closed.

2.15. *a)* $f_{\max}(2, 3, 1) = \$35.$

b)

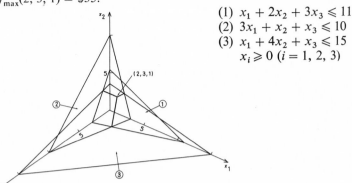

$$(1) \quad x_1 + 2x_2 + 3x_3 \leqslant 11$$
$$(2) \quad 3x_1 + x_2 + x_3 \leqslant 10$$
$$(3) \quad x_1 + 4x_2 + x_3 \leqslant 15$$
$$x_i \geqslant 0 \ (i = 1, 2, 3)$$

CHAPTER 9

Section 1
1.1. *a)*

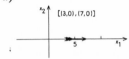

b)

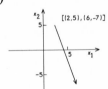

1.2. *a)* i) $(3, 0); (7, 0).$
     ii)

b) i) $(2, 5); (6, -7).$
     ii)

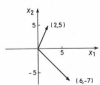

1.3. *a)* $p \neq q$; same components, but p a column and q a row vector.
     b) $p \neq r$; different components—p a two-component and r a three-component vector.
     f) $q = t$; same components—both row vectors.
     i) $r = v$; same components—both column vectors.

1.4. *b*) (3, 11).

1.5. *a*) $(u_1, u_2, u_3, u_4, u_5, u_6)$.

1.6. *c*) $\begin{pmatrix} 4 \\ 10 \\ 3 \end{pmatrix}$.

1.7. *c*) $(13, -13, 7)$.

1.8. *a*) Addition impossible; two column vectors with different number of components.

1.9. *a*) -15.

1.10. *a*) Not possible; first is a column and second is a row vector.

1.11. *b*) $-\frac{1}{23}P_2 + \frac{7}{23}P_3 = P_1$.

1.12. *a*) $-5P_1 + P_2 = \begin{pmatrix} 0 \\ 0 \end{pmatrix}$.

b) $k_1 P_1 + k_2 P_2 = \begin{pmatrix} 0 \\ 0 \end{pmatrix}$ if and only if k_1 and k_2 are both zero.

1.14. *a*) i) $2x_1 + x_2 = 50$ $2x_1 + x_2 = 0$
                  $3x_1 + 4x_2 = 90$ $3x_1 + 4x_2 = 0$
   ii) Nonhomogeneous system with a unique solution; homogeneous system with a trivial solution only.

   b) i) $4x_1 + 6x_2 = 120$ $4x_1 + 6x_2 = 0$
                     $x_1 = 12$ $x_1 = 0$
                     $x_2 = 16$ $x_2 = 0$
   ii) Nonhomogeneous system with no common solution; homogeneous system with a trivial solution only. Special case.

   c) i) $4x_1 + 6x_2 = 120$ $4x_1 + 6x_2 = 0$
                  $2x_1 + 3x_2 = 60$ $2x_1 + 3x_2 = 0$
   ii) Nonhomogeneous system with infinitely many solutions; homogeneous with nontrivial solutions.

1.15. *a*) i) $f_{max} = 0.2x_1 + 0.3x_2 + 0.2x_3 + 0x_4 + 0x_5 + 0x_6$.
     Subject to
$$x_1 + 4x_2 + 2x_3 + x_4 + 0x_5 + 0x_6 = 80,$$
$$2x_1 + x_2 + 2x_3 + 0x_4 + x_5 + 0x_6 = 95,$$
$$2x_1 + 3x_2 + x_3 + 0x_4 + 0x_5 + x_6 = 90,$$
$$x_j \geqslant 0 \; (j = 1, 2, \ldots, 6).$$
     ii) $3 : 3 : 6$.

1.16. *a*) *Initial Solution:* $X_1 = (0, 0, 0, 80, 95, 90)$.
     $f'_{max} = 0.2(0) + 0.3(0) + 0.2(0) + 0(80) + 0(95) + 0(90) = 0$.
     First Iteration: $X_2 = (45, 0, 0, 35, 5, 0)$.
     $f''_{max} = 0.2(45) + 0.3(0) + 0.2(0) + 0(35) + 0(5) + 0(0) = \$9$.

Second Iteration: $X_3 = (24, 14, 0, 0, 33, 0)$.

$f'''_{max} = 0.2(24) + 0.3(14) + 0.2(0) + 0(0) + 0(33) + 0(0) = \$9$.

Third Iteration: $X_4 = (30, 5, 15, 0, 0, 0)$.

$f^{IV}_{max} = 0.2(30) + 0.3(5) + 0.2(15) + 0(0) + 0(0) + 0(0) = \$10.5$.

1.17. *a)* Let $o = (0, 0, 0, \dots, 0)$

and $u = (u_1, u_2, u_3, \dots, u_n)$.

Then

$$o + u = (0 + u_1, 0 + u_2, 0 + u_3, \dots, 0 + u_n)$$
$$= (u_1, u_2, u_3, \dots, u_n)$$
$$= u.$$

1.18. *a)*

$$x_1 + x_2 = \begin{pmatrix} -1 \\ 3 \end{pmatrix}$$

1.19. *b)*

Trader	Profit	Loss
1		$203
2	$243	
3	51	

1.20. *a)*

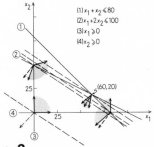

(1) $x_1 + x_2 \leqslant 80$
(2) $x_1 + 2x_2 \leqslant 100$
(3) $x_1 \geqslant 0$
(4) $x_2 \geqslant 0$

Section 2

2.1. $A : 1 \times 1$ matrix; $B : 1 \times 3$ matrix.

2.2. $A = A^T = (2)$.

$$B^T = \begin{pmatrix} 1 \\ 0 \\ -2 \end{pmatrix}.$$

2.3. *c)* Two $m \times n$ matrices such that $a_{ij} = a_{ij}$ for every ij where $(i = 1, 2, 3, \dots, m)$ and $(j = 1, 2, 3, \dots, n)$.

2.4. *a)* Addition not possible since $E : 3 \times 3$ and $F : 3 \times 2$.

b) $\begin{pmatrix} 9 & 0 & 5 \\ 4 & 4 & -12 \\ -4 & 15 & -1 \end{pmatrix}$

2.5. *a)* $\begin{pmatrix} -2 & 1 & -12 \\ 12 & 10 & 19 \end{pmatrix}$

2.7. *a*) $BC = -5$.

  b) $IC = \begin{pmatrix} -3 \\ 4 \\ 1 \end{pmatrix}$.

2.8. *a*) 3×2.
  b) 3×3.

2.13. *a*) $f_{min} = 8u_1 + 12u_2$,
      subject to
        $u_1 + 3u_2 \geqslant 5$
        $2u_1 + 2u_2 \geqslant 6$ $u_i \geqslant 0 \ (i = 1, 2)$
      where
        $u_1 = $ the productivity value per hour of machine A,
        $u_2 = $ the productivity value per hour of machine B,
        $u_1 + 3u_2 \geqslant 5$: for producing one model E carving knife one hour
          of machine A times its value u_1 plus 3 hours of machine B
          times its value u_2 should be worth at least \$5.00, the profit to
          be realized from selling one knife model E,
        $2u_1 + 2u_2 \geqslant 6$: same as above for model S knives,
        $f_{min} = 8u_1 + 12u_2$: minimize the 8 hours of machine A times its
          value per hour u_1 plus, etc.

$$\begin{pmatrix} 1 & 0 & -\frac{1}{2} & \frac{3}{4} & 2 \\ 0 & 1 & \frac{1}{2} & -\frac{1}{4} & 1 \end{pmatrix} \qquad f_{min}(2, 1) = \$28$$

  c) $f_{max} = 36u_1 + 16u_2 + 14u_3$
      subject to
        $1.2u_1 + 0.2u_2 + 0.1u_3 \leqslant 0.03$
        $0.4u_1 + 0.4u_2 + 0.8u_3 \leqslant 0.05$ $u_i \geqslant 0 \ \ (i = 1, 2, 3)$
      where
        u_1, u_2, u_3 represent the value of an ounce of protein, fat, and
          carbohydrates, respectively.
        $1.2u_1 + 0.2u_2 + 0.1u_3 \leqslant 0.03$: 1.2 ounces of protein times its
          value u_1 plus, etc., required for cereal A should not exceed
          3 cents per pound.
        $0.4u_1 + 0.4u_2 + 0.8u_3 \leqslant 0.05$: same as above for cereal B.
        $f_{max} = 36u_1 + 16u_2 + 14u_3$: maximize the 36 ounces of protein
          times its value u_1 plus, etc.

$$\begin{pmatrix} 1 & 0 & -\frac{3}{10} & 1 & -\frac{1}{2} & 0.005 \\ 0 & 1 & \frac{23}{10} & -1 & 3 & 0.12 \end{pmatrix}$$

$u_1 = 0.005 + \frac{3}{10}u_3; u_2 = 0.12 - \frac{23}{10}u_3.$
Let $u_3 = 0$. Then

$$f_{max}(0.005, 0.12, 0) = \$2.10.$$

2.18. *a*) i) $\begin{pmatrix} 1 & 0 & 0 & -\frac{2}{24} & -\frac{5}{24} & \frac{11}{24} & 1 \\ 0 & 1 & 0 & \frac{10}{24} & \frac{1}{24} & -\frac{7}{24} & 3 \\ 0 & 0 & 1 & -\frac{2}{24} & \frac{7}{24} & -\frac{1}{24} & 2 \end{pmatrix}$

$$x_1 = 1; \ x_2 = 3; \ x_3 = 2.$$

g) i)
$$\begin{pmatrix} 1 & 0 & 0 & 1 & \frac{2}{6} & 0 & \frac{2}{6} & 2 \\ 0 & 1 & 0 & -2 & \frac{8}{6} & -1 & \frac{2}{6} & 1 \\ 0 & 0 & 1 & -3 & \frac{10}{6} & -1 & -\frac{2}{6} & -1 \end{pmatrix}$$

$$x_1 = 2 - x_4;\ x_2 = 1 + 2x_4;\ x_3 = 3x_4 - 1.$$

2.19. *a)* $f_{max} = (5 \quad 6)\begin{pmatrix} x_1 \\ x_2 \end{pmatrix}$,

subject to

$$\begin{pmatrix} 1 & 2 \\ 3 & 2 \end{pmatrix}\begin{pmatrix} x_1 \\ x_2 \end{pmatrix} \leqslant \begin{pmatrix} 8 \\ 12 \end{pmatrix}$$

$$\begin{pmatrix} 1 & 0 & -\frac{1}{2} & \frac{1}{2} & 2 \\ 0 & 1 & \frac{3}{4} & -\frac{1}{4} & 3 \end{pmatrix}$$

c) $f_{min} = (0.03, 0.05)\begin{pmatrix} x_1 \\ x_2 \end{pmatrix}$

subject to

$$\begin{pmatrix} 1.2 & 0.4 \\ 0.2 & 0.4 \\ 0.1 & 0.8 \end{pmatrix}\begin{pmatrix} x_1 \\ x_2 \end{pmatrix} \geqslant \begin{pmatrix} 36 \\ 16 \\ 14 \end{pmatrix}$$

$$\begin{pmatrix} 1 & 0 & 1 & -1 & 0 & 20 \\ 0 & 1 & -\frac{1}{2} & 3 & 0 & 30 \\ 0 & 0 & -\frac{3}{10} & \frac{23}{10} & -1 & 12 \end{pmatrix}$$

$$x_1 = 20;\ x_2 = 30.$$

2.20. *a)* $(14, -4)$; $\begin{pmatrix} 59 \\ -64 \\ -4 \end{pmatrix}$.

b) $(31, 37, -32)$; $\begin{pmatrix} -23 \\ 46 \\ 31 \end{pmatrix}$.

2.22. *a)* B: \$6.77.
      b) \$6.64.

2.23. *a) i)* $A^{-1} = \begin{pmatrix} -\frac{1}{2} & \frac{1}{2} \\ \frac{3}{4} & -\frac{1}{4} \end{pmatrix}$ *ii)* $X = \begin{pmatrix} 2 \\ 3 \end{pmatrix}$.

CHAPTER 10

Section 1

1.4. *a)* $\begin{pmatrix} 1 & 0 & -1 & 2 & 60 \\ 0 & 1 & 1 & -1 & 20 \end{pmatrix}$.

$$X = \begin{pmatrix} -1 & 2 \\ 1 & -1 \end{pmatrix}\begin{pmatrix} 100 \\ 80 \end{pmatrix} = \begin{pmatrix} 60 \\ 20 \end{pmatrix}.$$

1.7. *a)*

P_r	c_j Solution Vectors	0.20 P_1	0.30 P_2	0 P_3	0 P_4	0 P_5	P_0
0.30	P_2	0	1	1	−1	0	20
0.20	P_1	1	0	−1	2	0	60
0	P_3	0	0	0	−2	1	0
	z_j	0.20	0.30	0.10	0.10	0	18
	$c_j - z_j$	0	0	−0.10	−0.10	0	

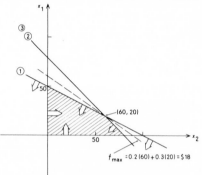

(1) $x_1 + 2x_2 \leqslant 100$
(2) $x_1 + x_2 \leqslant 80$
(3) $2x_1 + 2x_2 \leqslant 160$

b)

P_r	c_j Solution Vectors	0.20 P_1	0.30 P_2	0 P_3	0 P_4	−M P_5	0 P_6	P_0
0	P_3	0	0	1	−2	1	−1	0
0.30	P_2	0	1	0	1	−1	1	20
0.20	P_1	1	0	0	0	1	−1	60
	z_j	0.20	0.30	0	0.30	−0.10	0.10	18
	$c_j - z_j$	0	0	0	−0.30	0.10−M	−0.10	

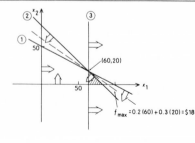

(1) $x_1 + 2x_2 \leqslant 100$
(2) $x_1 + x_2 \leqslant 80$
(3) $x_1 \geqslant 60$

1.8. *a)*

P_c	c_j Solution Vectors	60 P_1	50 P_2	M P_3	M P_4	0 P_5	0 P_6	0 P_7	P_0
60	P_1	1	0	$\frac{4}{5}$	$-\frac{1}{5}$	0	$-\frac{4}{5}$	$\frac{1}{5}$	22
60	P_2	0	1	$-\frac{3}{5}$	$\frac{2}{5}$	0	$\frac{3}{5}$	$-\frac{2}{5}$	6
0	P_5	0	0	$-\frac{4}{5}$	$\frac{1}{5}$	1	$\frac{4}{5}$	$-\frac{1}{5}$	0
	z_j	60	50	18	28	0	-18	-28	1620
	$c_j - z_j$	0	0	$M-18$	$M-28$	0	18	28	

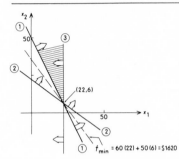

(1) $2000x_1 + 1000x_2 \geqslant 50{,}000$
(2) $3000x_1 + 4000x_2 \geqslant 90{,}000$
(3) $x_1 \leqslant 22$

$f_{min} = 60\,(22) + 50\,(6) = \$1620$

1.9. *a)*

P_r	c_j Solution Vectors	5 P_1	6 P_2	0 P_3	0 P_4	P_0
6	P_2	0	1	$\frac{3}{4}$	$-\frac{1}{4}$	3
5	P_1	1	0	$-\frac{1}{2}$	$\frac{1}{2}$	2
	z_j	5	6	2	1	28
	$c_j - z_j$	0	0	-2	-1	

c)

P_c	c_j Solution Vectors	0.03 P_1	0.05 P_2	M P_3	M P_4	M P_5	0 P_6	0 P_7	0 P_8	P_0
0.03	P_1	1	0	1	-1	0	-1	1	0	20
0	P_8	0	0	$-\frac{3}{10}$	$\frac{23}{10}$	-1	$\frac{3}{10}$	$\frac{23}{10}$	1	12
0.05	P_2	0	1	$-\frac{1}{2}$	3	0	$\frac{1}{2}$	-3	0	30
	z_j	0.03	0.05	$\frac{1}{200}$	$\frac{12}{100}$	0	$-\frac{1}{200}$	$-\frac{12}{100}$	0	2.10
	$c_j - z_j$	0	0	$M-\frac{1}{200}$	$M-\frac{12}{100}$	M	$\frac{1}{200}$	$\frac{12}{100}$	0	

Section 2

2.2.

F \ A	A_1		A_2		A_3		Tons Available
F_1	$10	(40)	$30	(30)	$40	0	70
F_2	$30	0	$30	0	$30	(30)	30
F_3	$30	0	$20	(25)	$20	(30)	55
Tons required	40		55		60		155

$$I_{13} = -10 \qquad I_{22} = 0$$
$$I_{21} = -20 \qquad I_{31} = -30$$
$$f_{\min} = \$3300$$

2.3. *a) i)*

c_j		10	30	40	30	30	30	30	20	20	M	M	M	M	M	
P_c	Solution Vectors	P_1	P_2	P_3	P_4	P_5	P_6	P_7	P_8	P_9	P_{10}	P_{11}	P_{12}	P_{13}	P_{14}	P_0
20	P_9	0	0	1	−1	−1	0	0	0	1	1	0	1	−1	−1	10
30	P_6	0	0	0	1	1	1	0	0	0	0	1	0	0	0	50
20	P_8	0	0	−1	1	1	0	1	1	0	−1	0	0	1	1	20
10	P_1	1	0	0	1	0	0	1	0	0	0	0	0	1	0	40
30	P_2	0	1	1	−1	0	0	−1	0	0	1	0	0	−1	0	35
z_j		10	30	30	10	30	30	0	20	20	30	30	20	−20	0	3550
$c_j - z_j$		0	0	10	20	0	0	30	0	0	$\binom{M}{-30}$	$\binom{M}{-30}$	$\binom{M}{-20}$	$\binom{M}{20}$	M	

2.4. *a) ii)* $I_{13} = -10 \qquad I_{31} = -30$
$$I_{21} = -20 \qquad I_{32} = 0$$
$$f_{\min} = \$3550$$

2.6.

$\diagdown$ L / G	L_1	L_2	L_3	Available Buses
G_1	12 ③	14 0	13 ③	6
G_2	14 0	12 ④	15 ⑤	9
G_3	10 ⑤	18 0	19 0	5
Required buses	8	4	8	20

$$I_{12} = -4 \qquad I_{32} = -10$$
$$I_{21} = 0 \qquad I_{33} = -8$$
$$f_{\min} = 248 \text{ minutes}$$

CHAPTER 11

Section 1

1.3. *a, b, c)* $f(x) = x^2/100$.

x	Δx	y	Δy	$\Delta y/\Delta x$
500		2500		
	100		1100	11
600		3600		
	100		1300	13
700		4900		
	100		1500	15
800		6400		
	100		1700	17
900		8100		
	100		1900	19
1000		10,000		
	100		2100	21
1100		12,100		
	100		2300	23
1200		14,400		
	100		2500	25
1300		16,900		
	100		2700	27
1400		19,600		
	100		2900	29
1500		22,500		

$x + \Delta x/2$	550	650	750	850	950	1050	1150	1250	1350	1450
$\Delta y/\Delta x$	11	13	15	17	19	21	23	25	27	29

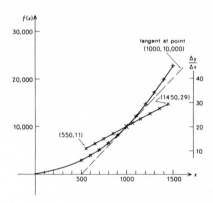

1.5. *a*) At $x = 300$, $\dfrac{\Delta y}{\Delta x} = \dfrac{\Delta x}{100} - 4$.

Δx (parts)	10	1	0.1	0.01
$\Delta y/\Delta x$ (dollar cost)	−3.9	−3.99	−3.999	−3.9999

Hence, at $x = 300$ the marginal rate is -4. When a run contains 300 parts the average cost of production decreases at a rate of $4.00.

At $x = 700$, $\dfrac{\Delta y}{\Delta x} = 4 + \dfrac{\Delta x}{100}$ and the marginal rate is 4.

1.8. *a*) $\displaystyle \operatorname*{limit}_{x \to 05} \frac{1000}{x} = \frac{\operatorname*{limit}_{x \to 50} 1000}{\operatorname*{limit}_{x \to 50} x}$ [by 1.8.3]

$$= 1000 \operatorname*{limit}_{x \to 50}\left(\frac{1}{x}\right) \qquad \text{[by 1.8.2]}$$

$$= 20 .$$

Function continuous since—

I $f(50)$ is defined,

II $\displaystyle \operatorname*{limit}_{x \to 50} \frac{1000}{x}$ exists,

III $\displaystyle \operatorname*{limit}_{x \to 50} \frac{1000}{x} = f(50) = 20.$

1.9. *a*) $\displaystyle \lim_{x \to 3} \frac{3-x}{6-2x} = \lim_{x \to 3} \frac{3-x}{2(3-x)}$

$$= \lim_{x \to 3} \frac{1}{2} \lim_{x \to 3} \frac{3-x}{3-x}$$

$$= \tfrac{1}{2} \cdot 1 = \tfrac{1}{2}.$$

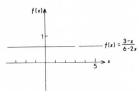

Function discontinuous at $x = 3$ since—
I. $f(3)$ is not defined.

b) Function discontinuous at $x = 0$ since—
I. $f(0)$ is not defined.
II. $\displaystyle \lim_{x \to 0} f(x)$ does not exist.

$$f(x) = \frac{100}{x^2} \quad x \geqslant 0$$

Section 2

2.2. *a*)   i) $\displaystyle f'(t) = \lim_{\Delta t \to 0} \frac{\Delta y}{\Delta t}$

$$= \lim_{\Delta t \to 0} \frac{f(t + \Delta t) - f(t)}{\Delta t}$$

$$= \lim_{\Delta t \to 0} \frac{[-1.5(t + \Delta t) + 100] - [-1.5t + 100]}{\Delta t}$$

$$= \lim_{\Delta t \to 0} \frac{-1.5t - 1.5\Delta t + 100 + 1.5t - 100}{\Delta t}$$

$$= \lim_{\Delta t \to 0} (-1.5)\frac{\Delta t}{\Delta t}$$

$$= -1.5.$$

ii) If $f(t) = -1.5t + 100$, then

$$
\begin{aligned}
f'(t) &= D_t(-1.5t) + D_t 100 && \text{[by 5]},\\
&= D_t(-1.5t) + 0 && \text{[by 1]},\\
&= -1.5 D_t(t) && \text{[by 3]},\\
&= -1.5 && \text{[by 2]}.
\end{aligned}
$$

iii) The rate at which a \$100-loan is discounted is \$1.50 per month.

e) i) $f'(x) = \text{limit}_{\Delta x \to 0} \dfrac{\Delta y}{\Delta x}$

$$= \text{limit}_{\Delta x \to 0} \frac{[-(x + \Delta x)^2 + 20(x + \Delta x)] - [-x^2 + 20x]}{\Delta x}$$

$$= \text{limit}_{\Delta x \to 0} \frac{-x^2 - 2x\Delta x - (\Delta x)^2 + 20x + 20\Delta x + x^2 - 20x}{\Delta x}$$

$$= -2x + 20.$$

ii) If $f(x) = -x^2 + 20x$, then
$$\begin{aligned} f(x) &= D_x(-x^2) + D_x(20x) &&\text{[by 5]},\\ &= -1 D_x(x^2) + 20 D_x(x) &&\text{[by 3]},\\ &= -1 \cdot 2x + 20 \cdot 1 &&\text{[by 4 \& 2]},\\ &= -2x + 20. \end{aligned}$$

iii) For a given x number of miners the rate of change in the daily coal output is $-2x + 20$ tons.

2.3. *a)* Let $f(x) = 50x + 3000$. We wish to prove that $f'(x) = 50$.
Proof:
If $f(x) = 50x + 3000$, then
$$\frac{\Delta y}{\Delta x} = \frac{[50(x + \Delta x) + 3000] - [50x + 3000]}{\Delta x}$$
$$= \frac{50x + 50\Delta x + 3000 - 50x - 3000}{\Delta x}$$
$$= 50 \frac{\Delta x}{\Delta x}; \text{ and by (2.2), we have}$$
$$f'(x) = \text{limit}_{\Delta x \to 0} \frac{\Delta y}{\Delta x} = \text{limit}_{\Delta x \to 0} 50 \frac{\Delta x}{\Delta x}$$
$$= 50,$$

since the limit of a constant is the constant itself.

QED

g) Let $S(p) = -1000p^2 + 10{,}000p$. We wish to prove that $S'(p) = -2000p + 10{,}000$.
Proof:
If $S(p) = -1000p^2 + 10{,}000p$, then
$$\frac{\Delta y}{\Delta p} = \frac{[-1000(p + \Delta p)^2 + 10{,}000(p + \Delta p)] - [-1000p^2 + 10{,}000p]}{\Delta p}$$
$$= \frac{-1000p^2 - 2000p\Delta p + (\Delta p)^2 + 10{,}000p + 10{,}000\Delta p + 1000p^2}{\Delta p}$$
$$= \frac{-2000p\Delta p + 10{,}000\Delta p + (\Delta p)^2}{\Delta p}; \qquad \frac{10{,}000p}{\Delta p}$$

and by (2.2), we have

$$S'(p) = \lim_{\Delta p \to 0} \frac{\Delta y}{\Delta p} = \lim_{\Delta p \to 0} \frac{-2000p\Delta p + 10{,}000\Delta p + (\Delta p)^2}{\Delta p}$$

$$= -2000p + 10{,}000.$$

QED

2.4. *a)* $f'(x) = 30x^5$.
e) $f'(x) = \frac{3}{2}\sqrt{6x}$.

2.5. *a)* $f'(x) = -12x + 1$.

2.6. *a)* $f'(x) = 0$.

2.7. *a)* $f'(x) = 10x(x^2 + 3)^4$.

2.8. *a)* $y' = 60x^5$; $y'' = 300x^4$; $y''' = 1200x^3$.
b) $g'(x) = \frac{3}{2}\sqrt{6x}$; $g''(x) = \frac{3}{4}\sqrt{\frac{6}{x}}$; $g'''(x) = -\frac{3}{8}\sqrt{\frac{6}{x^3}}$.

2.9. *a)* $f''(x) = 0$; since sales change at a constant rate of 50 units, the rate of the rate is zero.
g) $S''(p) = -2000$; since sales change at a rate of $-2000p + 10{,}000$ units for a given value of price p, the rate of this rate is a constant -2000.

2.11. *a)* $D_x\left(\dfrac{x^2 + 2x - 5}{5}\right) = \dfrac{2x + 2}{5}$.

2.13. *a)* $\dfrac{d}{dx}\left(\dfrac{1}{x^2 - 1}\right) = -\dfrac{2x}{(x^2 - 1)^2}$.

2.16. *a)* Let $p = 3$. Then
$$S(3) = 21{,}000 \text{ and } S'(3) = 4000.$$

Thus, $y = 4000x + 9000$.

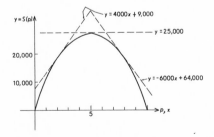

Let $p = 5$. Then
$$S(5) = 25{,}000 \text{ and } S'(5) = 0. \text{ Hence } y = 25{,}000.$$
Let $p = 8$. Then
$$S(8) = 16{,}000 \text{ and } S'(8) = -6000. \text{ Hence, } y = -6000x + 64{,}000$$

Section 3

3.4.   *a*) At $f'(x) = 0$, $x_1 \approx 183.51$ and $x_2 \approx 1816.49$ and
$$f(183.51) \approx 4335.20,$$
$$f'(1816.49) \approx 21,709.30.$$

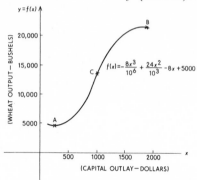

Since $f''(183.51) > 0$, point A (183, 4335) on the graph is a minimum.
Since $f''(1846.49) < 0$, point B (1846, 21709) on the graph is a maximum.
At $f''(x) = 0$, $x_3 = 1000$ and $f(1000) = 13,000$.
Since $f''(900) > 0$ and $f''(1100) < 0$, point C(1000, 13,000) on the graph is an inflection point.

3.5.   *a*) $P(x) = -8x^2 + 80x + 9600$.
  c) \$9800.
  d) 280,000 pounds; \$0.035 per pound.

3.6.   *a*) $R(x) = -10x^2 + 80x + 2000$.

3.8.   *a*) $x = 4$ units.
  b) $P(x) = -2x^2 + 16x$.
       $P(4) = \$32$.

3.16. *a*) Base 2×2; height 4 feet.
  b) \$4.80.

3.21. *c*) (1, 3).

3.22. *a*)

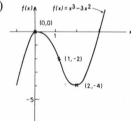

3.23. *a)*

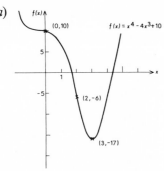

CHAPTER 12

Section 1

1.2. *a)* i) $f'(t) = -1.5.$

ii) $y = \int f'(t)dt = \int (-1.5)dt = -1.5t + C.$

iii) $f(0) = -1.5(0) + C = 100; \therefore C = 100.$

c) i) $g'(d) = 0.00625.$

ii) $y = \int g'(d)dd = \int (0.00625)dd = 0.00625d + C.$

iii) $g(0) = 0.00625(0) + C = 1.00; \therefore C = 1.00.$

1.3. *a)* $y = x^2 + 6.$

1.5. *a)*

$x + \Delta x/2$	250	350	450	550	650	750
$\Delta y/\Delta x$	-3	-2	-1.5	-0.5	2.5	5.5

b)

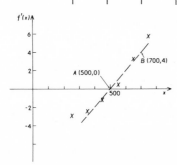

c) $f'(x) = x/50 - 10$; from points A and B.

d) $f(x) = x^2/100 - 10x + 3000$, $200 \leqslant x \leqslant 800$.

e)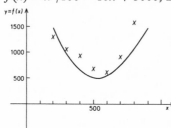

1.8. *a)* $y = 3x^2/2$.
    c) $y = 4x - 2$.

1.9. *a)* $y = -3x^2 + 2x + 3$.

1.10. *a)* $y = x^3 + C$.
    b) $y = x^4 + C$.

1.11. *a)* If $y = \int (4x^3 - 4x^2 + 4)dx$, then

$$y = \int (4x^3)dx - \int (4x^2)dx + \int 4dx \qquad \text{[by 5 \& 6]};$$

$$= 4\int x^3 dx - 4\int x^2 dx + 4\int 1dx \qquad \text{[by 3]};$$

$$= x^4 - \tfrac{4}{3}x^3 + 4x + C \qquad \text{[by 2 \& 4]}.$$

1.12. *a)* $\int (2x + 5)^3 dx = \dfrac{(2x + 5)^4}{8} + C;$

$$D_x\left[\frac{(2x + 5)^4}{8} + C\right] = \frac{8D_x(2x + 5)^4}{64}$$

$$= (2x + 5)^3.$$

1.13. *a)* $y = \int [(2x + 3)(x - 2)]dx$

$$= \int (2x^2 - x - 6)dx$$

$$= \tfrac{2}{3}x^3 - \tfrac{1}{2}x^2 - 6x + C;$$

$$f(x) = D_x[\tfrac{2}{3}x^3 - \tfrac{1}{2}x^2 - 6x + C]$$

$$= 2x^2 - x - 6$$

$$= (2x + 3)(x - 2).$$

1.14. *a)* ± 8 square feet; $A = 1600 \pm 8$ square feet.

1.15. *a)* $y = \int \left(-\dfrac{5}{4z^6} \right) dz$

$$= -\frac{5}{4} \int z^{-6}\, dz$$

$$= \frac{1}{4z^5} + C\,;$$

$$D_z\left[\frac{1}{4z^5} + C \right] = \tfrac{1}{4} D_z(z^{-5})$$

$$= -\tfrac{5}{4} z^{-6}$$

$$= -\frac{5}{4z^6}\,.$$

1.16. *a)* $D_x[kF(x) + C] = k D_x[F(x)] + D_x C$
$$= k D_x[F(x)] + 0$$
$$= kf(x),$$
where $f(x) = F'(x)$.

1.17. *a)* $y = \dfrac{x^3}{3} - \dfrac{x^2}{2} + 5 \ln |x| + C.$

Section 2

2.5. *a)*

i)

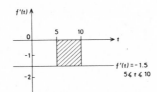

$$A = -\int_5^{10} (-1.5)\dot{d}t = 7.5.$$

ii) The discount from the end of the 5th to the end of the 10th month is $7.5.

c) i)

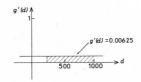

$$A = \int_{100}^{1000} (0.00625)dd = 5.625$$

ii) Air freight increases by $5.625 per pound as distance increases from 100 to 1000 miles.

2.6. *a)* Yes, since costs savings will be $54,000.

b) $t = 5.5$ years.

c) $t = 6.5$ years.

2.9. *b)* $18.

c) $P(x) = -2x^2 + 12x$.

2.10. *a)* $A = 7000$.

b) When investment increases from $500 to $1000, total wheat output increases by 7000 bushels.

c)

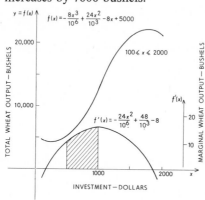

2.14. *a)* i)

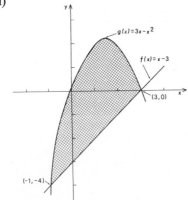

ii) $A = 10\frac{2}{3}$.

2.17. *d)* i), iii)

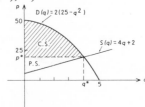

ii) C.S. $= 85\frac{1}{3}$.

   P.S. $= 32$.

CHAPTER 13

Section 1

1.2. *a)* $x \approx \$4,792,850.$
   $q \approx 6,093,073$ tires.
   $P(6,093,073) = \$314,291.$
   b) (1) $x \approx \$1,239,130.$
      $P(5,700,000) = \$2,570,870.$
      (2) $q_1 \approx 5,615,151$ tires.
      $q_2 \approx 6,475,757$ tires.
      $x_1 \approx \$3,531,760.$
      $x_2 \approx \$6,372,750.$
      $P(5,615,151) \approx 0.$
      $P(6,475,757) \approx 0.$

1.6. *a)* $C'' = \dfrac{2DS}{x^3} > 0$ since $D > 0$, $S > 0$ and $x^3 > 0.$

1.9. *a)*

x	$x/4$	DS/x	$C(x)$	$I/2$	DS/x^2
400,000	100,000	225,000	325,000	0.25	0.56
500,000	125,000	180,000	305,000	0.25	0.36
600,000	150,000	150,000	300,000	0.25	0.25
700,000	175,000	128,571	303,571	0.25	0.18
800,000	200,000	112,500	312,500	0.25	0.14

1.10. *a)* $x = 2000$ motors.
   $C(2000) = \$4000.$

   $\dfrac{D}{x} = 20$ orders.

1.11. $C\left(\sqrt{\dfrac{2DS}{I}}\right) = \sqrt{2DSI}.$

1.12. *a)* $x = \sqrt{\dfrac{2D(S+F)}{I}}.$

1.16. *a)*

x	R	S/Kx	$D\sqrt{x}$	$C(x) - R$
25	0.01	0.080	0.050	0.130
36	0.01	0.056	0.060	0.116
49	0.01	0.041	0.070	0.111
54.2	0.01	0.037	0.073	0.110
64	0.01	0.031	0.080	0.111
81	0.01	0.025	0.090	0.115
100	0.01	0.020	0.100	0.120

1.18. *a)* $C(x) = \left(\dfrac{x}{2} + R\right)I + \dfrac{D}{x}S.$

Section 2

2.7. *a)* $D_x e^{2(2)} = 109.196$.
  b) $f'(2) = 7082.80$.

2.8. *a)* $f'(x) = 0.69315e^{0.69315x}$.

2.9. *a)* 6.9634.
  b) 1.08560.

2.12. The machine given in this problem since at optimal $T^* = 10$ $V(T) = \$7444.95$.

CHAPTER 14

Section 1

1.1. *a)* i) $S = \{HHH, HHT, HTH, HTT, THH, THT, TTH, TTT\}$
  ii)

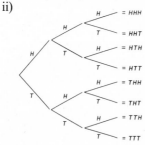

  iii) $S_1 = \{0, 1, 2, 3\}$, where numbers $0, 1, 2, 3$ denote number of tails.

  b) The same as in *(a)*.
  e) i) $S = \{BB, BG, GB, GG\}$, where $B =$ boy and $G =$ girl.
  ii)

  iii) $S_1 = \{0, 1, 2\}$, where numbers $0, 1, 2$ denote number of girls.
  f) i–iii) The same as in *(a)* by letting $H = B$ and $T = G$.

1.2. *a)* $S = \{PP, PN, PD, NN, NP, ND, DD, DP, DN\}$
  b)

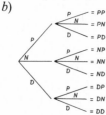

  c) Let $S_1 = \{P, N, D\}$. Then
$$S_1 \times S_1 = \{P, N, D\} \times \{P, N, D\} = S.$$

1.6. *a)* Suitable.
  b) Not suitable.

1.7. *a)* Suitable.
  b) Not suitable.

1.10. *a)* $S = \{AW, AR, BW, BR\}$

1.12. *a)*   *b)*

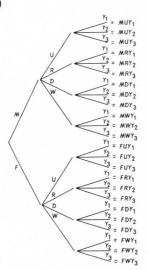   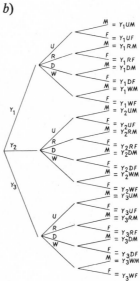

The number of classes does not change since $2 \times 4 \times 3 = 3 \times 4 \times 2$
$$= 24.$$

Section 2

2.2. *a)* $E \quad = \{A_d, K_d, \ldots, 2_d\}$.
  b) $F \quad = \{A_s, A_h, A_d, A_c\}$.
  c) $E \cup F = \{A_s, A_h, A_d, A_c, K_d, \ldots, 2_d\}$.

2.3. *a)* $E \quad = \{BBB, BBG, BGB, BGG\}$.
  b) $F \quad = \{BBG, BGG, GBG, GGG\}$.
  c) $E \cap F = \{BBG, BGG\}$.

2.7. *a)* (1) $E_1 = \{(1, 1), (1, 2), (1, 3), (1, 4), (1, 5), (1, 6), (2, 1), (2, 2), (2, 3),$
              $(2, 4), (2, 5), (2, 6)\}$.
  b) (1)   "A double is thrown."

2.8. *a*) $S = \{ABC, ABD, ABE, ACD, ACE, ADE, BCD, BCE, BDE, CDE\}$.

2.9. *a*) $E \cap F = \{AW\}$.
$\quad E' \quad\;\; = \{BW, BR\}$.
$\quad E' \cap F = \{BW\}$.
$\quad F' \quad\;\; = \{AR, BR\}$.
$\quad E \cup F \; = \{AW, AR, BW\}$.

2.11. *a*) $n(E \cup F) = 4$.
$\quad$ *b*) $n(E \cup G) = 8$.

2.12. *a*) $n(E \cup F \cup G) = 12$.

2.16. *a*) $S_3 = \{M \cap I, M \cap N, F \cap I, F \cap N\}$.

CHAPTER 15

Section 1

1.1. *a*) Probability of $\frac{1}{52}$ is assigned to the event since experiment can be repeated a great number of times under identical conditions.
$\quad$ *b*) No probability can be assigned to this event since the events "monthly sales" cannot be repeated in the future under identical or nearly identical conditions.

1.3. *c*) $S = \{BB, BG, GB, GG\}$.
$\quad P_r(\{BB\}) = \frac{1}{4}$.

1.5. *a*) $\frac{1}{2}$; *b*) $\frac{1}{4}$; *c*) $\frac{5}{18}$; *d*) 0; *e*) $\frac{1}{9}$.

1.7. *a*) $\frac{1}{3}$; *b*) $\frac{1}{3}$.

1.8. *a*) $\frac{1}{2}$.

1.9. *a*) $\frac{1}{2}$; *b*) $\frac{1}{10}$.

1.10. *a*) $\frac{1}{2}$.

1.11. $P_r(2_D) = (0.01)^2$.
$\quad P_r(3_D) = (0.01)^3$.
$\quad P_r(R_D) = (0.01)^r$.

1.14. *a*) $P_r(B' \cap P) = \dfrac{n(B' \cap P)}{n(\mathcal{U})} = \dfrac{200}{1000} = 0.20$.

1.16. *a*) (1) $\frac{1}{2}$.
$\quad$ *b*) (1) 1 to 1.

1.17. *a*) 0.25; *b*) 0.15; *c*) 0.25.

1.19. *a*) $\frac{1}{3}$.

1.21. *a*) Independent.
$\quad$ *b*) Dependent.

Section 2

2.1. *a*) $\frac{1}{2}$.

2.2. *a*) $\frac{1}{2}$; initial sample space reduced; events independent.

2.3. *a*) $\frac{1}{3}$; initial sample space reduced; events independent.

2.4. *a*) $\dfrac{245}{99,900}$.

2.5. *a*) $\frac{3}{51}$.

2.7. *a*) $\frac{1}{2}$.

2.9. $\frac{5}{11}$.

2.10. *a*)

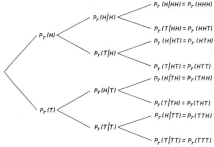

    b) $\mathcal{U} = S \times S \times S = \{HT\} \times \{HT\} \times \{HT\}$.

    c) $P_r(HHH) = P_r(H) \cdot P_r(H|H) \cdot P_r(H|HH) = \frac{1}{2} \cdot \frac{1}{2} \cdot \frac{1}{2} = \frac{1}{8}$

2.12. $P_r(GGG) \approx 0.49$.

2.13. $P_r(A) = \frac{2}{5}$; $P_r(A/B) = \frac{2}{3}$.

2.17. *a*)

Section 3

3.1. *a*) 216; *b*) 120.

3.3. *a*) 40 if two particular displays can be displayed in other windows; 24 if such displays are reserved exclusively for third window.

3.4. *a*) 720.

3.7. *a*) (1, 1), (2, 2), (3, 3), (1, 2), (1, 3), (2, 3), (2, 1), (3, 1), (3, 2).

3.9. *a*) 1200.

    b) $\left(\dfrac{1}{1200}\right)^3$; $\dfrac{(1199)(1198)}{(1200)^2}$; $1 - \dfrac{(1200)(1199)(1198)}{(1200)^3}$.

3.12. *a*) $1 - \dfrac{100 \cdot 99 \cdot 98 \cdot \ldots \cdot (100 - r + 1)}{(100)^r}$.

3.13. *a*) 120.

3.15. 79,380.

3.17. *c*) $(1)(1)^5 + (5)(1)^4(-0.01) + (10)(1)^3(-0.01)^2 + (10)(1)^2(-0.01)^3 + (5)(1)(-0.01)^4 + (1)(-0.01)^5$.

3.18. *a*) 126.

3.19. *a*) Approximately 1.062.

3.20. *a*) $0.008 + 0.096 + 0.384 + 0.512 = 1.00$.

3.21. *a*)

No. Heads	0	1	2	3	4	5	6
Probability	0.016	0.093	0.235	0.312	0.235	0.093	0.016

CHAPTER 16

Section 1

1.6. *a*)

Demand	8	10	13	16	17	18	20	25	29	36
Ratio	$\frac{1}{11}$	$\frac{2}{11}$	$\frac{3}{11}$	$\frac{4}{11}$	$\frac{5}{11}$	$\frac{6}{11}$	$\frac{7}{11}$	$\frac{8}{11}$	$\frac{9}{11}$	$\frac{10}{11}$

b)

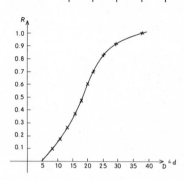

c)

$X \leqslant x$	10	15	20	25	30	35
$F(x)$	0.20	0.40	0.66	0.80	0.92	1.00

$X = x$	10	15	20	25	30	35
$f(x)$	0.20	0.20	0.26	0.14	0.12	0.08

1.8. *a*)

$X = x$	\$5	\$4	$-\$2$
$f(x)$	$\frac{6}{36}$	$\frac{14}{36}$	$\frac{16}{36}$

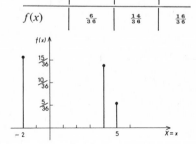

b) $E(X) = \$1.50.$

1.9. *a)* $f(0) = \binom{3}{0} (\tfrac{1}{2})^3 = \tfrac{1}{8}$.

$f(1) = \binom{3}{1} (\tfrac{1}{2})^2(\tfrac{1}{2}) = \tfrac{3}{8}$.

$f(2) = \binom{3}{2} (\tfrac{1}{2})(\tfrac{1}{2})^2 = \tfrac{3}{8}$.

$f(3) = \binom{3}{3} (\tfrac{1}{2}) = \tfrac{1}{8}$.

1.13. $1.80.

1.16. *a)* $2450; *b)* $122.50.

Section 2

2.1. *a)*

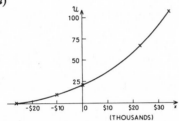

(THOUSANDS)

2.2. *a)* Contract T.
 b) Contract S.
 c) Contract T.

2.6. *a)* $R(D) = \begin{cases} 5D - 4Q & \text{if} \quad D \le Q \\ 1Q & \text{if} \quad D > Q \end{cases}$

				Stock Q			
Demand	4	5	6	7	8	9	10
4	$4*	$0	−$4	−$8	−$12	−$16	−$20
5	4	5*	1	−3	−7	−11	−15
6	4	5	6*	2	−2	−6	−10
7	4	5	6	7*	3	−1	−5
8	4	5	6	7	8*	4	0
9	4	5	6	7	8	9*	5
10	4	5	6	7	8	9	10*

b) $Q^* = 6$.

c)

				Stock	Q			
Demand	0	4	5	6	7	8	9	10
4	4*	0	4	8	12	16	20	24
5	5*	1	0	4	8	12	16	20
6	6*	2	1	0	4	8	12	16
7	7*	3	2	1	0	4	8	12
8	8*	4	3	2	1	0	4	8
9	9*	5	4	3	2	1	0	4
10	10*	6	5	4	3	2	1	0

d) $E(L_a{}^*) = \$2.50$.

e) $EVPI = \$2.50$.

2.10. a) $P_r(D < j) < \dfrac{7}{7 + 3} = 0.70$; $Q^* = 3$ dozen.

b) $E(R_3) = \$11.00$.

c) $EVPI = \$5.10$.

d) $Q = 4$ dozen.

e) $\$20$.

Section 3

3.4. a)

r	0	1	2	3	4 or more
$P_r(R = r)$	0.531	0.355	0.098	0.015	0.001

3.5. a) 0.961.   d) 0.730.

b) 0.114.   e) 0.251.

c) 0.678.   f) 0.938.

3.8. a) $q = \frac{1}{3}$.

b) $q > \frac{1}{3}$.

c) $q < \frac{1}{3}$.

3.12. a)

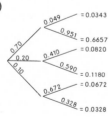

INDEXES

INDEX OF A SELECTED NUMBER OF
EXAMPLES AND CASES

INDEX OF SUBJECTS